BIOLOGICAL RHYTHM RESEARCH

BIOLOGICAL RHYTHM
RESEARCH

by

A. SOLLBERGER

Metabolic Ward, Highland View Hospital, Cleveland, Ohio (U.S.A.)
Secretary of the Society for Biological Rhythm

ELSEVIER PUBLISHING COMPANY

AMSTERDAM - LONDON - NEW YORK

1965

ELSEVIER PUBLISHING COMPANY

335 JAN VAN GALENSTRAAT, P.O. BOX 211, AMSTERDAM

AMERICAN ELSEVIER PUBLISHING COMPANY, INC.

52 VANDERBILT AVENUE, NEW YORK, N.Y. 10017

ELSEVIER PUBLISHING COMPANY LIMITED

12B, RIPPLESIDE COMMERCIAL ESTATE, BARKING, ESSEX

LIBRARY OF CONGRESS CATALOG CARD NUMBER 64–14175

WITH 189 ILLUSTRATIONS AND 2 TABLES

PRINTED IN THE NETHERLANDS

Dedicated to two
Swedish Pioneers
ERIK FORSGREN
and
JAKOB MÖLLERSTRÖM

FOREWORD

Rhythmic phenomena in the animated world early claimed the attention of the naturalists. One needs only recall LINNEAUS' famous flower clock, which was founded on the fact that the flowers of various plants close and open at different times of the day but each so regularly that one could set a clock by them. A further phenomenon which demanded attention was the sleep movements of the leaves of many plants. Such periodic plant behaviour was studied in detail by, for instance, ROSE STOPPEL. Its exogeneity or endogeneity long remained a matter of dispute. However, it was gradually realized that the 24-hour periodism is in no way restricted to the plants, but occurs in all living beings. Rhythms of the body temperature in man were discovered by JÜRGENSEN, 15 years after the introduction of thermometry by WUNDERLICH. In 1927 FORSGREN discovered the periodic alternating storage of glycogen and bile in the liver, thereby opening up a wide field of 24-hour-periodic phenomena to investigation. Thus a new branch of science unfolded, biological rhythm research, which slowly acquired manifold interconnections with the other biological sciences, including medicine. In 1937 seven scientists—five physicians, one botanist and one zoologist—founded an international society for the study of biological rhythms. Since then this new and interesting scientific discipline has spread all over the world. As is so typical of our time, the accumulated wealth of observations and experiments is well-nigh impossible for the single scientist to grasp.

Dr. SOLLBERGER, for many years the secretary of the mentioned society and also intimately connected with rhythm research through his own investigations, has in this work endeavoured to present a comprehensive review covering the whole field. In this presentation the various problems of biological rhythm research are examined. Much space is devoted to the theoretical background of this science. Data gathering techniques and especially the mathematical treatment of the material, the dependency of the rhythms on internal factors and on external conditions, as related to the time of day, lunation and seasons, and finally the most important findings in botany, zoology and medicine; all these aspects are explored. Thus a work has been created which both introduces this new domain and through its comprehensive presentation facilitates an orientation within it, not only to the specialist but also to much wider circles in science. Dr. SOLLBERGER has certainly earned our gratitude for all his laborious, scrupulous and diligent work on this book.

A. JORES

PREFACE

Undoubtedly, the reader has come across many manifestations of biological rhythms. The latter represent functions inherent in the living structure and appearing in all its expressions, also being most sensitive to shifts in the physical environment. This makes biological rhythm research an interdisciplinary science. It äts well into the space age, discussing – as it does – cosmic influences. Lately, cybernetics and computers have widened the future scope.

Nevertheless, biological rhythm research is a young science. Though the endeavours of the last 30 years have produced a wealth of data, yet we know little about the origin and mechanism of biological rhythms. There are thus many problems to challenge the young and the unprejudiced scientific mind. We have, for instance, to apply the knowledge of rhythms in medical diagnosis and therapy. We must also identify the environmental synchronizing agents and their action on the body, which involves the question of how to isolate a specimen perfectly from external influences.

One aspect is the analysis and comparison of simultaneously recorded physical and biological rhythms. This requires complicated statistical computations, that are, unfortunately, somewhat uncertain. There exist few well-established methods of time series analysis. A large literature is founded on the theory of stationary time series; rhythms are, however, eminently non-stationary. New methods of analysis have to be found. Once, when explaining this state of affairs to an inveterate antirhythmologist, I was informed that one should not work in a field where nothing can be proved. This is a kind of wisdom, however, which could never add anything to human knowledge.

This book purports not only to offer comprehensive information on biological rhythm research, but also to provide a basic understanding of future problems. It opens with a short introductory orientation of the whole field (Chapter 1).

The bulk of the book is divided into four parts. Part I discusses the spontaneous oscillators, leaning on cybernetic concepts (Chapters 2-4). This leads up to the biological counterpart, the endogenous rhythm or 'biological clock', and the problem of the time sense (Chapters 5-7). A few special subjects are added here (Chapters 8-11), viz. chronopathology, developmental rhythms, population cycles and basimetry.

Part II deals with such rhythmic phenomena in the environment as may control the biological rhythms, and with their possible pathways of action (Chapters 12-17), including the concepts of photoperiodism and thermoperiodism. This leads to a discussion of animal navigation (Chapter 18).

The natural sequel to the first two parts would be a presentation of the exogenous rhythms, that is, the synchronized endogenous rhythms. However, any serious discussion of biological control demands some knowledge about the mathematics and physics of periodic phenomena. Part III introduces this subject. Chapter 19 presents several rhythm models in addition to those given in Chapter 4. Chapters 20 and 21 outline the statistical analysis of time series. Chapter 22, finally, is intended to present the mathematical background for the handling of rhythms.

Part Three thus deals with problems of rapidly growing importance in biological rhythm research. Especially, the mathematical presentation is wide, including the essentials of differential equations, phase planes, complex variables and transform functions. The emphasis is not on mathematical stringency or teaching but on an attempt to develop a general understanding of the subject.

Being thus acquainted with the components of a biological rhythm system (Parts I and II), we may now try to couple them together, using the instructions in Part III. Thus we arrive at the exogenous rhythms, Part IV. Chapter 23 resumes the theoretical considerations of the previous chapter, as applied to the control of vitrating systems, also emphasizing the energy aspect of rhythmic processes. Chapter 24 discusses the actual control of biological rhythms. The remaining Chapters 25-27 survey the exogenous rhythms with regard to the different periods of duration (*e.g.* 24-hour, lunar and seasonal rhythms), and to the fields of study (botany, zoology, physiology and medicine).

I have strived to make each section in the book a complete whole, rather repeating a line of thought than breaking the continuity with cross references. To facilitate orientation, a paragraph numbering system is used. The numbers, appear on top of the pages, but also in the figures and formulae, linking text and illustrations together. The subject index indicates the paragraph in which the item appears.

The references are extensive, though the field is now so enormous and the papers so scattered that it is impossible to make a comprehensive list. I have also had to lean upon the literature compilations of other authors and want to express my gratitude in this respect to all anonymous contributors.

The numbering system of the references aims at brevity and adjustability. Though new, it is almost foolproof. The author's name is found in the alphabetically arranged reference list, whereupon the number (showing in the left margin) jumps to attention. The numbering is renewed for each new name. If there are several authors with the same name, they are distinguished by the range of numbers. 0-199 represents one author, 200-399 another, 400-599 yet another, *etc.* Three-figure numbers starting with 1, 3, 5, etc. indicate the presence of co-authors (equal to the usual notation *et al.*).

In trying to write an integrated presentation of biological rhythm research, I was aware of the wide span of sciences which had to be covered, and which a single investigator cannot really hope to encompass. I beg the reader to endure such inadequacies as may have arisen therefrom. All criticism is welcome. On the other hand, one learns much from the attempt to cover such a pronouncedly interdisciplinary field and there are few things as satisfying as new knowledge. I hope that the reader may feel some of the enthusiasm I experienced.

I started on this book years ago in Sweden, while residing at the Anatomical Department of the Caroline Institute. Most of the work was, however, performed in Puerto Rico, at the Pharmacological Department of the Medical School. I am indebted to Dr. José del Castillo for the wholehearted support which was offered there in the form of leisure, stimulating criticism and secretarial help, and which made it at all possible for me to finish the book.

Especially, this book would not have been possible without the devoted help and healthy criticism of many friends. A profound gratitude goes to my wife who not only patiently endured all my author's woes and whims for four long years, but also helped with much of the typing and indexing and sat through innumerable evenings of proof-reading. Most of the figures have been prepared with remarkable draftsmanship by Miss Margaretha Anderson, the rest by Miss Jean DeBell, Miss Maj Bergman, Mrs. Barbro Perey, Mr. S. Pettersson and Mrs. Ulla Söderbäck. Miss Carmen Chico has helped with the indexing and produced several perfect editions of type-scripts. I am also grateful to the publishers for giving me a free hand with the layout and the figures for the book, and for their efforts to produce only the very best in the way of printing.

Many improvements in the book are due to the valuable discussion and advice by Drs. James Dickson, Hun Sun, Richard Levins and Lawrence Stark. More than anything else, however, I have profited from the discussions with Miss Jean DeBell (M.S.), which saved me from innumerable pitfalls in the formulation of my thoughts.

San Juan, September 1964

A. SOLLBERGER
Professor of Pharmacology,
University of Puerto Rico Medical School

CONTENTS

INTRODUCTION

CHAPTER 1

Introduction

1.1– This introduction serves several purposes. It discusses why biological rhythms should exist. It defines their basic properties. It draws a broad outline of the contents of the following chapters. This should help considerably in the study of the present book.

Biological rhythm research is a young though rapidly expanding science which embraces many disciplines: botany, forestry and agriculture; various branches of zoology; veterinary and human medicine; biochemistry, physiology, psychology and pathology; mathematics, statistics, cybernetics and philosophy. It is already difficult for a single student to cover all aspects. Let us, nevertheless, try to build up the concept of biological rhythms from the simplest possible premises, to interrelate the various subfields, and to present the essential problems of today and tomorrow.

1.2 – Living matter displays incessant movement; in space and time. We may call the study of the temporal aspect 'chronobiology'. Indeed, complete cessation of movement means death.

Time is the medium in which biological rhythms revolve, the independent variate in our graphs. Yet, we know almost nothing about it. According to older philosophers time was a measure of movement, in the modern version it reflects the increase in entropy. Maybe it is an entity of its own, maybe serial with time measuring time measuring time. Perhaps, time is vectorially related to space, or included in the concept of events (with dimensions duration – mass).

Rhythms constitute only one type of movement, the periodic fluctuation of values between two limits, regular chronobiological variation.

The existence of rhythmic variation in biology is evident, whatever the reason. Let us start with some simple considerations, as visualized in Fig. 1.2a, alternatives I-III.

1.3 – *The Rhythmic Universe* (*cf.* Fig. 1.2a, alternative I). All living organisms are set into the solid framework of the physical world, the structure of which pulses with an abundance of 'external rhythms': diurnal, tidal, seasonal, solar, sidereal. The capacity to follow them, to oscillate, would certainly enhance the survival potential of a species. Early man and his prey possessed 24-hour activity patterns, the poikilothermic and hibernating animals follow the seasonal changes in temperature, the tiny shore animals march up and down the beach with the tide. The construction of our bodies (randomly, genetically and selectively determined)

[3]

should therefore include components which are capable of rhythmic function. They do not necessarily have to be formed for this purpose but they must exist. Neither need they be absolutely conditioned by the environment. Once being present, for whatever reason, they might sometimes be expected to oscillate even if the external world is removed.

The capacity for oscillations may, then, be passive, the rhythm being entirely driven by some external forcing agent, a synchronizer or a 'Zeitgeber'. It might also be active, representing spontaneously oscillating systems with natural periods. Some of them, with frequencies approximately equal to that of the external rhythm may have been favoured by evolutional selection. Or, a harmonic or submultiple of the natural frequency may just happen to come sufficiently close to the external one. In both cases, a complete synchronization is possible. If no synchronization occurs, the natural frequency takes over.

1.4 – *The Energy Storage Rhythm. Energy Conservation* (*cf*. Fig. 1.2a, alternative II). There is an incessant change between feeding and resting, *i.e.* between energy storage and energy utilization in the body. This is a basic physiological phenomenon, conditional for our adaptation to the need for rapid action and survival.

An animal may have to wait many days before finding food. Even if surrounded by mountains of glucose it could not eat continuously, surely having other rituals to perform as well. Actually, we constantly encounter situations which demand instantaneous action, with an immediate release of stored energy. Let us take an extreme example: If I suddenly have to run at the sight of a lion, my muscles will work at the expense of glycogen stored in their cells. Otherwise, I would have to go in search of food, masticate it, swallow it, digest it, transport it from the alimentary canal to the blood stream, take it to the muscle cells and metabolize it there. The whole action would consume more energy than it produces and would be too slow.

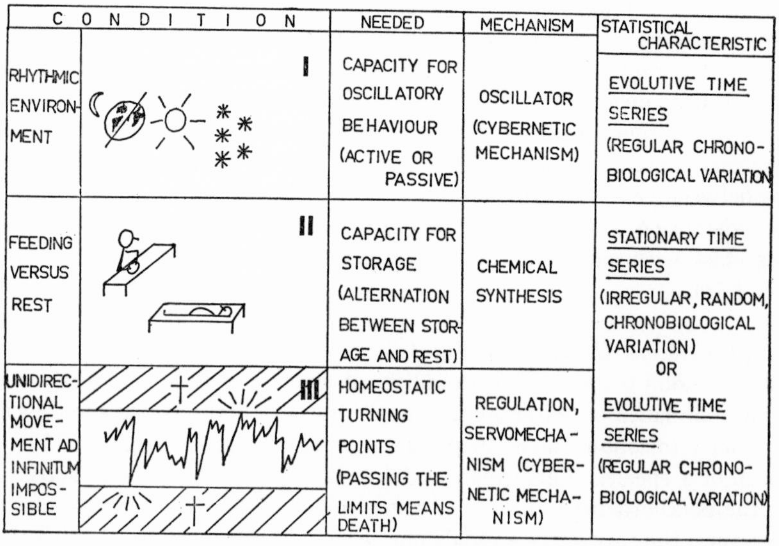

C O N D I T I O N		NEEDED	MECHANISM	STATISTICAL CHARACTERISTIC
RHYTHMIC ENVIRON-MENT	**I**	CAPACITY FOR OSCILLATORY BEHAVIOUR (ACTIVE OR PASSIVE)	OSCILLATOR (CYBERNETIC MECHANISM)	EVOLUTIVE TIME SERIES (REGULAR CHRONO-BIOLOGICAL VARIATION)
FEEDING VERSUS REST	**II**	CAPACITY FOR STORAGE (ALTERNATION BETWEEN STOR-AGE AND REST)	CHEMICAL SYNTHESIS	STATIONARY TIME SERIES (IRREGULAR, RANDOM, CHRONOBIOLOGICAL VARIATION) OR
UNIDIREC-TIONAL MOVE-MENT AD INFINITUM IMPOS-SIBLE	**III**	HOMEOSTATIC TURNING POINTS (PASSING THE LIMITS MEANS DEATH)	REGULATION, SERVOMECHA-NISM (CYBER-NETIC MECHA-NISM)	EVOLUTIVE TIME SERIES (REGULAR CHRONO-BIOLOGICAL VARIATION)

Fig. 1.2a. Some simple considerations concerning the causation of biological rhythm.

Clearly, the lion would be digesting me long before I could possibly digest any-thing myself. Or, if I have a gun which reduces my problem to merely flexing a finger, even this action requires the release of stored energy.

Thus, for any action the living entity needs energy, which is released instantly and which must be replaced immediately afterwards. There has to be an incessant change between storage and utilization. The ravenous appetite of the hibernating animal when emerging is, now, easy to appreciate. The energy storage variation may be irregular or regular. An example of the latter is our sleep-wakefulness rhythm.

1.5 – Without the energy storage system, an animal would have to float in a sea of food in splendid isolation in order to survive. Some unicellular organisms and the fetus come close to this. They would, however, perish promptly on separation from the source of food unless provided with built-in storage functions, *e.g.* the ability to form water-insoluble energy-rich substances such as glycogen and fat.

1.6 – The energy storage also aims at minimizing the total metabolic expenditure, *i.e.* at energy conservation. Actually, the body struggles hard at this. For instance, an excessive energy loss through the ultrafiltration of the blood in our kidneys is carefully prevented by a readsorption in the tubules (*e.g.* of glucose). The glycogen supply in the cells is incessantly replenished even at starvation, though it means a glyconeogenesis, a resynthesis from fat and protein. An example of how much energy such meticulous biochemical mechanisms conserve is that witnessed by the physician in cases of non-regulated diabetes. Here, we may find a ruthless squan-dering of enormous amounts of energy and energy-carrying substances through the futile feeding of a ravenous appetite and by a break-down of the own body substance with a rapid loss of weight.

Storage largely occurs through synthesis in the living organism, as does also the construction of the cytoplasmic framework of the body. Synthesis means *negative entropy* (entropy reversal), the local creation of order from disorder.

1.7 – *Limiting Conditions. Unidirectional Movement* (*cf.* Fig. 1.2a, alternative III). It is a common experience in physiology that there are limits to many processes, that unlimited unidirectional temporal movement is impossible. A slight rise in blood pressure may be valuable, increasing the pressure gradient for the exchange of low-molecular substances between the blood and its surroundings. It cannot, however, rise very far because there is a limit to the force with which the heart and the blood vessels can contract and press upon the blood as well as to the pres-sure which the vessel walls tolerate. The blood pressure has to turn and decrease again. – The blood-sugar-regulating release of glucose from the liver glycogen cannot proceed unbalanced. The stores in the liver would soon be exhausted. They have, thus, to be constantly refilled.

Actually, unidirectional movement is against the principle of energy conserva-tion. Such a system is sustained by the continuous conversion of one energy form into another with a concomitant heat production, a steady increase in entropy. It can only proceed as long as fuel is constantly thrown in at one end and waste products constantly removed at the other end. It stops when it runs out of fuel.

This would have happened to the animal kingdom long ago, if the plants had not continuously reversed the metabolic processes involved, turning waste into fuel again.

1.8 – *Homeostasis, Servomechanisms and Oscillators*. The observations of the limiting condition in biology gave rise to the concept of 'homeostasis', a precursor of modern cybernetics. When a function approaches a limit, the body counter-regulates. Actually, it tries to keep the levels of internal activity constant, working like a 'servomechanism'. Such systems are built upon the principles of *feedback*. They continuously search an equilibrium. If displaced from this state by some agent, they return to it. If such disturbances occur at random the function of the system in time may be described as an irregular chronobiological variation, if they describe a pattern, a passive, regular chronobiological variation would ensue. The regularity is forced upon the system from without.

The equilibrium is often a steady level of action. It may, however, also be dynamic, *e.g.* an oscillation. In this case, the biological feedback mechanism would act as an 'oscillator', characterized by active, regular chronobiological variation.

1.9 – *Time Series*. The three outlined mechanisms (Fig. 1.2a) cause fluctuations of biological variates between two limits. The movement may be classified as passive or active and regular or irregular chronobiological variation. Combinations may occur. The distinction is important for the theoretical analysis of rhythms, where the irregular forms may be compared to stationary time series and the regular forms to non-stationary time series.

In the stationary time series, the values fluctuate at random around a certain level or trend line. Given one value, at a certain time, we can never accurately predict the value at any other time, except stating the probabilities of it being so or so far from the trend line. These probabilities are unchanged in time. In practice, however, inertia prevents a completely random variation; that would amount to something like instantaneous random teleportation. Two successive values will therefore differ less than expected, causing serial correlation.

In the non-stationary time series, the rhythmic behaviour is known *a priori*. If one value is given, others have to deviate and can be predicted in time. In biological rhythm research the emphasis has slowly shifted from the stationary to the non-stationary aspect. The early students had to prove that biological rhythms existed, that they were 'not' stationary time series. Now, we can sometimes accept that the function *is* non-stationary and instead ask for its detailed characteristics.

1.10 – *Feedback*. The action of biological systems can be described in cybernetic terms where the interaction between parts is analysed as a flow of information, and self-regulation is explained in terms of feedback. Feedback, unfortunately, is as easy to understand in principle as it is difficult to handle mathematically (involving differential equations and nonlinear functions). They constitute systems where retrograde action occurs. If a process (information) runs from link to link in a mechanism, feedback exists if a later link acts back upon an earlier one, stimulating or depressing it, establishing a closed loop of action. In its simplest form this is equivalent to a mutual interaction between two variates, Fig. 1.10a.

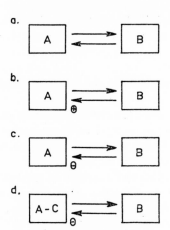

Fig. 1.10a-d. Types of feedback. $+$ = positive feedback, $-$ = negative feedback, c = reference value.

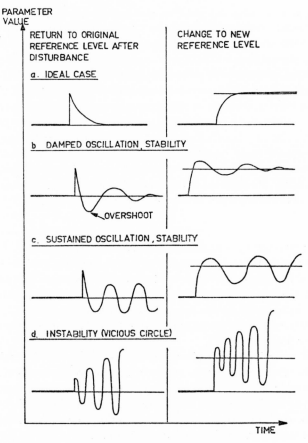

Fig. 1.12a-d. The oscillatory behaviour of servomechanisms.

1.11 – In *positive feedback* (Fig. 1.10b) the activity increases at each turn of the loop, until the limits of standstill or breakdown are reached. This corresponds to the vicious circle in psychology or pathology. Under certain circumstances the function oscillates regularly between an upper and a lower limit. In disease this may appear as a series of crises with intervening remissions.

1.12 – In *negative feedback* (Fig. 1.10c), the activity is damped at each turn of the loop until a standstill is achieved. Servomechanisms belong here (Fig. 1.10d) but in them it is the deviation from a control or reference value (C) which is brought to zero as in the ordinary thermostat, Fig. 1.12a.

Servomechanisms are built for stability. It may therefore surprise the biologist that they can oscillate. Actually, they often do so owing to inertia in the moving system, which causes overshoot (Fig. 1.12b). After a disturbance, the system returns to the reference position through a series of damped oscillations. If, however, the feedback is retarded or amplified, the oscillation may become sustained (Fig. 1.12c), or even increase in amplitude (Fig. 1.12d). The difference between oscillators and servomechanisms is small.

1.13 – Examples of biological servomechanisms are the pupillary reflex, whereby the retina regulates its own illumination, the endocrine system with the interaction between the pituitary and the peripheral glands, or chemical coupling in the carbohydrate metabolism.

Under special physiological or pathological conditions biological systems may oscillate. Examples are the pupillary movements under amplified illumination (hippus), the hand tremor in ethylism or aged people, the menstrual cycle, the blood-sugar variations in diabetes, the vegetative fluctuation in periodic disease or the rhythms in psychopathology. Animal population cycles may belong here (perhaps explained by a predator–prey feedback); parallels might be epidemics, economic cycles, and periodic wars. Chemical equilibria may sometimes be upset and yield periodic fluctuations, as in oscillating electrodes. Periodic growth may occur owing to the maturation time (synchronized cell division) or the competition for food.

1.14 – As an analogy with physical oscillators, biologists usually distinguish between external rhythms, endogenous rhythms, and exogenous rhythms. The external rhythms are represented by the surrounding synchronizers (*e.g.* light, temperature, the surrounding activity and regimen, atmospheric conditions). The endogenous rhythms reflect the natural frequency of spontaneously working bio-oscillators. The exogenous rhythms represent the synchronized (forced, entrained) biological rhythms.

A machine, once built, will always follow the same working rules. Of course, we may modify its function at will. Such a change is, however, an external manipulation, and we cannot perform that adequately, without guessing, until we know the mechanism of the machine. Similarly, a study of biological rhythms should start with the rhythmic aspects of its construction, the endogenous, spontaneous rhythms, the 'milieu interne' of biological rhythms.

1.15 – *Endogenous Rhythms*. Theoretically, the endogenous rhythms should appear if the organism is perfectly isolated from all external influences. This may, however, be difficult to achieve. Instead, we try to control as many environmental factors as possible. We may then suspect endogeneity if a periodicity of the biological function under study persists under constant conditions or deviates in frequency from all the frequencies known to occur in the surrounding world. In practice, it may suffice to control the strong synchronizers, especially light, temperature and the surrounding regimen. If, under constant conditions, an organism reverts to a spontaneous rhythm it is said to 'free-run'.

The endogenous rhythms are caused by biological oscillators. They run with frequencies from 1000 c/sec to durations of one day, month, year or more. There are: rhythmic nervous activity (nerve impulses, electroencephalogram, tremor; tapping, chewing, walking and breathing rhythms); other rhythmic muscular contractions (wing beats, ear movements in bats, periodic opening of mussel valves, contraction waves in worms, peristalsis, gastric or uterine contractions, heart rates, pulse waves, blood pressure variations, etc.); mental activity rhythms (in reaction times, interpretation of ambiguous optic illusions, judgement of time durations and creativity); variations in depth of sleep or frequency of dreaming; protoplasmic rhythms (contracting vacuoles, ciliary motion, circumnutating movements of growing plant tendrils); cyclic water and ion exchange over cell membranes or electric biopotential fluctuation in plant roots; rhythmic glandular secretion; sexual cycles.

1.16 – *Circadian Rhythms*. Highly interesting are the endogenous rhythms with external correlates, where the natural period approaches that of external periods. They were earlier regarded as exogenous rhythms. However, they seem to persist even if the synchronizer disappears. The best-studied example is the 24-h (diurnal) cycle in unicellular organisms, plants, invertebrates and vertebrates (though lunar or seasonal counterparts may exist). At constant light and temperature the periodicity remains, though the period often deviates from 24 h (about 19-29 h). Such oscillations are called circadian (circa die = about a day) or endodiurnal. Many authors regard them as purely endogenous, favoured by genetical selection. For instance, they do not occur in plants bred in darkness, but may appear after one single short light signal and may proceed in the manner of damped oscillations; in animals similar periods may even become sustained. The sensitivity to light also displays circadian cycles, which may be used as a time scale for testing the length of the daylight period. Animals and plants can "judge" the proper time of the year for moulting or flowering in this way. Then, the circadian light cycle has to be synchronized by external agents. This 'photoperiodism' is governed by non-chlorophyll plant pigments sensitive to red and far-red light or by neuro-endocrine pathways in animals.

1.17 – *Temperature Independence*. Another remarkable quality of the circadian rhythm is the temperature independence. Metabolic processes usually speed up with rising temperature (Q_{10} = quotient of metabolisms at 10°C intervals = 2-3). Similarly, endogenous rhythms should increase in frequency. This usually applies to endogenous rhythms without correlates but *not* to the circadian ones (Q_{10} only 0.9-1.3). Different explanations exist, *e.g.*:

(1) *Diffusion* processes are included in the feedback loops. Q_{10} for diffusion is small.
(2) *Molecular rhythms* used as timers, in the same way as ammonia or quartz vibrations may be used for controlling the period of a 24-hour clock by *demultiplication* (counting of each nth impulse).
(3) Servomechanisms with stable frequencies may be constructed out of temperature-dependent parts, a kind of temperature compensation.
(4) The rhythms are really somehow exogenous.

1.18 – *Time Sense. Animal Orientation.* The synchronized circadian rhythm is probably responsible for the remarkable time sense of the plants and animals, the 'biological clock'. Plants know at which hour to open their flowers, which enabled LINNAEUS to construct his 'flower clock'. Bees can be trained to feed at certain times. Many people can wake up in the morning at predetermined hours. A time sense (a chronometer) is also needed in true orientation, especially across the longitudes.

Animal orientation may work by simple 'taxis' (towards or against light, smell, wind, current, gravity) or through visible references, 'landmarks', with calculation of the angle between the directions to the reference point and the goal, the target angle. If the reference point moves, however, the target angle may change continuously, as when the sun, the moon, or maybe even the stars are used. Then the true time must be known, to evaluate the position of the reference point. This occurs in true animal migration, whether the movements with the tide of tiny shore inhabitants (*e.g.* crabs or beach fleas) or the travel between continents of birds or fish. The animals keep the direction sense when removed from the natural habitat if the celestial body is visible. If taken to another hemisphere blindfolded they usually keep the old circadian time and accordingly use the wrong target angle for some time, when seeing the sun again, until re-synchronized with external events. The mysterious 'homing' capacity of pigeons from places which they have never seen before, has called forth a series of other theories on animal orientation, from inertial guidance to extrasensory perception.

1.19 – *External Rhythms. Synchronizers.* We may distinguish between 'dominant synchronizers', with clear strong effects and 'weak synchronizers'. Dominant synchronizers are light, temperature (especially in plants) and the surrounding regimens (specially in *Homo*). If present, they effect synchronization. If they are absent, the others may take over, but usually freerunning occurs.

The problem is to define the weak synchronizers. Which are they? Can they act simultaneously with or only in the absence of dominant synchronizers? Which external factors can *not* act as synchronizers? Does it have to be 'full synchronization', as with the dominant agents, or is there such a thing as 'relative synchronization' (as may be observed between freerunning coupled oscillators)?

Actually, in our experiments with constant external conditions, we can never be quite sure, (1) that we know all the physical forces acting upon the body or all frequencies which may appear in them; and (2) whether they do not still act upon the organism interfering in some way with the endogenous rhythms. The ideal site for our experiments would, presumably, be the emptiest place in space between the galaxies, though ... Who knows? We do not know the forces which create new galaxies out of hydrogen clouds. Vast magnetic fields seem to be involved in the creation and sustenance of matter. Where in space do radiation, magnetism and gravitation really cease to operate? What is gravitation? Neither can we with untroubled conscience absolutely deny the presence of parapsychological forces or the holistic concept of all universe as one single gestalt, as a philosophical superstructure where all things are interconnected, though the burden of proof might not seem to rest with us.

Perhaps, we should restrict the term 'weak synchronizers' to such agents which may obviously substitute for the absent dominant ones, such as sound, vibration, atmospheric humidity or pressure; and designate the others as 'subtle synchronizers'.

1.20 – The possibility for the existence of subtle synchronizers has also helped to promote new views on our sensory mechanisms. Earlier physiologists generally required the presence of a tangible sensory organ for each active modality of stimulus. Now, the space-age forcibly reminds us that we have a gravitation sense (if only the collected information from the stretch receptors and the labyrinth). The influence of the cosmic radiation has long been discussed. The effect of magnetic and electrostatic forces upon life is studied. Perhaps the action is directly upon the sensitive ion equilibria of the cell membrane, upon the orientation of the free radicals, or upon the organic colloids. Even inorganic colloids seem to be influenced by cosmic events, maybe affecting the quasi-crystalline structure of the water. Forces of this kind may perhaps also be modulated by other external factors and carry information through to the organism. This field of study is important for our attempts at adaptation in space.

1.21 – The estimation of cosmic periods requires reference points which may,

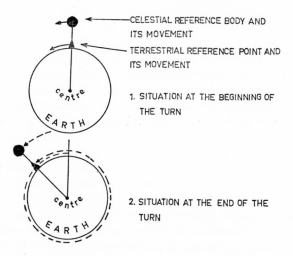

Fig. 1.21a. The use of reference bodies in determining the duration of cosmic cycles.

themselves, be in motion, Fig. 1.21a. The values will therefore vary with the reference. There is, for instance, a sidereal day, a solar day, and a lunar day (about 50 minutes longer than the others). Other cosmic cycles have also been advocated as synchronizers, *e.g.* various sunspot periods. Such connections are more difficult to prove.

1.22 – *Synchronization.* Different kinds of synchronization occur. Phase synchronization is comparable to the setting of a clock. Often, one single signal suffices for this. Frequency synchronization is comparable to the speed adjustment of a clock. Full synchronization would mean that the exogenous rhythm should follow the external agent perfectly at steady state. Before this is achieved, the system usually runs through a series of more irregular transients. The usual mathematical approach to forced oscillations is to determine the conditions necessary in the system for attaining full synchronization. One condition is that the forcing frequency and the natural frequency of the system must not differ too much, which holds for circadian rhythms. Partial synchronization has been less explored. In nonlinear systems synchronization with harmonics or subharmonics of the driving force may occur. There also exists the possibility of frequency transformations.

1.23 – Biological frequency transformation is postulated in the 'autophasing' theory of circadian rhythms, where a true 24-h input of subtle synchronizers is supposed to be transformed in the organism at random to produce a circadian output. An analogy would be two equal gear-wheels where the driving wheel works at a certain rate and the other is slipping somewhat, running at another rate. The mechanism is supposed to help in the adjustment to the normal environment, where the *synchronizing events* continuously change their timing though the average frequency remains 24 h, *e.g.* sunrise and sunset hours. The circadian rhythm would then eternally 'hunt' the external one, searching phase synchronization with it.

1.24 – Another question is which of the events in the external rhythm act upon the organism. Is it the values of the function itself or the changes in those values (proportional or differential synchronizers)? Is it both? Or are there other specifiable events which may trigger reactions in the biological system? Can the organism perceive the direction of the process; or does it react similarly to equal changes in the external variate whichever the direction, unidirectionality (can it for instance distinguish between dawn and dusk or do these two stimuli cause equal effects)?

1.25 – *Interaction Between Rhythms.* Biological systems contain innumerable oscillators with different frequencies. These may interact. Furthermore, synchronizing agents may modify this by acting upon one or several of the bio-oscillators. There may also be several conflicting synchronizers each trying to force one or several of the natural rhythms. They may even act upon different parameters of one single (nonlinear) oscillator. The situation will necessarily be complicated. The mathematical and physical models for this are the coupled oscillators.

1.26 – Two rather different kinds of interaction may be mentioned here, super-position (beats) and relative coordination (frequency coupling). Superposition is the phenomenon found in wave-theory, where the effect of different influences at a certain point are mathematically additive. Relative coordination is usually found when 'relaxation oscillators' (energy slowly stored and suddenly released, as opposed to the regular shift between kinetic and static energy in the pendu-lum) are coupled together. In this case, the oscillators try to find some kind of compromise, either a common intermediate frequency or some kind of phase relationship between different frequencies. If the oscillators run too much out of phase, one of them may skip a beat, or jump phase, or a sequence of irregular beats are intercalated. This is seen in the relation between auricular and ventricu-lar heart beats in cardiac block.

1.27 – *Exogenous Rhythms*. Normally, the dominant synchronizers are always present (exceptions may be arctic conditions, wherefrom interesting experiments emanate). Most publications on biological rhythms concern the clearly exogenous rhythms, especially the synchronized circadian ones. There are few functions in plants and animals which do not exhibit a 24-h behaviour. Seasonal rhythms are also universal. Beautiful examples of lunar influences exist, such as the movements of shore animals or of marine life (*e.g.* eels or the palolo worm).

1.28 – *Experimental Approach*. The study of biological rhythms may involve different modes of approach: (1) experiments with modification of the external influences; (2) comparison between recorded rhythms and analog models, physical or mathematical; (3) mathematical and statistical analysis of recorded rhythms.
   All three methods have their disadvantages: (1) in experimental modifications one can never be certain that all external influences are really under control; (2) there already exists a disconcerting number of models. It is remarkable how one and the same function may be mimicked by several constructions built upon the most conflicting theories; (3) the mathematical and statistical analyses are highly complicated.

1.29 – *Recording and Description of Rhythms*. Periods may appear in time or space. The latter may often be regarded as memories of the former (phonograph records, our rhythm graphs, or rhythmic growth patterns such as tree rings).

1.30 – Periodic phenomena may exhibit many shapes (Fig. 1.30a), *e.g.* discrete impulses, sinusoid waveforms, relaxation oscillations or various combinations. One important synchronizer, the 24-h light changes, forms a combination of the impulse and sine wave (Fig. 1.30a). Furthermore, its shape varies continually. Often, the transitions between light and darkness are relatively abrupt, especially in experimental set-ups, and may perhaps be regarded as two discrete signals (light-on and light-off, dawn and dusk).

1.31 – A rhythm proceeds at a certain speed. The velocity can be represented by the derivative of the periodic function. Another definition, the angular velocity, stems from the fact that a sine curve may be derived from a vector rotating at

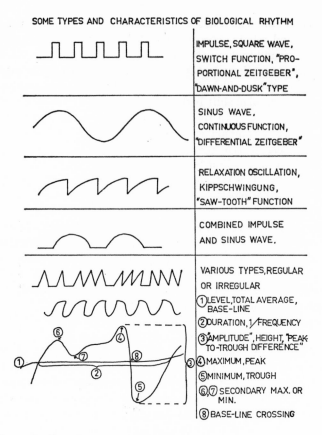

Fig. 1.30a. Some rhythm shapes and definitions.

constant velocity (Fig. 1.31a). The speed is then expressed as degrees or radians per time unit. Any one point on a cycle may be described by an angle between 0° and 360°. The phase angle gives the distance of this point in degrees from any arbitrary position on the time scale or from the corresponding point on another cycle (Fig. 1.31b). Non-sine curves may be regarded as having a variable angular velocity or at least an average angular velocity per cycle.

1.32 – Periodic signals may also be used to carry further information, through different kinds of amplitude and frequency modulation. In biological rhythms, considerable noise may also be added. The final curve may have a quite complicated and irregular shape.

1.33 – Owing to the variability in the exogenous rhythm curves an accurate description is difficult. Simple models as those in Fig. 1.30a do not suffice. Two alternatives exist. Either conventional statistical methods are used in defining the data; this usually entails a considerable loss of information and accuracy in the process. Or, a strict mathematical description by use of the harmonic analysis is performed. Here, the difficulty lies in the computational labour and in the evaluation of the results.

1.34 – Some simple statistical criteria of description are shown in Fig. 1.30a, such as the level, height (range), duration (or frequency), and timing of peaks or other

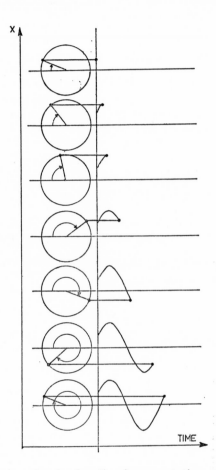

Fig. 1.31a. The generation of a sine function from a rotating vector.

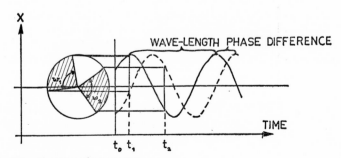

Fig. 1.31b. The phase angle concept.

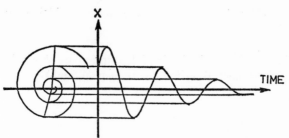

Fig. 1.31c. The generation of a damped sine function from a spiral.

events. Levels, ranges and frequencies may be interrelated in various ways. Timing successive peaks in circadian rhythms has yielded important data. – Activity rhythms, where activity is recorded per time unit, are not truly continous functions, which is a theoretical disadvantage. However, they have yielded a wealth of information about biological rhythms.

The ideal study should embrace the use of all information in continous rhythm functions from single individuals combined into larger groups. Telemetering methods of recording are always preferable.

1.35 – Many important modern descriptive methods are related to the 'harmonic' or 'Fourier analysis', *i.e.* a representation as the algebraic sum of a series of sine

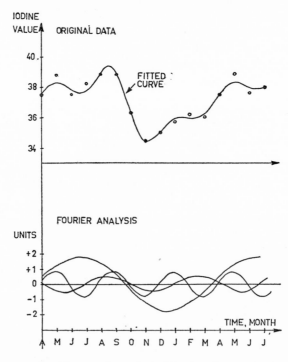

Fig. 1.35a. An example of harmonic analysis. The fitted curve is obtained by addition of the harmonics. The observed data deviate from the fitted curve. Adapted after Bliss.

functions of different frequencies and amplitudes, Fig. 1.35a. These frequencies must be multiples of the fundamental harmonic, else the curves do not cancel out at the nodes. If the main period is not known *a priori,* a series of different funda-mental harmonics have to be tried (say, with 22, 23, 24, 25, 26 hour durations).

The assemblage of sine curves describes the average rhythm perfectly. Any recurrent peak, trough or irregularity is reported. This does not necessarily mean that all the component waves exist as biological entities. In some cases, however, does the procedure have an evident biological meaning, as in the pattern of reflected waves in a pulse tracing.

Different types of harmonic analysis exist. They may be obtained by tedious mathematical computations or mechanical, optic and electronic computers. They include several modifications of straightforward Fourier analysis; autocorrela-tion (correlating a curve with itself, moved one or several steps out of phase); and cross-correlation. The results may be represented by 'an amplitude spectrum' (per-iodogram, frequencies on the x-axis, corresponding amplitude estimates on the y-axis); a 'power spectrum' (replacing the amplitudes with a variance estimate); or a 'phase spectrum' (phases plotted against frequencies).

1.36 – *Statistical Analysis of Rhythms.* After having achieved a description of our data we must test them for statistical significance. Even a series of random num-bers may form suggestive shapes if plotted and connected by lines. The statistical analysis may be applied either to simple statistical parameters (1.34) or to the harmonic description (1.35). The former case usually includes the use of conven-tional parametric or the newer non-parametric tests, which are based on the properties of the random "normal" Gaussian distribution. Tests for the significance of the Fourier pattern are based on the properties of the stationary time series, *i.e.* one proves that the rhythm is not stationary. This type of analysis derived much impetus from attempts to predict economical cycles. Somehow, the approach is peculiar, since biological rhythms are non-stationary time series. The direct statistical properties of these series have not attracted much attention.

1.37 – Conventional parametric statistical tests have been extensively used on biological rhythm data. However, their use and interpretation in case of non-stationary time series is much more uncertain than one would think. For instance, the standard deviations and other parameters of the frequency distribution vary in groups of data collected at different times in the cycle. This makes the appli-cability of such tests as the t-test or the analysis of variance doubtful. Probably, one should always at least try to use non-parametric tests instead.

Even measures such as the statistical average are uncertain, Fig. 1.37a.

It is easily seen that the "vertical" average may be misleading if phase differen-ces exist. On the other hand, the "horizontal" average cannot be calculated unless the amplitudes of the single curves are first equalized.

1.38 – Phenomena like those in Fig. 1.37a emphasize the importance of the 'time domain'. It is often helpful not to think in terms of values but in terms of the time when a certain value appears. This explains why such a simple para-meter as the peak-time has yielded so much information about biological rhythms.

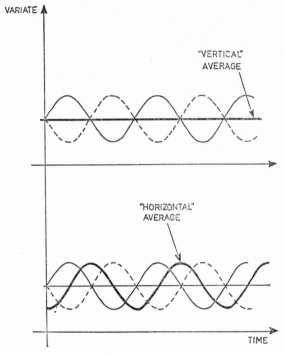

Fig. 1.37a. Possible average curves between cycles.

Consider the action of a synchronizing impulse on the random phase differences between a series of cycles. If there is any effect at all, the curves will come closer in time, Fig. 1.38a. This would reduce the "horizontal" variation between the curves. Here lies a possible method of finding external components in biological rhythms (20.30).

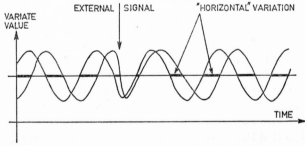

Fig. 1.38a. Synchronization effect on the horizontal variation between cycles.

1.39 – Tests for the 'Fourier method' are more complicated. The analysis may be carried through any number of harmonics. For judging when maximal information has been achieved various statistical procedures may be used. They may entail tests for the dominance of the amplitude or the power contributed by a certain harmonic. This comprises a comparison with the corresponding characteristics of the stationary time series which may be regarded as a conglomerate of all possible cycle frequencies and amplitudes, all with equal probabilities of existence. The latter is why the analysis of a biological rhythm by pure inspection is dangerous. If one looks energetically enough for a certain cycle in a random time series one is apt to find it sooner or later. It *is* there, together with all other possible cycles.

The 'analysis of variance' may be used in testing fitted average curves according to Fig. 1.35a. One computes the variance of the observed data around the calculated curve. As long as real new harmonics enter, the variance decreases significantly. If it does not, the additions are meaningless.

One difficulty from the biological point of view is that most types of harmonic analysis require long stretches of cycle records. They may, however, be adapted for single cycles, where data from different subjects replace the individual succession of rhythms.

Another difficulty derives from the serial correlation in biological data, which causes periodicities. The use of moving averages, or integration of the curves strengthens the serial correlation and may give unwanted components in the harmonic analysis.

1.40 – Special statistical problems arise when we investigate connections between external and biological rhythms. One possible approach was outlined in Fig. 1.38a. Usually, one tries to search the respective Fourier wave patterns for common elements. This is difficult. The driving rhythm and the exogenous one do not really have to coincide either in phase, frequency or shape. On the other hand, the occurrence of two similar cycles may easily be a pure coincidence. The statistical comparison would still yield a 'significant' result (nonsense correlation). A method which is seldom used in biology but which should be applied often is the cross-correlation analysis. It is calculated as the autocorrelation, but between two different curves.

1.41 – As can be seen, biological rhythm research is an interdisciplinary science which covers a very wide field. In order to facilitate contacts between workers in the field, the 'Society for Biological Rhythm' was founded in 1937. It also aims at arranging conferences (1937, 1939, 1949, 1953, 1955, 1957, 1960, 1963), establishing a library and developing a suitable nomenclature. A consistent terminology is, however, presently difficult to develop, partly owing to our lack of knowledge concerning the mechanisms behind the biological rhythm phenomena. Numerous synonyms are being used.

1.42 – We have now made an introductory survey of biological rhythm research to facilitate the reading of the following chapters. For convenience, the material in this book is presented under four main headings, *viz.*:

PART I

ENDOGENOUS RHYTHMS

"So in one place the blood stops, in another it passes sluggishly, in another more quickly. The progress of the blood through the body proving irregular, all kinds of irregularities occur".

HIPPOCRATES – Breaths XIV.

This part deals with the spontaneous biological rhythms and mechanisms which may generate them or influence their setting. The reading is facilitated if the introductory Chapter 1 is studied first, especially sections 1.-18. The subject is developed in ten chapters:

CHAPTER 2

General Cybernetics

2.1 – Survival in a variable external world demands the capacity for self-regulation. This was long regarded as one of the typical properties of life as contrasted to dead matter. Comprehension of its working mechanisms has slowly developed from the concepts of adaptability, homeostasis and stress syndrome to information theory and cybernetics. The governing principle behind the phenomenon is the feedback, as discussed in the introduction (1.10-13, Figs. 1.10a-d and 1.12a-d). Cybernetics is a wide term (ASHBY[1], WIENER[2]) covering the general behaviour of machines, whether animate or inanimate.

2.2 – *Homeostasis.* We have seen (1.4-6) that a spontaneous, truly endogenous alternation between utilization and storage of energy, of *actio* and *reactio*, of entropy increase and reversal, is necessary for the maintenance of life. These fluctuations do not have to be rhythmic and may be regarded as the simplest form of chronobiological variation (1.2,8,9). However, there must be a certain amount of balance between the counteracting forces. Else, irreparable damage may befall the highly ordered complexity of the living entity. Especially, the organism must guard against extreme deviations, whether caused by intrinsic variation or extrinsic factors. As a matter of fact, we live in a rather hostile environment, threatened by a variety of noxious stimuli, even by too much and too little of what we need. The dangers of freezing or fire, flood or drought, suffocation and starvation, poisons and parasites, somatic and psychic disease, predators, accidents and wars are but a few examples. Furthermore, we consist of parts which are extremely vulnerable, being built of highly specialized cells or organelles which may succumb to even a slight shift in the surrounding temperature, in pH, potassium contents, oxygen saturation or other parameters.

It is nothing less than a marvel that we can exist under such conditions. Actually, the cells of our bodies live in a 'milieu interne' (CLAUDE BERNARD) or 'fluid matrix' (CANNON) of high stability. This equilibrium is guarded by a wealth of biological regulators which fend off and neutralize any foreign influence.

The following quotations (CANNON) show how the comprehension of these phenomena developed.

CLAUDE BERNARD, 1860-78: "It is the fixity of the milieu interne which is the condition of free and independent life". "All the vital mechanisms, however varied they may be have only one object, that of preserving constant the conditions of life in the internal environment."

PFLÜGER, 1877: "The cause of every need of a living being is also the cause of the satisfaction of the need."

FREDERICQ, 1885: "The living being is an agency of such sort that each disturbing influence induces by itself the calling forth of compensatory activity to neutralize or repair the disturbance."

RICHET, 1900: "The living being is stable. It must be so in order not to be destroyed, dissolved or disintegrated by the colossal forces, often adverse, which surround it. By an apparent contradiction it maintains its stability only if it is excitable and capable of modifying itself according to external stimuli and adjusting its response to the stimulation. In a sense it is stable because it is modifiable; the slight instability is the necessary condition for the true stability of the organism."

CANNON, 1926: "In an open system, such as our bodies represent, compounded of unstable material and subjected continually to disturbing conditions, constancy is in itself evidence that agencies are acting or ready to act, to maintain this constancy."

"If a state remains steady it does so because any tendency towards change is automatically met by increased effectiveness of the factor or factors which resist the change."

"The regulating system which determines a homeostatic state may comprise a number of cooperating factors brought into action, at the same time or successively."

"When a factor is known which can shift a homeostatic state in one direction, it is reasonable to look for automatic control of that factor, or for a factor or factors having an opposing effect."

One may thus follow a broad line of development from CLAUDE BERNARD through the homeostasis concept of CANNON (who attributed the regulation mainly to the autonomous nervous system) and the adaptation syndrome of SELYE (who added the endocrine regulation) to WIENER[2], who systematized the study of the biological regulators and thereby created a new science, Cybernetics.

2.3 – *General Cybernetics*. In its most general form, cybernetics states the laws of 'behaviour of machines', whether simple or complex, whether mechanical or biological. The essential thing is not how they are constructed, but what they do. Widely different devices may yield the same result. A sine wave may be obtained from a mechanism of cogs and wheels, vibrating strings or an electronic device. We simply ask how information is being passed through the machine, and this is expressable in mathematical terms.

ASHBY's particularly lucid presentation of general cybernetics gives a good introduction to the subject. Consider what happens when we press the key on a piano, Fig. 2.3a, or the cybernetic analog, Fig. 2.3b. (Box notation is used; the boxes may represent a machine or a pure event; the arrows only show the direction and sequence of interactions, not quantitative relationships.)

The whole procedure, where an operator acts upon an operand, changing it to a transform, from one state to another, is called a transition. If the same operator acts on several operands we get a set of transitions, a transformation. If several fingers play simultaneously they together define a vector of states to be transformed. In most machines, a series of transitions follow each other in time forming a trajectory.

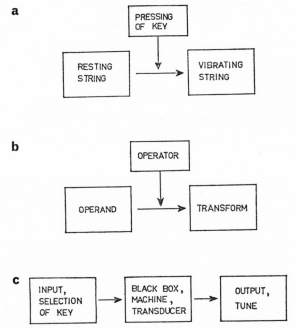

a

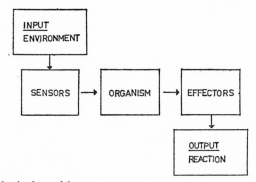

b

c

Fig. 2.3a-c. The piano playing operation.

2.4– Now, consider the piano as a machine (transducer) containing a number of possible transformations which may be chosen at will by selecting the proper keys. The operator is now the input of the transducer and the transform is the output, Fig. 2.3c. *Transducer* is the technical term for a machine. The expression 'black box' indicates that we need not know its construction, however complex, to

Fig. 2.4a. The biological machine.

Fig. 2.4b. The biological regulation machine I, *cf.* Fig. 2.6a.

make it work as desired or to investigate its function. The operation remains essentially the same if the string piano is replaced by an electric piano or an organ. The input (Eingangsgrösse) is delivered as a signal (disturbance, Störgrösse, stimulus, message, information) directly from the environment or changed by a transformator (sensor, Messwerk, réacteur) into a form suitable for the transducer. (The transformator is really just another transducer). The output (Ausgangsgrösse) represents the results delivered by the machine, either directly, of further manipulated to fit the environment by another transformator (effector, Stellwerk, effecteur). Compare this with a biological machine, Fig. 2.4a, and its homeostatic version, Fig. 2.4b.

2.5 – *Biological Regulation.* The living organism is a typical black box. We will never know its construction in detail, since it is as complex as the observer himself. We may nevertheless learn much about its action by studying how the external input affects the output of the organism, *viz.* the behaviour of the organism. The environment acts upon the organism (O) by way of disturbances (D) of the equilibrium between the environment and organism, bringing about the effect (E). Let us try some examples.

Prolonged iodine deficiency (D) in the food brings about an increase of the thyroid size (E, goiter) of the eater (O), coupled with a hypofunction of the organ. Prolonged psychic stress (D) may also excite the thyroid of a nervous person (O) to enlarge (E, hyperthyreosis). The appearance (D) of a hawk in the visual field of a small bird (O) causes the latter animal to lie still (E). The retinal picture of a BEM(bug-eyed monster, D), if realistic enough, may perhaps make the most astute of us (O) feel faint (E).

2.6 – The effect of disturbances on the organism may often be dangerous or deleterious to the entity. In order to counteract this, the organism will have to change either itself or the environment in some suitable way. This process is called *regulation.* The problem is to protect the 'milieu interne', *i.e.* to nullify the effect (E) of the disturbance (D) on the fluid matrix. Peculiarly, this is performed by organs in the 'milieu externe' (regulators) which are exposed to environmental manipulation but which themselves contain a fluid matrix. The distinction between a milieu interne and externe is functional, rather than morphological. Let us, simply, define the system as follows, Fig. 2.4b: The disturbance from the environment is received by the 'milieu externe' part of the organism (ME) which transmits an effect to the 'milieu interne' part of the organism (MI). This is also shown in Fig. 2.6a in a shorthand version.

The definition of the outer and inner milieus, which is tried here, may seem peculiar. Earlier investigators could draw a clear line between an individual and his environment. However, parts of the organism are *not* in constancy, though the component cells may be undisturbed. Furthermore, modern man builds his own environment to such an extent that it is truly only an extension of himself.

The regulator, R, which may be regarded as a part of the ME, now has to change either the environment, D(ENV), or the ME itself, O(ME), in order to nullify the effect on the MI, E(MI). See Fig. 2.6b.

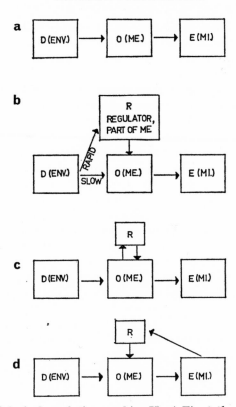

Fig. 2.6a-d. The biological regulation machine II, *cf.* Fig. 2.4b.

2.7 – *Regulation Paths.* From the informational point of view, we may say that D(ENV) represents a variety of influences, or information, which reaches the O(ME) and gives the effect E(MI). Without going into proofs (see ASHBY[2]) we may state that the E(MI) can also show variety, but never more than enters from the D(ENV). The significance of the regulator R is to block the passage of variety, or information, from D(ENV) to E(MI), *i.e.* to keep the output E(MI) of the organism constant against a variety in the input D(ENV). The regulation can set in at different stages in the system, see Fig. 2.6b-d. The arrows in the figure represent the flow of information, not the actual regulation. The latter may be performed by different organs and in different ways, such as changing the environment or damping out the disturbance during its passage in the ME.

2.8 – One type of regulation, Fig. 2.6b, occurs when the response sets in before the disturbance D(ENV) reaches the organism. The regulator R is directly informed about D(ENV) and modifies O(ME) so as to oppose D(ENV) when the latter arrives. The winter drop in temperature D(ENV) may expose us O(ME) to colds E(MI) unless we counterregulate by putting on warmer clothes. If we are far-sighted we may actually do this before the low temperature reaches our bodies. This type of regulation requires that the information from D(ENV) reaches R before it gets to the O(ME) and that R be swift so that O(ME) can also act before

D(ENV) arrives. Such anticipation or input prediction is possible if some rapid communication channel exists between D(ENV) and R, *e.g.* light, radio or the press, perhaps aided by the memory of previous events or by training.

2.9 – Unfortunately, perfect regulation is less common in biology. Consider now the situation in Fig. 2.6c. The regulator R is not informed about the disturbance D(ENV) until this has already reached O(ME) and brought about some kind of change in it. R is informed through O(ME). Still, R may block further passage to ME. If the winter D(ENV) comes unexpectedly, or if we are careless, we, O(ME), will actually freeze before we decide to dress appropriately. This regulation is less rapid and less efficient. Probably, the cold will be averted, but we cannot be certain.

2.10 – In Fig. 2.6d, the regulator is informed first when the dreaded event has timed. If we do not heed the signs of winter, we may actually catch a cold. Then however, we will regulate, partly by other means than merely donning heavy clothes, such as going to bed and taking pills. This regulation is inefficient but not without value. It may prevent us from getting a severe and perhaps lethal virus pneumonia.

2.11 – Physiology and medicine abound in examples of biological regulation. In starvation hunger urges the individual to eat. If necessary the precious blood glucose level is even upheld by a glyconeogenesis. – Thirst regulates the water

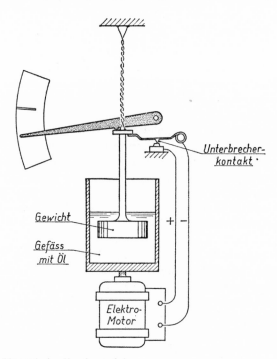

Fig. 2.12a. VON HOLST's feedback model.

intake. – Changes in body pH may be induced by accidental ingestion of acids or alkali, by excessive loss of H_2CO_3 in hyperventilation (bad habit, at hysteria or in crying children), or in diabetes (production of low-molecular fatty acids). They are countered by the buffer action of the alkali reserve (changes in available H_2CO_3 through regulation of CO_2 ventilation in the lungs) or by excretion of excess positive or negative ions in the urine (neutralized in the urine by other ions normally present in a non-ionic state in the body, such as phosphate from the bones or ammonia synthesized in the kidney from amino acids). – Degenerated blood vessels (in atherosclerosis) are strengthened by calcium deposits, the resulting increase in peripheral circulatory resistance is met by a rise in blood pressure. – Anoxia of the tissues is prevented by a rise in the amount of oxygen-carrying substance or in an increased circulation of the amount already present (tachycardia). As further regulatory measures we may administer oxygen, or remove such obstacles to free passage in the air-ways as may be present. We may even slow down the need of the tissues for oxygen by prescribing rest, antithyroid drugs or even hypothermia, which decrease the metabolism.

2.12 – *Definition of Feedback.* In the examples of biological regulation, Fig. 2.6, the actual regulatory process is not shown. It works according to the principle of

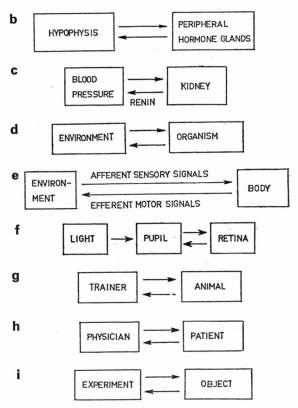

Fig. 2.12b-i. Various biological feedback examples.

feedback, as discussed in the introduction (1.10-13, Fig. 1.10). Before we enter into a systematic description of this phenomenon some examples, especially from biology, might be useful.

Feedback implies that a later state in a series of coupled processes (a trajectory, *cf.* 2.3) may act backwards and modify an earlier link, thus changing the subsequent outcome. If restricted to two links, this is in essence a case of mutual interaction. This may result in a steady-state balance between the two factors or else in periodic variations of the relations between them. Feedback is the foundation of 'robotics', and thus of our modern culture. Most machines work nowadays with feedback, even mechanical toys. There are fire-engines which run in a semicircle to the left → stop → hoist the ladder → retract it again → start → run in a semicircle to the right → stop → hoist ladder → retract ladder → start → run in a semicircle to the left → etc., re-enacting the whole sequence again and again as long as the system is supplied with external energy. Other examples from everyday technology are an ordinary buzzer, or the thermostatic temperature control in a house or in the biologists' water bath. VON HOLST[4] has constructed an instructive model, Fig. 2.12a, which also well demonstrates that feedback systems may work rhythmically. Fig. 2.12b-i lists a number of biological counterparts, to be discussed later.

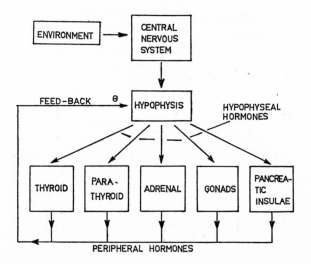

Fig. 2.13a. The endocrine feedback.

2.13 – *Biological Feedback Examples* (Fig. 2.12b-i). Illustrative examples of biological feedback may be found at any level of organization; in the body chemistry, endocrine system, nervous system and psychological interactions; in plants and animals. Take the endocrine balance (Fig. 2.12b) which results from a closed interaction cycle between the pituitary and peripheral hormone glands, according to the following scheme:

(1) increasing secretion of anterior pituitary hormone, APH
(2) transportation of APH with blood
(3) APH reaches target, peripheral endocrine gland
(4) peripheral gland secretes more hormone, PGH
(5) PGH passes with blood
(6) PGH reaches anterior pituitary
(7) PGH inhibits secretion of APH
(8) decreasing APH secretion
(9) decreasing PGH secretion
(10) PGH inhibition of APH secretion withdrawn
(11) increasing APH secretion

The system is depicted in Fig. 2.13a. It may reach an equilibrium aiming at keeping the blood PGH constant. The level as such is set by the hypophysis as controlled by the brain and the environment. If unstable, the system may oscillate between high and low hormone levels, as in the oestrus cycle. *Cf.* the insect endocrine system (DE WILDE) and MARTINI[300].

2.14 – The *renal blood pressure control* (Fig. 2.12c) aims at avoiding a drop in the glomerular filtration pressure in the kidneys:

(1) blood pressure decreases
(2) kidney circulation impaired (glomerular filtration of urine endangered)
(3) kidney anoxia
(4) kidney secrets the hormone renin
(5) renin passes with blood
(6) renin reaches blood pressure regulation centre
(7) blood pressure increases
(8) and so on as in the preceding example.

As a parallel, the spleen is supposed to secrete a hormone, which regulates the new-formation of erythrocytes, thus keeping a balance between blood destruction and formation.

2.15 – In the carbohydrate metabolism, several feedback systems may be traced, *e.g.* in the ATP (energy carrier) mechanism:

(1) glucose combines with ATP (adenosintriphosphate) and similar compounds which deliver the initial energy for break-down
(2) anaerobic metabolism, ATP reduced
(3) formation of "active acetate"
(4) "active acetate" enters the aerobic Krebs cycle which generates ATP
(5) ATP combines with glucose.

The box representation in Fig. 2.15a shows some ATP paths illustrated by broken lines.

The KREBS cycle ATP is thus linked to the initial anaerobic break-down of glucose and also to the glyconeogenesis, both of which deliver precursors to the citric acid. Glyconeogenesis brings additional glucose fuel to the anaerobic phase, especially at starvation and insulin deficit. Another feedback system operates between glucose and glycogen, mediated by ATP and free phosphate. The end stage in the KREBS cycle, the oxaloacetic acid, controls the formation of new citric acid from acetate, a positive feedback. If ketoplastic amino acids or fatty

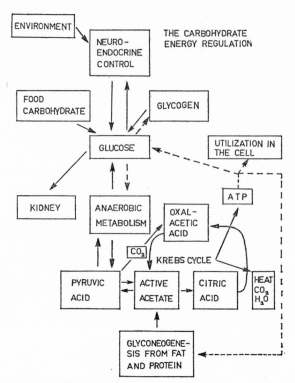

Fig. 2.15a. The carbohydrate energy regulation.

acids enter the KREBS cycle directly, the amount of oxaloacetic acid may rise and the acetate fixation increase. Simultaneously, the produced ATP will stimulate the anaerobic phase to produce more acetate fuel. If the energy demand of the cell increases, ATP is drained off and the free phosphate increases. This stimulates the glycolysis, yielding more fuel to the anaerobic and aerobic energy-liberating processes. If the cell needs less energy at rest the excess ATP promotes glyconeogenesis and glycogen formation from glucose, a storage in the cell.

In non-regulated diabetes and in starvation the disturbance would tend to decrease the ATP and increase the free phosphate. This would stimulate glycogenolysis, raising the blood and tissue sugar levels. If the energy deficit is severe, the only alternative is to increase the utilization of proteins and fat which may yield the necessary ATP in the KREBS cycle. The simultaneously increased amounts of oxaloacetic acid may, through the positive feedback, constantly increase the citric acid concentration, perhaps "forcing" it through the cycle. Glyconeogenesis, together with glycogenolysis, may raise the sugar levels. Both would tip the glucose and pyruvate concentration gradients in favor of the utilization of glucose, against the block.

All these reactions, based on metabolic feedback, may perhaps occur in the organism (DUNCAN, LANG[200], MÖLLERSTRÖM[14, 102]). They would seem to regulate the amount of available fuel according to the immediate demands of the cell. They are clearly combined into complicated networks and it is highly instructive to speculate about their function. It would not be surprising if such systems oscillate readily, especially if disturbed by disease. An analysis of such oscillations should yield information about the system. They must also underlie the 24-hour liver-glycogen cycles, which have been so extensively studied (See Chapter 25). Other examples of biochemical and intracellular feedback are given by CHANCE [100–101], GOLDACRE, GOTS, UMBARGER[1, 100], Conf. 1961e, Brookhaven Symp. 10.

2.16 – The *predator-prey* (parasite-host, Räuber-Beute) *cycle* (Fig. 2.16a) is one of the theories on animal population cycles (See Chapter 10):

(1) predator feeds on prey
(2) prey decimated
(3) predator starves
(4) predator decimated
(5) prey multiplies
(6) predator feeds on prey
(7) predator multiplies

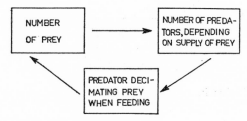

Fig. 2.16a. The predator-prey feedback.

There should be a ratio between the number of predators and prey which balances the regrowth of prey. An overactivity of the predators may well upset the balance, causing cyclic variations (or a complete extinction of the whole system).

2.17 – The *animal-plant feedback* (Fig. 2.17a) lies at the very basis of our existence. It is kept going by the incessant energy influx from the sun, striking a balance

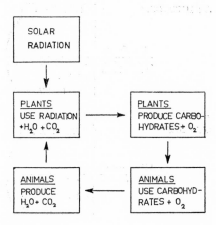

Fig. 2.17a. The animal-plant cycle.

between the number of green plants and animals, aided by the buffering action of oxygen and carbon dioxide in the atmosphere and the sea water.

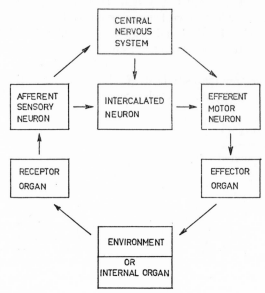

Fig. 2.18a. Neural feedback.

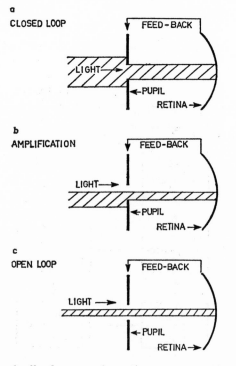

Fig. 2.19a-c. Pupillary feedback, very schematic.

2.18 – Nowhere is the feedback construction as obvious as in the nervous system, *e.g.* in the *reflexes* (Fig. 2.18a). These may be open as in the somatic reflexes, or closed as in the visceral counterparts.

The closed reflexes represent obvious feedback systems. However, the open reflexes may be regarded as closed through the environment, since the action of the system is usually to change the latter by removing the very cause of the stimulus. Actually, there is a continuous interaction between the organism and the surrounding world, of feedback character (Fig. 2.12d), where the nervous system is the main mediator, Fig. 2.12e (*cf.* 2.21).

2.19 – A good example of neural feedback is the *pupillary reflex* (Fig. 2.12f and 2.19a) which aims at keeping the illumination on the retina constant. It has the advantage of being easily manipulated experimentally by ophthalmological techniques (DRISCHEL, DUREMAN[100], LOWENSTEIN[100-101], STARK[2-5, 100-102, 104], STEGEMAN). The retina itself contains at least four regulatory mechanisms ensuring the adaptation of its receptors to the light intensity (STARK[3]).

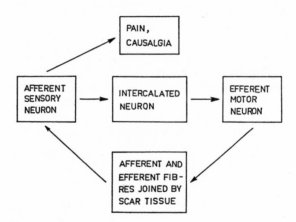

Fig. 2.20a. 'Causalgia feedback'.

2.20 – In *open reflexes*, the closing link goes through the environment (Fig. 2.18a). A "short-circuiting" may, however, occur within the body if the efferent and afferent nerve fibres are connected by scar tissue (GRANIT[100]), Fig. 2.20a. Here, the cause for sensory stimulation cannot be removed by the effector organ, impulses travel round the loop and persistant pain may result. This is one theory for the so-called 'phantom limb' pain, or the intensive and resistant pain which may occasionally follow upon tooth extraction, 'causalgia'.

A fascinating exposition of feedback in the central nervous system is given by ASHBY[2].

2.21 – The feedback rapport with the environment is one survival mechanism, as already discussed in connection with homeostasis and biological regulation (*cf.* 2.2,5-11,18). It may be of physiological or psychological character (Fig. 2.12d-e, h-g).

Psychological feedback arises if we add a teacher or trainer or an observer to the environment (Fig. 2.12g-h). There is feedback because they will change their behaviour according to the response from the subject. If we go to a really good doctor, Fig. 2.12h would actually change as in Fig. 2.21a, that is, the symptoms direct the treatment. A modern computer could do as well (and with less error) than the doctor, if programmed with the necessary symptom-treatment correlations. Such machines will certainly come, freeing the physician to do research, *i.e.* supplying still more data for the electronic brain.

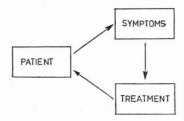

Fig. 2.21a. The future medicine.

The bonds which tie modern man to his environment are strong. We have more or less built our own surroundings. Functionally, we may even regard them as a part of ourselves. Thus the living organism extends further than his organic aspect and the limits between individual and environment become uncertain.

2.22 – *Feedback Theory.* We have now had a series of examples on biological feedback (2.13-21). The list could be extended indefinitely. Let us, however, turn back to the introduction on feedback in 1.10-13, 2.12 and Fig. 1.10, continuing from there systematically.

In the black box notation (2.3) feedback arises when the output is joined to the input (Fig. 2.22a) by a feedback loop, or branch.

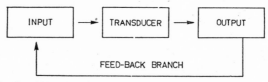

Fig. 2.22a. The feedback loop.

The feedback loop may be regarded as a channel of communication carrying a message between output and input. The transmission of this requires time. Usually, a time lag is no greater problem in communication theory, as long as the signal comes through without much disturbance (noise). In feedback theory, however, it constitutes a main problem and may create instability in the system.

Feedback may be positive or negative. In the former case it tries to maintain or increase its own supply. In the latter case its seeks to cut down its own supply.

2.23 – *Positive Feedback* (*cf.* Fig. 1.10b). Since this system increases its own input, it is also called a regenerative feedback. Unless balanced by an energy loss, it will work itself up to a limit where it either bursts, stops or turns in the opposite direction. In the latter case, the system oscillates between an upper and a lower limit. The difference between the end states increases steadily (the rich get richer and the poor poorer), *cf.* MARUYAMA. If the system stops, it may stay at either extreme. The neural feedback of Fig. 2.20a has two limiting states; no activity (rest) or full activity (pain). A steady increase is seen in the type of activity which the biologist calls a vicious circle, in psychology or in disease. It may either end by destroying itself (death) or by turning when reaching a limit. In the latter case, we have a crisis. If balanced by energy loss, it may turn into circular motion (Fig. 2.23a) as *e.g.* the KREBS cycle in steady state (Fig. 2.15a). If we observe a certain point of the system we may regard it as a ring oscillator.

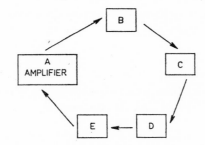

Fig. 2.23a. Circular motion.

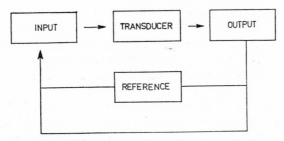

Fig. 2.24a. The reference value.

2.24 – *Negative Feedback* (*cf.* Fig. 1.10c). Since this system cuts down its own input, it always tends to stop at a zero resting level. If disturbed it tries to return to that state.

In a modified version, the servomechanism, the negative feedback is the leading principle of robotics. Here, it is the deviation from a preset level which is minimized, whether the system starts at lower or higher levels (Fig. 1.10d). As soon as it is disturbed, it tries to reestablish the initial level, it is goal-seeking. The preset level is the reference value (Fig. 2.24a). The mechanism continuously compares this with the actual output and aims at zeroing the difference. A good example is the thermostat set at, say, 37°C. If the controlled area gets colder or hotter, say, 35°C or 39°C, the difference of ± 2°C activates a mechanism which either increases or decreases the temperature. When it is again 37°C (difference 0°C) the mechanism rests until a new disturbance occurs. This is the way biological regulation has to work if it wants to keep the cellular matrix under constant conditions (*cf.* 2.5-6).

2.25 – *Energy Relations. Stability*. Feedback mechanisms are closed loop systems. Nevertheless, they need an energy supply to keep going, supplied by an amplifier. This addition has to be present but does not otherwise change the properties of the feedback. It does not necessarily enter the diagrams or calculations. If the power supply balances the energy loss in the loops, the system will work at a steady rate. If the amplification is greater (high gain) the system may get out of balance. The topic will be discussed in the next chapter. Since the feedback system is closed, all forces must balance. Wherever we start in the loop we may follow it through, adding all active magnitudes, with regard to sign. We shall then have a sum of zero when coming back to the starting point.

If the loop is opened the whole system stops functioning. Nevertheless, this is a useful procedure in testing feedback mechanisms. It is more difficult to do in biology than in engineering whithout destroying the system, but it has been done. Examples will be given later.

2.26 – A *closed loop system* has no special point of origin (Fig. 2.17a). Of course, one may more or less arbitrarily define one, *e.g.* the point of entry of the disturbance or the amplification. In other cases the origin is still more difficult to find, Fig. 2.16a. This reminds one of that classical enigma, Fig. 2.26a:

Fig. 2.26a. The classical feedback.

and of who was first. The Adam and Eve fable in the Bible shows that the problem was not easy to solve. With our modern knowledge we may, of course, say that the egg (protozoan cell) was first but that is simply to evade the issue.

2.27 – This chapter has introduced the concepts of biological regulation and cybernetics, including the basic properties of feedback systems. The next chapter will enlarge upon this, discussing the theory of servomechanisms.

CHAPTER 3

Servomechanisms

3.1 – In the preceding chapter the general cybernetic terms and definitions were given, ending with different types of feedback. One of the latter, the servomechanism, is of special importance in engineering and biology. It works by negative feedback, always trying to adjust itself to a certain reference value, *cf.* 2.24 and Fig. 2.24a.

3.2 – *Servomechanism Principles.* Fig. 3.2a is a more elaborate model of a servomechanism (autoregulator, Regelkreis, Automatic Control mechanism). The environmental input into the transducer (Regelwerk) may be regarded as its source of information, its ingoing signal (Eingangsgrösse, Störung, Störgrösse). Often this signal must be transformed to an energy form suitable for the transducer, in the sensor (Messwerk, Fühler, réacteur). Transformation (Kraftschaltung) may also be necessary at other stages in the system, *e.g.* at the output. This is performed by the effector (Stellglied, Stellwerk, effecteur). The power or the reference signal may also require transformation.

Let us call the transformed input *i,* the output (Istwert) *o,* and the desired input

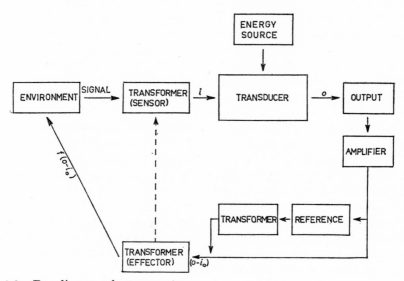

Fig. 3.2a. Box diagram of a servosystem.

(reference value, control value, Sollwert) i_o. The term $(o-i_o)$ represents the correction with which the feedback loop (Regelstrecke) acts upon the signal in order to keep $i = i_o$, (Regelabweichung). It may be regarded as an error which should be minimized.

3.3 – The servomechanism is thus a *goal-seeking* system which incessantly hunts the reference value. It may be controlled by adjusting that value, which may be kept constant or variable. If constant, the latter may represent the desired temperature in a thermostat-controlled waterbath, the 37°C of the human body, or the number (or size) of screws to be produced by a certain machine. It may be changed at will.

3.4 – In contrast to oscillating feedback systems (1.12-13) the servomechanism only reacts when the input is disturbed so as to differ from the reference value. As soon as this difference is eliminated activity ceases. On the other hand, it is promptly thrown into action whatever the magnitude of the disturbance (within limits) and whenever it appears. In practice the disturbances often occur at random and in such instances the servomechanism is said to be 'error-controlled'.

3.5 – *Examples of Servomechanisms.* A good example is the modern antiaircraft gun which constantly strives to diminish the angle difference between the radar-determined directions of the goal and of the exploding gunshells, until it hits with an uncanny precision. One of the first servomechanisms was the flywheel regulator in the steam engines.

In biology particularly good examples are found in the nervous system. Common signals are temperature, light, sound, touch and chemical stimuli. The sensory organs are transformers. Effectors are our muscles or glands. Our locomotion is governed by two typical neural servomechanisms, the position and direction controls. The pupillary system has already been mentioned (2.19). The endocrine feedback (2.13) has a control value set by the pituitary, as directed by the environment through the central nervous system.

3.6 – *Position and Direction Control.* Locomotor regulation involves two distinctly separate servosystems. One is concerned with the normal balance between muscles, the 'tonus', whether the body is immobile or in action. This is position control.

3.7 – The other type of locomotion feedback regulates the direction of the movement against a goal, the 'direction control'. It minimizes the angle between the direction to the goal and that of the actual movement, much in the same way as the antiaircraft robot. Actually, we always wobble a little (overshoot) around the true path, whether we try to walk towards a certain point, grab an object, hit a ball in tennis, or drive a car. Since a servomechanism is at work the absolute value of the initial deviation between aim and goal matters little. It will always be diminished. This explains *e.g.* why we can effortlessly change from driving a small European car, which requires deft movements on the steering wheel, to an American car, requiring heavy turns on the wheel.

There are two types of biological direction control. This has been studied *e.g.*

in eye movements, where the test subject is looking at a moving light spot (STARK[105-106], VOSSIUS, YOUNG[1, 100]). Larger changes in the position of the spot are followed by sudden coarse eye-jumps (saccadic control, *cf*. nystagmus) and this is smoothed out by a more fluent pursuit control, which is sensitive to velocity changes. If the subject is looking at a repeated pattern, a prediction control also enters, to make the process perfect. If a sine wave is prestented and the saccadic component dominates we get the picture of small stepladder-like jumps superimposed upon a sinusoidal eye movement track.

3.8 – *Prediction control* (Vorfühlregelung) is also used *e.g.* in shooting at a flying prey, which relies on our ability to estimate the future position of the object. Similar mechanisms are incorporated into the antiaircraft robots.

WIENER[3] describes a fascinating model with position and direction control. It is a small carriage which searches or avoids light (positive or negative phototropism). Steering is controlled by a photocell through an electronic direction control. The wheels are, however, also kept steady by a position feedback loop. The apparatus mimics the behaviour of the nervous system, especially under conditions of stress.

3.9 – *Open Loop Conditions.* A servomechanism is necessarily a closed system, *cf*. 2.25. For purposes of study it may be opened. How to do this is quite a problem in biology. In chemical systems, one component may be saturated. Control of the pupillary system is illustrated by STARK[3] (Fig. 2.19c). Here, the beam of light is so thin that the pupil cannot cut it off. The intensity of this beam may now be varied.

3.10 – The open loop can be manipulated from without at one end, the input, causing a series of reactions which are measured at the other end, the output (Fig. 3.10a). The relation between input and output will tell us quite a deal about the system.

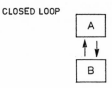

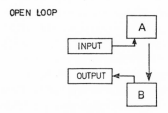

Fig. 3.10a. The closed and opened loop conditions.

3.11 – If left to itself the open loop may stop at one extreme. Let us see what happens if we open the animal-plant cycle as in Fig. 3.11a (*cf.* 2.17), as a purely hypothetical example.

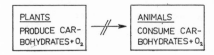

Fig. 3.11a. Opening of the animal-plant cycle.

Probably, the animals, being more sensitive, would soon loose their food source and starve to death. The green plants would continue receiving unexhaustable energy radiation as before. Their nutritional reservoir may like-wise be rather large. Their waste, O_2 and carbohydrates, would however accumulate indefinitely. Earlier or later the reaction:

3.11b $$n H_2O + n CO_2 \xrightarrow[\text{enzymes}]{\text{energy}} n O_2 + (CH_2O)_n$$

would reach an equilibrium and stop. Or, if only one life-form existed, with an unlimited supply of pure energy, it would nevertheless perish because it would be poisoned by its own waste or would eventually run out of material. If, however, another life-form with the reverse metabolism is added, life could continue as long as the radiation source persisted. This is an attractive theory of planetary life, which has been put forth.

3.12 – A less dramatic example of a broken loop occurs in deaf people. Normally, we hear our own speach and adjust it through feedback. If our voice, as we hear it, is too low, we raise it. If we cannot hear at all we shout.

3.13 – *Equilibrium and Amplification.* Servosystems are usually built for stability. They maintain a stable equilibrium, which may be static, unmoving except when disturbed, or dynamic, the balance between opposing movements in a chemical reaction or a steady, regular oscillation. If an equilibrium is unstable, it easily breaks down if the system is pushed away from the equilibrium (*cf.* ASHBY[2], CUNNINGHAM[2]).

In the following, we will first discuss some stable systems of special interest and then the conditions for instability.

3.14 – An important factor in this connection is the energy source, *cf.* 2.25. Amplification is always necessary since no system is frictionless. (The electrical superconductivity at low temperature is an exception.) The power may be introduced at any point in the system, *e.g.* as a signal amplification or feedback amplification. The net effect is the same. In essence, however, feedback is more a problem of how 'information' is transmitted in a loop, whatever the carrier (*cf.* 2.3-4).

If the amplification is moderate it will just keep the system going. If stronger, it will increase the feedback and rise the gain in the system. STARK[3] obtains high gain in the pupillary system by focussing a thin beam of light on the edge of the pupil (Fig. 2.19b).

However, with increasing gain in a servosystem the control becomes more difficult and the risk of instability increases.

3.15 – *Stability*. Well-balanced servosystems are stable, *i.e.* they return to the equilibrium after disturbance. The stability may be enhanced by some mechanisms. The animal-plant cycle (Fig. 2.17a) is balanced by the enormous reservoir of oxygen and carbon dioxide in the atmosphere as well as by the water in the sea. A simple model would be the water tank in Fig. 3.15a. Any fluctuations will be smoothed out.

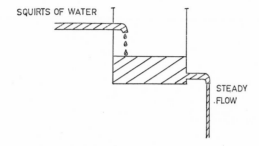

Fig. 3.15a. Stability through a reservoir.

An electrical capacitor may act in the same way. – The aorta transforms the periodic ejection of blood from the heart at systole into a steady stream in the arteries by dilatating and accomodating the whole blood mass (stroke volume) initially and then slowly contracting. – Bellows function similarly.

3.16 – *Ultrastability. The Homeostat.* Several feedback units may be coupled into larger systems, sometimes of high complexity. An important example is the homeostat of ASHBY[2] which mimics the function of the brain. Each homeostat unit contains a servomechanism system, characterized by certain parameters. After each disturbance the homeostat returns to the original equilibrium, always in the same manner (equal trajectories). The disturbance may, however, be so

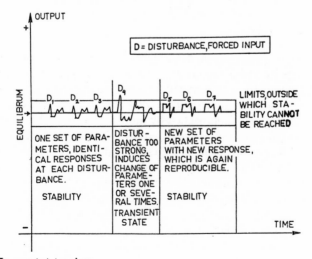

Fig. 3.16a. Homeostat tracing.

strong that the system is thrown out of gear and cannot return to the equilibrium. It will then, instead, change its own parameters, its own state, at random. Now, it tries again to reach a new equilibrium, against the disturbance, by a new trajectory. If this is still impossible it changes repeatedly at random until it finds a state in which it can attain stability. A tracing may look like Fig. 3.16a. The arrangement of the feedback loops between the four homeostat units A-D is shown in Fig. 3.16b.

Fig. 3.16b. Homeostat feedback loops.

The homeostat has two outstanding characteristics. It is remarkably stable, showing ultrastability. Its mode of reaction is random, it is error-controlled.

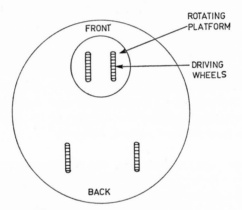

Fig. 3.17a. An error-controlled toy.

3.17 – *Error Control.* The random behaviour of the homeostat copies our own way of learning things by "trial and error" or, indeed, the whole process of evolution, where adaptation to the environment is a prime requirement. Indeed, *random behaviour ensures maximal success in an unknown environment.* One may use the analogy of the 'black box' approached by an experimenter who knows absolutely nothing about it (*cf.* ASHBY[1]). He may prod it, feel it, smell it, taste it, measure its weight and temperature, send currents through it, X-ray it, etc. Eventually, he may get a response, even if he only succeeds in breaking it. Note the similarity to the behaviour of a child confronted with a new object. It may also be taken as a perfect description of the development of 'Biological Rhythm Research', or of any science. Only when the black box has yielded a response will a more systematic investigation of its behaviour be possible.

    The random behaviour also appears in certain functional disorders of the nervous system, *e.g.* hysteria or the subcortical random movements of a caged or trapped animal, or in the postinfectious chorea (*e.g.* St. Vitus dance or dancing mania).

A simple mechanical model of error-control is furnished by a group of ingenious toys in the shape of bulldozers or flying saucers. They run in a straight line until they hit upon an obstacle, then turn at random into another direction. Viewed from below they look like Fig. 3.17a. When there is no obstacle the driving wheels go roughly in a straight line, the rest of the 'body' trailing like a tail. As soon as the front strikes an obstacle the body is wedged still and the platform rotates. Hereby the direction of the driving wheels changes. The ensuing direction is rather random. The apparatus has a remarkable capacity to find its way out of any traps, given time enough.

3.18 – *The Oscillatory Response.* When a servomechanism is disturbed, it tries to return to the reference value (*cf.* 3.2-3). A similar situation is met with if the reference value is suddenly changed. The reaction requires a certain time, the time lag. Furthermore, there is a certain amount of inertia in the system. Hence an overshoot easily occurs when the output value again approaches the reference value. Fig. 1.12 illustrates some possible ways in which a servomechanism may react to a disturbance. Ideally, there should be a rapid asymptotic approach to the desired value as in Fig. 1.12a. Such systems are, however, heavily damped and not very sensitive. In more mobile systems, the overshoot may cause oscillations, either transient damped oscillations (b, positive damping), sustained oscillations (c, zero damping), or wild fluctuations (d, negative damping), *cf.* 1.12-13. Examples of this will come later.

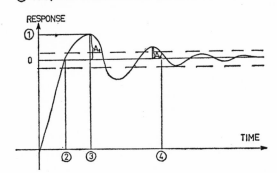

① MAXIMAL OVERSHOOT
② TIME FOR ERROR TO REACH FIRST ZERO
③ TIME TO REACH MAXIMAL OVERSHOOT
④ SETTLING TIME, TIME FOR RESPONSE TO SETTLE WITHIN A GIVEN PERCENTAGE OF THE SET LEVEL
⑤ FREQUENCY OF OSCILLATION OF THE TRANSIENT

Fig. 3.19a. A damped oscillation.

3.19 – *Transient Damped Oscillations.* A common servomechanism response to a disturbance is the damped oscillation. Damping may be increased, if necessary, by various means, *e.g.* by augmenting the resistance in the system (which, however, impairs its sensitivity) or by prediction control. The latter is possible if we know enough in advance about the general behaviour of the transducer. Also, the output values usually do not vary absolutely at random from moment to moment owing to inertia (creating serial correlation). In nonlinear movement the acceleration in the output may be used for a first approximation of the output-to-come.

The transient damped oscillation may be characterized in different ways, as shown in Fig. 3.19a, e.g. by magnitude and timing of maximal overshoot, by the settling time, or by the oscillation frequency. The settling time is reached when the oscillations are confined between certain predetermined limits. The frequency of oscillation is relatively constant. The surface between the curve and the zero level (Regelfläche) may also be measured as a gauge of the regulation efficiency (Regelgüte). In polar coordinates, the damped oscillation may be represented by a spiral (cf. Fig. 1.31c).

3.20 – *The Logarithmic Decrement.* Another characteristic of the damped oscillation is the logarithmic decrement (Dämpfungsverhältnis) which involves the amplitudes of successive oscillations (A_1, A_2, etc. in Fig. 3.19a):

3.20a $$\text{log. decr.} = \delta = \ln(A_n/A_{n-1})$$

Since the damping function (envelope) is often exponential, the decrement is usually relatively constant for successive amplitude quotients. It may be regarded as a measure of the energy loss of the oscillating system at each cycle (GREEN).

The inverse of δ will be a measure of the oscillation stability. It is usually called $\underset{\sim}{Q}$:

3.20b $$\underset{\sim}{Q} = -\pi/\delta$$

The number of complete oscillations needed to reach a certain ratio between the initial and final amplitude (A_1/A_n) is:

3.20c $$\text{oscillation number} = Q\,[\ln(A_1/A_n)]/\pi = -[\ln(A_1/A_n)]/\delta$$

3.21 – *Feedback Instability.* We have already seen that the balance in a servosystem is easily upset by a disturbance, to a greater or lesser degree (cf. Fig. 1.12b-d). Factors which favour such instability are primarily the time lag, resistance and high gain. The result may be oscillations, regular or irregular, with or without harmonics, steady or occasional, damped or undamped. They are common in living systems where complexity is the rule. The biologist may also find them in his equipment as superimposed undesired fluctuations, e.g. in the thermostat.

Let us list some instability conditions:

3.21a – *inertia, resistance, friction,* causing time lag.
  time lag (time delay, dead time, Totzeit), correction of overshoot comes too late.
  high gain (amplification), too strong feedback with heavy overshoot.
  dead space (dead zone), sensors not reacting in certain input intervals.
  hysteresis (backlash, free play), doublevalued output depending upon direction of input.
  noise, random fluctuations.
  information disturbances, e.g. small feedback loop which cannot transmit all information, faulty transformators or disturbances in the reference mechanism.

3.22 – *Feedback Resistance*. A large resistance will damp the overshoot but cause a time lag and lessen the sensitivity of the system. It should be large enough to prevent oscillations arising from noise in the input signal or in the system itself. If the resistance is too large, however, it can instead be reduced by the deliberate introduction of noise, *e.g.* in shape of very high-frequent oscillations, dither or jitter.

3.23 – *Time Lag*. The feedback action has to be reasonably swift, otherwise it will permit heavy overshoot and oscillations. In case of a periodic disturbance this effect is maximal if the phase lag is 180°. Actually, we then have resonance, the negative feedback is turned into a positive one and the system 'runs away', with increasing amplitudes of oscillation, *cf.* Fig. 1.12d.

The rapidity of information flow is important also in other contexts. The regulation in Fig. 2.6b is so efficient because the added channels D(ENV) → R, R → O(ME), and O(ME) → D(ENV) are swifter than D(ENV) → O(ME). To O(ME) the whole process will appear as a prediction of the influence from D(ENV), or a feedforward.

3.24 – *High Gain*. Amplification is needed to balance the power loss in the systems (*cf.* 3.14). If further augmented it tends to strengthen the overshoot and cause fluctuations. The high gain obtained in the pupillary feedback by focussing light on the edge of the iris (STARK[3], *cf.* Fig. 2.19b) causes considerable sustained oscillations in pupillary size. This phenomenon was earlier observed by ophthalmologists studying the anterior parts of the eye with a slit lamp, and was called induced pupillary hippus. – In the predator-prey feedback (*cf.* 2.16), one would expect stability; the prey multiplying in proportion to the hunger of the predator, both populations being stationary. However, the hunger of the predator would seem to introduce high gain, which might cause population cycles. The economic cycles in the business world and the periodic occurrence of wars may have a similar origin; greed is a deep-rooted instinct.

3.25 – *Combination of Time Lag and High Gain*. This increases the risk for instability. The pupillary servomechanism (STARK[3]) shows a relatively large phase lag but is stable because of the low gain. If the latter is stepped up oscillations occur, the hippus.

Other neurological feedback disturbances are probably the 'tremor' (shaking of hands and body) and the ocular 'nystagmus' (rapid movements of eye-balls to and fro). One type of tremor occurs in cerebellar disease. The hands of the subject are quite still at rest, but begin to shake when the person tries to control them. It signifies a disturbance of the neural direction control (3.7). The tremor increases continuously. It may be a happy disorder when stopping the chronic alcoholic from signing a bill for more drinks (another feedback, of course) but else it is a severe handicap. – Another type of tremor occurs in 'Parkinsonism', perhaps owing to a release of subcortical activities from cortical control. It is found in old people at rest and disappears in action. Probably, the defect lies in the neural position control (3.6). – Other pathological examples are the clonus, rhythmic muscle contractions, and the 'cogwheel' resistance of a joint against a moving force in spastic diseases.

3.26 – *Dead Space.* Faulty sensors may generate regular cycles. Imagine a thermostat which tries to keep an average temperature of 37°C but which responds first at deviations of ± 2°C. If the external temperature is 38°C nothing happens. If it is raised past 39°C, and then kept absolutely constant, say at 41°C, regulation brings the temperature down. Now, however, it continues to drop past 37°C. First when it reaches 35°C regulation occurs again. It now rises to 39°C, then sinks back to 35°C, and so on. We would get a system fluctuating steadily with an amplitude of 2°C and a level of 37°C, within a constant environment. Fig. 3.26a gives an example of thermostatic instability, with an amplitude of about 0.5°C and a period of 2-4 hours.

Similar things may probably happen with our own thermoregulation, *e.g.* in periodic fever (ASK-UPMARK). Normally, this is a servosystem controlled by the environment through the hypothalamus. – Perhaps the slow menstrual cycle, as opposed to the other more balanced endocrine servomechanisms, is due to a relative insensitivity of the hypophysis against the peripheral hormones.

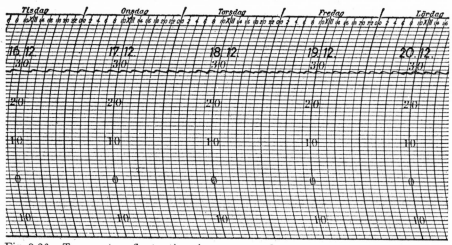

Fig. 3.26a. Temperature fluctuations in an empty thermostat chamber.

3.27 – *Nonlinearities.* No biological transducers have really linear trajectories. The exponential relation between the physical stimuli (disturbances) and the nervous output from the sensory organs are one example. The sensors also show 'adaptation' to the stimulus, a nonlinear influence. Other changes occur in pathology; hypersensitivity in trigeminal neuralgia and some psychic disorders, itching, or the keratitis following a loss of the corneal reflex.

3.28 – *Feedback Testing. Input-Output Diagrams.* A feedback circuit can be tested by a forced input and a recording of the output. These two variables may then be plotted against each other in a input-output diagram, for analysis. Usually, open loop conditions are used (*cf.* 3.9-12 and Fig. 3.10a). The testing signal is injected at one end and the result recorded at the other.

Any transducer may, of course, be tested in this way. There are some general types of response. The simplest type is the linear input-output system (Fig. 3.28a).

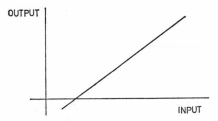

Fig. 3.28a. A linear input-output diagram.

Most real servomechanisms are however nonlinear, especially the biological ones, or only approximately linear within a limited range of input. Different parts of the loop may vary in this respect. The linear case is easier to handle mathematically. The nonlinear case is usually both swifter and more efficient. Examples of non-linear input-output relations are shown in Fig. 3.28b.

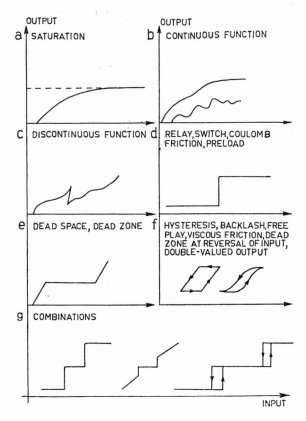

Fig. 3.28b. Nonlinear input-output relations.

Most of the illustrations in Fig. 3.28b are fairly obvious. There may be a limit to the output possible (a). A relay (d) switches between two possible outputs, as does a certain friction (d) or internal resistance in the systems, which has to be overcome before any change in output occurs. This type of friction (coulomb friction) is constant, not dependent of the input. Dead space (e) means a zone of input to which the apparatus is insensitive. Hysteresis, or backlash (f) signifies a change of characteristics, often during a period of dead space. It may involve viscous friction, where a correlation exists between input and resistance. Backlash occurs between gears, when the driving wheel decelerates and the other one is free-wheeling. Combinations of the various types occur (g). Compare this with 3.21a.

3.29 – *Feedback Testing With a Periodic Input.* Testing with a sine input has many advantages. The output is usually periodic too and it can always be analysed

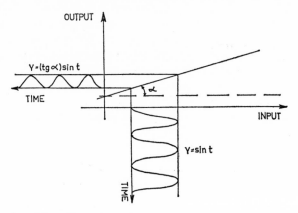

Fig. 3.29a. Sine input in a linear transducer.

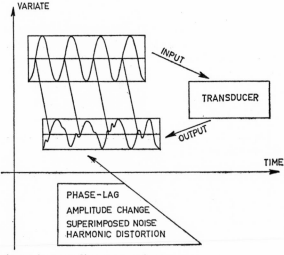

Fig. 3.29b. Sine input in a nonlinear transducer.

into components of the same type as the input (by harmonic analysis). The input runs through a whole series of velocity changes and by further varying its frequency the mobility of the system is rapidly explored. Usually, the input is made to run through a spectrum of frequencies automatically.

Let us test a 'linear' transducer with an oscillatory input (Fig. 3.29a). The output is the same wave, with changed amplitude. A corresponding example in the 'nonlinear' case is shown in Fig. 3.29b. The output is here characterized by the lag (phase lag between output and input) and a change in amplitude, measuring the gain. Furthermore, disturbances and nonlinearities show up as superimposed harmonics. All these transformations may be measured and evaluated.

3.30 – *Gain, Phase, Frequency Diagrams.* If the periodic input runs through a series of frequencies, the phase lags or gains may be plotted against the frequencies (Fig. 3.30a and b); *e.g.* in the phase-frequency diagram and the gain-frequency diagram (the BODE plot). In principle, the lags are measured as phase angle differences ($\omega°$) between input and output curves and the gains as the ratio between their amplitudes (A/A_0 = output amplitude through input amplitude).

The figures illustrate that the resistance in the system may tend to increase with the input frequency, also that the gain may vary with the frequency. A gain > 1 means an amplification of the signal in the system, if < 1 a resistance with energy loss.

Gain and phase lag may also be plotted in polar coordinates, the NYQUIST diagram (Fig. 3.30c).

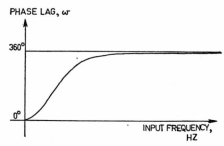

Fig. 3.30a. Phase frequency diagram.

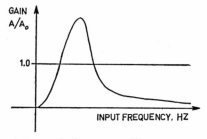

Fig. 3.30b. The BODE plot, a gain frequency diagram.

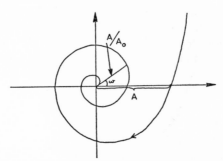

Fig. 3.30c. The gain phase diagram, Nyquist diagram, *cf*. Figs. 3.30a-b.

3.31 – One may use the term servomechanism in a more restricted sense, distinguishing between *regulator systems* and *servomechanisms*. In the former the reference is constant, as in the ordinary thermostat. In the latter the reference varies, unpredictively, as in driving. In both cases the system has to conform to the reference (controlling input). Our main interest lies somewhere in between; the controlling input is variable, but the variation is relatively regular. The biological applications of this will be dealt with later.

3.32 – This chapter has dealt with the properties of servomechanisms, especially the conditions for stability and the means of testing the systems. Biological applications will be discussed later. Good examples are given by ALBERTS, CLYNES, DRISCHEL, IBERALL[100], JENKINSON[1, 100], McKAY[200], MITTELSTÄDT, SCOTT[1-3, 100-101], SCHMITT, STARK[100-106], WAGNER[600-602]. There are also many text-books on information, cybernetic, servosystem, and oscillator theory; *e.g.* ASHBY, D'AZZO[100], BICKLEY[100], BODE, BOGOLIUBOV[100], BOWER[100], COSSA, KU, PASK, REICH, SHANNON[100], SMITH[400], STEWART[200], SUCKLING, WADD, WAGNER[400], WIENER. We have also seen in this chapter that servomechanisms readily fluctuate when disturbed and that they may be turned into regular oscillators. The next chapter will explore this aspect.

CHAPTER 4

Oscillators

4.1 – The previous chapters have discussed the problems of biological regulation, as controlled by feedback systems. We have seen that some of these function rhythmically, either under normal conditions or if disturbed or unbalanced. A servomechanism, built for stability, may turn into an oscillator by a slight change in parameters. This chapter will describe some different types of oscillators of more general character in physics, chemistry and biology, ending with some points regarding their mode of action.

4.2 – *Energy Relations*. The flow of energy through the oscillating system is per- haps easier to visualize than in case of the regulators. A continuous supply of power (*i.e.* a certain amplification) is needed to balance the energy loss (*cf.* 2.25). If the amplification is less (gain < 1) the process damps out. If it is greater (gain > 1) the velocity increases until the system breaks or is re-balanced by a concom- itant increase in resistance (viscous friction, *cf.* Fig. 3.28b). The energy delivered now oscillates regularly between two possible states, *e.g.* potential and kinetic, and a continuous energy transformation takes place. – The movement of the pendulum bob lifts it high so as to store potential energy. Gravity pulls, releasing the latter into movement again. – Current builds up potential condenser charge, the latter delivers current. – The buzzer electromagnet moves the spring, building up ten- sion, which is then released, activating the coil again.

4.3 – The power is often released into one of the two energy states and has to be applied when the system is in the right phase, *i.e.* rhythmically, creating resonance. Usually, the oscillator itself triggers this release of energy by feedback, as in case of the buzzer. One may say, for instance, that the balance in a watch cuts off small packets of power from the spring, delivering them to the rotating wheels rhythmically.

Oscillators perform very regularly. Whatever aspect of their action we study we will find that a certain position returns at certain intervals with great precision. They work through feedback, but one should realize that one cycle does not usually correspond to one 'turn' in the feedback loop, but to a number of these.

4.4 – *Ring Oscillators. Circular or Cyclic Motion*. A simple type of oscillator is the closed circular system, described in 2.23, Fig. 2.23a. Studying a certain point, *e.g.* the C-D link, we will find that it becomes activated at regular intervals, rhythmi- cally. Amplification occurs each time the process reaches A. A similar but more continuous mechanism is provided by an object moving in a circle. If there is continuous flow, one point in the flow will 'meet' any point in the surroundings regularly.

Examples are closed transport systems such as a conveyor belt or the blood circulation, water wheels, gear wheels, a stone flung in a circle at the end of a rope, a pendulum given a sideward push when at its turning point, a satellite, a current rotating in a supercooled ring conductor, or a muscular contraction going in circles in a loop cut from a heart preparation.

4.5 – The circular motion executed by rotation of a pendulum, a satellite or a wheel is exemplified in Figs. 4.5a and b.

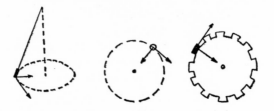

Fig. 4.5a. Circular motion. From left: pendulum, satellite, wheel.

In these cases we have a driving tangential force, and a centripetal force which continuously causes a change in the direction of the movement (acceleration). One could perhaps say that the movement determines the position and the position controls the direction of movement.

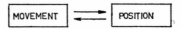

Fig. 4.5b. Circular motion viewed as a feedback.

4.6 – A system in circular motion may be used for transport, like a conveyor belt, or may passively transport mass (*e.g.* a water wheel) or energy (*e.g.* gears). In biology we have the blood circulation with all the material it carries. An example is given in Fig. 4.6a. It also illustrates how the transport capacity may be varied; through an increase of frequency, or an increase of amplitude (relative load, concentration; or volume, capacity).

4.7 – *The Pendulum. The Simple Harmonic Motion.* The pendulum is a common oscillator model, Figs. 4.7a, b. The retracting component of the gravitational force increases with increasing distance of the bob from the vertical position. Eventually, it equals the driving force and the bob turns. Let us assume the amplitude of the swing (y) to be very small and call the angle of deviation Ω. We may then approximately set sin $\Omega = \Omega$, which gives a simplified expression for the restoring component of the gravitational pull. The calculation develops as shown in Fig. 4.7b.

Thus we arrive at a differential equation of the second order, formula 4.7c with solutions 4.7d or 4.7e, *i.e.* a sine wave, 'a simple harmonic'. Formulae 4.7f show the

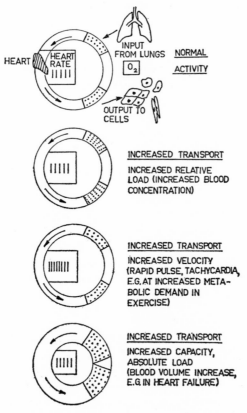

Fig. 4.6a. Transport by circular motion, oxygen from lungs to tissues.

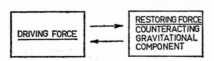

Fig. 4.7a. The pendulum feedback.

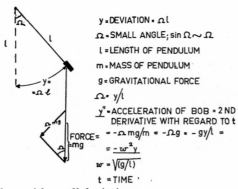

Fig. 4.7b. A pendulum with small deviations.

relations between the two forms of the solution and some definitions. The derivations and formulae may be found in any elementary textbook, *e.g.* SEARS[100], SMITH[200].

4.7c $\qquad\qquad\qquad\qquad$ $y'' + \omega^2 y = 0$

4.7d $\qquad\qquad\qquad\qquad$ $y = a \cos \omega t + b \sin \omega t$

4.7e $\qquad\qquad\qquad\qquad$ $y = A \sin (\omega t + \phi)$

4.7f

$$A = \sqrt{(a^2 + b^2)} \qquad \phi = \text{phase angle}$$
$$b = A \cos \phi \qquad \phi/\omega = \text{phase shift along time axis}$$
$$a = A \sin \phi \qquad 2\pi/\omega = \text{period}$$
$$\tan \phi = a/b \qquad \omega/2\pi = \text{frequency}$$
$$A = \text{amplitude} \qquad \omega = \text{pulsatance}$$

4.8 – The above formulae describe a simple harmonic motion. They hold under the assumption that the restoring force is proportional to the displacement. This is approximately the case *e.g.* in surface waves or string instruments, and especially in mechanical vibrating systems where the acceleration is determined by the magnitude of the driving force, BICKLEY[100]. Here, two important parameters are the stiffness and the inertia. The pulsatance increases with the stiffness and decreases with the inertia.

4.9 – *Electronic Oscillators.* Another model is the oscillating electronic circuit, which includes a capacitor (condenser), a resistor (resistance) and an inductor (coil); Figs. 4.9a and b. The condenser releases its charge with a rising current against the ohmic resistance and the inductive resistance of the coil. When the current decreases, the coil inductance sustains it and charges the condenser again, though with opposite sign. The condenser then empties in the other direction, and so on. If there were no resistance, the oscillations would go on indefinitely. As it is, we get damped oscillations (*cf.* 3.18-20, Fig. 1.12).

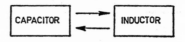

Fig. 4.9a. The electronic circuit feedback.

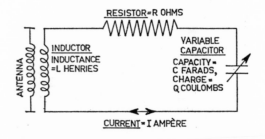

Fig. 4.9b. The electronic circuit oscillator.

4.10 – The differential equation describing the action of an electronic circuit is represented in formula 4.10a (symbols from Fig. 4.9b). 4.10b is the same in more general terms, *cf.* 4.7c. Roughly, one may say that the coil delivers acceleration, the resistance determines the velocity, and the charge the magnitude of the current.

4.10a	$Lq'' + Rq' + (1/C)\, q = 0$
4.10b	$y'' + ay' + \omega^2 y = 0$
4.10c	$Rq' + (1/C)\, q = 0$
4.10d	$y' + ay = 0$
4.10e	$q = K\, e^{-t/RC}$
	$\ln (q/K) = -t/RC$

If the resistance is zero ($R = 0$) we get back formula 4.7c, *i.e.* an undamped sine wave. If the inductance vanishes ($L = 0$) we get formula 4.10c. This represents a steady exponential decay, as is seen in the solutions 4.10e (*cf.* 3.18-20 and Fig. 1.12a).

4.11 – The general formula, 4.10b, has many solutions depending on the definitions of its parameters. It may generate several types of exponential decay or oscillations. The latter may be sustained or increasing, damped in various ways, or of a not uncommon type called relaxation oscillations (4.13). The mathematical problems involved will be discussed in Part III of this book. The reader is also referred to textbooks on mathematics and oscillations, *e.g.* BOGOLIUBOV[100], LOTKA[3], SMITH[200].

4.12 – *Audio Feedback.* One type of electronic oscillators is obtained by feeding the output from a triode back to its own grid over a feedback coil (Fig. 4.12a). Even without coils the triode may oscillate if grid and anode are joined in a suitable way, since the latter acts as a capacitor, affecting the grid charge (electrostatic induction). In other cases, the oscillations may be generated within special tubes with very swift feedback between the electron stream and a series of special grids.

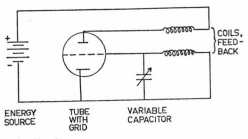

Fig. 4.12a. The audio feedback.

4.13 – *The Relaxation Oscillator.* The name relaxation oscillation implies the sudden release of slowly accumulated and stored energy followed by a reaccumulation. During the latter period the process appears refractory, relaxation period. The release occurs when the energy is large enough to overcome a certain resistance in the system, *cf.* dead space, 3.26,28. The theory has been developed by VAN DER POL[1-4, 100-101] and later, in biology by BETHE[1-9, 100-101], VON HOLST, and KOUMANS. VAN DER POL also built a simple electronic model (Fig. 4.13a). It consists of a capacitor (condenser) slowly charged from a battery and instantaneously discharged when the voltage is large enough to short-circuit it through a neon lamp

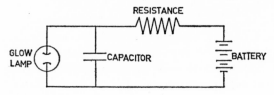

Fig. 4.13a. A relaxation oscillator.

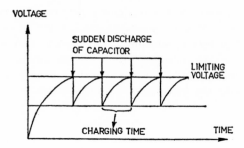

Fig. 4.13b. A relaxation oscillation.

(which then flashes). The voltage across the capacitor oscillates in a typical way, a 'saw-tooth' voltage (Fig. 4.13b). The relaxation oscillation curve may be generated by a formula, 4.13c, derived from formula 4.10b.

4.13c
$$y'' - (a - 3\gamma y^2)\, y' + \omega^2 y = 0$$
$$a/\omega > 1$$

4.14 – VAN DER POL gives numerous examples of relaxation oscillations; a vessel which is filled continuously and tips over periodically, a pneumatic hammer, the scratching noise of a knife on a plate, the squeaking of a door, a steam engine with too small a flywheel, more complicated electronic models which perfectly mimic the electrocardiogram (heart action record). The sound of an Aeolian harp is due to air eddies building up against the string and blowing away (the frequency of this sound depends on the properties of the air and is quite independent of the natural period of the oscillating string). The movement of the electronic beam across the television screen is another example; or the formation of drops from a liquid.

The emptying of the heart or the bowel or the urinary bladder, many a crisis in disease are further examples of relaxation oscillations.

4.15 – *Bistable Oscillators*. One peculiarity of the relaxation oscillation is the swift, switch-like shift from one extreme position to the other, in one direction. Some oscillators act in this way like relays in both directions, with two stable end-points, between which they are made to vary, the bistable oscillators. As soon as they are pushed from one extremity they seek the other. Examples are the buzzer or a rocking arm with its centre of gravity above the pivot.

Actually, any process which apparently changes between rest and sudden activity may be regarded as bistable. In that case the relaxation oscillators (4.13-14) belong here, with all their biological applications, and also positive feedback systems which go towards either one of their extremes or oscillate between them (2.23); ALBERTS, McKAY[200]. Bistable oscillators may be used as counters. McKAY discusses their negative resistance property and the possibility of constructing biological computers, using *e.g.* algae.

4.16 – *Chemical Oscillators. Oscillating Electrodes*. Autocatalytic chemical reactions display feedback since the amount of a certain compound directs its own formation. It has also been shown that such systems may oscillate under suitable conditions, *cf.* FRANCK[3, 100], HEDGES[100-101], HIRNAIK, LOTKA[1-2], SKRABAL. Starting from the law of mass action for the equilibrium between three isomers or for a series of reactions $S_0 \rightarrow S_1 \rightarrow S_2$ where S_2 influences its own formation autocatalytically, differential equations are obtained which under suitable conditions approach formula 4.10b, and may generate damped or maintained oscillations. The amplitude of the oscillation depends on the concentrations. The frequency of the oscillation is independent therefrom and characteristic for each chemical system (HIRNAIK). Periodic dissolution of metals may occur, generating periodic ionic and electrical activity, oscillating electrodes.

4.17 – Conditions for biochemical feedback and oscillation occur abundantly in the living organism, *e.g.* in the nerves (4.20) or in the metabolism (*cf.* 2.15). Another important factor controlling such mechanisms is the diffusion of chemicals in the cells. Perhaps, these properties even underly the control of protoplasmic motility, *cf.* RASHEVSKY[1], WEINBERG.

4.18 – Some examples of inorganic chemical oscillations which have been studied are:

(1) Periodic H_2 formation at the dissolution of a Ni-Fe alloy in H_2NO_3, of Cr, Zn, Fe, Al, Mg, Mn, Cd in HCl, of Zn in H_2SO_4, of Na-Hg and Ca in H_2O, of Na in ethyl- and *n*-butyl-alcohol.
(2) Periodic variations in electric potential between an electrode and the solution it is immersed into: Fe in H_2NO_3 + HCl or Co in HCl + CrO_3.
(3) Periodic O_2 formation by decomposition of H_2O_2; either in iodic acid + H_2SO_4 or catalytically by Hg in a slightly alkaline solution.
(4) Periodic CO formation; formic acid in H_2SO_4.
(5) Periodic interaction between $BaSO_4$ and Na_2SO_4.
(6) Periodic luminescence when air is leaking into a vessel containing phosphorus.

4.19 – *Nerve Models*. The system Fe-electrode/H_2NO_3-solution has attracted special attention. An iron wire in nitric acid acquires an oxide covering which protects it against further action of the acid. The equilibrium is however unstable. If it is disturbed at one point (*e.g.* by electric stimulation or contact with a more reactive metal), an action potential travels along the thread, representing a moving redox reaction. Other threads in the same solution will also be influenced. The model mimics the excitation processes in nerve fibres remarkably well. If the thread is covered with a series of short glass cylinders, simulating the "isolating" myelin sheath and the Ranvier constrictions of nerves, the process travels swifter. It may be characterized as a relaxation oscillation (4.13-14) inasmuch as the oxide has to be slowly rebuilt before a new impulse is possible (*cf.* BONHOEFFER[1, 100-101], FRANCK[1-2], FREDENHAGEN, LILLIE, OSTWALD).

4.20 – *Neural Activity*. In the nerve fibre the unstable equilibrium is represented by the concentration of cations (especially K^+ and Na^+) along the nerve membrane. The passing of an impulse (action potential) involves the transport of ions across the membrane. Similar phenomena follow the contraction waves in muscle fibres. In medicine, electrical activity may be measured at various sites in the body, *e.g.* the Electro-Cardio-Gram (heart muscle action), Electro-Myo-Gram (muscular action), Electro-Encephalo-Gram (brain waves), Electro-Retino-Gram (retinal activity), Electro-Dermato-Gram (skin resistance). The last is used as an indicator of vegetative nervous activity, REGELSBERGER[1-2, 200-201], WAGNER[3]. The input to the afferent nerve fibres is usually delivered by sensory organs. These transform the stimulus into action potentials, the frequency of which is roughly proportional to the logarithm of the disturbance (pulse frequency modulation). Under conditions of constant stimulus the nerve fiber may discharge rhythmically in the manner of relaxation oscillations, though adaptation and unidirectionality may interfere, *cf.* CLYNES, HILL[1]. – Rhythms in the EMG during shivering were found by YAMAMOTO[100].

4.21 – *Periodic Growth*. Growth, whether of individuals or populations, contains a positive feedback element. The parent determines the offspring, which forms the parent-to-come, *cf.* Fig. 2.26a. This may be a balanced system with an exponential increase in time (compound interest). The simplest example is that of free growth, where the rate of increase (y′) is proportional to the number of units already present, formula 4.21a with solution 4.21b (*cf.* 4.10 d-e).

4.21a	$y' = ky$
4.21b	$y = ce^{kt}$
4.21c	$y' = ky\,(1-y/L)$
4.21d	$y = 1/2\,L(1 + \tanh\,[1/2\,k^{-1}\,L^2(t-C)])$

4.22 – More realistic growth models include limiting factors or, more generally, an interaction between the parent-offspring feedback and the environment (competition, limited food supply, immigration, *etc.*), Fig. 4.22a. One may introduce an asymptotic saturation limit (L) to the population (the lower limit being zero), and arrive at equation 4.21c with solution 4.21d, which is the logistic law of limited growth, *cf.* SMITH[200].

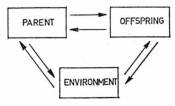

Fig. 4.22a. Population feedback.

4.23 – Normal population growth contains, however, also time lags, such as (1) a certain 'reaction time' before the organism responds to the environment and (2) a certain 'reproduction time' between successive generations. If these are included the mathematics yield differential equations of type 4.10b under certain conditions. Actually, there may occur damped or steady state oscillations around the saturation level. The first type is more common. The latter occurs if reproduction is large or the reaction time long. Obviously population cycles may occur without predators, *cf.* 2.16. For mathematical discussions and experimental verification see *e.g.* conferences 1954b and 1957d, also HUTCHINSON, MORAN[2], NICHOLSON, PRATT[1], RASHEVSKY[2], SLOBODKIN[1-3, 100], WANGERSKY[100-101].

4.24 – We have now given a series of examples of oscillators, both mechanical and electronic models, as well as applications in the chemical and biological sphere. Let us also summarize some of their general properties, though we will return to the subject often enough throughout this book.

4.25 – *Natural Frequency.* If activated, any particular oscillator works at a certain rate, the natural frequency (characteristic frequency, Eigenfrequenz). This is constant and solely determined by the construction (parameters) of the system (capacitance, resistance, inductance, elasticity, friction, mass, *etc.*). Examples are vibrating strings and forks, motors, metronomes. We thus have a rhythmic output at constant input (excluding the signal which sets the system in motion). The frequency is usually very stable, which permits us to use oscillators as clocks.

4.26 – Spontaneous oscillations also occur in biology, *cf.* 1.15-16, where they are called 'endogenous rhythms'. Unfortunately, far too many synonyms are being used, *e.g.* natural frequency, natural period, freerunning rhythm, circadian rhythm (reserved for near-24-h periods), ESSO (Endogenous Self-Sustaining Oscillation), eigenphasische Rhythmen, intrinsic rhythm, environment-independent frequency, spontaneous frequency, autochrony, internal rhythm, autonomous rhythm, persistent rhythm, endonomous rhythm. The term endogenous rhythms is also sometimes used as a synonym for oscillations located in the body's anatomical or physiological inside. This use should be avoided.

4.27 – *Changes in Natural Frequency.* Changes in the oscillatory frequency may be effected either by impressing variations from the outside upon the system or by a single change in any of its parameters. In the former case, forced oscillations may occur. In the latter, the natural frequency is simply changed and thereafter

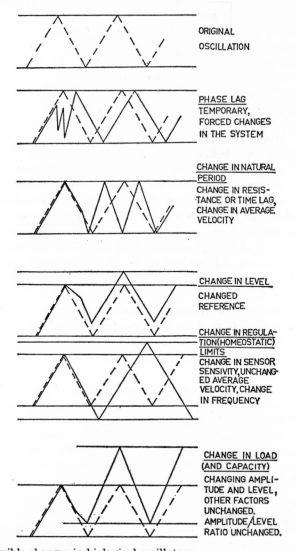

ORIGINAL
OSCILLATION

PHASE LAG
TEMPORARY,
FORCED CHANGES
IN THE SYSTEM

CHANGE IN NATURAL
PERIOD
CHANGE IN RESIS-
TANCE OR TIME LAG,
CHANGE IN AVERAGE
VELOCITY

CHANGE IN LEVEL
CHANGED
REFERENCE

CHANGE IN REGULA-
TION(HOMEOSTATIC)
LIMITS
CHANGE IN SENSOR
SENSIVITY, UNCHANG-
ED AVERAGE
VELOCITY, CHANGE
IN FREQUENCY

CHANGE IN LOAD
(AND CAPACITY)
CHANGING AMPLI-
TUDE AND LEVEL,
OTHER FACTORS
UNCHANGED.
AMPLITUDE/LEVEL
RATIO UNCHANGED.

Fig. 4.27a. Possible changes in biological oscillators.

Fig. 4.27b. Capacity change in a linear relaxation oscillator.

constant again. Complicated feedback systems (*e.g.* in electronics) are often difficult to stabilize, and may sometimes change their natural frequency spontaneously by feedback to their own parameters. The homeostat was an example, 3.16. In biological oscillators such changes are to be expected in view of the complexity of the systems. The phase lag, velocity, capacity, average velocity, regulation (homeostatic) limits, the reference value or still other parameters may change. Some possibilities are depicted in Fig. 4.27a, and especially for relaxation oscillators (4.13-14) in Fig. 4.27b. In the latter a change in the capacity will affect not only the amplitude but also the frequency. Combinations of the illustrated effects may occur.

4.28 – *Coupled Oscillators*. All the many oscillators in the living organism may be expected to interact. There are several possible ways of interaction; forced oscillations, resonance, interference, frequency demultiplication (one oscillator counting off a whole number of the others' beats for each one of its own), 'magnet effect' (relative coordination, different integer relations between the frequencies of the oscillators), and transformations such as between gears. In biology the last might be effected by many devices, *e.g.* one cyclic chemical transport system loading another one of different capacity, nervous and endocrine rhythms directing the metabolic rhythms catalytically, sliding effect owing to energy loss in one system, *etc*.

4.29 – *Forced Oscillations. Resonance*. An oscillator or a set of coupled oscillators may be forced to adopt a certain frequency. Usually, they accept the driving frequency only if it does not differ too much from their own natural frequencies. They may also, if nonlinear (*cf.* Fig. 3.28b), change to a harmonic or subharmonic of the input rate. The other types of interaction mentioned in the previous paragraph are also possible. Interactions between oscillating systems often require some time to settle down into a steady state, passing through a series of intermediate stages, transients. The subject of oscillator behaviour will be treated in Part III of this book.

4.30 – Many oscillatory systems which are set in motion by a sudden disturbance provide damped oscillations. If these latter are to become sustained an external triggering influence must be applied; at the same rate and in phase with the spontaneous system. Else, a braking effect occurs, which is maximal at a phase difference between the spontaneous oscillation and the triggering impulse of 180°. If we give a pendulum (4.7) a slight push at each turn it may oscillate regularly, *cf.* 4.3. Such a mechanism may be built into the oscillator by feedback (as in a clock). If we push a little harder, introducing high gain (3.24), the amplitude of the swings will increase slowly. In the electronic radio circuit the oscillations in the antenna coil (Fig. 4.9b) push the oscillating circuit in a similar way by inductive coupling. However, the characteristic frequency of the circuit must match that in the antenna. This is accomplished by adjustment of the variable condenser (tuning in).

4.31 – *Noise*. Noise in a system represents a series of undesired disturbances or frequencies. It may consist of absolutely random influences, 'random noise', or an oscillation of much higher frequency than the actual one. It may be generated from without or within the mechanism (thermal noise or changes caused by nonlinear transformations, *cf*. 3.29). We may try to make the system insensitive to it by increasing the resistance (3.22). Especially with high gain systems we want at all cost to avoid noise, since, once there, it will be amplified in the same manner as the meaningful operations (*e.g.* the humming sound heard if we turn up the radio volume control). It tends to drown out the information signals we want to receive. It may be generated by the Brownian movements of electrons and molecules in resistors or radiotubes (shot noise); appear as similar movements in the air around a microphone membrane; as vibrations; or as thousand and one activities in our vicinity, which are meaningful as such but bear no relation to our own activities. We recognize them as various types of humming noises, pips and howls in the wireless, 'snow' on the television set, vibrations in machinery, sounds of cars and aircraft or the babble of conversation in a restaurant.

4.32 – *Biological Noise*. Biological information is particularly noisy since we can seldom isolate the particular function under study completely from the rest of the organism. It is a particular headache in biological rhythm research to define what is signal and what is noise in our records. We will do well to devote considerable attention to the problem of obtaining a large 'signal-to-noise ratio', as in other branches of communication technique. This may be obtained by choosing homogenous strains of animals, ensuring as constant an environment as possible and by using accurate methods of assay. Another approach, which is often forgotten by the biologist, is to choose adequate statistical methods of analysis (*cf*. Part III). The latter may be remarkably efficient even in rather noisy material. After all, statistics is largely a method of handling random noise.

4.33 – On the other hand, noise means movement and may be used to overcome the static resistance in a system, so-called 'dither' or 'jitter'. A system already in movement is usually easier to direct swiftly than a nonmoving (dead) one. In biology movement is everpresent. The absolutely nonmoving biological system is dead and cannot usually be set into motion or directed at all. It is quite possible that one function of endogenous biological rhythms may be that of noise, to keep the system in motion, so as to minimize its inertia and increase the velocity of its reactions.

The resting pupil shows a high-frequency 'unrest' (STARK[4]) which does not influence the actual shutter-function of the pupil. It is injected from outside the loop and may have the purpose of increasing its reactivity.

4.34 – *Biological Oscillators*. Before cybernetics, it was a dictum that machines could no attain self-regulation, whereas the living organism could do so. Today, we know that there is no essential difference in this respect. – The biological feedback systems are extremely complex and possess a relatively large time-lag. Hence, they will readily become disturbed, with oscillations as a consequence. We might expect fluctuations of damped character triggered from the environment. We might even find sustained ones controlled by a constant environment (*cf*. 3.26) or by pathological changes in the servomechanisms. It has already been pointed out

(1.3) that the possibility of adapting to external rhythms would enhance the survival value of the individual, singling him out by the random selection of evolution. In this connection it would be immaterial whether the necessary feedback systems were designed for the very purpose of oscillation or for other purposes. Anyhow, oscillating biological systems are very common. If spontaneous, they are called endogenous rhythms.

4.35 – When confronted with endogenous rhythmicity in an organism we should always try to establish on what feedback system it is based. If finding the answer, we might then ask for the parameters and the way in which these determine the amplitude, characteristic frequency and other peculiarities of the rhythm in question. Actually, then, the endogenous biological rhythms tell us about the mechanism and the setting of the body regulators. The time is also nearing when an investigator might predict the conditions for oscillation in his own biological system.

4.36 – This chapter has dealt with the properties of oscillating systems and also given some examples of biological oscillators. The next chapter will discuss that most important medium in which they operate, time, and how it can be measured by the living organism, the time sense.

CHAPTER 5

Time, Time Sense and Biological Clocks

5.1 – *The Independent Variable*. The preceding chapters have dealt with the conditions for biological regulation and oscillation. These processes occur in time. Time is the independent variable in our graphs, usually represented on the abscissa (x-axis). The dependent variable is our measurement data, usually plotted along the ordinate (y-axis). The dependent variable may be regarded as moving in time. We may emphasize this fundamental character of biological data by naming them temporal moving variates.

5.2 – *Theories of Time*. It is remarkable, then, that we know almost nothing about one of our most fundamental variables, time. There exist theories enough to suit any taste (*cf.* DUNNE, EDDINGTON, GREGORY[100], GRÜNBAUM, PERPEET, POULET, RUSSEL[1]) but no real criteria for choosing among them. We may think of time as a unique axiomatic property of the physical world. We may regard it as a pure consequence of movement. We may consider it as a subjective phenomenon.

We may accept the MICHELSON-MORLEY experiment, LORENZ' explanation of it and EINSTEIN's relativity theory, including the axiom of the constant light velocity; if so we may regard time as a dimension with a reversed vectorial relationship to the three ordinary dimensions.

5.3 – We may even postulate a hierarchy of times in a serial universe, in which we envisage future and past as existing alike, with an observer moving in the direction of future, his progress being, however, timed by an observer moving in another time dimension, who is, in turn timed by yet another observer in yet another time dimension, and so on *ad infinitum*. In this case we accept the existance of precognition.

5.4 – Even more disheartening than viewing the multitude of theories about time is to list the things we do not really know about it. If time be regarded as a flow of something; is it then continuous or discontinuous, linear or nonlinear? Is there one absolute time, or only observers' times, differing from individual to individual? What relation bears time really to matter and to motion? Could time exist without matter? How would we experience time at the velocity of light? When did time start, if it ever did? Why does time seem to move in one direction only, time's arrow? Could we move in the other direction? If so, is time travel possible or would it give rise to an insuperable time paradox, each travel in to the past or future (*e.g.* simply by precognition) continuously changing both past and future (feedback)?

Why is our perception of time so uncertain? If we can really dream hours of happenings into seconds of other observers' time, as still asserted by some, does that mean that we can interchange temporal and spatial structures in our minds? Or is time's flow subjective?

5.5 – *Events*. Many things only exist for a certain time. We may regard them as events, with the dimension energy-duration. If the duration of an event is very long, the energy may approach zero, a quite appropriate description of ghosts and materialisations, if we choose to accept such phenomena. Since events have a duration we may also define a frequency for them. Actually, a periodic process is the perfect event, possessing a definite amount of both energy and duration. A quantum might be a rhythmic phenomenon, an amount of energy existing during a certain time. The HEISENBERG uncertainty principle might relate to a succession of identical events in time, with random location in space, *e.g.* the position of the electrons in the atomic shell.

5.6 – *Entropy Time. Logarithmic Time*. A modern explanation of time's arrow is to reinstate the old definition of time as created by movement and measure the latter by entropy (see GRÜNBAUM, WIENER[2]). Entropy increases steadily and this would make time unidirectional. However, the universe must not be infinite. Segregated, closed or open, entropic systems would have slightly different times. If the universe is finite, matter and time may be imagined to have had a beginning, after which the entropy change started. In that case time might be logarithmic. Something similar may occur with individual times, since our rate of growth from birth on is approximately logarithmic and since we spend more energy when working or concentrating hard than at rest, and our metabolic turnover slows down at old age. Time perception varies so; FISCHER[901], FRAISSE[6], SCHALTENBRANDT, WHITROW.

5.7 – *Cyclic Time*. If time could reverse its direction, we would probably not be aware of it. There might be isolated entropic systems with reversed entropy-time. Let us assume, however, that the universal time may reverse its direction regularly. If, now, we moved with time and time went backwards we would see processes reverse themselves, without noticing any change in the time flow. For all we know, time may be cyclic, *cf*. GRÜNBAUM. In that case we would have a perfect clock, time itself, common to all individuals, for setting the individual rhythms. Alternatively, such concepts as a rhythmic alternation between the dominance of the space and time vectors, or regular sequences of events might be constructed.

5.8 – *Chronometers*. Whichever theory is correct; when adapting time as the independent variable in our formulae and graphs we discard all speculations as to its real properties. However, we still need a means of measuring time, clocks. The simplest type of time-piece is the interval timer which only measures a pre-set duration, as with an unwinding spring or the hour-glass. An alarm clock is used in the same way. If the hour-glass is provided with a scale, time may be measured continuously. If it turns automatically when running out we get a chronometer. But then it has been transformed into an oscillator. Any oscillating system may be used as a true clock, from the incredibly stable high-frequency vibrations of ammonia, cesium atoms and quartz crystals, through celestial movements (sun dial) to pendulum time-pieces, spring watches and electronic circuits or tubes. A large set of interval timers with all possible durations would also do but is unpractical.

5.9 – We may use oscillators for measuring isolated time events on any scale, relative time, or to inform us about the universal time. In the latter case the clock must be set, both with regard to a suitable period (usually 24 h) and phase. The phase may coincide with the local longitudinal time or with a general universal time (identical on all parts of the earth). Setting may be done with the aid of cosmic events. If these are only observable on the part of Terra turned towards them, they will give us 'local time' as well as the period, depending on the rotation of the earth. Universal time requires an agent observable all over the globe simultaneously, such as the daily 'earth potential' fluctuations (*cf.* BROWN[7]) or instantaneous spread of information on one local time, *e.g.* 'Greenwich time'.

The period adjustment of a clock simply means a suitable transformation of the output from an oscillator. This may be done through gearshifts or demultiplication (counting off a certain number of beats). We may even drive several clocks of different periods and phases by one central oscillator. – Aviation offices usually have two clocks, one set at Greenwich time and one at local time.

5.10 – *Biological Clocks.* Living organisms have a remarkable sense of time. This involves both the capacity to measure time intervals and to orient in local or universal time. They must, therefore, possess clocks. These may be exogenous clocks like our watches or the sun, being consulted at will, perhaps continuously; or they may be built-in mechanisms, endogenous clocks. There may be special interval timers and special chronometers, or only the latter, used for both purposes.

The biological clock is important to the animals and plants. They have to 'know' the time of day and year to react with maximum efficiency to the environment. Plants must 'know' when to start growing or flowering or when to open the flowers; arthropoda when to time the various stages of metamorphosis; fishes when to reproduce; and birds when to molt. The clock also controls that enigma of physiology, animal migration. This will be discussed later.

5.11 – *Exogenous clocks* for the living organism might be inherent in the basic properties of space and time, or involve the movements of the earth, moon, sun and stars or resultant changes in electro-magnetic forces, gravity and even other less well-known forces (subtle environmental clues). These things will be discussed in Part II of the book.

5.12 – *Endogenous clocks* may perhaps be interval timers, represented by the accumulation or breakdown of metabolic or endocrine products, by some relaxation time or even damped oscillations. In that case it has to be reactivated anew each time by some suitable signal. The clocks may, perhaps, also be true organic oscillators situated in a special part of the organism or they may simply be one aspect of all the numerous feedback systems in the body.

5.13 – Wherever the clock, there must be special organic tissues engaged in measuring time. They might be special receptors, special centres integrating the information from several sensors and informing the rest of the body, or whole clock mechanisms. They should be localizable. However, we do not know where they are to be found. The nervous system is certainly involved in higher animals, but plants judge time, too. External stimuli, such as light or temperature (and their receptors) are certainly important in setting the clock, but periods are also found which do not correspond to any of the known external agents. There may be one or several clocks, perhaps with different settings in different organs. If there is a 'master oscillator', what is its frequency? If the clock is exogenous, can it then show only local time or perhaps even universal time?

The universality of the biological clock indicates that it must be localized in the most fundamental aspects of the cells. More, we do not truly know. Much effort and ingenuity has gone into attempts to unravel the mystery. The question of the exo- or endogeneity of the clock is still discussed. If we have a perfect 24-h period its exogeneity might be taken for granted. Is it, however, just passively read from an exogenous clock, or do we have an endogenous oscillator which is merely controlled from the outside (cf. 5.9 and 4.29)? The 24-h period does under certain circumstances change to another one, say 22.6 hours. This might prove that the forcing agent has been removed. However, it might also mean that only the setting of period and phase in one extension of the clock has been changed, the hidden central timer still keeping an externally controlled 24-h period.

It may be that the nucleic acid metabolism is deeply involved in time keeping. It is sensitive to visible and UV-light as is the phase-setting of biological rhythms (EHRET[5]).

What we really lack is a method for the analysis of data, powerful enough to distinguish between external and endogenous components of the clock.

5.14 – *Time Duration Sense.* Sometimes, it is only necessary for the organisms to measure the duration of a certain time stretch, irrespective of the time of day. When they 'choose' the time of the year for flowering, migration or molting (cf. 5.10 and Congress 1960c, BÜNNING[20, 29], CLOUDSLEY-THOMPSON[28]) they do this by 'observing' the annually changing light-duration of the day. When it reaches and passes a certain value the reaction comes with remarkable accuracy; only a few days may suffice. Such phenomena have been extensively studied, not least by the botanists, especially by BÜNNING. Here, we may visualize some interval timer

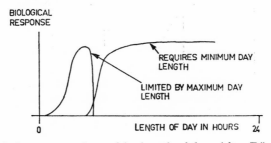

Fig. 5.14a. Biological response triggered by length of day. After BÜNNING.

mechanism (5.8), obtained by genetical selection. The timer might be started at some point such as the onset of light or darkness, running only as long as the new condition prevails and only precipitating a reaction if it is permitted to run out (or calling forth a reaction proportional to its duration when stopped, *e.g.* by darkness). Fig 5.14a illustrates the quantitative aspects of the time duration sense.

There may also be several timers, acting in a certain sequence. Some plants require a certain proportion and a certain sequence between length of dark and light periods in order to flower. Generally, an organism will have to 'know' if the days are lengthening or shortening in order to 'distinguish' between spring and autumn.

5.15 – There are, however, also cases where the pre-set time duration may be chosen at will, as in a person determined to wake up after a certain amount of sleep. This would seem to rule out the interval timer, unless we assume that individuals are born with a large set of timers with different time constants. Instead the mechanism comes suspiciously close to being a real clock, a time orientation sense.

5.16 – *Time Orientation Sense.* Many facts indicate that the biological time-indicators must be true chronometers which may be consulted at will. Men may estimate the time of the day correctly, even if abruptly aroused out of sleep. Many animals need chronometers for navigation in migration. These problems are closely tied up with the concept of the endodiurnal rhythm (today more generally called circadian rhythm) introduced by BÜNNING. Actually, there is no doubt that we have oscillating systems with a 24-h period (when synchronized), which could be used as a chronometer. Most of the body functions behave in this way. Ample examples will be given in Chapter 7 and in Part IV of this book.

Most authors assume the circadian rhythm to possess a period of nearly 24 hours, being truly endogenous and having been developed through natural selection. The period and phase are normally controlled and sustained by external events, but the curve shape is not that of the external light-darkness cycle. The endodiurnal cycle (in a more restricted sense) consists of oscillations in the sensitivi-

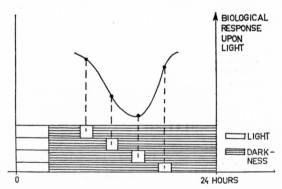

Fig. 5.16a. Testing the endodiurnal photosensitivity curve by light stimuli.

ty to light, with alternating phases of photophil (light-triggered) and scotoph (inhibited by light, darkness-triggered) reactions.

The endodiurnal periodicity of photosensitivity may be beautifully demonstrated by initiating the rhythm with light and then, during the ensuing darkness, testing the photo-response of some suitable function by giving short light stimuli at different times during the darkness or by varying the length of the latter, BÜNNING, BÜNSOW, HAMNER, SCHWEMMLE (see Congress 1960c). The phenomenon has been demonstrated in many plants and for many of their functions. The experiments run more or less as indicated in Fig. 5.16a. The response shape may recur if the darkness (with light-breaks) is continued through several days. However, the endodiurnal rhythm seems to be the same, whether the plants require short daylight periods (short-day plants) or long ones (long-day plants), Fig. 5.16b, and for day- or night-active animals. A 'skeleton' day may be used, with short illuminations only, representing 'dawn and dusk' (PITTENDRIGH).

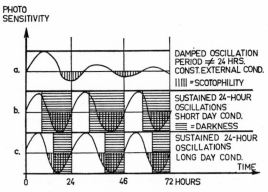

Fig. 5.16b. The endodiurnal cycle, according to BÜNNING.

5.17 – Relation between Time Duration and Time Orientation Senses. It must be realized that the various effects which may be measured in Fig. 5.16a are delayed. They demand several identical consecutive cycles before appearing and may happen later, not necessarily at the time of testing with the light shock. It is generally supposed that certain products accumulate during the light (or darkness) phases and that they call forth the desired effect if present in certain amounts. This would be in the nature of an interval timer.

Let us take the flowering of a short-day plant as an example. The 'dawn', or light-on signal, starts something going (a photophil process) in the plant. When the darkness comes (early in the day) the process probably stops and continues during the following light period, until enough has accumulated to call forth the desired effect. If, however, the light goes on too long, the peculiar result is that it inhibits the process. It inhibits something which should already have happened. This can, of course, only occur if the effect is delayed. The remarkable thing is also that exactly the same inhibition is achieved with a very short light stimulus given during the darkness. As soon as light strikes the plant during the wrong part of the day, something (a scotophil process) seems to be started, which neutralizes the photophil process or its effect.

5.18 – Now, the circadian process is probably the same in short and long-day plants. However, the periods of the cycle in which the organism 'chooses' a photophil or a scotophil reaction are determined by the nature of the plant, cf. Fig. 5.16b.

The mode of coupling between the circadian 'clock' and the 'interval timer' or the character of the latter are unknown. The degree of association seems to vary from a very close one in plants to almost none in birds (MARSHALL[1-6], WILSON[500-503]), or in aphids (LEES[6]). In hens, egg-laying can be kept maximal by very small amounts of light if dispersed throughout the day at certain hour-intervals, each one probably starting some interval timer. Apart from this, however, birds also have the ordinary circadian rhythms. The seasonal time of migration and testicular involution in birds is controlled by the day-length. – In aphids, long-day conditions produce parthenogenetic offspring and short-day conditions egg-laying offspring, an interval timer working, LEES[6], cf. LADERMAN[100].

5.19 – In cases where the duration to be perceived may be set at will, as in human awaking, or when we are required to judge the time of day, the use of a time orientation sense seems to be required. The clock is probably the synchronized circadian one. But how does the organism read it? In predetermined awaking, we use it as an alarm clock. These mechanisms are completely unknown.

5.20 – The sensitivity of the organism to other factors than light may also vary, e.g. to temperature or drugs, as will be discussed later. Also, which is most important, the sensitivity to phase-setting is influenced (WILKINS). This would seem to accelerate the process of synchronization considerably. Individual randomly-timed cycles with location in one half of the day would not be affected, whereas those located in the other day-half are shifted so as to meet the former.

5.21 – We have here used the circadian rhythm as an example of biological 'clocks'. However, there would also seem to exist lunar clocks and annual clocks. Littoral animals follow the moon among other things when navigating. Annual rhythms are legion. Here, the question of endo- or exogeneity is making itself felt; proponents for both exist. These rhythms will be discussed in Chapter 7 and Part IV of this book.

5.22 – *Time Sense in Plants.* Most examples of interval and continuous timing have been demonstrated with plants. In no field of science is biological rhythm research as old as in botany, where photoperiodicity was an early problem and accurate recordings of the rhythms were possible. According to BÜNNING, the French astronomer DeMAIRAN described in 1729 experiments where rhythmic movements of plant leaves (turning against the sun) continued in darkness. He was followed by DUHAMEL, ZINN, CANDOLLE, DUTROCHET, SACHS[1-2], HOFMEISTER, PFEFFER, DARWIN[100] and SEMON, from 1758-1905. Even LINNAEUS[1-2] used the time sense of the plants when constructing his famous 'flower clock', where the numerals of the clock face were represented by flowers opening their blossoms at the corresponding times. This clock has been reproduced by CLAUSER and BAILLAUD[101]. – The discussion will be continued in Chapter 7.

5.23 – *Time Sense in Animals.* The circadian variability has been verified in most animals. Classical experiments on time sense were performed with bees (*e.g.* BELING, GRABENSBERGER[2], KALMUS[1, 3], LINDAUER, RENNER, WAHL). If the insects are trained to receive food at a certain time of the day, they will later unerringly return at that time every day, *i.e.* 24 hours later. A good example is the following (RENNER[5, 7]): Bees were trained to collect sugar water regularly between 8:15 and 10:15 in Paris. When flown to New York they appeared at 3:00 local time, *i.e.* 24 hours after the last appearance. Both experiments were carried out in closed chambers with constant light and temperature. Even if completely shut off from external influences the bees keep the time.

A bird 'clock', corresponding to LINNAEUS' flower clock has also been constructed, showing the awakening time of these animals, *cf.* CLAUSER and SZYMANSKY[2].

The discussion will be continued in connection with circadian rhythms (Chapter 7) and animal migration (Part II).

5.24 – *Time Sense in Man.* Many people can tell the time of the day correctly without consulting a clock, even if awakened out of deep sleep. Others may wake up at any predetermined time, irrespective of the duration of sleep, not only at the usual trained hour of rising. Most readers have probably experienced this themselves, coming awake shortly before the alarm signal. Even after several days of isolation this time sense may still function. The mechanism works, also, under hypnosis and therefore early attracted the interest of the hypnotists. However, the precision is probably not larger than under normal conditions. There are individual differences in the accuracy of the time sense, about 20% are very good at it. Read CLAUSER, also BOND, BORING[100], BRUSH, EHRENWALD, FROBENIUS, GROSS[200], HALL[200], OMWAKE[100], STERZINGER.

5.25 – There are different ways of studying the time sense:

(1) Ordering the subject to *wake up at a certain time,* varying both this and the length of sleep.

(2) Waking up persons irregularly and ask them to *estimate the time.*

(3) Letting people *wake up spontaneously* at the accustomed time and measure the accuracy of this.

(4) Giving a *post-hypnotic command* to do a certain thing a certain time after release from the trance. At the correct time the subject feels a compulsion to do the thing in question without knowing why.

(5) Keeping subjects under *constant conditions* (or changed conditions) and control whether he keeps his old "time habits" or time sense. This has also been applied to animals, *cf.* preceding section and animal navigation. GARTENLAUBE's orangutan more or less kept his true Javanese sleeping times through his whole life in spite of being transported west (according to CLAUSER).

(6) Asking the subject to judge short time intervals. Remarkably enough some lengths of time are judged better than others and these values seem to form a rhythmic pattern based on a short period of 0.35-0.75 seconds, the *indifference point.* One may wonder whether this has something to do with the frequency of a supposed basic oscillator.

(7) Studying the influence of *metabolically active compounds* on the time sense. Quinine seems to affect the human time sense.

(8) Trying to *disorient* the subjects *in time*. EIFF[1, 100] and LOBBAN[2] tried this by changing the environmental time, either by cutting off a time period of subjective awareness through narcosis or surrepticiously resetting the clocks in an unchanging environment. In both cases the body functions seemed to split, some more following the objective time, others more the subjective time, though containing components of both. Some clocks, or extensions of *the* clock, were reset, others not.

(9) Studying subjective or pathological time perception. When we dream or work, subjective time may run very fast. Children experience time in quite another way than the aged. In the psychoses very peculiar experiences of time occur, from a sense of absolute standstill to that of a rapidly drawn film. Similar effects are evoked by LSD (FISCHER[901]).

5.26 – We have now studied biological regulation, oscillators and time sense. The next step will be a systematical survey of the various endogenous rhythms (Chapters 6 to 11), before we turn to a discussion of environmental factors and exogenous rhythms.

CHAPTER 6

Endogenous Rhythms without External Correlates

6.1 – The previous chapters have dealt with biological regulation and oscillators. The latter may be classified as endogenous rhythms and cover a large scale of spontaneous frequencies.

One may distinguish between two groups of bio-oscillators, those which have an external correlate (24-hour, lunar, seasonal) and those which have not. The latter are usually thermosensitive and speed up their frequencies with increasing temperature, as would be expected from biochemical processes. The endogenous rhythms with correlates seem, however, to be relatively temperature-independent, with constant frequency, *cf*. 1.17. How this frequency-stability is achieved is completely unknown, though many theories exist.

This chapter will cover the endogenous rhythms without correlates. We will start with a short introductory survey of these rhythms, including examples of their general properties. Then follows a discussion of some more well-known periodicities, mainly in man, such as brain waves, human perception rhythms, spontaneous central motor rhythms (tapping, walking), heart rate, pulse and respiration. The second half of the chapter gives a more general survey of endogenous rhythms without correlates, classified into microrhythms (rapid rhythms, duration less than one hour), macrorhythms (slow rhythms, durations about one hour to one week) and long-term rhythms (durations > one week), in the order of descending frequency throughout. Another classification which has been proposed is ultradian (period < circadian), circadian, and infradian (period > circadian), *cf*. Conf. 1961a, pp 13, 15.

The rhythms to be described here are mostly sustained oscillations though damped oscillations also occur. They exist under normal or experimental conditions. Pathological rhythms have, usually, other frequencies, reflecting deep-seated changes in the oscillating transducers themselves. They will be discussed separately in Chapter 8.

6.2 – *Short Survey of Spontaneous (Non-correlate) Biological Rhythms*. All organisms (plants, invertebrates and vertebrates alike) abound in spontaneous rhythms with durations ranging from milliseconds to years, *cf*. 1.15. It is not so wide a range if compared to the 'cosmic scale' of periodicities, which varies from the region of 10^{23} c/sec (electromagnetic radiation), to planetary orbits requiring hundreds of years for one complete cycle; however, it provides many interesting phenomena. The upper frequency limits are found in nervous transmission and fibrillar musculature, maximally about 2000 c/sec (Hz). Well-known are some of the natural rhythms in man such as the EEG waves, the heart rate or the respiratory frequency. – The various rhythms may be classified either according to frequency, phylum or organic system. The frequencies tend to cluster into groups. Each organic tissue, for instance, displays some typical periods or groups of periods.

The 'neural rhythms' are either concerned with the generation of impulses in single neurons (1-1000 c/sec), or constitute oscillating systems built of several neurons and sometimes including non-nervous tissue (*e.g.* musculature), with frequencies from about 20 c/sec to durations measuring hours. Related phenomena are the limits for our perception of rhythms (5-50 c/sec), or rhythms in our perception and our mental activity (duration usually 1/3-80 sec).

'Myorhythms', rhythmic muscular activity, are also conspicuous, whether involving the striated type (walking, chewing, tapping, breathing; 0.3-8.0 c/sec) or the nonstriated one (vascular tonus, peristalsis *etc.,* durations 10 sec to 40 days). They are really controlled by the nervous system, whether voluntary or autonomous.

True 'myogenic rhythms' exist, though, in the heart musculature, and in the invertebrate fibrillar flight musculature; the latter contracting at a higher rate than that of the nervous impulses which reach it (35-2200 c/sec).

An important type of endogenous rhythms is found in the very basis of organic life, the cytoplasm itself. It is closely linked to the problem of 'protoplasmic motility' and underlying metabolic phenomena, *e.g.* rhythmic contractions in plasmodia (duration 20-200 sec); pulsating vacuoles; ciliary movements in unicellular organisms (about 40 c/sec) and epithelia. By a rotation of the growth zone in plants spiralling movements of tendrils or roots are induced, circumnutation.

6.3 – *General Properties of Spontaneous (Non-correlate) Biological Rhythms.* Most natural rhythms are regulatory in character. The respiratory cycle is a typical example of a closed reflex feedback, Fig. 6.3a. Examples of how such mechanisms

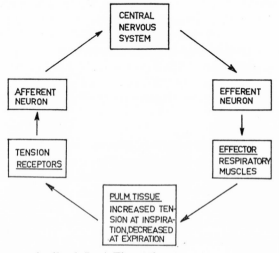

Fig. 6.3a. Respiratory feedback I, *cf.* Fig. 6.8b.

can be analyzed by servomechanical techniques have been given for the pupil (STARK, cf. 2.19, 3.9,24). Another example is SCOTT's studies of bean root potentials, to be discussed later.

Several natural rhythms also behave like 'relaxation oscillations', e.g. the cardiac metabolic cycle, where the muscular carbohydrate is rapidly broken down at the systole, to be rebuilt slowly during the diastole, cf. 4.13-14.

6.4 – The natural frequency differs from organ to organ and even within parts of one and the same organ. The auricles of the heart beat more rapidly than the ventricles, if the normal 'coupling' between their functions through the PURKINJE system and their triggering by an autonomous pacemaker are cut. Actually, parts of the auricles, in *Homo*, have a natural frequency of about 70 beats/min and the apex of the heart about 20 beats/min (NUSSBAUM). The phenomenon may also be observed in isolated portions of the embryonic heart musculature.

6.5 – In spite of being spontaneous, natural oscillators may still be 'controlled' from other sources, including external ones. The heart rate rises with the degree of body exercise or excitement as does the respiratory rate, in order to supply the tissues with enough oxygen and fuel. This regulation is achieved by the autonomous nervous system through servomechanisms superimposed upon the primary ones. One example would be the respiration-promoting effect of increased CO_2-levels in the blood, affecting the body pH, which in turn acts upon a receptor situated in the neck controlling the medullary respiratory centre.

6.6 – The constancy of our milieu interne (2.2) is largely upheld by feedback regulation, whether aiming at unchanged levels or regular oscillations. These mechanisms are very sensitive and we might expect many diseased conditions to call forth changes, resulting in a number of damped and sustained oscillations which do not normally occur. Actually, the physician meets a vast number of such 'pathological rhythms'. The natural periods may assume almost any value depending on the type of disease, the individual and the organ affected. It is, perhaps, not always realized by the botanist and zoologist that the diseases are really Nature's own vast experiments and that there is practically no experiment which has not been made sometime, somewhere in Nature.

6.7 – The various rhythms in our own body are, of course, interrelated in many ways, cf. 1.25. An example is the coordination between the pulse and the respiratory frequency. During inspiration the heart rate rises slightly as compared to the expiration (respiratory arhythmia). HILDEBRANDT[3-5, 7-12, 14, 16, 20, 100, 104] has constructed a pulse-respiratory quotient. The value normally varies around 4 but also shows a pronounced 24-hour rhythm, a clear correlation with the barometric pressure, and increased fluctuations in conditions of disease or convalescence. The coupling is performed in the central nervous system, joining the circulatory and respiratory centers, KOEPCHEN[1-2, 100], cf. ANDERS. – Biological coupled oscillators (4.28) underlie the various relations between auricular and ventricular cardiac rhythms which may be observed in incomplete atrio-ventricular block. 2-3-4 auricular beats/ventricular beat may occur or one of the latter may be dropped at regular intervals, *etc.* Phenomena of this kind were called relative coordination by VON HOLST (*cf.* BETHE[5-7]). They lend themselves well to servomechanical analysis, CLYNES.

6.8 – The natural rhythms may also show bursts with intervals of lesser rate; a rhythmic fluctuation in the natural frequency, signifying beats in the system. The respiratory arhythmia (6.7) was one example. Normal respiration also varies slightly in a periodic manner. Under pathologic conditions the phenomenon may become pronounced, the so called CHEYNE-STOKE respiration (*cf.* HEGGLIN[200]) where bursts of rapid breathing (0.5-1 c/sec) alternate with respiratory standstill,

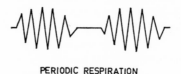

PERIODIC RESPIRATION

Fig. 6.8a. CHEYNE-STOKE breathing.

Fig. 6.8a. The condition is caused by some derangement in the regulation of the respiratory rate owing to anoxia and increased CO_2-concentration in the blood, perhaps an overload of the system in Fig. 6.8b. – Other kinds of rhythmic alternations are sometimes found in attacks of organic disease, *e.g.* swelling of certain joints, which may alternate regularly with psychiatric symptoms, *e.g.* depression.

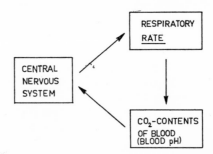

Fig. 6.8b. Respiratory feedback II, *cf.* Fig. 6.3a.

6.9 – *Natural Rhythms in the Nervous System* (5-200 c/sec). Since a nerve fibre is refractory during 1-2 msec an upper theoretical limit is set for the possible frequencies; about 500-1000 c/sec. In practice, the figure seldom exceeds 200c/sec. If several fibres are working simultaneously higher combined frequencies might be obtained. The intensity of the nerve message is communicated by pulse frequency modulation (19.14).

6.10 – The complicated interplay of nerve cell potentials which are recorded in the electroencephalogram (EEG, brain waves) runs at frequencies from 1-60 c/sec:

6.10a

Delta	waves	– 0.5-3.5	c/sec.
Theta	,,	– 4-7	,,
Alpha	,,	– 8-13	,,
Beta	,,	– 14-18	,,
Gamma	,,	– 20-30(-60)	,,

The frequencies tend to be lower in infants (theta, STARK[1]) than in adults (alpha) and to rise with increasing nervous activity in the series; stupor (slow delta)- deep sleep (delta)- superficial sleep (sleep spindles)- relaxation (alpha)- attention (alpha, beta)- grand mal (epilepsy, gamma). At superficial sleep peculiar bursts of beta waves are superimposed periodically upon a delta rhythm (sleep spindles). The alpha waves appear most clearly if the visual cortical activity is excluded by closing of the eyes. KLEITMAN in his famous work on the physiology of sleep and dreams has also studied the sleep EEG, cf. GOODENOUGH[100], SHAPIRO, OSWALD[200]. In epilepsy there are typical EEG changes with both delta and gamma components; the former may be correlated with blood sugar, ENGEL[302]. The EEG pattern is complicated (MÜLLER-LIMMROTH[100]) and varies with the focal location in the brain and the position of the leads.

Modern brain studies (cf. FREEMAN, GASTAUT[100]) are profiting from the cybernetic approach and the use of implanted probes (even in the reticular formation of the brain stem). A problem is the peculiar inability to pin down the memory function at any particular site in the brain. The changes in the EEG during the learning of conditioned reflexes is being studied. The bold dream of the future is, of course, that we should be able to decodify the EEG message, to tell what happens in the brain and what thoughts are shaped within. However, this goal is remote, though large investigations exist on wave patterns in different localities and conditions, complicated computer analysis of wave patterns, also three-dimensional visualization of leads. Unfortunately, the mathematical analysis of rhythms is difficult and EEG patterns are extremely complex.

6.11 – Within the complicated EEG pattern some of the more familiar behaviour of servomechanisms and biological rhythms have been reported (DAVIS[600], FREEMAN[1-5], HOAGLAND[100], HUGGER, LIPP[100], WIENER[2]), such as a lowered amplitude with increased frequency or with cold, an alpha frequency rise with temperature, frequency modulation and coupled oscillator phenomena, or damped oscillations with overtones upon stimulation. According to WIENER the EEG rhythms may be the result of a synchronization (gating) of neuron action with the purpose of permitting synaptic facilitation, addition and inhibition. The reaction time in Homo varies throughout one alpha cycle, CALLAWAY[100].

HALBERG has shown that mice EEGs register heavy disturbances as soon as the animal is confronted with a human being. It shows how careful we must be when handling our experimental animals, particularly in biological rhythm research. Telemetering techniques are always to be preferred.

6.12 – Rhythm Perception, Flicker Fusion (5-50 c/sec). The higher nervous frequencies are not perceived as rhythmic phenomena. We hear sounds with frequencies from 20-20000 c/sec through rapid frequency-modulated nerve signals as continuous gestalts. There is a certain lower limit for our ability to distinguish between consecutive events. One indicator of this is the flicker fusion test, where the limit for the perception of stroboscopic light signals lies at a frequency of about 5-50 c/sec depending on the light intensity. At higher frequencies we see a steady light. The phenomenon is used in cinematography.

6.13 – *Natural Motor Performance Rhythms* (1-8 c/sec). There is also a limit to the rate at which we can perform voluntary rhythmic actions, as apparent in the tapping test, chewing test, or the walking test (either the standing gait or the natural walking), cf. ANDERS, FRAISSE[1-5, 100-104], KOCH[1], WATANABE[300]. The movements may be recorded graphically, optically or electromyographically. The subject (*Homo*) may either perform at the most spontaneous and satisfactory pace, or as fast as he can. The highest frequency is always about 7c/sec. The spontaneous rhythms vary around 2 c/sec and at this level there is also a minimum interindividual variation. This frequency is also slightly higher in children and mentally retarded persons than in healthy adults.

It is interesting to note that the 2 c/sec rhythm occurs in the EEG alpha wave as a period of superimposed frequency variations. If this phenomenon is due to beats (1.26) the difference between this frequency and the alpha frequency gives a value of about 7 c/sec (HUGGER).

6.14 – The tapping and walking rhythms may well be regarded as the natural frequency of a neural feedback system, depicted in Fig. 6.14a. Either we may have a spontaneous frequency of about 2c/sec or it may be controlled by outer factors, *e.g.* a voluntary command towards a maximal rate of about 7c/sec. Another type of setting occurs if we ask a subject to follow a leading rhythm, *e.g.* a metronome or music. We may test his capacity for perceiving rhythmic patterns in this way. This is of special interest for students of music.

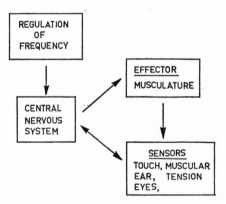

Fig. 6.14a. Motor feedback.

At spontaneous tapping one often automatically forms the taps into more complicated patterns. We also have the habit of hearing the perfectly regular sounds of a clock either as 'tick-tock' or 'tock-tick'. It seems even reasonable to assume that the highest rates commonly employed in the playing of music is set partly by our tapping limit.

6.15 – Summing up, then, we may say that the frequency of nervous impulses seems to vary from about 1-200 c/sec. The highest rate of nervous feedback oscillation in *Homo* would seem to lie around 7c/sec, simultaneously setting the upper frequency for rhythmic movements. It also appears as a component in the EEG. Through interference with other central nervous periodicities a most natural, spontaneous activity frequency of about 2c/sec may arise. – It is interesting to note that the heart rate lies in the same region, 0.5-6 c/sec. – One may also speculate upon the significance of the EEG frequencies. Perhaps the theta, alpha and beta waves (4-18 c/sec) represent normal feedback oscillation, the gamma waves (20-60 c/sec) bursts of activity in single neurons or 'parallel' groups of neurons, whereas the delta waves (0.5-3.5 c/sec) and pathological waves of similar frequencies are either interference phenomena or destabilized servosystems. It is possible that the change from theta to alpha rhythm during development represents a slow maturation in the capacity of the nervous feedback systems.

6.16 – *Heart Rate in Man* (0.5-6 c/sec). The 'pulse' is one of the oldest known spontaneous organic rhythms. The frequency is about 60 (35-100) beats/min and fairly regular in an individual, though it rises with exercise and body temperature (8-10 beats/1°C). Under pathological conditions it may be as high as 345 beats/min (paroxysmal tachycardia, *cf.* WHITE). Again, thus, we find about the same upper limit as in case of neural mechanisms, 6 c/sec (*cf.* 6.15). This is not peculiar; the heart contains a relaxation feedback mechanism and is further controlled by the autonomous nervous system.

It has already been mentioned that the individual parts of the heart musculature have natural contraction frequencies of 20-70 beats/min (6.4) and that they may desynchronize in heart block (6.7), also that there is a coupling with the respiratory rhythm. The electrical correlate of the cardiac cycle is shown in Fig. 6.16a. It may nowadays also be recorded 'intra-utero'. The heart rate in newborns is 140 beats/min. Twenty-four hour changes in the ECG occur, HILDEBRANDT[108], KLEITMAN[105]. The finer variations in the duration of the ECG waves have been studied by JORDAN. Rhythmical $\frac{1}{4}$-, $\frac{1}{2}$-, and 1-minute variations in the human heart rate exist, even persisting in cardiac 'arhythmia'. The blood flow in human musculature displays 1-minute periods, HILDEBRANDT[105]. Rhythmic heart-rate variations were also observed in other animals, LOOMIS[100].

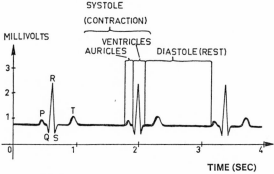

Fig. 6.16a. The human ECG.

6.17 – *Pulse Wave in Man*. Each pulse is a pressure wave in the blood, generated by the heart systole. The pressure in the blood vessels therefore varies cyclically, Fig. 6.17a. It may be registered in many ways: *e.g.* by intrarterial probes; volume changes recorded in superficial vessels (mechanical or photoelectric sphygmometers); volume changes in digits and limbs (plethysmography); over the heart itself; in arteries, veins or capillaries. With a suitable actograph, the ballistocardiograph, the momentum given the body by the pulse wave can be used to yield an estimate of blood volume.

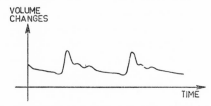

Fig. 6.17a. Photoelectric sphygmogram from the right radial artery.

The pulse curve is rather complicated. It may contain components from several moments in the cardiac cycle or adjacent vessels; also interference with reflected waves from the vessel walls, the latter especially in disease, *e.g.* arteriosclerosis. The mechanical character of the phenomenon makes it well suited for harmonic analysis. It is one of the few instances of biological rhythms where this method has a 'direct' biological meaning (LOBEL).

6.18 – *Respiratory Rate in Man* (0.3 c/sec). Respiration has already been cited as an example of neural feedback, Figs. 6.3a and 6.8a-b. The normal rate varies from 14 to 20 c/min in adults, 30-60 c/min in the newborn. The respiratory cycle is complex and followed by changes in many body factors, such as the acid–base

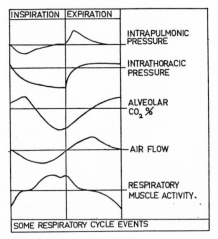

Fig. 6.18a. Respiratory cycle events, *cf.* RUCH[100].

balance of the blood, which also takes part in the regulation of the respiratory rate. Some events in the cycle are pictured in Fig. 6.18a.

Slight periodic variations in the respiratory frequency are normal, *e.g.* at high altitudes, at sleep, old age or in newborns but may be accentuated in the CHEYNE-STOKE respiration, Fig. 6.8a, as an indicator of regulation disturbances. Another respiratory type is the BIOT breathing where all inspirations are equal in depth. Actually, normal pulmonary ventilation contains a set of periodic variations with approximate durations of 1, 4, 9, 20, 40 and 150 min., GOODMAN. The respiratory rhythm is one example of a biological servomechanism where the loop may be broken and pulmonary input and output registered separately, as by YOUNG (quoted in RUCH[100]). See also NAHAS.

6.19 – *Feedback Path Dimensions. Frequency and Animal Size.* The previous sections have mostly been concerned with rhythmic activity in *Homo*. The speculation was advanced that the maximal speed of neural feedback lay around 7 c/sec and the natural one around 2 c/sec (6.15). One may, however, suppose that loops of different complexity should exist. Actually, one should be able to calculate the possible oscillatory rates if one knew the composition of the actual system and had quantitative information on the neuron, *e.g.* rate of discharge (1-50-200-500-1000 c/sec), synaptic delay (0.5-1.0 msec), length of nerve fibres and conduction velocity in them (1-10 cm/msec) as well as data on the non-neural components, *e.g.* length of muscle fibres. In general, cortical systems (with small distances between neurons and without non-neural components) should oscillate more rapidly than local motor feedback systems (with intramural plexa), and the latter should perform faster than motor functions regulated by feedback through long nerve trunks. Actually, the EEG contains components faster than the 7 c/sec. of the motor system.

6.20 – Furthermore, *small animals* should oscillate more rapidly than larger ones, having shorter neuron paths, smaller mechanical mechanisms, *etc.* Actually, there is, in a double logarithmic system, a linear inverse relationship between the heart rate or respiratory rate and body size (*cf.* BERTALANFFY, MAYNARD[2-3], MEIDINGER, SKRAMLIK). The heart rate in mammals varies from about 1000 beats/min in the dwarf bats (4 g body weight) to 20 beats/min in the elephant (2000 kg body weight). The upper limit is here about 17 c/sec. The respiratory rate (for birds and mammals) varies from about 4 c/sec to 4 c/min. There are similar size relationships during the individual growth.

6.21 – *Endogenous Microrhythms in General.* (Durations up to about one hour). The rapid oscillations in single neurons and voluntary nervous feedback, as well as in the perception of rhythms have already been extensively discussed (6.9-15, 19).

'Wing frequencies' in insects and hummingbirds (MACHIN[100], PRINGLE[1], SOTAVALTA, STOLPE[100]) may be recorded by measuring the pitch of the sounds produced or with the aid of stroboscopes. Values between 18 and 1000 beats/sec have been recorded. The highest frequencies are found in animals with fibrillar muscles, which are controlled by nervous impulses but run faster than these, 'myogenic rhythms'. This indicates the presence of a metabolic feedback within the cells, which may deactivate the contractile fibres periodically at high speed (an activity not followed by changes in the membrane potential of the fibre). If the insect wings are amputated the contraction frequency rises. It may be recorded as 'thoracic vibrations'. The highest value was found by SOTAVALTA, in midges, 2200 c/sec (normally 600-1000 beats/sec). Lower wing frequencies are reported in locusts (18 beats/sec), beetles (35-40 beats/sec), moths (50 beats/sec) and flies (150-200 beats/sec). The wing frequency in hummingbirds is 20-50 beats/sec.

6.22 – *Bats* may perform antero-posterior movements of the ears in sonar localization, at a frequency of 50 c/sec, NOVICK, PYE. The sounds emitted consist of about 5-10 pulses/sec. Each pulse has a complicated wave spectrum which varies between species. This may help in the identification of the proper echo. Both amplitude and frequency modulation of the signals occur. *Cf.* the pattern in bird song and insect sounds (FISCHER[900], KOEHLER[200], WALDRON, WALKER).

The mammalian body surface vibrates continuously, minor tremor, 8-30 c/sec (SUGANO).

6.23 – The *cilia* of unicellular organisms or epithelia perform around 2-20-40 beats/sec (GRAY[1-2, 100], MACHIN, RIVERA), *e.g.* in 'undulatory propulsion'. There is a clear temperature dependence. The sea urchin spermatozoa generate about 35 waves/sec, travelling at a rate of 800-1000 μ/sec along the cilia, imparting a velocity of around 200 μ/sec to the organism. The movement is essentially similar to that of the snakes. The ciliary movements have intrigued many investigators because of the obvious mechanical correlates. They cannot be entirely explained by simple movements at the bases of the tiny ciliary fibrils. *Cf.* BISHOP.

6.24 – Rhythmic contractions of the *locomotor musculature* in Holothuroidea (sea-cucumbers) may run at a rate of up to 16 c/sec, in segmented worms (Annelida) at about 3-4 c/sec. The legs of Myriapoda move at 6 c/sec (BETHE[100]). Locomotor contractions of medusae perform at 4 beats/sec (PASCHER).

6.25 – Certain types of *optical illusions, e.g.* ambiguous figures, may be used for studying oscillations in our 'mental perception'. A well-known example is the staircase which is alternately interpreted as seen from above and below, at a certain frequency. Another, the HERING illusion, has been studied by HOLT-HANSEN[2].

Fig. 6.25a. The HERING illusion.

If a triangle is observed its sides seem to oscillate. The effect is still more pronounced in Fig. 6.25a. The vertical straight lines seem curved. The curvature oscillates under suitable conditions inwards and outwards with an average duration of 1.5 sec (0.1-4.0).

Mental periods tend to lengthen with fatigue and decreasing strength of the stimulus. If the intensity is near our perceptive limen (*e.g.* faint sounds) we may alternatly perceive them or not (SEASHORE[100]). The same applies to our ability to distinguish between stimuli of different intensity. – Rhythms occur also in the clearness of memory images with durations of 2-4 sec (LANGE[400]).

6.26 – In *mental performance* we may observe fluctuation of the 'reaction time' or the rapidity of mental 'calculations', such as dotting squares, addition, subtraction, *etc.* (PHILPOTT, VOSS). We cannot concentrate continuously.

Many observers have found periods in mental perceptions and performance, usually with durations in the regions of 2-3, 10-15, 25-30 and 60-80 sec but also longer, up to 3 h. Careful studies were performed by PHILPOTT, who considers the durations to increase exponentially from the commencement of activity, with an average ratio of about 2 between successive cycle durations (*cf.* HOLT-HANSEN[1]). This reminds one of the theories on logarithmic time (5.6). If this is true it complicates the application of servomechanical analysis. Also, a logarithmic time-scale will have to be used in any periodicity analysis. Waves set up at different occasions are also said to interfere with each other.

6.27 – An allied problem is our ability to judge 'time intervals'. Certain time lengths seem to be judged more accurately than others, apart from a general tendency towards underestimation (GLASS, PHILPOTT). Such lengths seem to be about 0.35, 0.75, 1.50, 2.2-2.5, 3.5-3.8, 5.0, 6.2-6.4, 7.8, 9.3 sec, *etc,* with approximate increments of 1.2-1.5 seconds. Best of all the intervals, 0.35-0.75 sec seem to be estimated, the 'indifference point'. The other values may be multiples of this. Studies on the time sense were made as early as around 1880 by WUNDT and his disciples (ESTEL, GLASS, MEHNER) in opposition to FECHNER, who sought to found the phenomenon on the logarithmic WEBER law.

6.28 – One type of periodic activity is exhibited in closed muscular circuits, of the type circular motion (4.4). A muscle ring cut from a turtle heart ventricle and 10 cm in diameter passes contraction waves which make a complete turn in 6-7 sec, 'circus contraction' (*cf.* GARREY, MINES).

6.29 – *Protoplasmic streaming* in cells may either display circular motion or periodic reversal of direction (KAMIYA[2-4, 100-101], SEIFRITZ). The cell pulsates with a period of 10-200 sec (average rate of flow 70 μ/sec), increasing with cell age. The rhythmic fluctuation in protoplasmic flow must be closely connected with the basic energetic metabolic processes of living matter. It is followed by rhythmic potential variations which may continue, however, if the protoplasmic flow is stopped.

SEIFRITZ made a fascinating film demonstrating the protoplasmic flow in plasmodia. (It was also shown at the seventh Conference of the Society for Biological Rhythm, Ref. 1960a, by courtesy of the United States Information Service

which had included it in an international release intended to demonstrate the use
of 16 mm film in teaching). If the protoplasmic flow was temporarily stopped, it
later started at such a point in its cycle, as if it had been going on continuously.
This indicates deep-seated mechanisms, which are not even influenced by rather
drastic changes in the protein state. It was also beautifully demonstrated how
stimulating drugs tended to 'liquefy' the protoplasm, whereas narcotics tended to
'solidify' it (gel-sol reversibility).

The energy for the protoplasmic movement is probably delivered by ATP
obtained through glycolysis, acting upon myxomysin (= myosin B) and resulting
in a mechanochemical coupling. It is stopped by glycolysis poisons but not by
respiratory ones. A series of harmonics and beats are observable on the plasma
flow curve (KAMIYA[2]). The frequency is temperature-dependent (Q_{10} = 1.6-2.6). –
In *Euglena* the protoplasmic streaming may appear as rhythmic changes in cell
shape with a frequency of 3-6 c/min (KAMIYA[1]). – RASHEVSKY suggests that
oscillating biochemical systems coupled with the diffusion mechanisms may influence tissue contractility, *e.g.* 'amoeboid movements'. Here, larger cells should
have longer periods than smaller ones.

6.30 – JENKINSON[1, 100], McAULAY[100] and SCOTT[1-3, 100-101] found oscillations of the
bioelectric potentials in bean roots growing against a resistance. The period was
usually around 5 min (4-30 min). No similar variations in root growth occurred.
The oscillations were nearly sinusoidal and displayed typical damped transients
(3.19) of equal frequency if the plant was disturbed. The source is assumed to be
biochemical or biochemical-bioelectrical negative feedback servomechanisms involving auxines, with action upon the permeability of the cell membranes, *cf.*
NEWMAN and the 24-h variations in tree potentials, BURR.

6.31 – In the *non-striated musculature* several superimposed classes of rhythms
seem to be created by the autonomous control centres. The blood pressure shows
rapid variations (*cf.* FLEISCH[100], KOEPCHEN, MATTHES, RUCH[100], WAGNER[600]) with
durations of 10, 15-25 and 60 seconds as well as 2-15 minutes. Similar variations
have also been observed in the peripheral as well as the hepatic and splenic blood
flow (CERLETTI[100], GRAF[100, 400], TATAI[100, 103]). The heart beat, including the
superimposed 15, 30 and 60 sec variations in its rate, as well as the pulse wave were
already mentioned (6.16-17).

6.32 – In the gastro-intestinal *peristalsis* different classes of contraction frequencies exist (*cf.* KARLSSON, LARKS[100-101], RUCH[100], WEICKER, WEITZ[100-101]): *e.g.*
6-13 contractions per min (dog, rabbit, colon in *Homo*); 0.5-5 contr./min (stomach,
small intestine and colon in *Homo*); 0.2 contr./min (evacuation of colon); as well
as durations of 5-20 min and 1 h (ventricle). Intestinal villi in the dog contract
rhythmically with 6 contr./min. Actually, the non-striated musculature in general
(*e.g.* spleen, urinary bladder, uterus, penis and scrotum) contracts rhythmically,
with the following durations:

6.32a

ventricle	30-120	sec
small intestine	5-7	,,
	12-15	,,
	30-60	,,
large intestine	12-15	,,
	30-60	,,
	5-20	min
	60	,,
spleen	32-53	sec
urinary bladder	12-15	,,
,, (straining)	60	,,
uterus	10-180	,,
scrotum and penis	30-60	,,

In scrotal contractility (tunica dartos) WEICKER found periods of 30-150 sec (3-4 min at sleep). At moderate loads both amplitudes and frequencies rose with increasing tension. At higher loads the frequency acted in the reverse. Cold increased the rate, heat decreased it. Adrenaline increased the frequency, atropine decreased it.

ALEXANDROWICZ describes pulsating ganglia in octopods (8-35 beats/min), and BOOZ periodic contractions in the guinea-pig portal vein (1-20 beats/min).

6.33 – The *embryo amnion* of egg-laying vertebrate species displays rhythmic contraction, probably to ensure fluid circulation. In hen eggs the frequency is about 10-16 contractions/min (BAUTZMANN[1-3, 100-102]). *Cf.* the uterine contractions in mammals, which occur also in the non-pregnant state.

In mussels contractions in the striated part of the valve adductors may be observed at a frequency of 20 contr./h (BARNES, KOSHTOYANTS[100], SALANKI). Actual opening and closing of the valves, performed by the non-striated portion, occur at a much slower rate, with durations of 5-60 h. – Marine worms display activity rhythm durations of about 7 and 40 min, directed by two different nerve centres (WELLS[1-5, 100-102]).

6.34 – Cockroaches display 10-50 min periods in the CO_2-metabolism. There is a pronounced temperature dependence ($Q_{10} = 2.9$). The amplitude is also affected (WILKINS[5]).

The exocrine glands may function periodically. The pancreatic juice is produced in waves of 10-30-60 min durations (BALZER[100]).

6.35 – The central nervous system also produces some rhythms of the same magnitude. At strong illumination the 'corneo-fundal potential' shows a few damped oscillations with a period of about 30 min (KRIS[3]).

The depth of sleep and frequency of dreaming displays 60-80 min periods (KLEITMAN[11], SHAPIRO). Light sleep is often heralded by eye movements and EEG changes. Infants show an activity rhythm of about one-h periods, slowly merging into the adult 24-h cycle (HELLBRÜGGE[1, 101], KLEITMAN[10, 12, 102-103]). The erectio membri virilis occurs with about 80 min intervals (the 'biological hour') during the night (OHLMEYER[100]).

Lizards show 80-min activity rhythms under constant conditions (TAYLOR[1]).

6.36 – *Endogenous Macrorhythms in General.* (Durations from about 1 h to 7 days). The 'circumnutation' of plants (the spiralling movement of tendrils brought about by a regular rotational change in the location of maximal cell growth and swelling) shows a period of 1-4 h/360° (BAILLAUD[1-7], BARANETZKY, GRADMANN, MIEGE, TRONCHET[1-2, 100-101]). Bean roots grow in a similar manner with a period of about 2-h (SCOTT[1]). – MALM observed 4-6 h periods in the water balance over the cell membrane of yeast cells immersed in NaCl-solutions of varying concentration.

6.37 – 4-5-6-8-12 h variations have also been reported in *Homo, e.g.* in gastric secretion (LEVIN[100]), renal functions, blood platelet counts (4-5 h, GISS), or in disease (MENZEL[4, 5, 7, 15-17, 100-102]). Some of these periods are submultiples of the 24-h cycle. Several interpretations of such a behaviour are possible. The circadian period may arise out of them simply by accentuation of some peaks and suppression of others (*cf.* Chapter 9). The body might be able to measure time on the 24-h scale by counting off a certain number of combinations of the 4-12-h rhythms (*cf.* frequency demultiplication, 4.28). On a more sophisticated level, the circadian period may be regarded as a subharmonic of the shorter cycles. On the other hand, the latter may arise as harmonics of the former owing to biological nonlinearities. Or, the short periods might have been favoured by evolutionary selection together with the circadian one since they will all give minima at 24-h intervals. Actually, some external correlates may also be imagined, *e.g.* the ascending or descending limbs of the sun path or the tides.

6.38 – Periods embracing an irregular number of days also exist, *cf.* DERER. Some sexual cycles certainly belong here, *cf.* next chapter. Especially in human pathology 4-5-6-7-8-10-day periodicities are reported. How common they are under normal conditions is more difficult to state. Healthy people are more seldom scientifically observed during such long time periods.

JEREBZOFF[6-7] found a 52-h rhythm in the ring formation of mushrooms.

6.39 – The discussion in connection with 'hour'-rhythms (6.37) may, in principle, also be applied to the 7-day period (the week) as a sub-unit of the monthly 28-day cycle (*cf.* next chapter). However, the real occurrence of lunar cycles in vertebrates is debated, though they clearly exist in invertebrates, where, however, the exogenous connections are obvious. Truth is also obscured by the old superstition of the sevens as sacred numbers. The existence of an endogenous 7-day period is therefore uncertain. Of course, one should expect our 'weekly' activity pattern to recur in several body functions. Conversely, one might speculate upon the reason for our week schedule. Either it is purely arbitrary or else it draws its origin from an endogenous 7-day rhythm, however generated. In the latter case this rhythm would not necessarily have to run in phase with the calendar week, though it would tend to be timed by it. Yet another possibility would be an interference between a freerunning circadian rhythmicity and the 24-h day. The circadian period would then have to be about $24 \pm 24/7$ h $= 24 \pm 3.4$ h $= 20.6$ or 27.4 h. At least this lies within the possible range of observed circadian periodicities. Such a mechanism could also easily generate a number of longer periodicities, 8-9-10-20 days or more.

6.40 – *Endogenous Long-term Rhythms* (Durations > 7 days). Endogenous counterparts of the lunar and seasonal cycles may exist, through natural selection, though this is debated. Perhaps the human sexual cycle belongs here. – The lifespans and reproduction times of plants and animals constitute natural periods, some up to several hundred years in duration. – In wildlife, many animal populations are observed (*cf.* Chapter 10), mostly with the durations 3-4 y and 8-10 y. – Though most trees have seasonal rhythms of function some may change their leaves up to six times a year, others may only flower at several-year intervals, up to 60 years, ROMELL[2].

6.41 – Most people can observe a waxing and waning of their mood; from moderate depression to slight exhilaration. Such cycles may be pronounced in emotional disorders or psychic disease (*cf.* GALANT, GJESSING, HERSEY, MENNINGER-LERCHENTHAL, QUARRINGTON) *e.g.* in stuttering or mano-depressive psychoses. It can also be traced in the creativity of famous men, *cf.* MALL[2] and WEBSTER[1, 2, 4]. The latter has identified 33-week periods (7.6 months) in this respect as well as in disease, and relates them to the sunspot cycle of WOLF[400]. The crest coincides with that of the seasonal cycle each 11th period = 7 years. Aging is said to proceed in 7-year periods in *Homo* (KOTSOVSKY). In fact, many different periods of years have been reported in human behaviour such as frequency of great men, battles, religious movements (Refs. J.c., DAKIN, FELLOWS, STEPHEN): 1, 7, 9, 11 (sunspot?), 17.7, 22, 32, 57, 105, 142, 169, 250, 300, 400, 510, 603, 625, 800 and 1500 years.

6.42 – In *business* the problem of rhythm analysis is old and has stimulated both practical cycle analyses and mathematical-statistical theory, aiming at economical prediction. An enormous number of cycles have been proposed. The author picked up the following during a quick perusal of the literature: 84 hours, 17 and 29.5 days; 13, 15-16, 17-17.5, 33-34 and 39 weeks; 9.2-9.7, 11, 11.9-12.0, 13.3, 17, 17.8, 21-21.6, 22.7, 23.6-23.8, 26.5-27, 30, 32-33, 35.4-36.2, 38-38.8, 41-42, 46, 53 and 59 months; 5.5-5.6, 5.9, 6.3-6.4, 6.9, 7.4-7.6, 7.9, 8.2-8.6, 8.9, 9.2-9.9, 10.4, 10.8-11.2 (sunspot cycle?) 12.5-12.8, 13, 14.5-14.8, 16.7, 17.8 (much verified), 18.3, 22-24 27, 36-37, 50, 54-55, 59-61 and 159 years (Refs. J.c., J.d., HUNTINGTON[2]). – In agriculture (crops) and in forestry (tree-ring width, *cf.* DOUGLASS, GLOCK[100], HUNTINGTON[2], SIREN) many cycles have also been reported: 6 mths; 2.3-2.6, 3.9-4.2, 5-5.5, 8, 8.9-9.8, 11 (sunspot?), 16.7, 17.8 (*cf.* business cycles), 19, 22, 35-38 (Brückner period?), 54 and 100-year cycles.

6.43 – *Reliability of Longterm Cycle Estimates.* A word of warning should be inserted here concerning the many endogenous periods reported in literature. Many of these have never really been proven to exist, in the mathematical-statistical sense. In this respect there is a definite difference between microrhythms and longer periods. The former are usually regular and may be observed through many cycles. There is seldom any reason to doubt their occurrence. The longer periods are more uncertain. For obvious reasons long runs of observations are scarce and a few cycles do not suffice for a rigid analysis. Also, in a purely random time series, one may expect to find any cycle one is looking for (*cf.* 1.39). To prove the existence of the rhythms amounts to the problem of showing, on runs containing but few cycles, that the desired period is more frequent than all others.

In *Homo*, sick persons are usually observed for longer periods than healthy people. This facilitates the finding of longer periods in diseases. It is, therefore, not absolutely certain that 'pathological rhythms' are really longer than those observed in health, though it seems probable. Here, however, the possibility for establishing controls exists but it would make for expensive experiments.

The reader is certainly right in reserving his judgement regarding the existence of the longer periods reported in the literature until definite proof is there, especially so if a certain author succeeds in finding his particular rhythm everywhere. One exception may be such periods where external correlates exist. Unfortunately, the connections are not always clear. Often, various sunspot cycles and accompanying meteorological events have been advocated as external correlates. The direct connection is usually difficult to prove, especially since the possibility of genetic selection exists. Also, the actual rhythm and the correlate do not have to agree in timing; – not even to be absolutely equal in frequency. One may even imagine that some external correlates might have disappeared. On the other hand, the agreement may be purely coincidental, a non-sense correlation (*cf.* Part III).

Caution, thus, is due, but not excessive criticism. Proof is difficult to produce. Time will tell.

6.44 – As mentioned (6.39) number superstition may obscure the picture. The 'sevens' (7 days, 7 months, 7 years) play a great role in ancient thinking, *e.g.* with HIPPOCRATES. Other numbers have also been favoured, three and five (*cf.* WEBSTER[3]). Much discussed are the systems where sexual cycles are based on 7-day periods or multiples thereof (FLIES, RIEBOLD, TIETZE, *cf.* the criticism of HECKERT[3] and DERUDDER[13], also Chapter 7).

6.45 – After a preparatory discussion of servomechanisms and biological regulation we have studied one group of natural oscillators in biology, the endogenous rhythms without external correlates. Let us now turn to the endogenous rhythms with correlates, before we round off the subject of endogenous rhythms with some special studies of perinatal and pathological rhythms, as well as population cycles and basimetry.

CHAPTER 7

Endogenous Rhythms with External Correlates

7.1 – After studying biological regulation and oscillators we devoted the last chapter to temperature-sensitive endogenous rhythms 'without' correlates. There remains to discuss the endogenous rhythms 'with' external correlates. Many of these, at least, are temperature insensitive (*cf*. 1.17). They are also remarkably resistant to chemical influences. The best known of these cycles are the circadian freerunning rhythms which will be described first. This concept was already introduced in connection with the time sense (5.16-25, *cf*. 1.16-17), where the endodiurnal photosensitivity cycle of BÜNNING and its use as an interval timer and as a chronometer was discussed. The subject will return again in Part IV in connection with the 24-h synchronized rhythms, where studies in the different fields of biology will be summarized. Here we will confine ourselves more to the properties of the circadian rhythms than to any complete presentation.

Next will be discussed the noncircadian freerunning rhythms with external correlates, mainly the sexual cycle. For simplicity, some other animal sexual cycles are included here, though they probably do not have external correlates. Again, the lunar and seasonal rhythms will return for detailed discussion in Part IV, where especially the lunar rhythm of invertebrates and seasonal rhythms are reviewed.

7.2 – Many biological rhythms are obviously directed by external factors; 24-h, lunar, seasonal. One should expect them to disappear as soon as the external influence vanishes. However, the rhythm often persists, though deviating somewhat in frequency from the external correlate. Such rhythms are generally supposed to be truly endogenous though favoured by nature through evolutionary genetical selection. If the phenomenon appears as soon as all external synchronizers (Zeitgebers, clues, *cf*. 1.19-22) are excluded the rhythm is said to be freerunning (HALBERG). Usually, it suffices to keep only the dominant synchronizers constant, especially light and temperature. Probably freerunning periods exist, corresponding to most external correlates, *e.g.* the day, the lunar month and the year. The first alternative, the circadian (circa die = about a day, HALBERG) rhythm is by far the best studied. The human sexual cycle would correspond to the lunar period. Endogenous seasonal rhythms are said to exist.

7.3 – *Circadian Rhythms*. The spontaneous circadian rhythms have been carefully studied by many authors on a large number of organisms, from algae to mammals (*cf*. sections 5.16-25, Refs. 1958a, 1960c, also ASCHOFF[1-3, 7, 9, 12-17, 103, 108], BALL[300-

[303], BROWN [1-5, 7-9, 101, 103, 107-111, 113, 115], BRUCE [100-101], BÜNNING [1-5, 8, 11-15, 18-25, 27-35, 100-105, 107], CLOUDSLEY-THOMPSON [4, 10-17, 20, 25, 28], FOLK [6, 102], HALBERG [4, 6-8, 10, 12-14, 102, 110, 121, 125], HASTINGS [1-3, 100-104], HOFFMAN [1-8], JEREBZOFF [2-4, 6-9], KLEINHOONTE, PITTENDRIGH [1-6], ROBERTS, STINSON, SWEENEY [1, 101, 103], WELSH [1-5], WILKINS). Most investigators start with 24-h controlled functions, submitting the organisms to constancy as regards light and temperature. After a number of irregular cycles, transients, the system usually turns to a new frequency, which is then kept unchanged. The frequency differs between individuals and species, but the periods never deviate much from 24 h. They usually stay between 19 and 29 h. Many of these frequencies have been tabulated by ASCHOFF [12, 14], BRUCE [1], PITTENDRIGH [3].

7.4 – In *plants* many rhythmic factors have been used for circadian studies; especially flowering and leaf movements, but also osmosis, water assimilation, turgor, CO_2 metabolism, acidity, phosphatase activity, seedling, root, and stem growth, ring formation in fungi, tendril movements, spore discharge, photosensitivity of pigments and bioluminescence. A well-studied plant is *Kalanchoë blossfeldiana*.

The technique of recording 'leaf movements' is singularly beautiful in its simplicity. It consists in tying a thread between the leaf and a kymograph, STOPPEL [12].

7.5 – In *animals*, circadian recordings have been made predominantly on activity rhythms, but also on such variates as chromatophores (BROWN [6-7, 9, 107], FINGERMAN [2, 4, 102], STEPHENS [3, 5], WELSH [1-4]) and metabolism. If the exogenous 24-h rhythms are added there are virtually no functions of life which have not been included. – Many types of 'actographs' have been devised for animals of all sizes, from revolving cages for mice to hanging fingerbowls for mud snails (CLOUDSLEY-THOMPSON [16, 28], GUNN [400], STEPHENS [1]).

7.6 – The peculiar circadicity of a large class of natural periods may be interpreted in many ways: (1) as acquired by natural selection; (2) as some kind of interaction between a weak 24-h synchronizer and a natural rhythm of quite other frequency; (3) as a weak 24-h synchronizer submitted to frequency transformation in the organism (autophasing, BROWN [12], *cf.* 1.23); or (4) simply as that submultiple of some purely endogenous frequency which comes closest to 24 h. STOPPEL also firmly believes in the exogeneity of the circadian rhythms. The problems will be discussed later.

7.7 – Several factors speak for the spontaneous character of the circadian rhythms. If plants are reared in constant light or darkness they exhibit no circadian rhythmicity. It may appear, however, after one single short impulse of the opposite condition, *e.g.* even a light flash of only 0.002 sec duration (in the fly *Drosophila*, PITTENDRIGH [1, 6]). This impulse is then also timing the rhythm, with a certain delay. Single stimuli may also reset the phasing. In plants the oscillations often die out after some periods in the manner of damped oscillations (this may also be explained by a desynchronization of several oscillators which were synchronized previously (WASSERMAN). The fluorescent unicellular alga, *Gonyaulax*, however, exhibits sustained circadian variations (HASTINGS[1-3, 100-106], SWEENY[1, 100-101, 103]) in light production (variations in luciferas-luciferin activity, *cf.* NICOL).

In animals the circadian periodicity is usually selfsustained. The frequency is dependent on the light intensity (ASCHOFF[14-17], *cf.* Part II) and spontaneous changes may occur (DeCOURSEY[1], PITTENDRIGH[6, 100], RAWSON[2]).

7.8 – In general, the circadian rhythm is, however, remarkably stable, with individual variations as small as 4% (ASCHOFF[15, 101], PITTENDRIGH[6, 100]). Between individuals there is a larger variation, and still larger between species, where *e.g.* one may be day-active, another night-active. The curve shape also varies strongly with the factors measured on an individual. The cycles may run inverse or parallel courses, or be phase-shifted (HALBERG[7-8, 10, 121]) or one may follow the differential curve of the other, depending on the way in which they are interrelated in the body (SOLLBERGER[3,100]). One process may even have different frequencies or phases in different parts of one organism (BALL[304], RICHTER[5]).

7.9 – Beautiful experiments were performed by BÜNNING[29] (*cf.* SEMON[1]) who, studying the circadian movements of plant leaves, crossed two plants with periods of about 23 and 26h. The crosses had a period of about 25 h. In some of the later generations the original periods recurred.

7.10 – *Circadian Graphs.* The circadian period may suitably be represented graphically as in Fig. 7.10a (see ASCHOFF[12, 17]). The plotted parameter may be the circadian maximum or minimum, onset or end of activity, *etc.* The period is easily read from the diagram. In the example given in the figure the parameter time has travelled 24 h forwards (b) during 7 days (a). The period = 24 + 24/7 h.

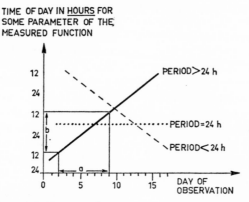

Fig. 7.10a. A circadian peak-time graph.

If, in the original records successive days are placed under each other we get another striking effect, especially in activity records, Fig. 7.10b. This technique was used by KLEITMAN[103] when studying the sleep-wakefulness rhythm in infants, *cf.* DeCOURSEY[2], GESELL, PITTENDRIGH[6], ROBERTS[3]. The breaks in the activity form linear patterns. A change in frequency is indicated by a change in slope.

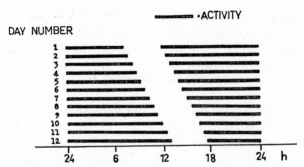

Fig. 7.10b. A circadian actogram.

7.11 – *Circadian Temperature Independence* (1.17, 6.1). In the living organism most processes are accelerated by an increase in body temperature, being largely governed by enzyme-dependent biochemical reactions. If the level is raised 10°C the normal metabolic rate is at least doubled (Q_{10} = 2-3). If the biological clock were of a biochemical character one might expect its velocity to behave similarly, *e.g.* a doubled frequency per 10°C increase in the body temperature. This may be easily tested in lower poikilothermic organisms (which tend to keep the environmental temperature) by submitting them to different levels of constant external temperature. Most endogenous rhythms behave as expected. However, the circadian frequencies are almost unaffected. Q_{10}, as calculated from the frequencies, usually lies around 0.8-1.3. This remarkable phenomenon is referred to as the temperature independence of the biological clock, even though there is a slight influence. The phenomenon should not be confused with other effects, such as the phase-shifting by pulses of changed temperature or the thermoperiodism, which is the temperature equivalent of photoperiodism. That will be discussed later.

The temperature independence is an important physiological phenomenon. As PITTENDRIGH remarks, sensory organs must possess this characteristic, else they would all become temperature receptors. Its rhythmic aspect has attracted many investigators: *e.g.* BROWN[111], BRUCE[101], BÜNNING[1, 29, 31, 34-35, 102, 107], BÜNSOW[4], FOLK[103], GROSSENBACHER[2], HAMNER[3], HASTINGS[103], KALMUS[1, 2, 6], PITTENDRIGH[1, 6], RAWSON[4], RENNER[4], SWEENEY[103], WAHL[1], WENT[2, 3, 6]. Many of the findings have been tabulated (SWEENY[103]), including *e.g.* plants, luminescence in cells, colour changes in crabs, time sense in bees and activity in mammals. In homeothermic animals such studies are more difficult since the thermoregulation control must first be overcome by artificial means (except in hibernating animals). Some investigations exist, however, especially in bats (RAWSON[4]).

7.12 – The Q_{10} for rhythms may be calculated from two determinations of the cycle duration (P_2 and P_1) at the temperature T_2 and T_1 respectively (*cf.* RAWSON[4]):

7.12a $$Q_{10} = (P_2/P_1)^{10/(T_1 - T_2)}$$

7.13 – *Explanations of Temperature Independence.* The Q_{10}-values for rhythms are obviously small and cannot be explained by the ordinary biochemical temperature influence. Though the true explanation is not known, many theories have been put forth:

(1) If the clock is really exogenous, it should be truly temperature independent (BROWN[10, 111]).
(2) Temperature-compensation, *e.g.* the relation between several parallel, normally temperature-dependent biochemical processes, or the coupling of two such processes which inhibit each other, or a temperature compensating biochemical servo-system (BRUCE[101], HASTINGS[103], SWEENEY[103]).
(3) Intramolecular energy oscillations, somehow governing the biological clock. This would perhaps agree with the more and more emphasized structural organization of the cell into solid elements, *e.g.* membranes. Such oscillations are rather independent of temperature, (BRUCE[101]).
(4) Diffusion in the cell. The Q_{10} of diffusion processes is of the same magnitude as the actual values recorded for rhythms. Semipermeable membranes would be important in such connections. Macromolecules would diffuse slower than small ones (WENT[6]).

7.14 – The first theory is obvious. – The temperature-compensation theories would allow for Q-values < 1, as has been observed (HASTINGS[103], SWEENEY[103]). Many investigators feel that temperature-compensating devices should be rather variable, whereas the Q_{10} effect is rather consistent in one animal. However, SCHMITT[1] points out that stable temperature-independent feedback systems may easily be constructed out of temperature-dependent parts.

7.15 – Diffusion may be one solution. Though most biochemical reaction sequences are probably lodged in the mitochondrial membranes, a fair amount of diffusion also occurs in a cell. If, now, the clock is a biochemical oscillator, the frequency of the oscillation would increase with the velocity of the reactions in its loops. However, the velocity would be set by the slowest process in the loop, and this might well be a diffusion process. Such a feedback-diffusion theory would explain the general level of the Q_{10} values and yet allow of a certain variation around this. In principle, it demands that these values be larger than unity. Lower values would have to be explained by biochemical inhibitory processes.

The diffusion theory has other consequences. The enzymes have a large Q_{10}. The effect would, however, not be an increased loop velocity but an increased capacity of the system (*cf.* Figs. 4.6a and 4.27a). For comparison imagine a barge ferrying marching soldiers over a river. The marching velocity of the soldiers (= diffusion) is rather constant but the barge (= enzyme) would have to run faster the larger the troop. The capacity of the land for carrying soldiers is rather unlimited (= diffusion capacity). Thus the diffusion would determine the velocity of the system and the enzyme would determine the capacity of the system. The same holds for the phenomenon which we usually call an increased metabolic rate in an individual. This does not mean that a constant amount of energy is juggled quicker and quicker around in the body. It rather indicates an increased load on the pre-existing system; the caloric intake and waste production is correspondingly increased.

7.16 – The increased load on a frequency-constant system will show up as a change in amplitude of the cycle. The temperature effect has not been much studied in this respect. Exactly those rhythmic factors which are mostly used, *e.g.* activity or plant leaf movements, are less well-suited as measures of metabolic fluctuations. In some cases, a clear relation between temperature and amplitude, at constant frequency, appears. In studies of melanophore rhythms of fiddler crabs (BROWN[111]) the amplitude rises with temperature. In the fluorescent *Gonyaulax* this relation is reversed (SWEENEY[103]). In yet other cases the results are less clear-cut.

7.17 – The temperature independence is only valid over a certain temperature range, usually 10-30°C. Especially at lower temperature the rhythm may tend either to disappear or to break into a higher-frequency low-amplitude run (BÜNNING[29, 34, 35]). The latter might indicate some change in the characteristics of the mechanism (*cf.* Fig. 4.27a). BÜNNING believes the freerunning rhythms to be relaxation oscillations and the low-temperature effect a lowering of the threshold (*cf.* Fig. 4.27b).

7.18 – *Circadian Chemical Independence.* A parallel to the temperature independence of the endogenous rhythm frequency is its relative insensitivity to toxic influences upon the cells. A number of cytoactive chemicals acting upon photosynthesis, nucleic acid synthesis and aerobic respiration have been tried (*e.g.* $NaNO_3$, NaCN, NaF, Na-arsenate, KCl, $CaCl_2$, $FeCl_3$, $CuSO_4$, $AgNO_3$, HgCl, *p*-chloromercuribenzoate, iodoacetic acid, iodothyreoglobuline, 5-fluoro-2-dioxyuridine, 2,4-dinitrophenol, urethan, phenylurethan, colchicine, EDTA, mono- and dichlorophenylurea, ether, quinine, euquinine, cocaine, β-indoleacetic acid, chloramphenicol, ATP, riboflavin, kinetin, gibberelin). The effect was tested among others on sporulation, bioluminescence in cells, plant movements, germ growth, bee dances, *Drosophila* activity, and hamster eosinophils (*cf.* BALL[300], BÜHNEMANN[3], BÜNNING[22, 27, 29], CHAUDRY[102], HASTINGS[2], KALMUS[2], WAHLSTRÖM, WERNER).

7.19 – The results obtained with chemicals are uncertain and divergent and not well understood. Generally, only slight effects on the period occur. In many cases, a clear damping of the cycle amplitude is observed, in other cases a variable phase-shifting effect. If the toxic action is heavy, high-frequency oscillations of low amplitude may occur, as in low temperature (*cf.* 7.17). It is possible that some surface-active drugs, alcohol, papaverine and narcotine increase the duration of the circadian cycles.

It is obvious, however, that no clear-cut effects on the endogenous frequency are obtained, such as would be expected if the endogenous clocks were essentially biochemical. The rhythm cannot be explained as a succession of assimilatory and dissimilatory states as was often assumed by the earlier writers on biological rhythms. The 'chemical independence' is indeed even more difficult to explain than the temperature independence. Several of the theories for the latter (7.13) do clearly not apply here. A biochemical feedback compensation mechanism of such perfect generality is difficult to envisage. Again, the diffusion theory (7.15) seems quite probable, including the effect on cycle amplitude. Where, however, does the driving energy originate?

7.20 – *Noncircadian Rhythms with Possible Correlates* (*cf.* 5.21 and 6.40). It may be that the circadian rhythms have become inborn owing to the ecological significance of the surrounding diurnal changes. For similar reasons we may expect circumlunar (in littoral animals) and circ-annual rhythms, though there is no certain proof of their endogeneity (*cf.* MARSHAL[6], NAYLOR[1]).

7.21 – *Sexual Cycles*. It is a fact that the human menstrual 28-day period lies in the region of the sidereal and synodic months ($27\frac{1}{3}$ and $29\frac{1}{2}$ days respectively). However, it is difficult to prove that the individual cycles are synchronized with the lunar month and they are not so *inter se* (*cf.* 17.4-6, 26.2-5, HECKERT[1, 2, 4], HOSEMANN, MENAKER[200]). Actually, the near-monthly duration could be a coincidence since many animals display quite other average durations of the estrus cycle (*cf.* REINBERG[100]):

7.21a

Dog	180	days
Chimpanzee	36	,,
Macacus	27	,,
Pig	21	,,
Cow	20	,,
Sheep	16	,,
Guinea-pig	15	,,
Rat and mouse	4-6	,,

The theories which regard these periods as multiples of 7 days were discussed in 6.44. They would allow us to treat these animal cycles as harmonics of the lunar period. It is, of course, also possible that the human sexual cycle was once synchronized with the lunar period.

7.22 – In many invertebrates, fish, reptiles and birds the sexual cycle is definitely seasonal, whether exogenous or circ-annual, mediated by the primitive neuro-endocrine system in lower animals and perhaps by the retino-hypothalamic connection in vertebrates. This will be discussed later. There are also peculiar examples where single individuals or species have dissociated completely from the usual periodicities, *e.g.* the plant *Breynia cornus* (FOLK[102]) in Buitenzorg which flowered every $5\frac{1}{2}$ months for 11 years, or the sooty tern which breeds every 9 months.

7.23 – *The Human Sexual Cycle*. The literature on this subject is enormous. The cycle, whatever its origin, is probably generated by a neuro-endocrine feedback (2.13). Most body factors follow it, *e.g.* sexual hormones in the blood and the urine, buccal, rectal and vaginal temperatures, basal metabolism, blood sugar, endometrial glycogen, water retention, body weight, pulmonary vital capacity, alveolar CO_2-concentration, arterial O_2-pressure, blood pH, serum bicarbonate, heart rate, sedimentation rate, erythrocyte and reticulocyte blood counts, differential blood leucocyte counts, serum protein, bile pigments, blood adrenaline, electric skin resistance, pupillary size, psychic activities, pain threshold, vaginal cytology and composition of the cervical mucous secretion as well as citric acid contents, viscosity and gravity of the urine (*cf.* BARTON[1], BERGMAN, DÖRING[1-9], [100-101], [104], FARRIS, HARTMAN, JACOBI, KLEITMAN[8], KNAUS, LARKS[1], OGINO, PERGOLA[1], [100], POMMERENKE, POTTER, SMITH[100-101], SHORR[100], TATAI[102], TOMPKINS, VOLLMAN).

7.24 – Measurements of the menstrual temperature cycle have become especially important. It is easy to record and presents (within a range of about 0.5°C) a pronounced drop during the menstruation and even more pronounced rise (Temperatursprung) during the days after ovulation. This is one of the signs used for defining "safe periods" or the time of optimum fertility (*cf.* BERGMAN, BETHUNE, FARRIS, FLIESS, HARTMAN, JACOBI, KLEITMAN[8], KNAUS, OGINO, POMMERENKE, POTTER, SCHLIEPER, SCHNEIDER[2], SCHWING, TOMPKINS, VOLLMAN, WERNLI). Aberrations in the sexual cycle show up clearly on the temperature curve, which may be used for diagnosis and control of treatment by the gynaecologist. The shape of the curve may change, the amplitude increase or the rhythm disappear.

7.25 – The events of the human sexual cycle are pictured in Fig. 7.25a (partly adapted from the careful studies of DÖRING). The main origin of the sexual cycle

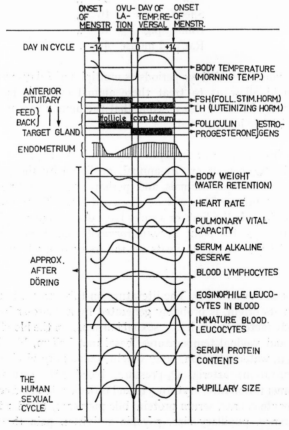

Fig. 7.25a. Events of the human female sexual cycle. Approximated after DÖRING.

seems to be a feedback oscillation between the anterior pituitary hormones (follicle-stimulating hormone, FSH, and luteinizing hormones, LH), the ovarian targets, *viz*. follicle and corpus luteum (folliculin and progesterone) as well as androgens (during menstruation) and placental estrogen (in pregnancy). Accompanying this are changes in the vegetative nervous balance and psyche, followed by variations in respiration, circulation, metabolism and reproductive organs. However, LAMPORT warns against an oversimplification of the feedback concept in this connection.

Several components of the sexual cycle system are of the relaxation oscillation (4.13-14) type, *e.g.* the slow maturation of the follicle and its sudden rupture, as well as the abrupt breakdown of the endometrium and its slow reconstruction.

7.26 – An endocrine sexual cycle is also said to exist in the human male, though this awaits definite proof. Pathological 4-week rhythms have also been described (MENNINGER-LERCHENTHAL).

7.27 – It is obvious from the last chapters that the question of the exo- or endogeneity of the circadian, circumlunar and circ-annual rhythms has not yet been settled definitely. It is difficult to exclude all rhythmic clues experimentally to one's own complete satisfaction. Even if the exogenous and freerunning frequencies are not equal, there might still be interaction. It is also hard to prove statistically whether there is or is not any external influence. There is further the wide range of organisms investigated, from unicellular systems to primates. Also, their mode of action and of interaction with the environment may differ radically. In plants and lower animals the light effect is rather direct on the whole organism, in higher animals the effect is indirect and mediated by the central nervous system. Furthermore, a large number of different functions has been recorded and their behaviour need not be identical.

7.28 – There are also several other cosmic cycles which have been advocated as correlates for biological rhythms, specially the sunspot cycles. They could conceivably reach us through the solar influence upon our atmosphere (*cf*. 6.41-43 and Chapter 17). The relations are, however, yet unclear.

7.29 – We have now in the last two chapters made a general survey of the endogenous rhythms. There remain, however, some special fields which have hitherto only been mentioned in passing; endogenous rhythms in pathology, the formation and development of individual rhythms, and population cycles.

CHAPTER 8

Chronopathology

8.1 – In disease, many of the body's temporal aspects may be changed; the rate of metabolic reactions or nerve information, the time perception, the time sense or the biological rhythms. The last aspect will be treated here.

In the previous three chapters on bio-oscillations, pathological rhythms have only been mentioned in passing, such as feedback disturbances (2.15,20,23, 3.12,24-27, 6.8) and alterations in the time sense (5.25) or the tendency towards longer periods (6.38,41,43).

8.2 – The rhythms found in disease may be derived from those in normal individuals, though changed in some respect owing to alterations in the structure carrying them (overload, transmission difficulties, loop breaks, *etc.*), with a change in the curve shape, frequency pattern or variation range. Other rhythms may arise owing to anomalies in the organism. In general, there is a tendency towards instability in the sick organism, either from overload of the regulating system (specially perhaps at the early reactive stages of disease) or from exhaustion (the late stages). Instability tends to create or enhance oscillations.

If the body is the target of excessive external or internal influences a number of stress mechanisms are evoked. These work by endocrine and neural feedback. If they are overburdened, oscillations have to be expected, either transient and damped (if the disturbance was temporary) or sustained (at constant disturbance). Furthermore, since most regulatory mechanisms in the living organisms are neural, it is not surprising that oscillatory diseases are especially common in this region. The increased sensibility of the organism with increasing age is another factor, as well as the general loss of energy in debility.

Biological rhythms also have many clinical aspects which will be treated more fully in Chapter 27. There are the problems of rhythms in early diagnosis, circadian changes in susceptibility to drugs (*cf.* FORSGREN, HALBERG, MENZEL, MÖLLERSTRÖM), seasonal diseases (*cf.* DERUDDER), shift work (*cf.* BJERNER, BROWNE, MENZEL, THIIS-EVENSEN). Some diseases may be also treated with rhythmic therapy, *e.g.* in balneotherapy (*cf.* HILDEBRANDT).

8.3 – A strict subdivision of the field is difficult to make. Perhaps, one may distinguish between pathological rhythms in the peripheral somatic or neural regions and in the central nervous system. The latter can be roughly subdivided into hypothalamic and cortical disturbances. The hypothalamic region may cause many rhythmic malfunctions in the whole endocrine and autonomous nervous apparatus. The cortical, psychic diseases are always combined with the former group, but the reverse does not have to be true. We will therefore, discuss 'peripheral pathological rhythms', 'neuro-endocrine pathological rhythms' and 'rhythms in the psychopathology', in that order, though they are often interconnected. The latter two are thoroughly discussed by MENNINGER-LERCHENTHAL.

8.4 – *Peripheral Pathological Rhythms.* The vicious circle in pathology has already been mentioned as an example of positive feedback (2.23). The disease becomes slowly worse and worse. Examples are the progress of such diseases as heart or kidney insufficiency or leukemia. In the first-mentioned case, it runs as follows: the heart cannot empty all the blood received → the chambers retain blood and increase in size (dilatation) → stasis of blood ensues in the veins, with slowed circulation, anoxia and a secondary increase in blood volume (regulation, probably caused by anoxia in the bone marrow in an effort to increase the capacity of the system, 2.6, 4.6) → the change in blood volume increases the load on the heart and anoxia worsens the energy situation → the cardiac capacity of blood transmission lessens and dilatation proceeds further → *etc.* Sooner or later the situation reaches the end of the system's capacity and life is endangered. In this case a crisis may save the patient. This may be a regulation (negative feedback) which is only evoked in extreme cases, *e.g.* massive diarrhea which empties the blood of the high amounts of urea accumulated in uremia (when the kidneys fail). Or it may be induced by treatment, *e.g.* digitalis in heart insufficiency strengthening the cardiac musculature, or nitroglycerine compounds in *angina pectoris* with threatening infarctation, relaxing the spastic vessels which carry blood to the heart. The vicious circle then starts again until next crisis and so on, the general situation slowly worsening throughout, until the ultimate limit is reached. The whole process resembles an irregular oscillation with a sloping trend. The crises are usually sudden and dramatic which adds a relaxation oscillation character (*cf.* 4.13-15).

8.5 – Another rhythm mechanism may be the *decreased energy reserves* in the diseased body forcing the individual to periodic rest and recovery, especially if the load on the organism rises simultaneously (MENNINGER-LERCHENTHAL). The author has sometimes observed a quite regular rectal temperature rhythm of this kind with a recurring low amplitude every 7 days and not synchronous with the social week events, in diabetic subjects. In this disease one may also observe periodic recurrences of aciduria in labile and easily exhausted patients, sometimes of such regularity that the next attack may be predicted fairly well.

Such ailments could also perhaps account more or less for partial or total defects in the synchronizing mechanism. In the latter case, freerunning may occur as pointed out by HALBERG[7]. In disease, the 24-h rhythm also tends to break up into short-period components (MENZEL[4-5, 7, 15-17, 100-102]), whatever the reason (*cf.* 6.37). Here, the tendency towards longer periods does not hold; another exception is the EEG (*cf.* 6.10-11).

8.6 – *Damped transient oscillations* during the recovery after a sudden disturbance (3.18) also occur. DERER gives many examples of such macroperiods (*cf.* 6.38) in human pathology after induced 'stress' such as X-ray treatment or other therapy. Examples are 4-7 day periods of blood constituents in rabbits after poisoning of the cerebrospinal fluid; steroid excretion and eosinophil blood counts following ACTH administration; blood leucocyte counts, urinary excretion and corticosteroid excretion after X-ray or antimetabolite treatment in conditions of increased leuco- or lymphocyte production; blood pressure in hypertensive subjects after hypotensive drugs; serum iodoprotein after thyreotropic hormone. More generally, X-ray treatment of plant and animal tissues are followed by a periodic growth recovery (LANGENDORFF[100]), e.g. in plant roots, reticulocytes, spermatogonia or myelopoiesis in the bone marrow (periods up to 40 days). The administration of drugs may give damped transients, e.g. in the circulation (HILDEBRANDT[21]).

8.7 – *Neuro-Endocrine Pathological Rhythms*. Direct 'trauma' upon the central nervous system may easily affect the internal regulation. The periodic character of epileptic motor and sensory fits has long been observed (*cf.* 6.10-11). They are caused by minute cortical scars which tend to synchronize the discharges in large units of nerve fibres. Other neural disturbances are the pupillary *hippus*, the cerebral and cerebellar *tremors* and the pathological *nystagmus* (3.24-25). Some other examples have also been given earlier, such as cardiac arhythmias (6.7, 16-17) and the CHEYNE-STOKE breathing (*cf.* 6.7-8,18). SCHMID[200, 300-302] described 7-20-day periods in the blood pressure of hypertensive subjects.

8.8 – Especially prone to oscillatory responses are the *hypothalamic* and related temporal cortical centres. Disturbances give rise to periodic variations in the endocrine and vegetative functions, including metabolism, body temperature and bone marrow productivity, as well as the vasomotor, gastrointestinal and connective tissue systems or the general activity. The 'causative agents' may be cerebral (especially pituitary) tumors, commotio, cranial fractures, disseminated sclerosis, encephalitis, syphilis, arteriosclerotic ischemia, cerebral hemorrhage, fever, also toxic serum constituents generated by neoplasms, infections or uremia. The symptoms are often accompanied by or alternating with psychotic disease (MENNINGER-LERCHENTHAL, RICHTER[4]). One way of observing the vegetative imbalance is to record the EDG (*cf.* 4.20).

8.9 – Actually, there is a large number of obscure cyclic diseases involving endocrine and autonomous nervous symptoms. A not uncommon component is abdominal pain without apparent cause. REIMANN has coined the term 'periodic disease'. The attacks often occur at 7-14-21-28 day intervals (RICHTER[5]); generally they may vary from 2 days to 6 months or more (48-h rhythms are not unusual) with the most common value around 20 days. The period may be remarkably constant for one individual or change slowly. The disease is twice as common in men as in women. It may start at any age and last a short time or the whole life (30 years have been reported). In women it may be obviously related to the sexual cycle. All these symptoms may cover a heterogenous group of diseases of essentially unknown origin. Such explanations as infection, hormone imbalance, or solar 7-day influences have been advanced. Probably, the origin is hypothalamic. At least, similar symptoms occur in cases of verified hypothalamic damage.

The common association with mental disturbances also points to a central origin. See BRICK[1, 100], GABINUS[100], HERTZ, LINDHOLM[100], LITHANDER, MENNINGER-LERCHENTHAL, REIMANN[1-4, 100-105], RICHTER[3-5], SHWAYRI[100], SIEGAL, TUQAN, WEINER[100].

8.10 – The periodic diseases may be characterized by rhythmic fluctuations in one or several of the following body factors and symptoms: Blood pressure, heart rate, vascular spasms, headache, migraine, dizziness, cutaneous hyperemia (reddening of skin), trombocytopenia (loss of blood platelets), purpura (capillary bleeding), nasal bleeding, anemia, sedimentation rate, white blood cell counts, splenomegaly (enlargened spleen), oedema, serum levels of potassium, calcium, cholesterol, creatine phosphate and total nitrogen, blood bicarbonate, pH, blood sugar, basal metabolism, O_2 consumption, respiratory quotient, alcoholism, body weight, hypothermia, hyperthermia (fever), female hormones and keto-steroids, excretion of ammonia, urea, phosphate, sulphate, chloride, cystine and pentoses, alkaptonuria, amount and specific gravity of urine, hematuria, abdominal colics or pain, gastro-intestinal ulcera, anorexia (loss of appetite), hunger, polydipsy, (abnormal appetite), diarrhea, acetonemic vomiting in children, stomatitis, sweat production, electrodermatographic changes, eczema, hair colour (not artificial), joint pain and swelling, gout, polyserositis (more or less general endothelial inflammatory response), peritonitis, iritis, digital pain, muscular paralysis, ocular movements, ataxia, angioneurotic oedema and other allergic responses, tremor, fatigue, sleep, restlessness, mood, nervosity, excitement and activity.

Periodic paralysis and K-metabolism are discussed by AITKEN[300], CONN[100], FUDEMA[100], GAMSTORP, GLYNN[100], GROB[100], JANTZ, MCARDLE, POSKANZER[100], ROWLEY[100], SHAKHNOWITSCH, SHY[100], TALBOTT, TALSO, VASTOLA[100].

8.11 – RICHTER[3-5] found cyclic activity in female rats as a result of peripheral thyroid hormone depletion obtained by thyroidectomy, radioactive iodine and toxic drugs. Normally the rats eat every 3rd-4th hour, drink every 2nd-3rd hour, defecate and urinate every 4th-5th hour. They have a gross activity rhythm running parallel to the sexual cycle of 4-5 days. The feeding activity, body weight and body temperature run inversely as compared to the activity curve. After the effected fall in thyroxin production peculiar damped oscillations occurred in the whole pattern, periods of normal activity rhythm alternating with rest periods of 8-14 days. The former periods tended to shorten progressively, the latter were unchanged. This could not be produced in all animals. The whole state could last for years. Thyroxin administration restored the normal conditions. The similarity to the sexual cycle behaviour is evident. Probably, the cause is the disturbance of the peripheral hormone feedback to the hypophysis (2.13). Similar activity rhythms in rats also occurred after severe stress (overload of ACTH-cortisone cycle), progesterone treatment, mechanically induced pseudopregnancy and cutting of the hypophyseal stalk as well as one case of spontaneous tumor pressing against the stalk. From this, the author concludes that a hypothalamic disturbance is the prime factor in evoking the oscillations.

8.12 – RICHTER[5] has also collected many own cases of periodic disease as well as reports from the literature. He points out that there are unusual and intriguing cases where several pathological rhythms of different periods and timing may coexist in the same person in different parts of the body, *e.g.* different joints in cyclic hydrarthrosis (*cf.* REIMANN). He has developed a shock-phase theory according to which the body abounds in cycles of different locality and phase which normally cancel out. The pathological influence is assumed to synchronize a number of these processes, producing an overt rhythm. Of course, one may also turn this around, assuming a release of normal rhythmic patterns from a central inhibition (MENNINGER-LERCHENTHAL).

RICHTER distinguishes between three types of oscillatory mechanisms: (1) peripheral tissue clocks, (2) central clocks (thalamus, hypothalamus, reticular system, hypophysis), and (3) homeostatic clocks, *i.e.* endocrine cycles. The last type is less exact than the others. Menstrual cycles may vary from 16-100 days, whereas the central clock of one patient operated flawlessly on a 48-h period for over 30 years.

8.13 – One type of periodic disease which has long been recognized is cyclic fever. An obvious cause is infectious parasites with parallel life-cycles (Chapter 10) as in malaria (72- or 48-h periods), brucellosis or relapsing fever. Another type depends on 'hypothalamic dysregulation'. ASK-UPMARK (*cf.* 3.26) has collected numerous examples. Cyclic fever seems to be common in afflictions of the reticulo-endo-thelial system, especially the bone marrow (primary and secondary bone tumours, myeloma, lymphogranulomatosis, leukemia, thrombocytopenia, anemias, poly-cythemia, osteoporosis, osteomyelitis, diseases of the liver and spleen. Several of the periods are multiples of the 24-h period (*cf.* 6.38).

8.14 – *Rhythms in Psychopathology.* As already indicated there is no real border-line between hypothalamic and psychic rhythmic disturbances. Here, however, the cortical region is also involved. Some cortical, though not mental, diseases were already mentioned (8.7). Periodic psychotic symptoms are followed by signs of hypothalamic disturbances, whether rhythmic or not. Almost any combination of the two types of central rhythmic disturbances may be found. The causative agent may be a diencephalic trauma or a more obscure cortical affection, as in the 'periodic psychoses'. These seem only to be rhythmic as long as the rapport with the hypothalamus is intact. According to MENNINGER-LERCHENTHAL they may turn into a continuous state after leucotomy (severing of the efferent paths from the cortex, usually in the frontal lobe). Especially, psychic aberrations of our basic urges such as feeding, sleep and sexual activity obviously act through the hypothalamic regulation. – The psychic diseases are nowadays regarded as metabolic diseases. A rhythmic behaviour may then perhaps arise if the responsive factor varies cyclically, bringing forth a reaction only when surpassing a certain level. – The transition between periods of pathological disturbance and the 'nor-mal' states (remissions) are usually very abrupt, without transients (*cf.* 4.29).

8.15 – Some general differences would seem to exist between the periodic psychoses and the pure brain stem afflictions. The former seem to be equally frequent in the two sexes (RICHTER[4]). They may be particularly regular. – The periods of mental disturbance may easily surpass 6 months. As a general rule in pathological central nervous rhythms the period tends to be longer the more cranial the localization of the disturbance in the brain stem (MENNINGER-LERCHENTHAL). This author also regards the rhythms as preformed primitive mechanisms, which are normally inhibited by the neopallium (cortex).

8.16 – The hierarchial system of higher nervous centres stabilizing (or inhibiting) the lower ones, which are intrinsically rhythmic in their action, is also stressed by SELBACH[1, 100]. He even gives examples from phylogeny. In 'rhombencephalic animals' the respiratory rhythm is irregular periodic, in 'mesencephalic organisms' it is more regular, though waxing and waning as in the CHEYNE-STOKE breathing (6.7-8). First in the 'diencephalic animals' the relative stability of our own breathing occurs. Parallels may be found in the temperature regulation and in children, where the stability of the servosystems increases with age, the damped oscillations more or less disappearing. SELBACH stresses the increased lability of the neuro-endocrine balance in psychoses and ascribes this to an impairment of the neural servomechanisms with increased dead space and high gain (3.24-26). The result is a sudden reaction, crisis, cf. 1.11, 2.23. When the bodily functions approach the widened homeostatic limits, a large overshoot occurs which takes the character of a complete reversal in the neuro-endocrine system. From extreme *sympaticotonia* (ergotropy, adrenergy) the patient is thrown into extreme parasympaticotonia (trophotropy, cholinergy, vagotonia) and reversely. A similar mechanism is seen in syncope (fainting). The crisis may be followed by damped oscillations (GJESSING[3]). SELBACH draws parallels with WILDER's 'Law of initial value' (Chapter 11). Other parallels are the ASHBY homeostat (3.16) and the relaxation oscillators (4.13).

8.17 – *Periodic* changes in the *psychoses* are conspicuous and have always interested the physicians, *e.g.* ARNDT, CRAMER[400], GEORGI, GJESSING, GORNALL[100], KRAEPELIN, KRETSCHMER, MALL, PILCZ, RICHTER[3-4], STAEHELIN. These rhythms occur both within the 'manic-depressive' and 'schizophrenic' regions. They may appear at periods of our life when the regulation mechanisms are already out of balance, *e.g.* the puberty or climacterium. They may also influence the 24-h rhythm of the subjects, even causing a complete reversal (GEORGI). Periodic variations have been described in: mania and depression, suicide tendency, excitement, elation, affectivity, anxiety, melancholy, apathy, delirium, amentia, paranoia, hallucination, catatonia, stupor, dreams, insomnia, poriomania (walking madness), smoking, kleptomania, pyromania, nymphomania, impotence, homosexuality, and pedophilia.

8.18 – GJESSING made painstaking records of the mental and metabolic changes of *periodic catatonia* in single subjects during long time periods (Fig. 8.18a). The patients were lying in bed with controlled food. The error in predictions of change in mental state was ± 1-2 days.

GJESSING distinguished between the interval (more or less normal state) and the reaction phase (catatonia, either slight reaction with excitement or heavy reaction with stupor). He observed a remarkable retention of nitrogen-containing substances in the body shortly before the onset of the reaction phase, followed by a compensatory increase in BMR, heart rate, blood leucocytes and N-excretion. He considered this nitrogen retention as the prime cause of the disease. He actually succeeded in shortening the catatonic phase by regulating the N-intake. Especially effective in abating the attacks was, however, thyroid treatment. This has been confirmed by others (e.g. MALL and GORNALL[100], cf. 8.11).

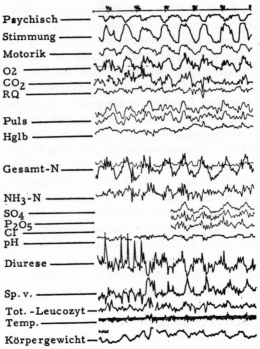

Fig. 8.18a. Periodic changes of metabolism in schizophrenic catatonia, according to GJESSING[3].

8.19 – This chapter has only been a short survey of the great field which pathological rhythms constitute. The emphasis has been on endogenous rhythms. Problems of control and synchronization will be brought up in the proper connections, also that of the clinical aspects (Part IV). For a further discussion, specially of the clinical problems, see DELL'ACQUA[2], AJELLO[100], ENGEL[300-301], FRANKE[201], GROTE, HAEBERLIN, HALBERG[2, 7, 10, 104, 106, 108, 111, 115, 117, 120-124, 129, 130, 137], HILDEBRANDT[4-5, 8-9, 11-16, 18, 20, 100, 102-104, 107-109], JORES[2, 4, 8-11, 100], MENZEL[1, 4-17, 21-25, 28-32, 100-103], MORHARDT, DERUDDER[1-17, 100], SCHULZ[200].

The next chapter will touch upon another specialized aspect of endogenous rhythms, their formation.

CHAPTER 9

Developmental Rhythms

9.1 – Very little is known about the development of biological rhythms, especially during the perinatal period. Since many periodicities are regarded as inherited (*e.g.* the circadian rhythm) and since the embryos develop in relative isolation one would expect these developmental rhythms to be endogenous. On the other hand, the isolation is not perfect. The mammalian fetus is profoundly influenced by its mother. Egg-shells are quite thin and translucent, as are many forms in the invertebrate metamorphosis.

9.2 – Many exogenous rhythms appear only after the birth of the individual, being developed gradually upon exposure to the external periodicities. This is especially the case in mammals who stand in rapport with the surroundings through a nervous system and which are born before this apparatus has matured. Several possibilities exist for the formation of the rhythms:

(1) The rhythm is *preformed* in basic embryonic functions and appears when *triggered* by external events (and is later synchronized).

(2) The rhythm is *preformed* and already *operates* in the embryo, as an endogenous rhythm.

(3) The embryonic rhythm may differ in *characteristics* from the adult one and is modified by or interferes with external stimuli at birth.

(4) The embryonic rhythm may already be *synchronized*. Remember that even if its frequency differs considerably from the external one, a synchronization on a harmonic level is still possible.

(5) The rhythms cannot appear until the neural and endocrine apparatus has *matured* and will therefore develop gradually, whether genetically predetermined or induced from without.

(6) One may actually expect *undeveloped servosystems* to have other characteristics than the adult ones. They should be less stable and oscillate readily. Their capacity should also be smaller, predisposing to higher frequencies and lower amplitudes.

(7) *No embryonic rhythms* exist, they are passively acquired at birth.

9.3 – There is altogether too little experimental evidence to decide between the possibilities. Since the circadian rhythms are thought to be inherited and since all living systems contain servosystems, one may reasonably assume that rhythms exist already prenatally. The primitiveness of the organism and the successive addition of higher controlling and damping centres during development indicate that the embryonic rhythm should differ in characteristics from the adult one and be changed after birth. As to synchronization, this is possible already prenatally, but some changes should appear after birth, when there is a stronger contact with the dominant synchronizers (1.19). – One type of spontaneous rhythm, the amniotic movement, was described in 6.33.

LEVINS (personal communication) suggests an intriguing possibility for explaining embryonic rhythms, which is related to periodic alternations between populations. Assume that several organ functions should happen to be more or less incompatible during development. They could then be separated in two ways, either 'spatially' (as happens with the metabolic waste in the egg), or 'temporally'. The latter would indicate a rhythmic alternation between the functions.

9.4 – *Development of Rhythms in Mammals.* Possibilities for 'intrauterine control' exist through the maternal blood circulation or uterine movements (*cf.* 6.33). Some endogenous rhythms do exist, *e.g.* the heart beat which can be recorded *intra utero*. Fetal movements may well turn out to have a rhythmic pattern.

9.5 – The main problem are the rhythms with external correlates. A persistent belief is that newborn babies are monothermic, without any spontaneous fluctuations in the temperature. This is not quite true. There seem to be 24-h variations, whether circadian or exogenous, though of small amplitude. The range of the variations rises from day to day (GYLLENSWÄRD, GOFFERJÉ, HELLBRÜGGE[1], JUNDELL, KLEITMAN[106], LANGE[200]). The same applies to the development of most body functions during the first half-year of life and on a smaller scale up to puberty, *e.g.* as regards the electrodermatogram, heart rate, blood sugar and urinary volume, or the secretion of Na, K, PO_4, creatine and creatinine (*cf.* Conf. 1961a, FUNCK, HELLBRÜGGE[1, 100, 101], HOHAUS, KATHAN, NIGGESCHMIDT, RUTENFRANZ[1-2, 100]). There is also the question of the special sensitivity of children, leading to typical infantile seasonal morbidity rhythms (*e.g.* DERUDDER; 26.17-20), and the mental instability at puberty, predisposing to psychosis (8.17).

9.6 – An apparently endogenous periodicity is to be found in the 'sleep-wakefulness' pattern of young infants, as reported by KLEITMAN[6, 10-12, 102, 103] (*cf.* BÜHLER[100], GESELL, HELLBRÜGGE[1, 101], RUTENFRANZ[2]). The cycle duration was somewhat less than one hour and corroborated by studies of eye movements and actograms. Self-demand feeding seemed to occur at intervals which were integers of this rhythm. Slightly longer rhythms seem to occur during sleep in adults (EEG, sleep depth) with periods of 60-80 min (6.35). One wonders whether this is a continuation of an embryonic rhythm.

9.7 – The *birth trauma* may probably set up damped oscillations during the first hours of life, *e.g.* in blood pressure or heart rate, though this still awaits confirmation.

9.8 – *Development of Rhythms in Birds.* It is difficult to tell what actually happens *intra utero* in mammals. Unfortunately, the mammalian fetus or young is never completely independent. Among the higher animals the embryonic conditions may, however, be studied in birds, where the eggs can easily be kept under controlled conditions. Such studies have been made on the liver glycogen rhythm in chick embryos (ELFVIN[100], PETRÉN[2, 100], SOLLBERGER[3, 5]). The embryos probably

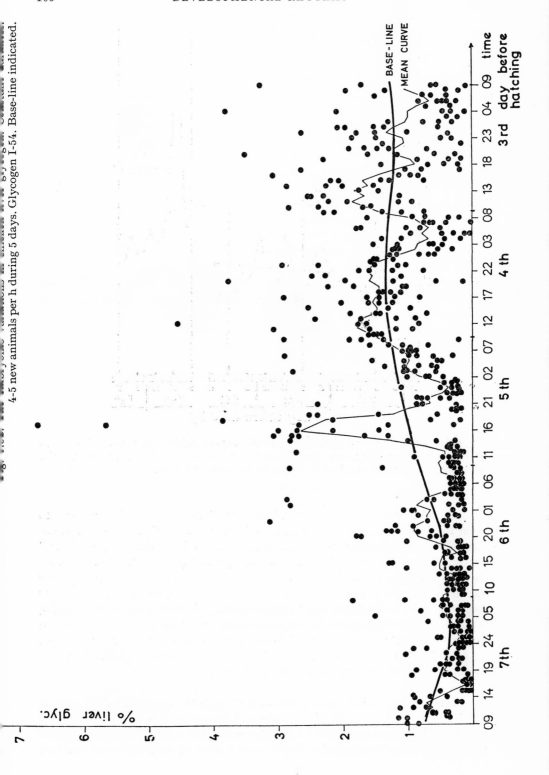

4-5 new animals per h during 5 days. Glycogen I-54. Base-line indicated.

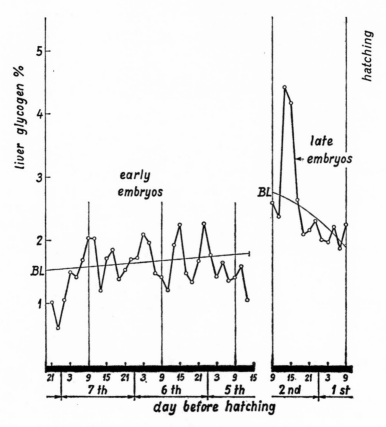

Fig. 9.8a. The liver glycogen rhythm in chick embryos under constant conditions, as well as in newborn and older male chickens under normal conditions and starvatoin. 12-16 new animals every 2nd h. After PETRÉN-SOLLBERGER.

generate 3-4 irregular cycles a day (*cf*. Figs. 9.8a-d). Some kind of change seems to occur the days before hatching, in anticipation of the adult rhythm (Figs. 9.8a-b). Immediately after hatching the circadian glycogen rhythm appears (Fig. 9.8a), well synchronized with external rhythmic events, if present (Fig. 9.8d). The embryonic rhythms are demonstrated in Fig. 9.8c (upper part), and the adult ones (under various conditions) in Fig. 9.8d, pictured as relative variations. Fig. 9.8c suggests something like: first a freerunning 'high-frequency' rhythm; then the freerunning is stopped (some kind of synchronization?); and one of the peaks is enhanced in preparation for the circadian period (which appears immediately after hatching). – *Cf*. similar studies on the O_2-consumption and activity before and after hatching (BARNWELL[1], HEUSNER[100], HIEBEL[100], SZYMANSKI[1]).

9.9 – One problem in this connection is the noise in the embryonic data, part of which may be explained by a phase-dispersal between individuals. However, some interindividual synchronization (egg heat generated in a small space and against the thermostat?) must exist, else the cycles should cancel out completely. And how

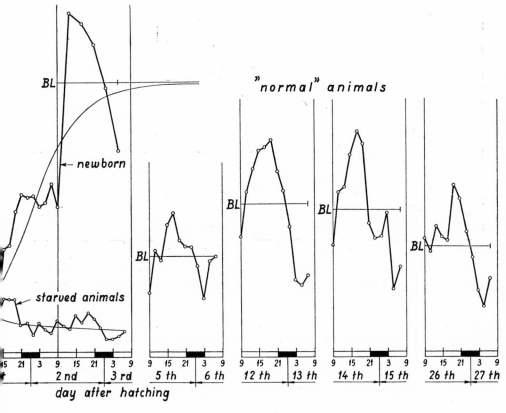

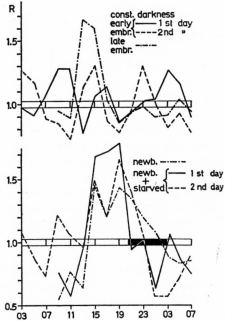

Fig. 9.8c. Relative variations during 24 h of chicken liver glycogen in embryos and newly hatched animals. Same material as the four left hand series in Fig. 9.8a.

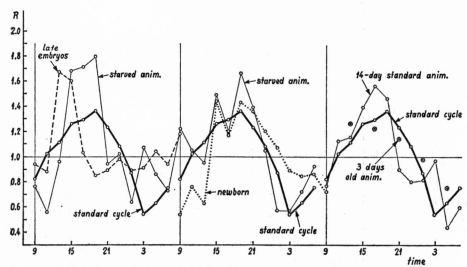

Fig. 9.8d. Relative variations of chicken liver glycogen in some embryonic, newborn and older series of animals, corresponding to Fig. 9.8a. The 'standard cycle' is an average of the 5-, 12-, and 26-day old adult cycles. After PETRÉN-SOLLBERGER.

should all these phenomena be tested statistically (*cf*. Part III)? The possibility of a prenatal synchronization (somehow?) cannot be ruled out either.

9.10 – An interesting parallel is the progressive decomposition of circadian rhythms into 'hour-rhythms' in disease, as observed by BLUME[1-2, 4, 6] and MENZEL[4-5, 7, 15-16, 100-102], *cf*. 6.37.

9.11 – *Evolutionary Aspects*. Apart from the idea that some rhythms have been acquired by natural selection, little is known about the subject. It is clear that rhythms appear even in unicellular organisms. What develops is an increasing complexity in the apparatus which carries the rhythms and its coupling to the external world. In many invertebrates the light penetrates directly through the body itself with direct action of some kind. In higher invertebrates this action is on the neurosecretory system, either through a translucent body or the eyes, especially the *ocelli* (*cf*. also 24.18).

In vertebrates, the nervous system becomes increasingly important in the control of rhythms. The pathways of the light influence are not clear. Maybe the pineal eye or the postulated retino-hypothalamic connections are involved (see 13.15-17). The evolving system with additions of new and higher inhibitory centres and its stabilizing effect on endogenous rhythms was mentioned in 8.16. There may also be a tendency towards successively slower rhythms with increasing size and complexity.

9.12 – In invertebrates, the total development of the individual occurs during the metamorphosis period. In some instances, the adaptive value of a rhythmic behaviour seems clear (*cf*. CLOUDSLEY-THOMPSON[20, 27-28]). The emergence from the insect pupae occurs at a certain time of the day, when conditions for survival are favourable. Mating (also in higher animals) occurs at certain times in relation to the day, moon quarter and season (cf. Part IV). This results in a simultaneity of action which favours a high number of offspring and survival.

9.13 – Much discussed is the 'nocturnalism' (night-activity) or 'diurnalism' (day-activity) of insects. (Note that this is really the correct use of the word diurnal.) CLOUDSLEY-THOMPSON[1, 8, 14, 18-20, 23, 26-28] points out that the integument plays a decisive role in this connection, especially in hot climates. Arthropods with a waterproof cuticle (insects and arachnids) can venture out into the sun without risk of dessication. Those without (woodlice, some millipedes and centipedes) are nocturnal, since only then the air is humid and cold enough. There are exceptions among the former group, which are actually nocturnal, too (scorpions, cockroaches, stickinsects), probably for secondary reasons, such as competition with other species.

The development of an efficient thermoregulation (JOHANSEN) has helped in the fight for survival against heat and cold. Other solutions were hibernation (26.6) and migration (Chapter 18). The capacity to orient was also used by the lower animals to anticipate and follow the tidal movements on the beach.

9.14 – Another aspect on the ecology of rhythms are the animal population cycles which will be discussed in the next chapter.

CHAPTER 10

Population Cycles

10.1 – In previous chapters the endogenous rhythms have been discussed, including their mechanisms, occurrence, evolution and ecology. One ecological aspect which has caused much discussion is that of the animal population cycles.

There are many theories and a large literature. Good introductions are Conf. 1954b and 1957d.

10.2 – When counting the animals of a population in the wild or under suitable experimental conditions, one may often observe cycles of remarkable regularity. An old example is the periodic migration of the lemmings. There seem to be two major durations. A 3-4 year cycle has been observed in lemmings, voles, muskrats, rabbits, fox, grouse bird, owls and hawks. This also applies to the sex-ratio of the populations (PITELKA). An 8-10 year cycle occurs in lynx, mink, arctic fox, hare and grouse. And 35-year cycles have been observed in ducks, perhaps related to the BRÜCKNER cycle (cf. 17.12). The phenomena may be well developed in certain regions of the world and absent in other parts – in the same animal. The geographic areas in question are however very large, such as the whole of Canada or a belt round the northern hemisphere between 50° and 30° latitude.

10.3 – *Theories.* The causes of the natural population cycles are not really known and many theories exist. There are also mathematical and experimental models. The latter usually consist of carefully controlled *micropopulations*, which demonstrate the aspects of periodic growth. Some theories are:

(1) The population cycles are simply 'random cycles' caused by serial correlation (cf. Part III; COLE[200-202], PALMGREN[4]).
(2) They are 'exogenous rhythms' with unknown synchronizer (ERRINGTON, ROWAN[7]).
(3) They are caused by a 'predator-prey feedback' (cf. KLOMP, LACK[1], TINBERGEN[100], UTIDA, VOLTERRA, also 2.16).
(4) There is a high population density, generating 'stress', which leads to self-destruction, relaxation-oscillation-like, or to migration (cf. CHRISTIAN, KOSKIMIES); a population pressure.
(5) There is 'periodic growth' (4.21-23) including competition for food (cf. HUTCHINSON, MORAN[2], NICHOLSON, PRATT[1], SLOBODKIN).
(6) There is a 'synchronization of life-cycles' or reproduction times by external or interindividual agents.
(7) There is an interference between the lunar and seasonal cycles with 3-4 and 9.6 year periods (cf. SIIVONEN[100]).

10.4 – *The Random Theory.* The animal population data are often 'noisy', and it is also difficult to collect runs long enough for a statistical frequency analysis. This has led to some authors rejecting any causation in the data. To complicate matters further, we can only use one value per year (the yearly average) in the wildlife population curves, since there is a pronounced seasonal trend which must be eliminated. Furthermore, a series of random figures tends to exhibit peaks at certain intervals depending on the serial correlation and the definition of peaks (*cf.* 1.34,39 and Part III, also COLE[200-202]). Some of the observed cycles are, however, entirely too regular for such an explanation to be valid (*cf.* ERRINGTON, HICKEY, MORAN[2], ROWAN[7]).

10.5 – *Exogenous Aspects*. The existence of an unknown synchronizer cannot be ruled out completely, especially with regard to the geographical distribution of the rhythms. It has been suggested that the phenomenon of latitudinal passage holds for this type of cycles (WING). This should be carefully tested. The population periods are also said to recur both in the weather, business and tree-ring data (*cf.* 6.42, HUNTINGTON[2]).

10.6 – *Ecological Aspects*. *Mixed Populations*. The predator-prey mechanism certainly exists but its precise significance is unknown. Parallels are 'epidemics' and 'pandemics'. Population cycles may, however, exist even in areas where no predator-prey feedback would seem to be at work.

An 'increasing population density' may act directly, effecting a change in the animal physiology, or indirectly through interaction with the environment, *e.g.* competition for food.

The 'direct density effect' has been observed in captive or isolated groups of animals, which periodically run wild and die with all signs of a neuro-endocrine stress shock (CHRISTIAN, DEEVEY, ERRINGTON[2]). The migration of the lemmings may belong here. This does not necessarily have to be coupled with an actual competition for food. It seems as if the animals cannot 'stand a throng'. The effect may, of course, be an adequate reaction developed by genetic selection for the purpose of avoiding over-population. The author has observed the phenomenon in caged chickens, which may peck each other even if there is plenty of food available. One may wonder whether our periodic disposition towards fighting wars is an example of predator-prey feedback with high gain or a population density effect.

LEVINS considers the fate of 'mixed populations' in a certain environment. The component populations may possess different degrees of fitness with regard to the environment and to group incompatibility. The proportions between them will tend to adjust so as to maximize the fitness of the whole population. In extreme cases either sub-population may vanish. Another solution is a spatial separation of them, even to the degree of a search for different ecological niches. Yet another solution is a temporal separation of the sub-populations, *i.e.* a rhythmic alternation, especially if the environment fluctuates, itself. The seasons are a good example of such fluctuations.

Actually, examples exist of genetically determined variations in one and the same population with the seasons; *e.g.* LEES'[6] findings on the sexual development of aphids (*cf.* 5.18), and KALMUS'[10, 15] populations of *Daphnia* with different body shapes at different times of the year.

10.7 – *Periodic Growth*. This field has already been discussed (4.21-23) in connection with the oscillators. There are several factors which may upset the conditions for feedback stability. One is precisely the indirect density effect (10.6) which works by competition for food. (If the food is represented by the plant kingdom the system herbivores-plants may even be regarded as a predator-prey feedback system.) Another factor in periodic growth is the 'reproduction time' and this leads to the synchronization theory (10.8-10).

It is with regard to the periodic growth that we possess several brilliant experimental studies of animal populations (*cf*. NICHOLSON, PRATT[1], SLOBODKIN, UTIDA). SLOBODKIN uses *Daphnia* of such homogeneous populations that all life-cycles are synchronized and obtains characteristic periodic growth. These rhythms are of longer duration than the actual lifecycles (50-100 days as compared to a few days). Limiting conditions (density effects) are avoided. The importance of the 'age-size distribution' of the animals is stressed; at a certain composition of this, balance is struck, else periodic growth ensues.

10.8 – *Synchronization of Life-Cycles*. The synchronization of life-cycles or reproduction times will obviously generate population cycles. Normally, individual cycles are phase-dispersed and cancel out. Any kind of shock which temporarily arrests or accelerates certain parts of the life-cycle and not others will tend to synchronize them. Take ordinary cell division. This is actually an example of biological feedback, the relation between metabolic need and surface area of the cell determining when division is to occur. Such cycles may be synchronized if the cell *mitoses* are all arrested at a certain stage, *e.g.* by use of mitotic poisons, hypothermia or calcium depletion (ROBBINS[100]). Upon release from the agent all cells will start at the same phase of development.

10.9 – A suitable light regimen may under circumstances have a similar synchronizing effect (LORENZEN). According to RICHTER[5] the trauma of disease may bring about a synchronization of normally phase-dispersed peripheral organ rhythms, the shock-phase hypothesis (*cf*. 8.12).

10.10 – Some *exocrine glands* secrete periodically, their individual cells being synchronized by autonomous rhythmic stimuli (HIRSCH[1-3, 100], JÄRVI, KRIJGSMAN). – There are human parasites with synchronized life cycles, *e.g.* in malaria. – In newbuilt suburbs, where only young people settle, a life cycle synchronization may be quite conspicuous. – Wars tend to eliminate the middle age group.

10.11 – With this chapter we have finished our study of the endogenous rhythms. Before turning to the external rhythms, though, there remains to discuss a field of study, which is to some extent related to that of biological rhythms, namely basimetry. This concerns the relations between initial values and changes in biological variates.

CHAPTER 11

Basimetry

11.1 – In the previous chapters we have discussed biological regulation and oscillators. It was pointed out that the former works like a servomechanism, trying to keep the body function at certain levels or at least between certain limits, against random disturbances from the outside. Certain disturbances (*e.g.* drugs) are, however, non-random and aim at changing the level of activity, the setting of the biological servosystem (*cf.* Fig. 1.12, right side). Apart from the oscillations that may accompany the change, there may also be certain relations between the strength of the stimulus and the change in level, unless we are working with a switch function (Fig. 3.28b and 4.15). Actually, rather complicated biological mechanisms seem to be at work which also generate a correlation between the initial level and the change. Basimetry devotes itself to the study of these phenomena, which have many points of interest in common with biological rhythm research.

11.2 – *Law of Initial Value* (*L.I.V.*). When giving prescriptions for his patient, the physician not seldom gets unexpected results. A certain drug may have a good effect in one subject and only a slight effect in another person. There may even be cases of a complete reversal of the usual response, a so-called 'paradoxic effect'. Such reactions are not uncommon in the treatment of neuro-endocrine disorders.

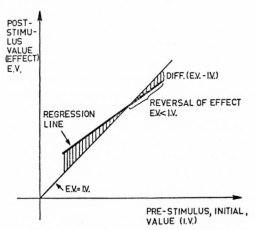

Fig. 11.2a. The law of initial value, L.I.V. The relation between post- and prestimulus value.

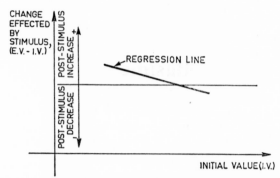

Fig. 11.2b. The law of initial value, L.I.V. The relation between change and prestimulus value.

WILDER, around 1930, observed a pattern in this behaviour by relating the effects to the initial value of the function studied. He found that "the larger the initial excitatory state of a function the smaller its sensitivity to further stimulation and the larger its sensitivity to inhibitory agents; and conversely". In case of extreme initial values there may, furthermore, be no reaction at all, or a 'reversed effect'. Numerically, the relation may appear as in Fig. 11.2a. This is essentially a regression between post- and prestimulation values (poststimulation value = E.V. = effect value, prestimulation value = I.V. = initial value) with an angular coefficient less than unity, and may be so tested statistically. The effected change is represented by the vertical lines.

Another way of visualizing the relation is by plotting the change (E.V. – I.V.) directly against the prestimulus value (I.V.), as in Fig. 11.2b. Statistical tests should, however, not be performed on this regression, since the X- and Y-axis values have one factor in common. The pictorial representation may, however, preferably be made in this way.

11.3 – WILDER called the relation the "Law of Initial Value" (L.I.V., Ausgangswertgesetz) and denoted its study as basimetry (cf. Ref. J.b., Conf. 1960a, 1961c, also HAYDU, HILDEBRANDT[16], HUNGERLAND[100], POLAK[100], SELBACH[2], STALLING, WAGNER[4], ZIPF). It is not a strict law, since there are exceptions, but it is important to remember for the biologist. WILDER's Rule was originally formulated for the autonomous nervous functions and from empirical observations, but it may be found active in almost all realms of the biological sciences. The psychiatrists have been especially interested since paradoxical and very sudden reactions are quite common, the so-called crises. Shock treatments of various kinds may precipitate the crisis.

Some examples of the L.I.V. may be cited. It is a common experience, e.g. that nicotine stimulates when the smoker is tired or depressed (vagotonia), but soothes when he is upset or restless (sympathicotonia). Hypotensive drugs may have a good effect in hypertensive patients, but a slight effect in normotensive, and may sometimes even give the opposite response in hypotensive persons, all with the same dose. Alternatively, the dose required to achieve a certain drop in blood pressure may be quite small in hypertensives and large in hypotensives.

11.4 – The physiological background to WILDER's Rule is complicated. Though the phenomenon is not uncommon in medical pharmacology, it more seldom appears in experimental pharmacology with its heavy drug dosage. This has exposed it to much criticism. It has even been suggested that the L.I.V. is a purely random statistical phenomenon (HUNGERLAND[100], POLAK[100]).

If we assume that the stimulus only causes a constant change from one level (the average I.V.-level) to another (the average E.V.-level) we get the situation in Fig. 11.4a. The ellipse represents the values, where the average I.V. differs from the average E.V. though there is no correlation between the E.V. and I.V. values; *i.e.*, there is no special tendency for high E.V. values to be coupled to either high or low I.V. values or *vice versa*. No L.I.V. phenomenon occurs.

If, however, the change (E.V. – I.V.) is compared to I.V. a correlation appears. If random values are collected two by two and if the first one in the pair is extreme (high or low) then the second one tends more towards the centre of the distribution, simply since two extreme values in succession is a rare occurrence. This is the so-called central tendency in random values. Thus, the average E.V. for each possible value of I.V. always tends to be the same, a constant, and the difference between this and I.V. will vary systematically (the vertical lines in the figure). The I.V. is thus only correlated with itself; minus a constant (r = 0.71). Another way of expressing this is to say that the variates I.V. and (E.V. – I.V.) have one common factor = I.V.

The effect appears whether the variation occurs between individuals or represents the error in one individual, also if the E.V.- and I.V.-levels are equal (no change) as long as there is some random variation in the values. This superficial way of explaining the L.I.V. is rejected, if the E.V. and I.V. are directly and significantly correlated, as in Fig. 11.2a.

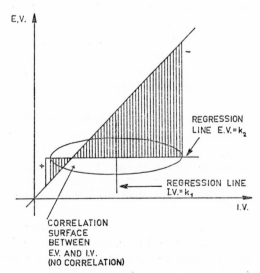

Fig. 11.4a. The false L.I.V.-effect. No correlation between pre- and poststimulus values.

11.5 – *Repeated Stimulation*. If a series of stimuli is given, WILDER's Rule would demand that each successive stimulus have less effect than the preceeding one. The function in question would tend to level off asymtotically in time (WILDER[11]). If we simplify the Rule into its most elementary form, we could state that each change is inversely proportional to its initial value. Going towards smaller and smaller changes and a continuous stimulus we approach the differential formula 11.5a. Its solutions are families of parabolas with the axes coinciding with the X-axis, formula 11.5b. Clearly, WILDER's Rule is related to the WEBER-FECHNER logarithmic dose (stimulus) – response law.

11.5a $y' = a/y$

11.5b $y^2 = 2ax + c$

11.6 – *Paradoxic Reactions*. If the values approach the asymptotic value (homeostatic limit) a 'paradoxic reaction' could, furthermore occur, turning the process in the other direction. After dropping for a while, the values would revert to the old behaviour and so on, a regular oscillation ensuing (*cf.* the dead space oscillation in a constant environment, 3.26, and periodic growth, 4.22).

11.7 – Paradoxic reactions may be interpreted as homeostatic turning points, or relaxation oscillations or just one aspect of a regular oscillation. One thing differs however from our earlier discussions, because we are now dealing with reactions upon heavy disturbances deliberately forced upon the system from without. Paradoxic reactions are not uncommon in biology, *e.g.* in the neuro-endocrine region or psychiatry. The allergic hay fever patient, *e.g.*, knows how rapidly he may become insensitive to the nasal decongestant he uses and how, at last, the swelling may even become worse than before, after a very short period of effect.

11.8 – *Rhythmic Aspects*. There are several rhythmic aspects in WILDER's Rule. It could generate cycles in steady state under load (when pushed against a homeostatic limit, *cf.* 11.6). Actually, even an ordinary non-disturbed biological rhythm behaves similarly; if a value is close to the peak and on the way up (high initial value) a reversal (paradoxic reaction) is to be expected. If the values are low, and going down, the opposite reversal will happen.

11.9 – If a stimulus is now introduced into the rhythmic process (or even starting one, *e.g.* a damped oscillation) it may conceivably act in different ways:

(1) It may just 'accelerate' the rhythm (whichever the direction) with unchanged limits, thus shortening the time till the paradoxic reaction.
(2) It may act as in 1, but with widened limits, in either or both directions.
(3) It may only push in one direction, either with the rhythm or against it, with or without widened limits.

Examples exist. Well-known is the reactive hypoglycemia shortly after a heavy meal. The blood sugar is first pushed high, then drops more than normally within widened limits. Similar phenomena are seen in orthostatic persons with a labile nervous system and under stress (*cf.* LUNDBERG).

11.10 – It should be remembered that the recording of an initial value does not tell anything of the direction of a presumed rhythmic (or non-rhythmic) process. However, there is both an 'initial value' and an 'initial direction' of a biological movement and both should be studied. Almost nothing is known about these conditions in drug therapy.

11.11 – We have now touched on another aspect of rhythms, namely that these constitute one of the factors which cause the fluctuations in the basal values underlying the basimetric phenomena. Other factors are random, pathological, or interindividual variations.

Basimetry demands a changing sensitivity to drugs with the rhythm. Such effects are well-known (*e.g.* in the 24-h rhythms, 5.16 and 7.3-19, also Part IV) and are important in therapy. The sensitivity to drugs usually differs from day (sympathicotonia) to night (parasympathicotonia). The diabetic patient is very sensitive to insulin at night, when 8-16 I.U. may give unwanted reactions, whereas he may tolerate many times as much during the day. However, there must be more than a mere relation to the initial value at work in such variations, since the whole metabolism and physiology of an individual partakes in the rhythmic movement, with profound changes in sensitivity.

The author has also seen typical basimetric relations in the blood pressure and pulse response to catecholamines in newborn infants (CONTIS, LIND and SOLLBERGER, to be published). They could be explained simply as a series of damped oscillations set up by the 'birth trauma' and conditioning the drug response.

11.12 – WILDER's Rule has proved its value in medicine. It reflects the work of complicated biological systems, which are yet but poorly understood. Many relations to the study of biological rhythms exist, but remain to be clearly defined in the future.

11.13 – We have now finished the study of endogenous rhythms. Before turning to the exogenous rhythms we will, however, study the external physical cycles as well as diverse rhythm models and the statistical treatment of such data.

PART II

EXTERNAL PHYSICAL RHYTHMS

"All things by immortal power
Near or far
Hiddenly
To each other linked are,
That thou canst not stir a flower.
Without troubling of a star".

FRANCIS THOMPSON

(cited by VAN DER POL).

This part deals with the external physical rhythms around us, their mode of action and their periods. The reading is facilitated if the introductory Chapter 1 is studied first, especially sections 3 and 18-21. The subject is developed in seven chapters:

CHAPTER 12

External Agents

12.1 – In Part I we have studied the spontaneous endogenous rhythms. It was also pointed out that these phenomena may be governed by external 'synchronizers' (cf. 1.3,19) through some kind of interaction, yielding 'exogenous rhythms'. We will now discuss which the external agents may be, which frequencies they exhibit, and how they are utilized in animal navigation. This first chapter will give a general introduction to the problems.

12.2 – The external agent may be: (1) a single impulse or a change in level, sometimes repeated discontinuously at random (disturbances). It may affect the phasing (phase synchronization) of a rhythm; (2) the agent may exhibit a constant influence. Though not a very natural condition it is often used in experiments on rhythms. Such a state cannot change a cycle directly but may constitute one condition for its existence (cf. 3.26). The frequency of a circadian rhythm may, e.g., differ at different levels of the constant activity; (3) the agent may vary continuously and at random; (4) it may display periodic changes, continuous or discontinuous, giving frequency synchronization.

It is, of course, the fourth alternative which interests us most. However, when discussing the mode of action of a synchronizer on the body, we will first study the steady state behaviour under different constant conditions, then the periods which may exist.

12.3 – *Synchronizers*. The external rhythms may determine the duration, shape and level of the exogenous response but, most importantly, its timing. In the latter capacity they are also called Zeitgebers (time givers), time clues, time cues, entraining agents, or timing factors. Their properties have most stringently been exposed by ASCHOFF[3-4, 6, 9, 12-17] who coined the term "Zeitgeber".

12.4 – We do not really know how many of all the external influences we respond to. In some instances, the connection is obvious. If we carry appropriate sensory organs we may record light (intensity, colour and polarization), sound and vibration, smell and taste (chemoreception), temperature, pressure-tension, position and change in velocity, activity in general. Usually, the sensory organs are more sensitive to changes (e.g. rhythms) than to steady stimuli. There are species differences. Smell and taste are of less importance to us, though periodic stimuli of this kind should be acceptable synchronizers under special circumstances. On the other hand, chemoreception is of prime importance to many animals, such as amoebae and insects.

12.5 – Though our knowledge about the synchronizers is deficient, we may tentatively distinguish between three kinds: dominant synchronizers, such as light, temperature or the surrounding regimen; weak synchronizers which may presumably take over if the dominant ones disappear, *e.g.* biometeorological influences; subtle synchronizers of more uncertain character, mainly theoretical cosmobiological cues.

12.6 – It probably matters less through which sensory channel the information is carried. It is the temporal pattern which is important. There are also certain influences which act upon the organism though we do not know exactly how the body receives them. Earlier physiologists used to require the presence of a clearly demonstrable sense organ to accept external influence. However, reactivity is a basic characteristic of all living things, and any part of the organism or a cell could act as a receptor towards more direct influences. The weather sensitivity of arthritic people is almost legendary. In central Europe some persons may be almost totally incapacitated by sudden changes in atmospheric pressure, the Föhn. Seashore animals have adapted themselves to the movements of the tide, caused by lunar gravitational influences. There are reports which indicate that animals may be sensitive to gravitational, magnetic and electrostatic fields or other cosmic events, such as sunspots. The electrostatic forces in the air also act upon the aggregation state of the fine particles in the natural aerosol and may affect the respiratory passages in this way.

Visible light is not the only radiation around us. Animals and plants may be sensitive to infrared or ultraviolet light. It is also being discussed whether we may not be sensitive to the radio-waves. Even the cosmic radiation may be a factor of importance since the intensity of its impact upon the earth's surface is regulated by the atmospheric pressure.

12.7 – *Identification of Synchronizers.* The problem is how to ascertain whether periodicities in all these surrounding factors affect us or not. There are two modes of approach, experimental and statistical. In the experimental approach we either isolate the subject completely from one or several of the factors, or present varied artificial stimuli of the same modality.

In the statistical approach we record as many factors as possible, simultaneously and under natural or experimental conditions, both from the organism and the external world. One then looks for a parallel behaviour in the curves, *e.g.* with various kinds of frequency analysis. It involves a considerable amount of computational work. Unfortunately, the evaluation of the results is fraught with difficulties. It does not suffice to find two periodicities which run parallel. This may easily occur at random (nonsense correlation). Actually, there is normally a variable time lag between the synchronizer and the biological function. These do not even really have to have equal frequencies. Cycles may even arise from random material during the statistical treatment. These problems will be more extensively discussed in Part III.

12.8 – The synchronizer may determine the duration, shape, level and timing of the biological process. Of these, its action on the frequency and timing (entrainment) has been chiefly investigated, whereas little attention has been awarded the actual shape of the curves. – When timing the activities of several animals the synchronizer will simultaneously have the effect of synchronizing the action of the various animals *inter se*.

Factors of importance in this connection are: the strength of the synchronizer, the strength of the endogenous rhythm, the type and degree of coupling between them, the type and characteristics of the synchronizer as well as of the factor measured.

12.9 – The purpose of a synchronizer is to inform the organism about the period and phase of universal time. If the target reacts or not with entrainment is another problem. The question of whether circadian rhythms are endogenous or exogenous depends upon whether weak synchronizers are still able to inform the organism about universal time or not, whether the organism cares to react to this or not, and whether such an entrainment has to be complete or may be incomplete, *e.g.* taking the shape of circadicity.

12.10 – *Interaction between Synchronizers*. The synchronizers may differ with regard to the strength of biological action, with some of them dominating. The strongest are light and temperature, which act upon well-defined sensory transducers and which are almost always present in nature. The weaker synchronizers have also been called residual periodic variables (PITTENDRIGH[3, 100]), since circadicity appears as soon as light and temperature are kept constant. There may perhaps be a continuous spectrum of action from strong, full entrainment to weak, partial entrainment.

12.11 – Interaction between synchronizers could occur either before or after they reach the organism. For instance, there is a cosmic influence upon our weather. Also, the atmospheric pressure may regulate the incidence of cosmic rays upon the terrestrial surface. The possibility of a 'subtle carrier' signal being modulated by the other factors exists.

One may also envisage a competition between the synchronizers in their biological action, or between different centers activated by different agents, but we know little about it. A competition between light and temperature stimuli occurs. The quality of the target organism should also be important, giving rise to differences between species and individuals. Old people are generally more difficult to entrain than the young. Several competing weak synchronizers, which differ in phase, might also conceivably give circadian periods.

12.12 – *Synchronizer Parameters*. The external agent may be constant, regular, or irregular; continuous (*e.g.* sinusoidal) or discontinuous (*e.g.* impulses or switch-like changes between all or nothing, or between signals of different intensity, *cf.* 4.13-15). Impulses may differ in duration, they may be single or repeated (regular or random). If the input is continuous, it may take almost any shape. Combinations between various types are possible, *cf.* Fig. 1.30a.

12.13 – The synchronizers may be natural or experimental. The latter are often idealized versions of the former. The slow normal transitions in light at dawn or dusk may be represented by an instantaneous switch-over. 'Constant conditions' only exist in the laboratory with a few exceptions (*e.g.* the external day or night at the poles). On the other hand, this may perhaps not be a physiological condition if the organism is built for a continuous adjustment to rhythmic changes. In that case one might expect reactions to constancy which are not normal. It has been suggested that instead of constancy one might apply 'stimuli at random' in time (TAYLOR[1]). One may also induce a feedback to the environment by training the organisms to regulate the synchronizer themselves.

12.14 – Another question is which events in the synchronizer cycle act upon the organism. The diurnal light cycle may either be regarded as a series of switch-like transitions between states of light and darkness of different durations. Or it may be the slow continuous changes in light intensity which count. (Actually the solar light-cycle is more or less a combination between a sine wave and an impulse, *cf.* Fig. 1.30a). It also differs with the seasons and geographical location.

In general, one may perhaps distinguish between three main types of synchronizer information (ASCHOFF[17], WEVER[1]): (1) the timing impulse (mostly occurring in experimental work); (2) the duration at any one level of signal intensity, the proportional Zeitgeber. How the transition from one level to another occurs is of lesser importance whereas the durations of the steady states is so; (3) The rate of change in the signal strength, the differential Zeitgeber. – With regard to the idealized laboratory light cycle the active synchronizing event may be the lengths of the light and darkness periods respectively, or it may simply be the moments when the change-over occurs, *viz.* dawn and dusk. An impulse really contains components of both the differential and proportional Zeitgebers. Which type of information is utilized by the organism is uncertain. ASCHOFF suggests that the proportional Zeitgeber affects the angular velocity of the output function whereas the differential one has a phase-shifting effect.

12.15 – It is also possible that the reactions differ with regard to the direction of the synchronizer movement. The organism may only be able to perceive increases or decreases. Or it may not be able to distinguish between them, only registering the rate of change (the unidirectionality of CLYNES). Or it may react more to one than to the other (asymmetry, STARK[4]).

12.16 – *Mode of Action.* How the synchronizer information is channelled in the body and how the synchronization is achieved is uncertain. The process usually requires 3-10 days (ASCHOFF[12]) and displays typical transients (*cf.* 4.29). As to the mechanism itself, we know virtually nothing, though many physical models may be constructed. Attempts to draw inferences from the transients have not yielded much information. There may occur beats, forced oscillations, influences upon the setting of the biological servomechanisms, damped oscillations, relative coordination, or multiple action upon one endogenous oscillator or upon several coupled oscillators. This will be discussed later.

12.17 – It is important to distinguish clearly between the three main modes of synchronizer action:

(1) *Physiological response*. Same as for the reaction to the stimulus in general physiology. Since the sensitivity of the organism varies rhythmically, the response will, however, do so, too.

(2) *Phase synchronization*. In this case, the variability in response under (1) is timed. It is actually timed by the very same stimulus, since this has also a phasing influence. Actually, the sensitivity of the organism to phase shifting varies rhythmically, too, which enhances the synchronizing action (*cf.* 5.20, DeCoursey[2], Wilkins).

(3) *Frequency synchronization*. Here, both phase and frequency are entrained by the rhythmic stimulus.

Some confusion has arisen from a failure to distinguish the first type of action from the two others. That the physiological response varies during the day does not mean that the rhythms are thrown apart or that synchronization is made difficult. Bünning's endodiurnal change in sensitivity to light (5.16) functions even though it is well synchronized by the 24-h light changes. The ease of synchronization of biological rhythms is one of the really well-established facts we have about them.

One may also remember that the circadian freerunning can be regarded as a continuous spontaneous phase shift (advancing or delayed) in search of synchronization with external events (*cf.* Brown's autophasing theory, 1.23), and that the variability in circadian frequency with the light intensity may enhance this (DeCoursey[1-2], Pittendrigh[6]).

12.18 – After this general presentation of the synchronizers, we shall discuss them one by one, starting with the photoperiodism. A more penetrating discussion of the mechanism of synchronization will be given in Parts III and IV.

CHAPTER 13

Photoperiodism

13.1 – After a brief exposé of the general properties of synchronizers, we are now going to study the most prominent of them, the light. Its action as such, the 'photoperiodism', differs completely from that of 'vision', up to the point of partly employing other wave lengths and other pathways in the organism. The vision aims at 'orientation in space', the photoperiodism at 'orientation in time'. This is achieved through a synchronization of body functions with the daily changes in illumination and through the estimation of the length of the light period as a measure of the time of the year. These things were already discussed in sections 1.16, 5.14-24. Another mode of action of light is the photochemical one (photosynthesis) as found in the plants or in our skin, or the diverse physical actions of strong radiation. Light also has a growth-directing effect on plants. *Cf.* Fig. 13.1a.

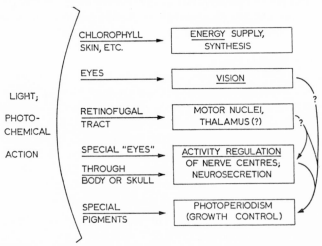

Fig. 13.1a. Various biological effects of light.

In plants, the photoperiodic activity has to be regulated so as to promote optimal photosynthesis in a variable environment. The processes are complicated and not yet fully elucidated. Good introductions are Conf. 1957f, 1960b, 1960c, BALDWIN[1], CURRY[100-101], RABINOWITCH, SANDOZ.

13.2 – *Radiation*. The spectrum of electromagnetic and corpuscular radiation is large and the living organisms are sensitive to most of it, the biological effect increasing with frequency and intensity of the disturbance. Special receptors, however, only exist in a short section of the electromagnetic system, in the region of the visible light. The basis is a photochemical reaction in certain pigments such as the plant chlorophyll and the rhodopsine of the eye or the synthesis of vitamin D, unsaturated fatty acids and melanin in the skin. Radiation may also heat the body, from the pleasant warmth of the infrared light to burns and wholesale destruction from roentgen, radium and atomic radiation. The penetrating capacity of the X-rays has been well utilized. Harder radiation may cause mutations or form destructive 'free radicals' in the tissues. A man may be killed if standing in the focus of a strong radar transmitter, not to mention the effects of the masers and lasers.

13.3 – Most radiations reach us from space, especially from the sun. The cosmic radiation may be generated by the stars and accelerated in their rotating magnetic fields. Some radioactive elements in the earth crust are also present. We are usually more or less exposed to all radiation, though the energy absorbing ionization layers of the atmosphere partly shield us. This means, however, that the atmosphere is both influenced by and acts upon the radiation. The filtration of the cosmic rays thus depends on the atmospheric pressure. It would take a shield of lead 5 m thick to exclude them completely. One of the famous experiments in biological rhythm research is that of KLEITMAN, who performed his measurements in the Mammoth Cave of Kentucky in order to shut out the cosmic radiation.

The radiation may also affect the organism indirectly through its influences upon the electric potential and ionization of the atmosphere.

13.4 – *Variations in External Illumination*. Most organisms are particularly dependent upon light for their existence. The conditions of illumination vary, however, considerably with the time of day and year as well as latitude, both with regard to light intensity, duration, and spectral composition (EBBESEN). One discontinuous feature is the daily break caused by the night, which turns the solar light changes into a mixture of sinusoidal and impulse-type variations (*cf.* Fig. 1.30a). On the other hand, there is also the lunar light. The properties of the illumination change under water, influenced by absorption and by the angle of incidence of the light. Atmospheric conditions are also active. Some of the natural fluctuations in the light conditions are demonstrated in ASHBEL, FOLK[102] (for various aspects of the optic influence, *cf.* BODEN[100], DETWILER, GRIFFIN[2], JENS, JANKOWIAK, LINKE[1], ONO[100], TAGEEVA[100], WATERMAN, WITHROW).

13.5 – *Action Spectra*. Any action of light is conditioned by the wave length. Many of its actions are based on photosensitive pigments (*cf.* FRENCH, HENDRICKS[4], OSTER, WITHROW), *e.g.* the plant chlorophyll or the visual purple in the vertebrate eye. Each pigment has a specific absorption spectrum for multicoloured light and certain regions where maximal adsorption occurs. It may be more or less equal to the action spectrum where the effectiveness of various wavelengths in promoting a certain response in the organism is measured, *e.g.* photosynthesis, phototaxis, flowering, germination of seeds, pigmentation of fruits, or skin erythema.

The action spectrum may be recorded in two ways. Either the quantitative biological response to a certain light intensity in all different colours is measured, or else the light intensity required to give the same quantitative response at different wave lengths. For this purpose spectrographs are used, usually with gratings, which split the white light into the colours of the rainbow. Very impressive are EHRET's[1-7] investigations into the action spectrum of mating in *Paramecium* with the aid of an enormous spectrograph. – UV-light has a strong action upon the phase-setting mechanism, and also upon the nucleic acid metabolism, plasma permeability and nerve conduction (EHRET[5], MURALT[100], VIRGIN[4]). One may wonder whether there is a connection. Perhaps it should also be stressed that incandescent and fluorescent lamps differ with respect to their contents of far-red radiation, the latter lacking it.

Fish show a peculiar reaction to light (DAVIS[800]). If submitted to a few minutes of strong light they become restless and sink to the bottom of the aquarium.

13.6 – The *light-active wave lengths* are mainly blue, red and infrared for plants and the whole visible spectrum for vertebrates. Many insects have their best vision in the ultraviolet. Green light is specially ineffective in plants.

For some literature on action spectra, see ALLEN[100], BRACKETT[100], BÜNNING[100], BUTENKO[100], CURRY[100-101], DARTNALL[100], DUYSENS, FISHER[600], HALLDAL, HASTINGS[105], MAGNUS[1], MARSHALL[300], MEIJER[1], SWEENEY[100], VIRGIN[2-3, 5, 7, 100], VOROBJEVA, VOSKRENSKAYA.

13.7 – *Photosynthesis*. The utilization of solar energy by the plant requires: (1) the reduction of inactive protochlorophyll to active chlorophyll pigments by light (blue, 445 mμ and red, 640 mμ); (2) photosynthesis by trapping light energy in chlorophylls and carotenoids (blue, 435 mμ and red, 675 mμ). Plants grown in darkness contain only protochlorophyll which has to be converted by light before full photosynthetic action is gained (VIRGIN[7-8]). The photosynthesis (*cf.* BRITTIN[100], SANDOZ) involves the fixation of CO_2 and H_2O by the chloroplasts, the reduction of CO_2 to $nC(H_2O)$, carbohydrates, and the formation of O_2. This action proceeds in light. However, the further processing of the carbohydrates by the plant requires more energy, obtained by the utilization of some of the oxygen in the ordinary KREBS cycle respiration. This reaction may proceed in the dark, and the two processes may alternate, resulting in circadian changes of the CO_2 handled by the plant, *cf.* WILKINS. Chlorophyll is the general photosynthetic pigment though there exist some others in very primitive plants.

13.8 – *Photoperiodism in Plants. The Red Far-red Pigment System*. The photoperiodism in plants uses other wave lengths and pigments than the photosynthesis. Chlorophyll-lacking saprophytic algae or mushrooms have yellow pigments stimulated by near-UV light (370 mμ) or blue light (445 mμ and 475 mμ) to regulate their phototropism. Many factors are governed in this way, even the protoplasmic viscosity (VIRGIN[1-5, 9, 100]).

13.9 – In *higher plants* we have the *red far-red* (R-FR) reaction involving a phytochrome pigment (HENDRICKS[4], MEIJER[100]). This exists in two forms which we may call the R- and FR-forms. Red light (660 mμ) changes the R-form into the FR-form. Far-red light (710 and 730 mμ) or darkness promotes the opposite reaction (13.9a):

$$13.9a \qquad\qquad \text{Pigm.R} \underset{\substack{\text{far-red light} \\ \text{or darkness}}}{\overset{\text{red light}}{\rightleftharpoons}} \text{Pigm.FR}$$

Red and far-red light thus each counteracts the biological action of the other. (The pigments are also slightly blue-sensitive.) The reactions promoted vary in a complex manner. Red light seems to stimulate plant growth in general (vegetative growth) and flowering (reproduction) in 'long-day plants'. Far-red light promotes flowering in 'short-day plants' and stem elongation. The flowering process also differs from the vegetative growth in being an inductive, cumulative process. For each day of suitable light regimen a certain amount of hormone, florigen, seems to be produced and stored, until a sufficient amount for the initiation of flowering is formed. The plant is thus able to *remember* earlier favourable days even if other conditions have intervened (*cf.* 5.14,17-18).

13.10 – After some exposure to white (or red) light most pigment is in the FR-form, which then promotes certain reactions during the ensuing darkness with a gradual return to the R-form pigment. If the white light period is ended by a stretch of far-red illumination, however, the previous light-effect is nullified and the subsequent dark-reactions disturbed. If we want special red or far-red light effects from a plant it has to have been exposed to the opposite light previous to that, else the pigment is in the wrong shape for sensitization. (Darkness may here substitute for far-red light.) Another result of the peculiar R-FR antagonism is that the promotive effect on growth is larger for red and blue light combined than for white light (WENT[3]), since the latter contains antagonistic far-red light and inactive green light. It is for the same reason that fluorescent light is more suitable than the far-red-containing incandescent light. Strong continued white light may even inhibit the chlorophyll synthesis and plant development (ARTHUR[100], HILLMAN[1]). It may also be mentioned that some early biological rhythm research botanists used red light as a substitute for darkness (as in the photographic laboratory) since the R-FR-system was not known. Many of these investigations were therefore erroneously interpreted.

13.11 – The R-FR system might conceivably function as a light-sensitive feedback oscillation system coupled to other oscillatory, time-measuring, metabolic, hormone, growth-inducing or reproduction-inducing systems in the plant. It probably also controls the conversion of protochlorophyll to chlorophyll. A plant grown in the dark, for instance, contains only R-pigment (and protochlorophyll), and exhibits no overt endogenous rhythms. However, even an extremely short exposure to light may induce a circadian rhythm (*cf.* 7.7). Perhaps it acts by setting the F-FR system in oscillation. Obviously, it cannot activate the photosynthesis, as such. In continued darkness or light, however, the oscillations are more or less rapidly damped. Perhaps this is due to the R-FR system being driven towards one of its extremes, *viz.* only R- or only FR-pigment. Such a state would, however, probably not be in equilibrium, and the system would be set in heavy motion as soon as a change in the condition occurs. Probably the R-FR system is intimately geared to the circadian rhythm of photosensitivity in plants (5.16-18, 7.3-19). The main difference between long- and short-day plants should then be the inverse reaction to R-FR stimulation.

HENDRICKS[1] gives a beautiful example of the importance of the photoperiodic control for the development of an organism. Two red maple trees were grown at the same total amount of radiation during 24 h. One, held on long-day conditions, was 10 feet high after 10 months. The other, under short-day conditions, reached only 6 in. after the same time. One may imagine the importance of such phenomena in agriculture and horticulture, but also in domestic animals, where it may be used for the control of the egg-production in hens or milk production in the dairy.

13.12 – *Photoperiodism in Invertebrates.* In invertebrates light may act on the organism through several pathways *e.g.* through their *eyes* or *directly through a translucent body* upon certain cell pigments (WILDE). The intermediate link between the photoreceptors and the body functions seems to be the release of 'neurosecretions' into the blood. Most insects have two types of eyes, (1) the *ommatidia,* which give space and colour perception and form the compound eyes; (2) the *ocelli,* on top of the head, which are only light-sensitive in general and whose function is not well understood.

In this connection HARKER's[6, 8-9] experiments on cockroaches are interesting. She found one neurosecretion in the suboesophageal ganglion which was controlled by the ocelli. Another neurosecretion in the other parts of the brain is controlled by the ommatidia, and also reaches the suboesophageal gland along a special nerve strand, controlling it in turn. Removal of the suboesophageal gland and cutting of the connecting nerve strand obliterated the circadian rhythm. However, suboesophageal ganglia transplanted to decapitated animals could initiate a circadian rhythm in these, in phase with that of the original donor animal.

This dual light control is reminiscent of the red far-red pigment system in plants and the neurosecretion part of the endocrine feedback in vertebrates. There are, however, other experiments with surgical removal of parts of the brain which partly conflict with the above (EIDMANN, FINGERMAN[1, 100-101]).

13.13 – The ommatidia can also record the *polarization plane* of the light, which is an aid in insect navigation (AUTRUM[100], v. FRISCH[3], JANDER[100], VOWLES, WATERMAN, WELLINGTON). Spore growth may also be controlled by polarized light (BÜNNING[108], ETZOLD, JAFFE[200, 300]).

13.14 – The *chromatophore* system in animals is also regulated by neurosecretion (invertebrate eye-stalks or the vertebrate hypophysis), controlled by optic stimuli through the eyes. The pigment may afford means for mimicry, thermoregulation, protection against strong light or a colourful display for attracting the female. One of the best-studied circadian rhythms is that of the colour changes in fiddler

crabs, which also show a pronounced temperature independence (Brown[3-4, 6-7,
9, 107], Fingerman[2, 4-5, 103], Stephens[3, 5]).

13.15 – *Photoperiodism in Vertebrates*. In vertebrates there is, generally, only one
photoreceptor, the *eye*, though a certain *dermal photosensitivity* may be retained,
e.g. the control of melanin pigmentation, vitamin D synthesis and the production
of unsaturated fatty acids by the ultra-violet light. Aberrations in the melanin
synthesis may give rise to remarkable cases of lethal skin photosensitivity.

From the eye there are, however, several communication channels to the rest
of the organism: (1) to the occipital visual centres of the *cortex* with their control
of body regulation and their connections with other cortical areas; (2) a more
direct connection with the motor nuclei in the *brain stem*; (3) probably also direct
links with the hypothalamus and its neuroendocrine control, the retino-hypothalamic connection (the heliotropic system, Hollwich, Scharrer).

13.16 – A *retino-hypothalamic tract* has not yet been isolated anatomically. There is,
however, indirect evidence for such diencephalic connections. They may also be
expected to exist from embryological reasons, since the retina has been developed
from this part of the brain. The subject was discussed at a conference for the first
time in 1963 (Conf. 1963b). Many possible pathways were described (Bilek[100],
Fiske[100], Gergen[100], Marg). Even the limbic system or the reticular formation
may be involved. The spectral composition of the active light differs from that
stimulating vision (Benoit[6]).

Ordinary light also penetrates directly through the skull in higher animals such
as ducks, rabbits, rats, sheep and dogs (Benoit[5], Brunt[200]). Especially the orbital
wall and the temporal region are thin. The hypothalamus seems to be directly
light sensitive (Benoit[6]). The physiological role of this light penetration remains
to be evaluated. – It has even been suggested that there might be an afferent
nervous inflow from dermal photoreceptors, directing the autonomous functions.

The retino-hypothalamic system would be the information channel of the photoperiodism in vertebrates, controlling, *e.g.* the metabolism, general activity and
sexual cycles through the vegetative nervous system and the neuro-endocrine
system (particularly the hypophyseal production of melanophore and gonadotropic hormones). *Cf.* also Bissonette[1-10, 100-101], Braden, Hague, Halberg[8, 116],
Jores[6, 9, 11], Jöchle[1-6], Lindsley[100], Marshall[2-6, 101-103, 200-202, 300], Radnot[1-4,
100-102, 104-106], Remler.

13.17 – The *retino-hypothalamic connection* constitutes an optical control of the
neurosecretion reminiscent of the mechanism in insects. In vertebrates, the
melanophore hormone regulation of the cutaneous colour is mediated in this way.
We may also recall the importance of the hypothalamus for the rhythmic regulation in the body (8.8-16). Jores has devoted many studies to the melanophore
hormone (intermedine) function in higher vertebrates. Other factors which are
controlled by light through the neuro-endocrine system are the water balance,
blood formation, eosinophil leucocyte rhythm (Radnot[100, 103]), serum cholin-
esterase, blood sugar, secondary sexual characteristics (Radnot[101]), thyroid function (Radnot[102]), suprarenal function (Radnot[105]) and sexual cycle. In blind

persons or experimentally blinded animals, these functions may be disturbed (HALBERG[8], HOLLWICH[2], JORES[6]). Animals born blind can develop circadian rhythmicity, though other synchronizers may, of course, substitute for the optical one (HALBERG[116], REMLER).

An important aspect of the optico-endocrine control are the sexual cycles (cf. 7.21-22, also Part IV). The annual cycles of gonadal development and migration in birds, fish and reptiles may be regulated in this way (e.g. BISSONETTE[1-10], [100-101], MARSHALL[2-6], [101-103], [200-202], [300]) as well as the sexual cycles in mammals (BRADEN, JÖCHLE[1-5]). The optico-hypophyseal connection may perhaps also explain the steadily increasing rate of growth and sexual maturity in our younger generations as the result of an increased overall illumination level.

Highly interesting is the parietal eye in lizards (cf. BARTHOLOMEW[3]) which may be a photoperiodic analogue of the insect ocelli.

13.18 – Effect of Light Intensity under Constant Conditions. Under constant conditions there can be no synchronizing action. However, some characteristics of the freerunning 'circadian rhythm' are nevertheless affected, the 'natural frequency' and the general 'energy level'. These seem to increase exponentially with the light intensity in light-active organisms (day-active animals and long-day plants) and fall in dark-active organisms (night-active animals and short-day plants). As regards the differences between light and darkness (= zero light) this may be formulated: period-in-constant-light > period-in-constant-darkness for nocturnal animals, and period-in-constant-light < period-in-constant-darkness for diurnal animals. This has been called ASCHOFF's Rule (PITTENDRIGH[6]). In general, furthermore, the period-in-constant-light is longer than 24 h for dark-active animals and shorter than 24 h in light-active animals, though this is no exact rule.

Beautiful studies on the effect of light on the circadian rhythm have been performed by ASCHOFF[2-7], [11-18], [101-106], [108], cf. DeCOURSEY, DIGBY[1], JEREBZOFF[4], JOHNSON[200], PITTENDRIGH[5-6].

13.19 – It may be recalled (7.7) that individuals reared under constant conditions often do not exhibit any circadian rhythm. A single disturbance may set it in motion. The most efficient signal is a light-shock which may be extremely short. A dark-shock may also be used, but this requires time periods of several hours. In continuous darkness or light, the rhythmicity often damps out, usually faster in light. In plants, the most rapid damping occurs with constant far-red light (cf. 13.10-11). Sometimes sustained oscillations occur, specially in animals.

13.20 – In nature, constant light conditions are uncommon, though continuous light of remarkable stability occurs in the arctic regions (cf. LOBBAN[2]). Continuous darkness can be said to occur in blindness (cf. 13.17). In blinded mice (dark-active) the frequency rises, but slowly returns to the original when other synchronizers take over. In green plants, the circadian freerunning period increases with red light (650 mμ). A 0.4 lux intensity is too weak to elicit any light effects in animals, the limit lies around 4 lux. In plants, the upper limit of light intensity conforming to the ASCHOFF Rule lies around 6000 lux, under optimal conditions of temperature, humidity and CO_2 concentration. Higher light intensities may, instead, inhibit the plant activity (*cf.* 13.10).

13.21 – One may speculate upon the possible biological meaning of ASCHOFF's Rule. As compared to the synchronized 24-h cycle the freerunning rhythm may be regarded either as exhibiting a continuous advance in phase (period > 24 h) or delay (period < 24 h); DECOURSEY[2], PITTENDRIGH[6]. The external rhythms behave similarly. Though their average period is 24 h the phasing of the events within the cycle changes continuously. Thus the freerunning would make it possible for the biological rhythm to 'hunt' after the external rhythm for synchronization (*cf.* BROWN's autophasing theory, 1.23, 24.33). It is obvious that perfect synchronization will be difficult to achieve in nature, as contrasted to the precise conditions in laboratory synchronization.

13.22 – *Definitions.* Light is usually the strongest synchronizer. As an entraining agent it occupies such a large space in biological rhythm research that special notations are used (*cf.* ASCHOFF[16], PITTENDRIGH[6]):

13.22a

L	=	light
D	=	darkness
LD	=	a sequence of light and darkness signals
LL	=	continuous light (Dauerlicht)
DD	=	continuous darkness (Dauerdunkel)
τ	=	circadian period
τLL	=	circadian period in continuous light
τDD	=	circadian period in continuous darkness
a	=	duration of animal activity
ϱ	=	duration of animal rest
τ	=	$a + \varrho$

LD = 6 : 12 would mean a 18-h 'day' with 6 h of light followed by 12 h of darkness. ASCHOFF's Rule for nocturnal animals (*cf.* 13.18) would read τLL > τDD.

13.23 – By use of different LD-schemes, numerous experiments on synchronization and photoperiodism have been performed. The discussion of this will be delayed until Part IV. Now, however, will be given a short list of authors in the field of photoperiodicity and some related subjects, particularly with reference to the organism studied. The literature is enormous and the present list constitutes only an introduction. Further references on this or related subjects are found in connection with the discussions on time sense (Chapter 5), circadian rhythms (Chapter 7), action spectra (13.6) and animal navigation (Chapter 18), as well as 24-h, lunar and seasonal rhythms (Part IV).

13.24 – Light effects in unicellular organisms have been studied by *e.g.* BRACHER, BRUCE[1, 102], BÜHNEMAN[2, 5], EHRET[1-6, 101], HASTINGS[1, 100, 102, 104-106], KALLIO, LADERMAN[100], LORENZEN, PIRSON[1, 100], SWEENEY[1, 100-101], and in mushrooms by JEREBZOFF[1, 4-6], SAGROMSKY.

13.25 – Light effects in botany have been studied on bean and pea plants (BLANEY[100], BÜNNING[18-19], HAMNER[3], HIGHKIN[1], HILLMAN[2], KLEIN, NANDA[100]), on tomato plants (BONDE, HIGHKIN[100], HILLMAN[1]), especially on *Hyoscyamus* (HAMNER[3], LANG[1, 100], WASSINK[100]), on *Phaseolus* (BÜNNING[1-3, 105], EHRENBERG, FLÜGEL, LOCKHART, LÖRCHER, PFEFFER, STERN[100], STOPPEL[2-3, 5, 12]), on *Kalanchoë* (BÜNSOW, GREGORY[300], HARDER[100], SPEAR[1, 100]) and on *Xanthium* (BÜNNING[18], GREULACH[100], HAMNER[3], NITSCH[100]). *Cf.* ARNOLD[1], ARTHUR[100], BALL[300], BIALE, BOGORAD[100], BONNER, BORTHWICK, BROUWER, BROWN[108], BÜNNING[4-6, 8-15, 17, 20-21, 23-26, 28-29, 32, 34, 101, 104], CATHEY, CHOUARD[1, 100], CLAUSS[1-101], DARWIN[300], DOORENBOS[100], DOWNS, ENGEL[100], FINN, GALSTON, HABER[100], HAMNER[1-3, 100], HEIMANN, HEINTZ, HENDRICKS, INGOLD[100], JACOBS[100], KELLERMAN, KLEINHOONTE, KRIBBEN, LAIBACH, LEOPOLD, LIVERMAN, LONA, MEIJER[1, 100], MOHR, SALISBURY, SCHÖN, SCHWABE, STÅLFELT[4-6], STOPPEL[1, 9, 100-101], TOOLE, UEBELMESSER, VIRGIN[2-3, 5, 7, 100], WAREING[2-3], WELLENSIEK, WENT, WILKINS, WITHROW, WITTWER[100], WOLF[200].

13.26 – Light effects on invertebrates have been studied especially in snails (SANDEEN[100], STEPHENS[1, 100]), crabs (BROWN[101, 107, 112, 115], DEHNEL, FINGERMAN[1, 4, 100, 102-103], WEBB[1, 100]), crickets and locusts (CLOUDSLEY-THOMPSON[10-13], EIDMANN, FINGERMAN[101]), cockroaches (BÜNNING[33], CLOUDSLEY-THOMPSON[4, 11, 15], HARKER[3-9], ROBERTS[2-3]), aphids (HAINE[2], LEES[5, 7], MARCOVITCH) and flies, *e.g.* the fruit fly, (ALLARD, BATEMAN, BRUCE[1], DIGBY, PARIS[100], PITTENDRIGH[2-3, 5-6, 101], REMMERT, ROBERTS[1]). *Cf.* also BROWN[2], BÜNNING[100], CLOUDSLEY-THOMPSON[11], GIESE, KLEITMAN[13], LEES[1, 3-4, 6], WATERMAN, WAY[100]. Many kinds of spiders have been used for animal orientation studies. Bees and termites figure in many experiments on time sense.

13.27 – Light effects have been demonstrated in fishes (BULLOUGH[1-2], HARRINGTON), reptiles (BARTHOLOMEW[3]), and birds (ASCHOFF[105], BISSONETTE[1, 3-4, 6-8, 10], ENGELS, FARNER[1-2, 100], LOFTS[100], MARSHALL[3-6, 100-103], NALBANDOV, SCHILDMACHER[1-4], WAREING[3], WOLFSON[1, 3-4, 8-10, 100]), especially sparrows (BARTHOLOMEW[2], FARNER[3, 101-102], RILEY[1, 100], RINGOEN, WOLFSON[6-7]) and poultry, mostly hens and chicks, (ASCHOFF[103], BASTIAN[100], CLEGG[100], ELFVIN[100], FRAPS[1-3, 100], HAYS, KABLE[100], KIRKPATRICK[1, 100], MORENG[100], SCHILDMACHER[100], SOLLBERGER[3], STAFFE, WILSON[500, 502-503]). Numerous experiments on animal navigation have also been performed on fishes and birds (*e.g.* starlings and pigeons).

13.28 – Light effects in mammals have also been studied (BASSETT[100], BISSONETTE[2, 5, 100-101], HALBERG[3], JÖCHLE[2-3]), not least in squirrels (DECOURSEY, WELLS[200]), ferrets (BISSONETTE[3], DONNOWAN[100], HAMMOND, HART[2], HILL[300-301], MARSHALL[300], THOMPSON[1, 100]), hamsters (BRUCE[1], PITTENDRIGH[101]), mice and rats (ASCHOFF[2-3, 7, 104, 106], BRADEN, BROWMAN[1, 3], BROWN[110], BRUCE[1], FOLK[1, 3],

HALBERG[102-103, 107, 116, 133, 135-136], JÖCHLE[5], JOHNSON[200], PUNTRIANO[100], RAWSON[3], STINSON, TRIBUKAIT), cattle (HART[1], JÖCHLE[4]) and *Homo* (ASCHOFF[108], HALBERG[116], KLEITMAN[6, 100, 104], LEWIS[100-104], LOBBAN, RADNOT[1-3, 100-102, 104-105]).

To these lists of photoperiodic and related phenomena, we may add ASCHOFF[4-6, 9, 11-17, 101], BRACKETT[100], BROWN[3-4, 6-7, 9, 11-12, 100, 105-106, 109, 113-114], BULLOUGH[5, 7], HALBERG[7-8, 10-11, 134], LEPESCHKIN, LOEB, MAYERSON[100], MARSHALL[200-202], MATTHEWS[200], TOLLING[100], TONGIORGI, VERHEIJEN, VERHOEVEN[100], WASSINK[100]; also AMEN, BARKER[300], MACLEOD[100].

13.29 – We have now studied the most important of the synchronizers, light. Next come the other dominant synchronizers, especially temperature.

CHAPTER 14

Thermoperiodism and Surrounding Regimen

14.1 – In the previous chapters some general synchronizer characteristics as well as photoperiodism have been discussed. Light is one of the dominant synchronizers (1.19, 12.5). Another is temperature, especially in lower animals. If these both fail, the alimentary regimen or the general surrounding activity can take over, particularly in man.

14.2 – *General Effects of External Temperature*. The external temperature is subjected to marked 24-h and seasonal changes (FLACH). It ranges from desert heat to arctic cold. The general effect is for metabolism, diffusion, growth and average activity level to increase exponentially with the temperature. At a certain temperature optimal effects are achieved. Small animals, with a large relative body surface, are sensitive to hot climates owing to the risk of evaporation (*cf*. 9.13 and CLOUDSLEY-THOMPSON[1, 8, 11, 18-20, 23, 26-28]). Poikilothermic animals, which adopt the surrounding temperature, become lethargic when their metabolism slows down in the winter cold, initiating the state of obligatory hibernation. Some homeothermic animals may achieve the same effect actively during voluntary hibernation (hedgehogs, squirrels, bears; FOLK[2, 4, 6, 100-102], SUOMALAINEN[1-2, 100]). In both cases a pronounced dependency on the environment (BARTHOLOMEW[3]) occurs. Also, a seasonal rhythm (*cf*. Part IV) will be impressed upon the organism. Forced hypothermia (*cf*. JUVENELLE[100]) in higher animals is dangerous, leading to shivering, heart fibrillation and death; unless the temperature regulation is paralyzed, artificial circulation and breathing applied, and special resuscitation methods used. The evolution of the temperature regulation is complicated, with locomotion for reaching optimal temperature habitats, variations in activity and metabolic rate, insulation, surface heat exchange, and nervous thermoregulation with homeothermy (JOHANSEN).

14.3 – *Constant Temperature*. The remarkable temperature independence of the circadian rhythm (7.11-17), typical for endogenous rhythms with external correlates, has already been discussed. The conditions in these experiments were constant external temperatures, where the actual temperature differed from experiment to experiment. The phenomenon is important for poikilothermic animals. Otherwise, they would be unable to adjust to external periods. The temperature independence is, however, not absolute and only holds within limits. At temperatures lower than 10°C, the circadian period breaks down. Either the rhythm disappears (is 'frozen' with a resulting phase-shift after re-warming) or turns into a high-frequency, low-amplitude run (7.17). BÜNNING believes this to indicate that a relaxation oscillator is at work. In general, a decrease in temperature has a similar effect as darkness. In both cases, there is a tendency towards decreasing general energy expenditure, often manifested as a decrease in amplitude or level of the cycle (*cf.* 13.18).

14.4 – *Thermoperiodism.* Another effect is obtained if the external temperature is varied on a circadian basis. A transient lowering of temperature with constant light has the same general effect as a dark-shock in initiating circadian rhythms. Several hours of low temperature are, however, required. That temperature variations may substitute for a light synchronizer has been shown by WENT[1-6] on tomato plants. These require a certain 24-h light rhythm for optimal growth. The same effect may be obtained with constant light and temperature variation in the corresponding phase. The effects are not additive.

It may be that temperature is as important a synchronizer as light in higher plants (WENT[6]), and maybe more important in poikilothermic vertebrates, or in the molting of insects (GUNN[500], JOHNSON[100-102]). The earth temperature severely affects soil organisms and imparts seasonal rhythms to them.

14.5 – *Interaction Between Temperature and Light.* The interaction between external light and temperature in controlling the biological rhythms is fairly complex and not well understood. It probably varies from organism to organism. WENT has shown that at different temperatures higher plants require different light regimens for optimal growth. With increasing temperature shorter periods are required. The Q_{10} is consistently about 1.2-1.3, thus within the limits for the temperature 'independence' phenomenon and for WENT's diffusion theory (7.15). Also, the day-length is important. Therefore, plants from hot climates often cannot synchronize with the conditions in regions with cold weather, and die.

14.6 – The competing action of light and temperature in achieving phase synchronization has been submitted to beautiful experiments (PITTENDRIGH[100-102]) on the eclosion rhythm in *Drosophila*. Typical transients occur (*cf.* 4.29) and attempts have been made to infer something about the underlying mechanisms from these. In the experiments, which shall be further discussed in Part IV, light dominated at certain conditions and temperature at others. One possible explanation is the two-oscillator theory which assumes that one of the oscillators is light-sensitive, the other temperature-sensitive and that they entrain each other mutually, the former dominating (Fig. 14.6a). For plants, WENT[3] also stresses the dual mechanism (Fig. 14.6b).

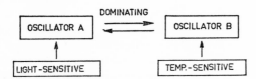

Fig. 14.6a. PITTENDRIGH's two-oscillator model.

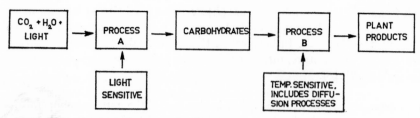

Fig. 14.6b. WENT's photothermoperiodic model.

For further references to thermoperiodism *cf.* 7.11-17, also BALL[302], FOLK[2, 6, 101], HIGHKIN[1], LEINWEBER, OLTMANNS, SCHWEMMLE[1-4, 100-102].

14.7 – *Alimentary and Metabolic Synchronizers.* If light and temperature are kept constant other factors may give entrainment. One of these is the feeding schedule.

When FORSGREN in 1927 realized that even metabolic products were subjected to a 24-h rhythmicity as represented by the liver function (bile and glycogen), a severe criticism ensued from the physiologists of that time, who were caught in a secure static model of life. It was held that the effect was purely alimentary. It was a remarkable feat of bi-valued logic of people, who gladly accepted the cardiac, respiratory, enterogastric and temperature rhythmicity but could not perceive a periodicity in the driving force of all physiological events, metabolism. Later, it was shown that the rhythm persisted under the conditions of starvation or regular, intermittent feeding. These conditions are frequently used in experiments since feeding at certain preferred times is a strong synchronizer. There are few things in our daily life, not least in hospitals or other institutions, which are as regular. Another possibility is 'self-selective feeding', which is then regarded as directed temporally by the other rhythms in the organism. Furthermore, children (if not spoiled) and animals automatically select the amounts and proportions of food-stuff which are best suited to their needs, a fact upon which many studies in nutrition are founded (COHN[100]). Selfdemand feeding has also been tried in infants.

14.8 – If feeding is used as a synchronizer, one must not forget that it may depend on other functions. Many animals do not eat in darkness. Feeding and drinking periods may differ. The composition of the food may be important, as in the study of diurnal rhythms in diabetes (*e.g.* MÖLLERSTRÖM[4-10, 12, 14, 17-22, 100-102]). The wild animals are dependent on the habits of the prey (*cf.* 10.3). Also, we do not know whether a continuous synchronization to the feeding rhythm occurs or whether this is normally repressed by the light stimulus. A caloric restriction may enforce the feeding influence so that it overrides the light synchronizer (HALBERG[10, 135]).

14.9 – It has already been mentioned that the circadian rhythm displays a chemical independence (*cf.* 7.18-19). This is not absolute. 'Respiratory poisons' tend to shorten the period somewhat. 'Surface-active agents' (alcohol, papaverine, narcotics) increase it. When the effect disappears the organism may return to the original state (BÜNNING[24-25, 29, 34-35]). Oxygen deprivation may act as a phase-setting agent (BALL[302]). Effects such as low-amplitude high-frequency runs, damped oscillations and phaseshifts also occur.

Very little is known about the administration of drugs as synchronizers, though it should be of interest in medicine.

14.10 – *General Surrounding Activity. The Herd Instinct.* Man is bound by many ties to his surroundings and his fellowmen, both physically and psychologically. Since man more or less creates his own surroundings the latter connection is important and synchronizes the activities of the individuals. In animals, the herd instinct is a parallel. It is interesting to see how caged chickens eat and move and sleep simultaneously.

The *synchronizing* effect of the herd instinct is valuable if assays are made on animals where only one determination on each individual can be had, *e.g.* liver glycogen (SOLLBERGER[6]). In other cases the animals should be isolated from each other.

A prominent component is noise, the hallmark of our pushbutton culture. Noise and vibration constantly reach us during the day and it requires considerable effort to isolate an experimental chamber from it. Another way out is to mask external disturbances by a constant sound. In the authors laboratory, the thermostatic device itself produced noise enough for this purpose (*cf.* ELFVIN[100]).

Our work is done at certain office hours, we attend movie, radio and television programs together at certain times, we feed together, we are plagued by the same noises. All these factors act as synchronizers. One exception are the sabbaths and holidays when our accustomed rhythm is disturbed. Some people are even notoriously ill at ease on holidays and vacations. One insulin laboratory found it difficult to perform standardization tests on animals on Sundays until the normal level of day noise was upheld by music-playing. The strict hospital regimen may play a part in therapy, as a synchronizer (*cf.* HALBERG[145]).

14.11 – Every now and then one will also be told that cows produce more milk with music. One may wonder whether the animal would prefer Bach or Spike Jones. (Even television has been tried.) Unless the cow is scared, the essential thing is perhaps a synchronizing action on the animal's 24-h rhythm.

One may, of course, speculate why so called 'primitive' music achieves such an immediate response in the unprejudiced listener through its rhythm and why the frequency lies in the region of muscle reflex action. Some kind of biological resonance might be a good guess. – The author once had the pleasure of talking to a lady who had found that her pulse was always beating synchronously with the dance music. She devoted considerable time to explaining the phenomenon. The observation is testable, of course, but it might contain tricky problems, such as the influence of the partner.

14.12 – We have now studied the dominant synchronizers. There remain many external factors which we know less about and which may or may not be synchronizers. The next chapter will discuss the weak synchronizers, especially the influence of atmospheric conditions.

CHAPTER 15

Weak Synchronizers

15.1 – The previous chapters have described the dominant synchronizers. There remain, however, meteorological and cosmic influences to discuss. The former certainly act upon our bodies but we know little about their mode of operation and their role as synchronizers. If they have such an action, it must be relatively weak. We will now discuss the atmospheric factors, which may be considered as possible 'weak synchronizers' (cf. 1.19-20, 12.6).

Changes in the composition of the atmosphere may affect our conditions of existence deeply. Such influences are studied in meteorology. Little is known about their mode of action on the organism, though the fact that interaction exists has long been used in climatotherapy (balneotherapy, cf. HILDEBRANDT[4-5, 8-9, 11-18, 20-21, 100, 102-104, 109], LAMPERT, SCHWARTZE). The generalized study of the atmospheric influences upon living organisms has developed into a new science, biometeorology. A good introduction to our subject are the publications of the INTERNATIONAL SOCIETY OF BIOMETEOROLOGY (Ref.J.e., Conf. 1957e, 1960d; cf. also BERG[1, 3], DÜLL[1, 100-105], FLACH, FOLK[102], HUNTINGTON[2], MILLS[1], PETERSEN[200-201], DeRUDDER[1-2, 5, 7-8, 10-11, 14], SCHMID[1-2], TROMP).

15.2 – *Meteorotropic Agents.* The weather and the geographical conditions control many parameters in the air, such as the wind, pressure, temperature, humidity, ionization, electrostatic forces, ozone contents, and the aggregation size of the natural or industrial 'aerosols'. Some further literature is found in ASSMAN, BACH[100], DIGBY[2], FREY[200], GRIFFIN[300], HAGENTORN, HAINE[3-4], JÖCHLE[101], KÄHLER, KÖNIG[100-101], KÖSTER, KRUEGER[100], KÜHNAU, LINKE[2], MENGER, MENZEL[10], REITER STOPPEL[4, 6-8, 10-11, 101], TCHIJEWSKY[3, 5], UNDT, VERING[4, 6], WALLGREN; also BRENNAN[100], KERDÖ[100], KURASHIMA, SCHULZ.

15.3 – *Interaction with Other Synchronizers.* The variations of the meteorological factors are relatively irregular but are also impressed by the regular cosmic events, e.g. in a 24-h sequence. Conversely, they may disturb the action of other synchronizers on the organisms. This is one reason why the shape of an exogenous rhythm usually varies heavily from day to day even in one individual. The environmental temperature, e.g., is a composite synchronizer reflecting more or less random atmospheric conditions as well as a strong 24-h trend. Even the light may be influenced by atmospheric factors, being damped by clouds or subjected to dispersion in air layers of different density. The sunset colours are one example; the atmospheric ionization also changes at this time. The intensity of the cosmic rays is dependent on the atmospheric air pressure. The showers of radiation from solar eruptions set up reactions in the outer atmosphere effecting the degree of ionization and electro-magnetic phenomena. This may be observed as noise in the radio receivers. Even the moon acts on the weather (STUBBS).

As regards plants, it is important to know that the earth 'breathes' owing to its micro-organisms and that therefore 24-h variations in CO_2 and O_2 occur (KIL-BINGER), especially in relatively closed systems in contact with earth (e.g. hot-houses), cf. 13.7.

15.4 – *Meteorotropic Receptors*. One problem is how the body manages to perceive the meteorological influences. We have a temperature sense, of course. There must, however, also exist further transducing systems with even more direct pathways (cf. 1.20, 12.6). Anyone who has experienced pains in the head, joints or scar tissue at the passing of weather fronts or who has felt the vegetative reaction with a flushed face owing to cutaneous vasodilation after a short trip to the country knows it.

15.5 – There are many possibilities for meteorotropic reception. The air humidity and pressure may affect the *pulmonary function*. The size and electric charge of the aerosol particles determine their penetration and resorption in the lungs. The blocking effect of air humidity against the water evaporation from the skin may be a factor. The most radical theories envisage a direct action of the electrostatic charges (and magnetic fields) in the air upon the cell membrane and the sensitive ionic equilibrium across this boundary, or upon the colloid state of the cells, especially the nerve cells. Perhaps there is a direct action on the orientation of the free radicals.

We do not even know how many sensory mechanism are involved. One possibility is that one single of all the mentioned meteorotropic factors (e.g. the temperature) acts upon the body, being modulated by all the other conditions and acting as a carrier.

15.6 – *The N-method*. With single meteorological disturbances, a biological correlation can be tested by recording the desired parameter on consecutive days before and after the day of external influence, which is regarded as zero day (e.g. days −3, −2, −1, 0, +1, +2, +3) and averaging several series. The procedure tends to eliminate other trends in the values.

Meteorotropic influence has been described for many variables: e.g. correlations between weather fronts and book reading frequency; air temperature and student marks (HUNTINGTON[2]); or weather fronts and morbidity (MENGER, MEN-ZEL[10]). Even bacterial growth is influenced (VERING[6]), as well as the sexual activity in rats (JÖCHLE[101]). According to STOPPEL[4, 6-8, 10-11, 101], the electrostatic forces in the air direct the movements of plant leaves (cf. HAINE[4]).

15.7 – We have now discussed several synchronizers, including the meteorotropic ones. The next chapter will deal with the hypothetical cosmic influences, the so-called subtle synchronizers.

CHAPTER 16

Subtle Synchronizers

16.1 – After having discussed the dominant and the weak synchronizers, there remain the cosmic ties, the 'subtle synchronizers' (cf. 1.19-20, 12.5-6). The science upon which we will build is the 'cosmobiology'. Introductions to the field are Conf. 1958c, 1961d, BERG[2-4], BROWN[3-12, 100, 102, 104, 107-110, 113-114, 116-120], DÜLL[100-104], EUGSTER, LAURELL[1, 3-4], LINKE[1], PICCARDI, DERUDDER[12-13], TCHIJEWSKY[2, 4, 6-7], WING[2, 4-5]. More is found in ASSMAN[2], BACH[100], BARNOTHY, BARNWELL[100], BECKER[300, 400], BORTELS, BOUTE, GENERALES, GERENCSER[100], GIAIO, HAINE[4], MULAY[100], NELSON, POKROVSKY, SCHMID[2], SCHOSTAKOWITSCH, SCHULTZ[1-5], TAKATA[100], VERING[6], WEBB[102-103], ZINK[100].

16.2 – *Astronomical events,* more than anything else, set the pace for our synchronizers. These processes are rather regular and periodic as compared to the irregularity of atmospheric changes. It has already been pointed out that they will also affect the atmosphere and that their action may be modified by the atmosphere (15.3). The various movements of the earth, moon, sun and stars make an intricate but well-known pattern. Gravitational, magnetic and radiational forces are among their known expressions. The different periodicities arising will be described later. The strength of the earth's electric and magnetic fields follows such cycles. The solar radiations (heat, UV, corpuscular) imprint their patterns upon almost all atmospheric conditions. Indirectly, thus, the cosmic synchronizing influence is overwhelming. But can these factors also act directly upon the organism?

16.3 – If it is difficult to define any sensory apparatus with regard to the weak synchronizers, then it is still worse with the pervasive geophysical clues (BROWN). The physiologists hesitate to accept their existence. Evidence for the possible action of electrostatic and magnetic fields is just starting to turn up. Also, one easily tends to forget that our whole body, including the locomotor, circulatory and labyrinthine systems, is gravity-dependent.

16.4 – *Electrostatic and Magnetic Fields.* With regard to the delicate ionic equilibria in the body, it is not unreasonable to expect an external influence upon them. Some effects of electrostatic charges and magnetic fields seem to exist (Conf. 1961d, BARNOTHY, BARNWELL[100], BECKER[300], BOUTÉ, BROWN[10-12, 102, 104, 118, 120], DÜLL[100-104], GERENCSER[100], HAINE[4], MULAY[100], SCHMID[2], STOPPEL[4, 6-8, 10-11, 101], WEBB[102-103]; see also CLEMMOW, DAVIS[1100], DELEANU, LISSMAN[100], MACLEAN, SCHNEIDER[2], TEIXEIRA[100]).

Magnetism seems to affect the growth of organisms, *e.g.* in cancer cells or the blood-forming tissues. It is important that the animal remains in constant relation to the magnetic field for some time to achieve these effects. Human subjects seem to become disoriented in space if exposed to strong magnetic fields. Mental afflictions might be susceptible to variations in the earth-field (RAVITZ).

16.5 – It used to be felt that only strong magnetic fields could have any action. However, it would seem as if even the earth-magnetic field and experimental fields of the same magnitude suffice, as indicated in BROWN's[10, 12, 102, 104, 118, 120] experiments with the orientation direction of snails and flatworms. The animals can distinguish between magnetic directions. If an artificial magnet under the animals is turned to counteract the earth field the orientation changes according to expectation. Since the terrestrial magnetic field possesses rhythmic components derived from solar and lunar influences it may perhaps act as a carrier for these influences (12.11).

16.6 – *Solar Activity*. The intense solar activity as witnessed in the sunspots (*cf.* 15.3) acts upon the gravitational and magnetic fields of the earth. It also emits heavy radiation (heat, UV, visible light, corpuscular radiation). It affects the atmospheric ionization and the weather profoundly and causes disturbances in radio reception. It creates the 24-h light cycle. The DÜLLS[100-104] made very straightforward studies of suicide and general mortality rates as influenced by the solar and earth-magnetic activity, using the statistical N-method (*cf.* 15.6 and HUNTINGTON[2]). Numerous investigators have reported the 11-year sunspot cycle in their biological data.

16.7 – *Other Subtle Synchronizers*. 'Gravitation' is one of the geophysical factors which we have sensors for; the statoliths of the ear, the stretch-recording proprioceptors in muscles and joints, even the cell substance itself. The aviators receive valuable information from the pressure against the seat during acceleration (flying by the seat of the pants). The astronaut should be still more aware of it. Studies of the gravitational effects on growth have for instance been made in animal and human centrifuges; as regards animals for generations. Primitive animal orientation includes 'geotaxis' (Chapter 18).

The strength of the gravitational field varies with the geographic locality. It is influenced by the earth mass and rotation, also by the distant planets and stars. Its action is instantaneous. However, the phenomenon is not well understood, (*cf.* DICKE, WITTEN). – It is claimed that the position of the planets influences the radiation showers and the conditions for atmospheric radiowave reflection which are so important to our communication systems. A close study of this has led to a remarkable feat of prediction in radio 'weather' (NELSON).

It has even been suggested, from purely thermodynamic considerations, that the 24-h change between heating and cooling of the primordial earth was necessary for the formation of living protein (BLUM).

16.8 – Our sensitivity to *heavy radiations* is well known (cosmic rays, atomic radiation, X-rays, UV-light, *cf.* 13.2). Their possible action as synchronizers is unknown. The effect of visible light and adjoining bands was discussed in Chapter 13. Even the action of radio waves is being discussed. The influence of weak gamma-radiation on animal orientation was studied by BROWN.

Still more evasive influences may be postulated, from 'coriolis forces' and diffuse cosmic influences to ESP and instantaneous informational relationships in a scientific holistic world (GREGORY[100]).

16.9 – There are many experiments which suggest the presence of subtle synchronizers, though we cannot tell which they are. There are PICCARDI's investigations which show that the formation velocity of ordinary anorganic colloids, such as BiOCl or $Ca_3(PO_4)_2$, seem to be sensitive to cosmic forces (cf. BECKER[400], BORTELS, BOUTE, GIAIO, VERING[6]). A direct effect on the quasicrystal structure of water is supposed to exist. BROWN[1, 3-12, 108-110, 113-114, 116-117] recorded several factors continuously in a variety of organisms under constant conditions: such as the metabolism of potato plants, sea-weed, snails and crustaceans; oyster valve movements; and rat activity. From the curves, components could be extracted which showed variations with the lunar day, the solar day and the year, as well as the cosmic radiation. This was made by assigning each value its 'correct place in the time structure' in question and averaging over a large number of curves, thus cutting out other influences. The amplitudes of the single curves proved to follow the surrounding atmospheric pressure, in spite of the constant conditions. The investigators assume the existence of a 'subtle carrier', modulated by all external influences, and which is able to reach the isolated organism, informing it about the surrounding atmospheric conditions as well as of the position of the sun and moon, i.e. universal time.

Another puzzling phenomenon is the 'latitudinal passage' (WING), where the phasing of various biological cycles seems to vary with the earth latitude (cf. Chapter 17).

16.10 – How these various synchronizers could act upon the organism we do not know (cf. 1.19-20, 15.5). It has to be at the cellular level. A direct effect on the delicate ionic membrane equilibria, the orientation of free radicals or the colloid state has been advocated. In higher animals, this action may be on the nerve cells (LAURELL[4]). It has also been suggested that the very basis of living matter, the semicrystalline structure of the cell water may be affected, with secondary influences upon the proteins.

16.11 – *The Crucial Experiment.* One possibility of using the terrestrial rotation as a clock, as pointed out by HAMNER (Conf. 1960c, p. 70), exists if the organisms receive hypothetical signals from an unchanging place in space, whether radiational, gravitational or magnetical. He has devised several tests aiming at obscuring this effect, e.g. by placing plants horizontally on a rotating turntable. The latest development is to study the circadian rhythm on a turntable at the southpole. This would fool the organisms as to true time. There are however complicating factors. The magnetic and geographic poles do not coincide. The relation between these and their complicated movements in space may provide time clues. The experiments are in progress.

16.12 – *Conditions in Space.* An important question today is how man will react against the unfamiliar surroundings in space (GENERALES) with the absence of normal synchronizer clues and the introduction of new ones (STRUGHOLD). This has led to a considerable number of studies in space cabin simulators. These are chambers where the subject is isolated as completely as possible from external influences. Actually, it is an old technique in biological rhythm research, dating back to KLEITMAN's studies in the Mammoth Cave. Artificial synchronizers may also be introduced and the entraining mechanisms studied (*cf.* HAUTY). In general, there is a large variability in the capacity of human subjects to follow strange living schedules, depending on the individual psyche, age, *etc.* Some easily revert to the circadian period. – Submarines provide a similar constant environment, suitable for experimentation (KLEITMAN[14]).

16.13 – *The Circadian Problem.* Until we know for certain whether the weak and subtle synchronizers act upon our bodies or not, the question of the origin of the 'circadian rhythms' remains uncertain. It has been pointed out several times already that many of the facts about these rhythms, as we know them, may be interpreted both ways, as purely endogenous or as exogenous. BROWN points out that circadian rhythms seldom occur in normal conditions. They are products of unphysiological conditions. In nature, the entraining agent would be expected to be light or temperature. It is not impossible that other synchronizers may have a weaker, less direct action, resulting in an incomplete fixation of the rhythms (*cf.* the autophasing concept, 1.23). On the other hand, it is not necessary to exclude the endogenous rhythms. One could imagine a model with one endogenous noncircadian rhythm, as found in the embryos (Chapter 9) and controlled by a weak or subtle synchronizer. One popular reasoning about the circadian rhythms runs something like this: Since a circadian frequency deviates from any surrounding one it must be endogenous. This is not quite logical. It should be: Since a circadian frequency deviates from any surrounding one it must at least contain an endogenous component (which does not necessarily have to be equal to the circadian one or even sustained). What we really need is a method of analysis which would single out external components in a biological rhythm under natural experimental conditions.

16.14 – Many of the proposals made in this chapter may seem difficult to accept. As a matter of fact, a short contemplation shows that the scope of these problems is almost frightening to the modern mind. There are the holistic concepts of all things being interrelated. Gravitation and magnetism are dependent on the position of distant celestial objects. Why, that's almost astrology . . . Clearly, we must be careful in accepting such statements but also in rejecting them because of the negative associations they carry in our minds. The problem constitutes perhaps one of the most fascinating challenges to the biological scientist of today.

16.15 – We have now finished the discussion of which synchronizers there are, and their possible mode of action. It remains to classify the periods which they possess, and also to describe a phenomenon highly dependent upon them, the animal navigation. The next chapter lists the periods.

CHAPTER 17

Synchronizer Frequencies

17.1 – In the previous chapters, the various synchronizers and their actions were discussed. We shall now study the frequencies of the external periodic synchronizers.

The external periods are almost exclusively governed by 'astronomical events'; the movements of the earth and its natural satellite, of the sun and the stars. Most of the events are very regular. There are, however, more different periods than one would expect at first thought, and through interference they may give a still larger number. Most important are the day and the year, which create unequivocal exogenous periods of the same lengths. We will now consider the 24-h, lunar and seasonal cycles, followed by sunspot cycles and more remote events. Some general references are BROWN[10], FOLK[102], LAURELL[1, 3, 4], LINKE[1], QUILGHINI, ROTH, STRUVE[100], cf. 1.21.

17.2 – *Terrestrial Rotation. Twenty-four Hour Periods.* We are used to thinking of the 24-h period as the natural day. It is caused by the terrestrial rotation and corresponds to one turn of the planet around its axis. If we take a certain point on the earth crust, *e.g.* the Mount Everest, we want it to come back to exactly the same position where it started, after one day. This is however, impossible, since the earth centre is simultaneously moving in space. We thus need a reference point to pin down Mount Everest's position. Unfortunately, there is no stable reference point either, they all move. The problem is exemplified in Fig. 1.21.

The length of the 'day' thus depends on the reference point. The turning time with respect to the sun, the 'solar day', is close to 24 h. It is important in everyday life for us as well as for the wild animals. Yet the stars are theoretically better reference points because of their distance, which makes the movement of the earth during one day with respect to the celestial object rather small. In this case, we get the 'sidereal day', 23.9 h.

17.3 – The *lunar day* is 24.8 h. The true solar day actually varies by 16-20 seconds with the time of the year, owing to the elliptic earth orbit and the inclination of the equatorial against the orbital terrestrial plane. Our artificial 24-h day is therefore no absolute reality, *e.g.* for the wild animal. It may be so for us owing to the hour-controlled general activity around us. In view of the gravitational effect of the moon, the lunar day may be as real a period for the living organism as the solar day. The difference between these two days will also make the time of the passage of the moon and of the tidal effects travel through the solar day at a rate of slightly less than one hour a day, being 50.5 min later on each occasion. After one month they coincide; one example of beats between astronomical periods. Since there are two daily tides, there is an average tidal half-day of 12.4 h.

The 24-h periods are perhaps the most important of the external rhythms. The literature on them is enormous, and will be scanned in Part IV.

17.4 – *Lunar Periods*. The time of one lunar revolution around the earth must be determined in the same way as regards terrestrial rotation, with a reference body. This may be the sun, the stars or other celestial parameters. In this way many different months may be defined (DEWEY[2], STRUVE[100], WOLFE).

The time it takes for the moon to line up again with the sun is the 'synodic month' (29.5306 days, synodos = meeting). It is also the time between two equal lunar phases (*e.g.* full moon) since these are determined by the relation between sun and moon. – With the stars as reference, we get the 'sidereal month' (27.3217 days). – With the equinox (intersection line between the celestial equator and the solar ecliptic planes) as a reference we have the 'tropical month' (27.3216 days). – If, instead, the intersection between the lunar orbital plane and the ecliptic is chosen, the 'nodal' or 'draconic month' (27.2122 days) appears. – If the point of least distance between moon and earth is the reference we have the 'anomalistic month' (27.5546 days). – The 'calendar month' is 28-31 (30.44) days. – Thus:

[17.4a]   (Average month durations)
                    calendar month   30.44   days
                    synodic   ,,   29.53   ,,
                    anomalistic ,,   27.55   ,,
                    sidereal   ,,   27.3217   ,,
                    tropical   ,,   27.3216   ,,
                    nodal   ,,   27.21   ,,

17.5 – *Tides*. The gravitational influence of the moon upon our planet causes the 'tides' on the moon-near and moon-far sides of the earth. During one revolution of the planet any point on its surface will encounter the flood twice. The sun has a similar effect, about half as strong as that of the moon. When Sol and Luna are lined up with the earth, at new and full moon, the two heavenly bodies work together and give specially high tides. At the quarter phases of the moon the tide is at its weakest point. There are even ebb and flow waves in the earth crust and in the atmosphere. When the moon is high above the equatorial plane the two daily tides may differ considerably in height. Since there are two tides a day there is an average lunar half-day of 12.4 h. It makes beats with the 24-h cycle, forming a 14.8 day half-month period. – Since Luna always keeps one side towards the earth it rotates around its own axis at approximately the same period as it turns around the earth. Concerning physical tide effects see ADDERLEY[106], BRADLEY[100], CARTWRIGHT, CREUTZBERG, SCHÜBLER, STACEY.

17.6 – The tides are a strong reality to all animals living on the shore (*cf*. CARSON). They usually travel up and down the beach with the ebb and flow. It also means that they have to know in which direction to move, a matter of navigation. This is a more tricky problem than one would think. The animals must move before the flood and many are too small to perceive any larger clues in the close surroundings. If removed to a new environment the animals still migrate in the correct compass direction (*cf.* next chapter). The swarming of many sea animals is also coupled to the lunation (herrings, eels, palolo worms). Tidal and lunar periods are therefore not uncommon among the exogenous rhythms, especially in invertebrates. The lunar rhythms will be discussed more fully in Part IV. *Cf.* CASPERS, FINGERMAN[2-6], [103], HAUENSCHILD, JENS, NAYLOR[1], STEPHENS[1, 100]. It is still not known whether evolutionary residues of this persists in higher animals (*cf.* 7.21).

17.7 – *Solar Rhythms. Seasonal Rhythms.* The 'sidereal year' is $365^1/_4$ days. It denotes the time interval between two passages of the sun with respect to the stars, the true orbit time. The seasons are, however, more dependent upon the position of the sun in our sky and this is also influenced by the spin in the earth's axis of rotation owing to external gravitational forces. This makes the passage time between vernal equinoxes (one intersection between the equatorial and orbital planes), the tropical year, about 20 min. shorter than the sidereal one. There are even seasonal changes in the earths rate of rotation.

17.8 – The rotation of the sun around its own axis requires 25-33 days/revolution (differing with solar latitude). This value is peculiarly close to that of the sidereal month, which does not simplify the question of causation in biological rhythms. The velocity with which sunspots travel across the face of the sun is linked with its rotational period and sunspots seem to act upon the organisms, too.

The seasonal rhythms are transmitted to the organisms by changes in almost all environmental parameters, especially light variations and temperature. They create a pronounced exogenous rhythm in most species. The seasonal rhythms will be discussed in Part IV.

17.9 – *Solar Activity. Sun Spots.* The sunspots are some kind of deep, cooler vertices in the sun atmosphere. The 'solar flares' are elevated luminous eruptions on its surface. They are both accompanied by radiation and strong magnetic fields, which disturb the earth atmosphere and magnetic flux. The corpuscular part of the radiation is rather slow, taking 4-6 days to reach the earth. It is also scattered in the atmosphere so as to reach all sides of the globe simultaneously. – The solar constant is an overall measure of the solar luminosity.

The sunspots appear rhythmically with peaks each 11th year (11.1, range 7-16 years, *cf.* REID). Continuous records of the sunspot numbers exist since 1750. Since the polarity of the sunspot magnetic fields is reversed at each new cycle, a 22-year rhythm also exists. Many sunspot periods have actually been reported: 17 and 33 weeks (WOLF[400]); 3.4, 5.9, 8.8-9.2, 9.9-10.0, 11.1-11.7, 12, 17.7 (*cf.* business and tree-ring cycles), 22-23, 37, 80-83, 89 and 200 years. The solar radiation in general (*e.g.* the solar constant) displays still other periods: 21 and 27 days; 11, 21-23, 25 and 45 months; 7.6 years.

17.10 – Many authors have reported biological rhythms of similar periods as those of sunspots. Relations may reasonably be expected but are difficult to prove. Especially, the 11-year cycle has been spotted everywhere; in social crises, business, the weather, earthquakes and in biological variates. *Cf.* 6.41-43, Ref. J.c. and J.d., HUNTINGTON[2], TCHIJEWSKY[2, 4, 6-7], WEBSTER[1, 4].

17.11 – *Further Astronomical Cycles.* Further astronomical periods may be found, which might or might not be of biological importance. Some of them are far too long for our present powers of observation.

There is a small spin of the earth with relation to its own rotational axis, with a period of 14 months (variation of latitude, the 'CHANDLER period'). – There is a spin of the rotational axis itself with a period of 26,000 years (earth precession) and, superimposed upon this, smaller variations (nutation) owing to a spin in the moon's orbital axis (regression of the moon's orbital plane) with a duration of 18.6 years. – Solar eclipses occur usually about twice a year. They become more similar at intervals of 18 years and 11.3 days, the 'Saros'. This is slightly less than the moon orbit regression period and a multiple of the synodic month. – There are the various planetary orbits and pulsating stars of variable light intensity. In the latter, periods between 2 hours and 80 years may be found. Most common are about 0.5, 7 and 250 day durations.

There are obviously a large number of celestial periods. If they are furthermore supposed to interact in various ways, they will become numerous. This increases the risk of a random coincidence of astronomical and biological cycles and makes proof of causality still more difficult.

17.12 – *Weather.* The atmospheric conditions are rather dependent on celestial events (*cf.* Chapter 15). There is an enormous literature on cycles in the weather (river flood levels, rainfall, atmospheric pressure and temperature, earthquakes, ozone contents of the air). The studies aim at prediction. However, most of the variations, except the seasonal one, are too irregular for that purpose. Some of the correlates may also have disappeared. Many of the periods recur perhaps in solar events, tree-ring growth and business. Some of those reported are: 12 hours; 6, 13 and 28 days; 33 weeks; 12 (seasons), 12.3, 13, 20 (approximating the orbital time of Venus?), 22, 25, 27 (approximating the orbital time of Mars?), 29, 36, 44 and 51-55 months; 5.2-5.5, 7.3-7.7, 8.3, 9.0-9.8, 11-11.4 (sunspots), 13, 14.9, 16 (the 'WAGNER period'), 16.7-17, 17.7 (*cf.* business), 18, 22-23, 26, 35-37 (the 'BRÜCKNER period'), 45, 51-52, 65-66, 89, 95, 100, 130, 180, 450, 520, 700 and 40 000 years. *Cf.* Ref. J.c. and J.d., BROOKS, BRUNT[1-2], DEWEY[3-4], HUNTINGTON[2], LINKE[1], WING[3].

17.13 – *Latitudinal Passage.* Many rhythms seem to exhibit a peculiar geographic pattern as regards their timing. Generally, the timing becomes later with decreasing terrestrial latitude, from the poles towards the equator. Similarly, the timing of the sunspot maxima vary with the solar latitude. The phenomenon is called latitudinal passage. The cycle events seem to pass like ripples both in time and space, in the latter at a velocity of about 71% of the cycle period per 90° (pole to equator). The latitudinal passage is said to occur in many cyles of the most different types and wave lengths *e.g.* the lemming population cycles, weather data and tree-rings. The phenomenon of latitudinal passage should be carefully checked, since it definitely suggests a cosmic cause of the rhythm, if present.

The latitudinal passage has been studied by WING[1-2, 4-5] (*cf.* DEWEY[1, 3]).

17.14 – Closely linked to the celestial phenomena are the problems of navigation. Animals can navigate and this includes the need for timing. The next chapter will discuss this.

CHAPTER 18

Animal Orientation and Navigation

18.1 – In the last chapters we have studied the properties of various synchronizers. With the aid of these, the organisms can adjust their rhythms to the external time and periodicities. However, they can also use the external clues for orientation in the same way as our navigators do. True navigation also requires a chronometer in order to interpret the positions of the heavenly bodies. Hence the interest in biological clocks (*cf*. Chapter 5).

18.2 – Animals and man must be able to return to certain places they have visited before in homing and foraging. Some even do it without ever having seen the goal as in the migration of birds and fish. There are different ways in which such goal-seeking can be achieved, *viz*. random movement, spiralling, taxis, orientation and navigation. We will discuss these possibilities, the methods to study animal orientation and their application to invertebrates and vertebrates. Some general references are Conf. 1960c, 1961b, 1962d, ADMIRALTY MANUAL[1], LINCOLN, MATTHEWS[5], MITTELSTÄDT.

18.3 – *Random Movements and Spiralling*. Purely random movement in small spaces, such as is often exhibited by scared or trapped animals, will sooner or later take them to the correct place (*cf*. error control, 3.17). The same applies if the animals slowly spiral outwards from the starting point, until an appropriate landmark is perceived. Both methods may be seen as components even in the navigation of animals.

18.4 – *Taxis*. Taxis occurs if the goal is directly perceivable; it can be positive, the animals moving towards the clue, or negative, the animals avoiding contact. Taxis is common in lower organisms. The cybernetic phototropic machine has been mentioned (3.8). *Phototaxis* (*cf*. BIRUKOW[1-3], BRANDT[1], DRZEWINA, JAHN, VERHEIJEN) is common in insects which may try to keep a light source at a fixed angle to their side. This works if the light source is distant. If it is close it sets up a feedback system which results in a spiral path (SMITH[200]) towards the object. *Chemotaxis* is used by unicellular organisms and insects (even blood-hounds). Moths may localize their females at incredible distances in this way. Fish may perhaps be influenced by the smells carried by the water (HASLER[1, 3]) or affected by tactile stimuli in the ocean currents (Conf. 1961b). Wind may be a factor for land and air animals; however, migrating and homing birds do not follow it. *Geotaxis* (gravitational taxis) may be investigated in animals used to moving on vertical surfaces, *e.g.* walls (BIRUKOW[2, 5, 102], BRANDT[1], RENSING[100], TENCKHOFF-EIKMANNS). There will be a natural competition between light stimuli (direction upwards) and gravity (direction downwards). Surprisingly, the animals do not creep vertically. Instead they deviate laterally from the direction of pull by an angle which varies throughout the day in the same way as the sun angle.

18.5 – *Orientation*. If the goal is not within sight, we must at least know the direction in which to move until we perceive the target or other suitable landmarks. For this, we need a reference point. We can, then, establish a target angle between the directions to this spot and to the target, Fig. 18.5a (*cf.* the automatic antiaircraft gun, 3.5). Any landmark may perform as reference point, but it should be distant, because its direction then only varies little with the position of the orienting person. Good reference points are the magnetic poles (compass orientation) or the pole star. The direction of the latter is always parallel to the earth axis from whatever point of the earth the observation is made.

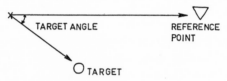

Fig. 18.5a. Orientation with respect to a reference point.

18.6 – The sun is often used as a reference point. However, despite its distance it moves so that the target angle changes throughout the day and one has to know the hour time to correct for this. One may observe the position of the sun projection on the horizontal plane and its angle with the northern direction, the azimuth. If Sol is observed directly, the target angle changes at a uniform velocity (constant angular velocity) whereas the corresponding angle in the azimuth plane, the sun angle, does not. Even if the sun is not visible, the polarization plane of the light will tell its direction. If the sun-observing organism lives in the water, it also has to correct for the refraction of the light in the water-air interface. If one has a clock, a short observation of the solar movements would make possible a prediction of the future sun path, including its highest point at local noon. The latter, whether observed or predicted, would give a phase setting of the clock. The period may be controlled by successive noons. The correction of the sun angle may either be made with aid of the clock or by assigning a certain correction directly to each position of the sun. It must, however, be kept in mind that the height of the sun varies with the seasons. Obviously, there are several parameters of the solar movement, which might be observed:

18.6a
     (1) Direction to the sun, direct.
     (2) Azimuth, horizontal direction to the sun.
     (3) Direction of solar movement.
     (4) Velocity of solar movement.
     (5) Change of velocity in azimuth angle.
     (6) Altitude of the sun (equal twice a day).

(7) Maximal altitude of the sun (varies with
    season and latitude).
(8) Change in solar altitude.
(9) Polarization plane of the light.

With regard to animal navigation, the problem is which of these solar parameters can really be perceived. However, it has not been definitely solved, cf. BRAEMER[2], HASLER[101], MATTHEWS[4-5], RENNER[7], SCHWASSMANN.

18.7 – Navigation. A more complicated mode of direction finding is necessary over large distances, viz. navigation (or bi-coordinate orientation). A coordinate system has to be erected in which the positions of both the navigator and the target are determined. The way vegetation in a forest grows, the direction of a compass needle, the direction of solar movement (though not at the equator) or the position of the stars may help to establish the coordinates. The position in the system may be derived by the observation of celestial objects with the aid of a chronometer and a sextant. The latitude is determined from the height of the polar star over the horizon; and, more theoretically, from the apparent changes in direction of a moving pendulum; or the movement of water in a circularly bent tube rotating around its own diameter, the Compton effect. The longitude is determined as the difference between the local time, as determined from the passage of the stars or the sun, and the simultaneous time of the zero longitude, either the Greenwich meridian or the longitude of the departure point (cf. 5.9). This involves the use of a chronometer set at the time of the zero longitude.

A new method of navigation is the inertial guidance system, employing gyroscopes and electronic integrators which record all changes in velocity and acceleration (including changes in direction).

18.8 – Animal Orientation and Navigation. Most animals have, for some reason, a more accurate orientation sense than we have. The capacity is widespread among the different species. It may be inherited or learned. Some birds and fishes migrate from one continent to another each year, even if the individuals have never seen the new place before. Pigeons are used as messengers owing to their strong homing tendency. The littoral (= shallow water zone) animals on the beach move in and out with the tides. Bees return unerringly to their honey source and even communicate the direction and distance to other bees. The language consists of special dances.

How the animals do all this is not accurately known. There are several possible methods which may be used. No doubt the sun is used by many species, but also moon and star navigation or inertial guidance are possibilities. The most important aspect for the biological rhythmologist is that many types of migration, especially over long distances, demand some kind of biological-clock function. The clock could somehow be set at universal time, or keep the sidereal time at the place of departure. It might be a period-corrected circadian timer. The setting could even be made with the aid of the actual new surrounding diurnal regimen (since this period is still 24 h, though with a different light-dark ratio) if no phase-shift is induced, and as long as the animal is stationary. One must not forget that a continuous observation of the actual local times would completely disorient the animal as to the oscillator period, since the travelling-day period is not 24 h.

18.9 – *The Experimental Approach*. Natural migration may be studied by marking the animals for identification when found (*e.g.* bird-banding), or by following them with aircraft (GRIFFIN[2], HITCHCOCK) or radar (EASTWOOD). They may also be provided with small telemitters.

18.10 – The animals may also be trained to select a certain direction by placing the food at a certain place beyond viewing distance at a certain time of the day. After some repetitions the animals learn to move in the correct direction at feeding times.

A popular experiment is to transfer the animals unexpectedly to a new place, and setting up living quarters with as similar landmarks as before, *e.g.* at another hemisphere or longitude. In such cases, the animals usually miss their target as if they were using the present azimuth but the previous local time (*cf.* PAPI[2] and 5.23). Assume, for instance, that they have learned to search for food at 10.00 o'clock at a sun angle of 35°. If the new place is 4 h earlier in sidereal time, the animals will misjudge time since they keep the old hours and will not search food until 14.00 o'clock local time. The azimuth is now another than at 10.00 o'clock in the place of origin, but the animals will still use a sun angle of 35°. This indicates that the proper sun angle is not inferred from the position of the sun but from an independent timer. After some time the animals have, however, adjusted to the new site and orient correctly again (RENNER[5-6]). The timer has then probably been entrained by the new external day cycle.

18.11 – More exact experiments may be made with the animals on a circular table or cage, with the home in the center and the target on the rim, with or without a faked sun (using mirrors or artificial light), *cf.* BIRUKOW[3], HASLER[101], HOFFMANN[8], PAPI[2-3], PARDI[2, 101-102]. If *e.g.* beach animals are taken from a habitat where they have to run east-west with the tide, they will move accordingly at the correct times if transferred to such a circular device with free view of the sun. The position of the animals is easy to mark on a diagrammatic representation of the table as a circular distribution, Fig. 18.11a.

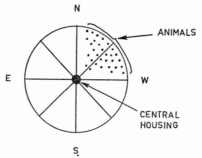

Fig. 18.11a. Migration movements on a circular table.

18.12 – *Orientation in Invertebrates.* Many species have been studied, *e.g.* spiders (BARTELS[200], PAPI[3-4, 101-102], TONGIORGI), pond skaters (BIRUKOW[3-5, 100-101], EMEIS, RENSING[100]), beach fleas (PAPI[2, 5, 100], PARDI[1, 4, 100-102]), ants and termites (BRUN, GRABENSBERGER[1], JANDER, SANTSCHI), locusts (UVAROV) and bees (*cf.* 5.23, BECKER[1], BELING, BOCH, V. FRISCH, GRABENSBERGER[2], KALMUS[1, 3, 11, 13], KLEBER, KÖRNER, LINDAUER, RENNER, WAHL, WERNER, WITTEKINDT, WOLF[1]). *Cf.* also BIRUKOW[2], BRUNS, FOREL, MEDIONI, PARDI[3].

Invertebrates seem only to employ orientation, not navigation. Most commonly they use the sun as a reference point but the moon may also serve as such (PAPI[5], PARDI[102]). The sun angle is continuously corrected for the shift in azimuth, hence the term 'photomnemotaxis'. This correction is not read directly from the position of the sun but with the aid of the biological chronometer. If the latter is reset (by light-darkness entrainment) the orientation is therefore correspondingly in error.

18.13 – There are three different ways of studying the sun orientation: (1) Under normal field conditions. Here, the target is still and the sun moves; (2) If a constant, artificial light source is given, the direction in which the animals seek food changes throughout the day in an oscillatory manner, corresponding to the sun angle which should have been used (BIRUKOW[3, 5]); (3) Only the food is visible but not the sun. This condition may be used with bees which seem to communicate the appropriate sun angle to their fellows by tail-dancing, in spite of the real simplicity of the situation. The indicated angle changes during the day (LINDAUER[5-6]). Under alternatives (2) and (3), the animals seem to report the diurnal change in azimuth only, not other solar parameters (*cf.* RENNER[7]).

Beach fleas which have been reared under constant conditions can use the sun for orientation immediately upon exposure to it. They do not have to learn its behaviour (PAPI[102], PARDI[4]). Since they are littoral animals (living in the shallow water zone) they try to escape from the tide. Their species must have learned the correct direction in their special habitat somewhen and transmitted the information genetically. The findings are interesting but somewhat controversial to the current theories of inheritance. The animals can also learn new directions, but this takes several days. Bees, on the other hand, which have to change the target direction often need some days to learn the solar behaviour at a new place before they can utilize the information for orientation (LINDAUER[6]).

18.14 – Arthropoda can record the polarization plane of the light as a clue in orientation (BIRUKOW[1], VON FRISCH[3], PARDI[101-102], WATERMAN). It has been suggested that vertebrates can do the same, by squinting.

18.15 – *Navigation and Migration in Vertebrates.* Many species have been studied, *e.g.* fish (BRAEMER, HASLER[1-3, 100-101], KOCH[200], ROWAN[2], SCHWASSMANN), and some reptile orders, including animals such as lizards and turtles (CARR[1-2], FISCHER[1, 100], GOULD). Many birds have been studied, *e.g.* garden warblers, blackcaps, ducks, geese, crows (BELLROSE, DAVIS[1], DIJKGRAAF, GRIFFIN[1, 100], HAMILTON[400, 500], HOFFMANN[3], KRAMER[1-8, 102], LACK[2], MEDIONI, PAUL[200-201], PENNYCUICK, PRECHT, RAWSON[2], ROWAN[1-4, 6], RÜPPELL[2], SAUER[1-4, 100-102], SCHMIDT-KOENIG[5], SEIBERT, WALLRAFF[5]), especially starlings (HOFFMANN[1-2, 7-8],

KRAMER[100], PERDECK[1], RAWSON[1], RÜPPELL[1]) and pigeons (GRAUE[100], KRAMER[101], [103], MATTHEWS[1-5], PRATT[200, 300-301], SCHMIDT-KOENIG[1-4], SCHNEIDER[200], WALL-RAFF[1-4]).

Fish and birds may travel over long distances in their migration and they have to master true navigation. Most enigmatic of all is the homing capacity of pigeons, which may be brought blindfolded to a completely unknown place and still find their way home.

18.16 – There is no doubt that both fish and birds can use solar orientation (*cf.* 18.5-6). Again, the azimuth is the most important solar parameter read by the animals, though the sun altitude has also been suggested. An interaction between daylength and sun altitude may perhaps give information about latitude and time of season (BRAEMER[2]). There is also the possibility of determining the longitude from the difference in the local observed solar day and the (perhaps still frequency-synchronized) circadian chronometer from the point of departure; and the latitude with the aid of the stars. SAUER's[1-4, 102] fascinating experiments with birds in a planetarium indicate that star navigation might be used, probably by aid of inherited star pattern imprints. Many birds migrate unerringly at night (HAMILTON[400]). In the planetarium, the star pattern may be changed at will. The animals then orient according to the correct local time and the false sky. They may also perceive the seasons in this way.

18.17 – However, we must confess that we do not really know how the animals actually navigate. Especially the homing of the pigeon is difficult to explain. Its performance is almost suggestive of inertial guidance (BARLOW[202]). This is not impossible since the inner ear can record the acceleration (including change of direction). This would automatically mean that the velocity may be computed as soon as a reference velocity is given (*e.g.* zero at rest). The knowledge might be integrated and stored by the brain. A timer is also needed.

There have even been offered as intriguing possibilities that the vertical branchial blood vessels in the fish may react to the 'coriolis force' when moving against the earth rotation; or that their labyrinths may be sensitive enough to interpret the intricate movements imparted by the reflected wave pattern from the shore (*cf.* GRIFFIN[2] and HASLER[3], including the following discussion). The latter would be a subtle parallel to the echo-localization in bats. A sensitivity to gravitational and magnetic forces is also within the theoretical possibilities. Even ESP has been suggested.

18.18 – *The Biological Chronometer.* It has been stressed repeatedly that a correct orientation in time is necessary in animal navigation and orientation. Though a very minute study of the sun's movements could yield many data (18.6a) probably only the azimuth is used. Under any circumstances, a comparison between the local longitude and the zero longitude can only be made with a chronometer (excluding the possibility of inertial guidance).

That the circadian clock is actually used is best shown by the fact that it may be changed and that this causes a corresponding error in the animal orientation. The resetting is easily achieved with artificial LD-changes. In pond-skaters, entrainment has even been possible to LD 5 : 5 schemes which is very unusual (13.22, BIRUKOW[5]). If the clock is stopped, *e.g.* by heavy cold, for a certain time, a corresponding error in orientation occurs (PAPI[102]). The chronometer also shares the circadian properties of temperature and chemical independence (7.11-19, RENNER[5]) and of damping out under constant conditions (BIRUKOW[5]). HOFF-MANN[8] kept the clock freerunning in starlings (constant dim light and tempera-ture). He could follow the effect on the activity cycles of the animals, thus knowing how much the chronometer would be retarded each day. After several days, the birds were set free and then made an error in orientation as predicted by the retardation.

18.19 – It has even been suggested that some birds possess a sextant (*cf.* DETWI-LER, GRIFFIN[2]). They have a peculiar pectinate projection of the retina which may cast a shadow. The organ is best developed in day-active birds. – It is also interesting to note that both the sun angle correction and the geotaxis angle seem to be governed by the same clock (RENSING[100]). – According to PAPI[5] and PARDI[102] a 'lunar clock' must also exist, since some animals orient well with the aid of the moon.

18.20 – As can be seen, there are many possible explanations of animal orientation and navigation. The methods certainly vary, from taxis in the simplest organisms, through sun compass orientation in invertebrates to true navigation in vertebrates. The mechanisms are largely inherited. The circadian rhythm may be used as a chronometer. However, the fact that animals can use a mechanism is no proof that they always do it. Perhaps, they may sometimes use inertial guidance, star naviga-tion or compass orientation. The problem of animal navigation is rather contro-versial for the time being. It is also closely tied up with that of biological rhythms.

18.21 – We have now studied the endogenous rhythms and the external physical rhythms. Before turning to the exogenous (entrained) biological rhythms a num-ber of more theoretical physical, mathematical and statistical problems must be elucidated. This is done in the next Part of the book.

PART III

MODELS AND MATHEMATICAL-STATISTICAL ANALYSIS OF RHYTHMS

"In fact, there is no such thing as the theory of any phenomenon, whether in biology or physics. There are always several possibilities of explaining a given set of facts . . .

An old oriental legend tells of a wizard who was asked a simple question by his wife and did not know the answer to it. His wife strongly reprimanded him for this, saying, "You are the counselor to our king, who pays you much money for your knowledge; are you not ashamed of not knowing such simple things?"– "My dear", replied the wizard, "the king pays me only for what I know. If he were to pay me for what I do not know, all the treasures of his kingdom would not be sufficient for that purpose".

RASHEVSKY – Mathematical
biophysics.

"The application of any specific statistical method to an economic problem should be made only if it can be handled and understood in economic terms".

TINTNER – The variate difference
method.

The two preceding parts have dealt with the endogenous and external rhythms. It would be natural to proceed with the exogenous rhythms. However, we must first become aquainted with the statistical and mathematical methods of treating biological rhythm data. This will be done here, in some detail. The approach is a little broader than absolutely necessary. It aims at making the biological rhythmologist understand the general principles in the mathematical and statistical treatment of time series. It was for the same reason that the theory of regulation, servo-mechanisms and oscillators was rather extensively discussed in Part I. How much the biologist can apply of this in his own work only he himself can judge, but he needs a broad understanding of the principles to decide about it.

Part III will thus treat the numerous attempts at formulating the biological time series in physical and mathematical models and the use of these in explaining the properties of biological rhythms. The reverse process is also treated, the mathematical and statistical analysis of recorded rhythms, especially with the view of isolating the exo- and endogenous components. The reading is facilitated if the introductory Chapter 1 is studied first, especially sections 9, 25-26, 28-40, but also Chapters 2-4. The subject will be developed in four chapters:

[163]

CHAPTER 19

Physical and Mathematical
Models of Rhythms

19.1 – The earlier chapters have discussed the endogenous and external rhythms. In the process, some physical models have already been described, *viz.* servomechanisms and oscillators (Chapters 3 and 4). Machines may perform rhythmically in space and in time. As to biological rhythms we know most about the latter aspect and little about spatial periodicity. This makes it difficult to evaluate the use of physical models in our field. Many of them are far too simple to apply to the complex biological machinery. However, they tell us much about the fundamentals of rhythmic time series and they are easy to understand.

   The work of machines can be described in mathematical terms, as has already been demonstrated for some oscillators (Chapter 4). Some formulae will be included here though no systematic presentation of time series mathematics is aimed at. This will instead be tried in later chapters (21 and 22). Many models may be purely mathematical.

19.2 – In applying models we are safe as long as we merely regard them as a kind of simplified description of the biological behaviour, where lesser nonlinear and random distortions are eliminated for the sake of clarity. It is dangerous to draw too detailed parallels between causations in a machine and in biological behaviour. Often, there are several different models which fit the experimental data equally well. In general, the usefulness of models is overstressed by the physicists who tend to disregard the complexity of biological events and relationships. On the other hand, the biologists may understress the usefulness since they often do not understand the models and since they more readily notice the discrepancies between theoretical and actual events. Perhaps the worst thing is when the biologist tries to make models himself, since he tends to accept the simpler ones without really understanding how many different versions can be constructed to illustrate one and the same event. During the last years a distressing number of theoretical models have been advanced to explain the behaviour of biological rhythms. It is typical though, that they are all about equally possible, but that they cannot be proved to apply. Actually, we know yet much too little about the biological rhythms for any excessive modelmaking. What is really needed is more experiments and more methods of analysis of available data. The latter is perhaps the least-explored field in biological rhythm research, though now rapidly expanding.

19.3 – *Spatial and Temporal Rhythmic Patterns.* Our physical surroundings are incessantly moving, from the parts of an atom to celestial bodies. In the external world, as well as in the living organism, there is an unceasing redistribution of material in space and time (KALMUS). Some of these changes are rhythmic.

In *space* we may have rhythmic spatial patterns such as the arrangement of thread in lace, grooves in a phonographic record, crystal lattices, earth crust configurations (VOLZ), or even the curves in our rhythm graphs. In *time* we may have rhythmic temporal patterns, as in a melody or the rattle of a machine gun. Often, spatial and temporal patterns may be combined, as in the movement of machinery, falling drops, sounding strings, nerve signals, or pulse waves. If we shake the ends of a cord sideways we will generate spatial waves moving in time. The two patterns may sometimes be interconverted. A record may be played, the sound of a singer may be recorded on tape. In such cases the spatial pattern may be regarded as a memory of the temporal one. Our rhythm graphs are spatial memories of temporal happenings.

19.4 – The events in biological rhythms are chiefly temporal. Exceptions are spatial patterns resulting from rhythmic growth. In plants, we find the seasonal tree rings, and the ramifications in trees (BAILLAUD[102]) or in pine cones. The latter possess fascinating geometric properties (McCULLOUGH, personal communication). Mushrooms may grow in concentric rings (BISBY, HALL[1], JEREBZOFF, SAGROMSKY). In animals, there are the segmentations of the body; the rhythmic colour pattern in butterfly wings, bird feathers, or tiger furs (*cf.* WILLIER); bands in the enamel of deciduous teeth.

19.5 – One peculiar rhythmic spatial pattern is the distribution of cellular and nuclear sizes in some organs, *e.g.* the liver. They may be collected in classes, where each class has twice the volume of the preceding group. The phenomenon is

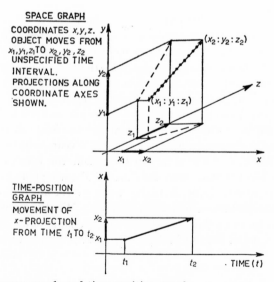

Fig. 19.6a. The space graph and time-position graph.

little understood, but it indicates some growth peculiarity. The cells are not poly-ploid, *cf.* BERTALANFFY, JACOBJ, KELLER[1], V. MARCK.

19.6 – *Motion*. Motion may occur in different ways. There is rectilinear and curvilinear motion in space. In time it may proceed at varying velocity. Bodies are put into motion by forces. If the latter disappear the movement proceeds rectilinearly at constant speed (theoretically). If the force is steadily applied the rectilinear motion increases in speed with constant acceleration, or various types of curvilinear movement appear. With changing force, the acceleration may change. At constant increase in acceleration (surge) enormous velocities or distances are soon reached. When studying a space graph, showing the change in position along a linear path, or the linear projection of three-dimensional movement on a coordinate axis (x, y, or z), we may also plot the position (say x) against time (t), obtaining a time-position graph, Fig. 19.6a.

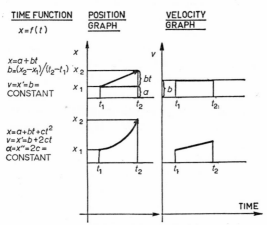

Fig. 19.6b. The time-position and time-velocity graphs.

The velocity of the object is given by the first derivative of the time function, the acceleration by the second derivative. The velocity may be plotted directly against time, Fig. 19.6b, yielding a time-velocity graph. These are often used in the study of growth and aging processes.

19.7 – *Oscillatory Movement*. If an object just oscillates to and fro between two points in space, the path or trajectory in time may have many different shapes, *e.g.* as in Fig. 19.7a, *cf.* Fig. 1.30a. There is an infinite variety of possible shapes, from the most irregular to very simple ones. Examples of the latter are the square or rectangular wave (switch-function); the impulse, which may be generated electronically and is often used in neurophysiological work; the sine wave, which is the commonest of all models; the saw-tooth curve (relaxation oscillations, cf. 4.13-14); the cycloid, a series of arches generated by the movement of one point on a rolling circle (Nicolson[100]).

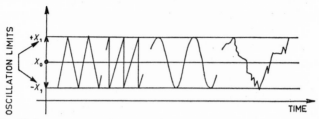

Fig. 19.7a. Oscillatory movements.

There are also other more complicated trigonometric functions such as the Lissajous figures, harmonic motion in two dimensions (Mitchell[1]) seen on the oscilloscope; or the function $y = \sin^2(1/x)$ which has a variable period (cf. Nicolson[100]). Variates of the type $y = a^{\sin x}$ become sinusoidal upon logarithmation (DeRudder[16]). Normally they are characterized by a thin high peak. A similar function can be generated from a standing ellipse in the same way as the sinusoid from a circle (Fig. 1.31a, cf. Jens[1]). Another peculiar oscillatory discontinuous function is $y = (-a)^n$, if $a \leq -1$ and n has integer values.

19.8 – *Harmonic Motions.* If an oscillation is caused by an agent which tries to bring the variate back to the resting level (x_0, in Fig. 19.7a) with a restoring force which is directly proportional to the deviation from x_0 we have simple harmonic motion (cf. 4.7-8, Bickley[100], Sears[100], Smith[200]). Examples are the up-and-down swings of a body suspended on a spring coil or vibrations in a rigid body. It may be regarded as a feedback between acceleration (or force) and velocity. At the extremes velocity approaches zero and changes sign, the acceleration is largest. At the center, the acceleration force is zero and the velocity largest, causing overshoot (cf. 3.18). Owing to friction the amplitude is slowly damped, unless amplification is provided for (cf. 3.14,19). The time of one oscillation is independent of the amplitude and constant, being set by the characteristic frequency (cf. 4.25-26). The movement in time is sinusoidal.

In a system swinging around a central axis, *e.g.* a pendulum or the balance wheel of a watch, the restoring force may be proportional to the angle of deviation instead of to the linear path of the swinging object. This is the angular harmonic motion. If the angle is small it approximates to a simple harmonic motion (cf. 4.7-8).

19.9 – The simple harmonic motion is the most common model of swinging systems, including analogs of the biological ones. It has several unique properties. In its simplest form the formula may be written $x = \cos t$. The velocity function $v = x' = -\sin t$. The acceleration $a = x'' = -\cos t$. If further derivatives are calculated it is found that they all have the same sinusoidal shape, only differing in phase by one quarter of the oscillation time (cf. Fig. 19.9a).

The sinusoidal curve may also be derived from a rotating circle, if the velocity of rotation, or angular velocity, is constant, *cf*. Fig 1.31a. Thus, each position on the curve may be represented by a phase angle as shown in the figure. The angular velocity is constant whereas the velocity of a point moving along the curve is variable (*cf*. Fig. 19.9a). The former may be expressed in degrees or radians per minute. The larger the velocity, the shorter the wavelength (duration of a cycle).

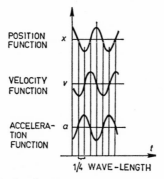

Fig. 19.9a. The sine wave derivatives.

Similarly, the phase difference between two cycles (equal in shape) may be expressed as a phase angle, if congruent points on the curves are compared (*cf*. Fig. 1.31b). This measure is independent of the time scale or the wave length of the cycle. The other possible measure is, of course, the horizontal (time axis) difference expressed in wave lengths. One may even compare two sine curves of different wave length by considering them to have a constant shift in the phase angle difference (Conf. 1960c, p. 148). Similarly, any curve shape may be described in comparison with the corresponding sine curve, as having an irregular shift in phase angle difference.

An exponentially damped sinusoidal oscillation may be illustrated as the projection of a spiral instead of a circle (*cf*. Fig. 1.31c).

The sine function will be discussed again in connection with the harmonic analysis (Chapter 21). A fascinating example of harmonic motion in biology and the mathematics necessary to describe it, is given by the undulatory propulsion of snakes or spermatozoa (*cf*. 6.23, GRAY[1-2, 100], MACHIN[1]).

19.10 – *Wave Forms in Space*. If a physical oscillating particle can impart its movement to a second particle through some kind of interaction (molecular attraction or pushes), the second particle to a third, and so on, a wave motion is propagated in space owing to the fact that the transmission from particle to particle requires time. It represents the transfer of a movement but not of matter across space, a travelling wave (Fig. 19.10a) The point in the diagram may illustrate a fishermans float moving up and down on the water. This is an example of a transverse pulse. If the single particles oscillate in the same direction as the wavefront movement we have a longitudinal pulse (as in sound waves). The oscillation may also consist of rotations with their axes on the propagation path, the torsional pulse.

19.11 – Under some conditions a travelling wave may be reflected at the end of the

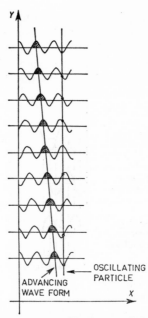

Fig. 19.10a. The relation between an oscillating particle and a travelling wave form.

Fig. 19.11a. A harmonic system of standing waves.

transmitting medium (*cf.* SEARS[100]). If new waves are repeatedly sent along they will interfere with the reflected ones, resulting in a standing wave. In the travelling wave the amplitude is constant and the wave front seems to progress. In the standing wave the wave front remains fixed whereas the amplitude changes. The latter may be conveniently studied with a piece of rope if one end is shaken. Reflection occurs at the other end, a little differently whether it is free (hanging rope) or fixed. The reader would do well to move his rope in circles, not side-ways. He may easily observe the nodes, the motionless points on the rope. It will also give him some insight into the remarkable act of handling a lasso. Similar reflection phenomena occur at the end of sounding tubes, whether open or closed.

Yet another situation occurs if both ends of a string are fixed and the intervening part tensed. Here both ends will be nodes in the resulting sinusoid standing wave. Its wave length may differ but it must be an integer fraction of the length of the string, 1/1, 1/2, 1/3 etc., string lengths being possible. This is a harmonic system of waves, Fig. 19.11a. Similar phenomena occur in a vibrating drum, in several dimensions.

Systems with multiple interacting reflected waves also exist. One example is the pattern set up by the pulse in the blood through reflection in the blood vessels (LOBEL). The wave system obviously changes with the quality of the vessels and an analysis of it may yield important medical information.

19.12 – *Velocity of a Wave*. The term velocity may have different meanings in a wave form:

(1) The velocity of propagation of the wave front = frequency × wave length.
(2) The velocity of one wave particle. In the example of Fig. 19.10a, it would be = frequency × 4 × amplitude.
(3) The velocity of the curve path (of an object supposed to follow the curve path) = first derivative of curve path formula:
wave path in time: $x = f(t)$
velocity: $x' = f'(t)$
(4) Angular velocity. Based on the rotating vector model of the sinusoid curve. It is constant for the sine curve and may for other rhythms be described in terms of deviations from this (*cf.* 19.9).

In biological rhythms we are usually concerned with alternatives (3) and (4). In general, wave forms in space are not so useful as models. Since all bodily reactions are ultimately of chemical character, we are more often concerned with substances which appear and disappear without travelling from site to site in the organism, *i.e.* time functions. Exceptions are the pulse wave and the transmission of nerve impulses (transverse oscillations of ions across the membrane).

19.13 – *Rhythmic Signals. Information*. With rhythms we mean the 'regular recurrence of something', usually in time. They may be discontinuous, with discrete impulses, or continuous, a wave form. They contain a certain measure of information (structure) as compared to purely random sequences of events, and may be used for conveying messages, signals. The simplest possible message is one impulse. Informationally it contains two alternatives (1 *bit*); something is *on* or *off*, *yes* or *no*, + or —. In the binary system this may be written 0 or 1.

'Series of signals' may be combined into larger informational units (ASHBY[1], SHANNON[100]). If the signals are absolutely independent and each allotted a certain position (as for instance traffic lights) and each has its own yes-or-no message, combinations of them may yield more information. A combination of four + or — signals gives 16 alternatives:

19.13a

alternative number	...... signals	1-4	....
1	+ +	+	+
2	+ +	+	—
3	+ +	—	+
4	+ +	—	—
5	+ —	+	+
6	+ —	+	—
7	+ —	—	+
8	+ —	—	—
9	— +	+	+
10	— +	+	—
11	— +	—	+
12	— +	—	—
13	— —	+	+
14	— —	+	—
15	— —	—	+
16	— —	—	—

The information (variety) in one or in four combined signals is:

19.13b

alternatives	logarithmic information units
2	$1\ bit = \log_2 2 = 1$
$2^4 = 16$	$4\ bits = 4 \times \log_2 2$ $= 4 = \log_2 16$ ($bit = $ *bi*nary dig*it*)

Obviously, the information is multiplicable, hence the use of logarithms as units of measurement, since they are additive. Another example: a deck of cards contains 52 alternatives or $\log_2 52 = 5.7$ *bits*, *i.e.* it could be exchanged for 5.7 impulses with two alternatives each. This is the language of the computers and also of the Morse system (here the two alternatives are long and short signals). Biological processes may also be described as a transfer of quantifiable information through the body (KALMUS[12]).

Information may also be regarded as an uneven distribution of energy, because its opposite, entropy, an even energy distribution, cannot possibly give any clues to anything (except that it exists). Such a view makes it easier to understand how the physicists can calculate the information in a chemical process or in the solar radiation. Information is sometimes equated with negative entropy.

19.14 – *Modulation*. The binary system is the simplest mode of communication. Another way is modulation, to imprint a message upon a carrier consisting of continuous wave forms or discrete signals (Fig. 19.14a). – In radio transmission both amplitude and frequency modulation may be used. – The nerves use frequency modulation of the nerve impulses (spikes, discrete signals). The signal frequency increases linearly with the logarithm of the sensory input. – A damped oscillation may be regarded as modulated by the damping function (3.19-20).

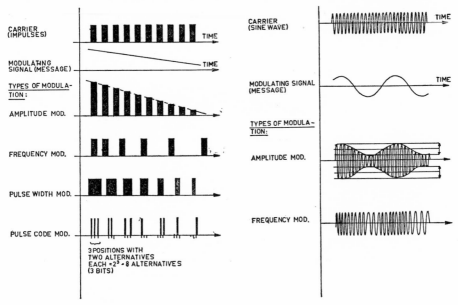

Fig. 19.14a. Modulation of a carrier signal.

19.15 – *The Biological Message*. This may be anything from simple alternatives (*e.g.* sleep – do not sleep) to complicated continuous wave forms (*e.g.* sound). A large group comes from the environment (*e.g.* light, temperature, touch), controlling the endogenous oscillators. Here, we may regard the body as a transducer with an environmental input (signal) acting upon a carrier, generated by the oscillators, and delivering an output, the modulated exogenous rhythm (*cf.* Chapter 2). It is not, however, always clear what constitutes the signal (*cf.* Chapters 15-16). Even the daily light–darkness changes constitute a problem. This message may be a continuous information on the light intensity. But it may also just give an alternative, light or dark. In that case the signals are two, *light-on* and *light-off*, or *dawn* and *dusk*. Both types of messages may exist (or even coexist), depending upon the sensitivity of the receiver organism (*cf.* 12.14).

From the rhythm viewpoint the relation between output and input in a transducer may occur in three different ways, rhythmic input, rhythmic transducer, or both.

19.16 – *Rhythmic Input and Nonrhythmic Transducer*. With a rhythmic input the transducer may or may not follow it. In the latter case the signal may be modulated by the nonrhythmic properties of the transducer (saturation, nonlinearity, delay, relay action, dead zone, backlash) yielding a transducer-modulated output, one kind of forced oscillation (*cf.* 4.29). Linear and nonlinear transformations were pictured in Figs. 3.28a and b; and some of their effects on a sinusoid input in Figs. 3.29a and b. In Fig. 19.16a some special cases are illustrated, *cf.* Fig. 19.37a.

Of course, the rhythmic input does not have to be sinusoidal; infinite variations of input and transformation are theoretically possible. – Of practical importance is the saturation phenomenon. Few transducers react linearly along the whole range of input. They tend towards an output limit, whether a piano string or the organism. The resulting nonlinear transformation upsets the normal balance be-

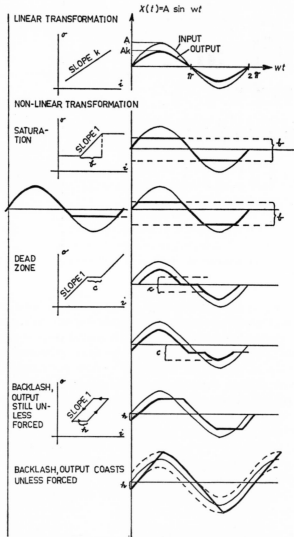

Fig. 19.16a. The modulation of a sinusoid input in transducers with different characteristics.

tween the 'particles' of the original sinusoid and calls forth all other possible vibrations in them. Since the end conditions, the nodes, are enforced a harmonic system of waves ensues (*cf*. 19.11). For the same reason any disturbances, even random, tend to set up a harmonic pattern in a transducer, since this is the only stable set of movements.

Fig. 19.16b compares the effects of linear and nonlinear transformation. In the nonlinear case the shape of the curve is changed. It now contains series of higher harmonics. We may also transform this situation into the mathematical problem of showing that the transformation $x = a + b \sin t + c (\sin t)^2 + \ldots + m (\sin t)^n$ represents a system of harmonics.

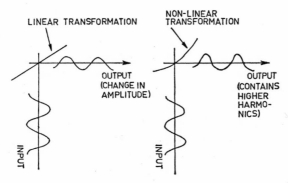

Fig. 19.16b. The effects of linear and nonlinear transformation on a sinusoid input, compared.

When a feedback loop is opened and tested with a rhythmic input, the conditions above apply. The information gained also tells us, however, how the closed loop will operate as an oscillator (*cf*. 3.29). The homeostat shows other examples of transformation of rhythmic signals (*cf*. 3.16).

19.17 – *Nonrhythmic Input and Rhythmic Transducer. Biological Coding.* In this case, the transducer would represent an endogenous rhythm. The conditions under constant input, *e.g.* light and temperature, have been discussed (12.2, 13.18-21). The various ways in which signals may be imprinted upon a carrier frequency was discussed in 19.14.

If a signal is sent through a transducer the output always shows an interference with various unintentional, more or less random oscillations, including harmonic

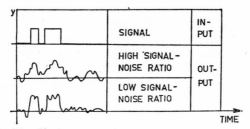

Fig. 19.17a. Signal with noise.

ones, noise, Fig. 19.17a (*cf.* 4.31-33 and 19.16). In communication theory the signal–noise ratio is very important. The higher it is the more difficult to bring out the message (decoding).

19.18 – The signal may also have to be coded by the sensors before passing on in the body and it may therefore constitute any conceivable transformation of the environmental influence. In many cases this is performed by the nervous system. The logarithmic (or exponential) response of the body is well-known, the WEBER-FECHNER Law or our mode of judging the strength of sounds in an exponential scale (in bels) instead of the absolute sound level (in phones). Theoretically, this law describes the behaviour of transducers with a constant signal–noise ratio at all intensities.

19.19 – It has also been suggested that the sensory organs are rate-sensitive, reacting upon the rate of change more than upon the level. This would facilitate the adaptation to new levels of general activity (rate of change = zero). From the cybernetic point of view, adaptation may be regarded as a 'lack of continuous information about the level of the stimulus'. The rate-sensitivity condition may be built directly into the feedback formulae (CLYNES).

Also non-nervous tissues may transform stimulus data. The logarithmic response to drugs is quite common in pharmacology and medicine. – With regard to biological rhythms it may also be pointed out that the stimuli contain two types of information: quantitative data and timing.

19.20 – *Rhythmic Input and Rhythmic Transducer.* The simplest solution is that the external agent, if strong enough, forces its frequency upon the endogenous oscillator, forced oscillations (4.29). Usually, this requires that the driving and the spontaneous frequencies must not deviate too much from each other. One example is the entrainment of the circadian rhythm by the 24-h solar day. In this case we are only considering a one-way flow of information, from the external agent to the transducer. Theoretically, the latter may also act back upon the former, establishing a feedback and coupled oscillator condition. In biological synchronization this is less common since the sources of the external stimuli are too strong and too remote for manipulation. For *Homo* it is easier since his environment is largely artificial. Since, however, he does not know much about biological rhythms and their mechanisms, he easily runs the risk of creating quite a havoc in his internal periods, intentionally or unintentionally.

19.21 – If the input cannot force the transducer, various kinds of one-way interferences may appear. The simplest type is additive interference, or superposition; as in the complicated sound wave composed of harmonics, or stationary waves resulting from interference with reflected waves (19.11). In physical wave forms interference signifies the action of several forces on one and the same component particle (*cf.* Fig. 19.10a). Any other type of interference, *e.g.* multiplicable, is of course biologically possible.

19.22 – *Beats.* Interference creates beats (*cf.* HALBERG[8], SEARS[100]) with periodic variations in amplitude (*cf.* amplitude modulation, 19.14). A good example is the CHEYNE-STOKE breathing, Fig. 6.8a. Generally, the phenomenon appears if two rhythms of different frequency interfere. The less the difference the longer the beats. Let us, for simplicity, start with two sine waves of equal amplitudes, and frequencies f_1 and f_2 (formula 19.22a). The resultant wave is given in formula 19.22b. It may be interpreted as a new wave of average frequency, $(f_1 + f_2)/2$; and periodic changes of the amplitude, which is represented by the expression $2A \cos [2\pi(f_1-f_2)/2]\, t$. The frequency of the amplitude variations is (f_1-f_2), it equals the difference between the component frequencies. This is not, however, a difference tone, which is a nonlinear phenomenon. In acoustics beats are common and heard as variations in the loudness of the tone, not as a new tone of lower frequency.

19.22a
$$y_1 = A \cos(2\pi f_1 t)$$
$$y_2 = A \cos(2\pi f_2 t)$$

19.22b
$$y = y_1 + y_2 =$$
$$= \left[2A \cos 2\pi \left(\frac{f_1 - f_2}{2}\right) t \right] \cos \left[2\pi \left(\frac{f_1 + f_2}{2}\right) t \right]$$

19.23 – *Difference and Summation Tones.* Now, let the system of beats, which represents a purely linear additive interference, take place in a transducer with nonlinear characteristics. As has already been mentioned (3.28-29), harmonics will then appear in the output. Furthermore, a peculiar transformation of the beats occurs, Fig. 19.23a, with periodic changes in the base-line. The latter will be observed as a tone, the difference tone, with the same frequency as the beat. The

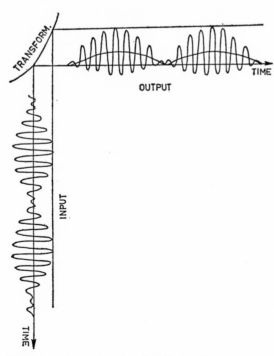

Fig. 19.23a. Nonlinear transformation in a beating system.

nonlinear transformation will, however, also affect each of the small cycles of the basic frequency, $(f_1 + f_2)/2$, giving rise to a series of harmonics. The first of this may be heard in acoustics and is usually called the summation tone, its frequency being twice that of the fundamental or $= f_1 + f_2$.

19.24 – *The Ringing Response.* A signal may also trigger damped oscillations in the transducer (*cf.* 7.7, 8.6, 13.11). This will now be superimposed upon the input, forming the ringing response (Fig. 19.24a). Repeated responses of this kind may interact, creating a sustained rhythm of other frequency than that of the signals (KENNETH[100]).

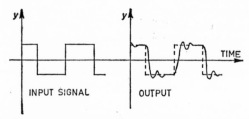

Fig. 19.24a. The ringing response.

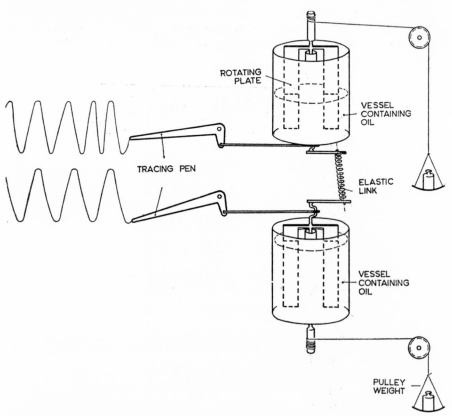

Fig. 19.25a. VON HOLST's model of relative coordination.

19.25 – *Interaction Between Rhythmic Transducers. Coupled Oscillators. Relative Coordination.* Apart from the mechanical superposition of the rhythms in several oscillators, there are other kinds of interference, where the two mechanisms act upon each other, each one changing the characteristics of the other (*cf.* 4.28). One type of interaction is the relative coordination of VON HOLST. Here, one may imagine an 'elastic link' (Koppelungsglied) coupling together several rhythms; this permits slow changes of relations between phases and frequencies but forces them back into a certain relation if they tend to slide out of it too much, the 'magnet effect'. A mechanical model is given in Fig. 19.25a. If the link is strong or the characteristic frequencies of the systems do not differ too much, a common middle frequency will result, an absolute coordination. If the link is weak, complicated patterns of frequency-relations may appear, relative coordination. If one of the partaking oscillators has a large inertia it will be more stable than the others and force them into certain relationships, a dominating oscillator. If the properties of the link are changed, sudden jumps in the relative coordination may occur from one type of relationship to another. Often the system tries to establish a certain, relatively simple frequency-relationship. Examples are given in Fig. 19.25b.

19.26 – The simplest type of coupling is unidirectional, where the first oscillator dominates the second, the second the third and so on, Fig. 19.25b (1-3). A series

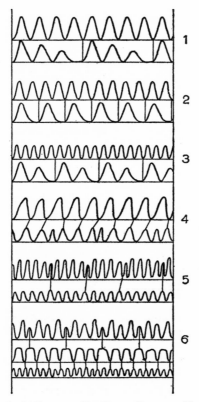

Fig. 19.25b. Examples of relative coordination, after VON HOLST.

of cogwheels may serve as an oversimplified model. One can see the motion proceed from unit to unit. In biology, the leading oscillator is often called the pacemaker. If the coupling disappears the parts start oscillating at their respective characteristic frequencies. Examples 1-3 in Fig. 19.25b are also examples of demultiplication, where each nth leading impulse triggers a response. This infers a capacity for periodic function in the second unit since it is able to 'count off' a certain number of input signals and then reset itself at zero. The transfer between decimal units in a mechanical calculator is one example. Some Geiger counters also use demultiplication circuits.

19.27 – If the coupling is multidirectional (mutual) more complicated relations obtain, Fig. 19.25b (4-6). Here, we find phase-drift; intercalated extra beats; and a tendency towards synchronization at relatively simple frequency relations, which may be fixed or change periodically.

19.28 – Whereas superposition primarily results in marked amplitude variations, relative coordination is chiefly concerned with frequency relations. The latter may show amplitude effects but these are of secondary importance. Fig. 19.25b(1) is rather an exception where a damped oscillation is dominated and reinforced by a leading unit.

19.29 – It is difficult to analyse the relationship between oscillators in relative coordination. One way is to make models. Much is gained from pure inspection of the graphs. Various methods of frequency analysis may help to establish which periods are involved. VON HOLST[3] also used another method where the successive cycles of one oscillator are superimposed, as are the corresponding time segments of the other rhythms, Fig. 19.29a.

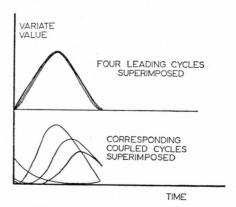

Fig. 19.29a. Relative coordination cycles superimposed, covering one complete cycle of the coupled system. Corresponding to Fig. 19.25b, ex. 1.

19.30 – Electric circuits may be made to interfere according to the superposition principle. However, there is a special type of oscillator which interacts as in relative coordination, and that is the relaxation oscillator (4.13-14). Indeed, the limiting capacity, at which the relaxation oscillator discharges, may be compared to a coupling link which becomes overstrained and throws the whole system into a new gear. Biological, chemical and electronic models of coupled oscillators have been studied by BETHE[4-7, 101], FRANCK[100], V. HOLST, HUGGER, VAN DER POL[4, 100-101], WOLLENSCHLÄGER.

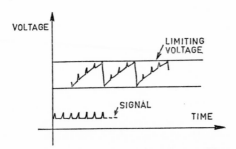

Fig. 19.30a. Frequency demultiplication in a relaxation oscillator.

If a relaxation oscillator of the type shown in Fig. 4.13b is fed with regular low-voltage signals a new phenomenon occurs, Fig. 19.30a. The signal is too weak to discharge the system during the beginning of the charging period, the oscillator is refractory. At the end of the relaxation cycle the signal triggers a response, simultaneously changing the frequency of the transducer, which in this case reacts to every 4th input impulse. This is frequency demultiplication. A strong signal resets immediately; one way of phase control in oscillators.

19.31 – *Some Biological Examples of Interaction Models.* Though physical models should be applied with caution, there are many examples of similar biological phenomena. – External rhythms forced upon a passive transducer occur in parasites which have to adopt the periodicities of the host (*cf.* BOSCH[100], HAWKING[1-2, 100]). – Various types of carrier modulation occur in the sonar localization of bats (*cf.* 6.22, NOVICK, PYE). – Beats are found in sound waves; the CHEYNE-STOKE breathing (6.8); the pulse waves (6.17, 19.11, LOBEL); the electroencephalogram (6.10-11); the electrocardiogram (6.16, SUCKLING); in the body temperature and urine excretion of arctic dwellers who were kept on an artificial day while simultaneously retaining their old rhythm (LOBBAN); or in the temperature of patients where institutional routine interferes with freerunning (HALBERG[8]); between 24-h and seasonal cycles (seasonal changes in 24-h amplitude). It occurs between the earth-rotation and moon-phase influences upon the tides (17.5), the daily amplitudes of which show monthly variations.

19.32 – Harmonic overtones with the possible occurrence of summation or difference tones is quite feasible in biological transducers which are certainly nonlinear. In testing opened biological feedback loops with a sine input the output contains harmonics (3.28-29).

The ringing response on relay signals may occur in the 24-h rhythm where HILDEBRANDT's[20-21, 104] investigations on cardiac and respiratory rates are suggestive of an interaction between a forced 24-h oscillation plus a damped oscillation set up at each new dawn (*cf.* the dawn-dusk theory of the 24-h light-action).

Interference of biological signals with noise is known to the ECG-specialist when he finds the AC-current of the mains in his curve. Whatever rhythm a biologist is studying he may expect a distortion of his curve by noise, *e.g.* from other related oscillatory processes in the body or unknown sources. The opened pupillary loop retains a high-frequency oscillation which may be thrust upon it from other brain centres. One may also speculate upon the possible role of noise in facilitating biological movement, a 'biological dither' (*cf.* 4.33).

19.33 – VON HOLST's examples of relative coordination, shown in Fig. 19.25b, partly represent the movements of different fins in decerebrated fish. The type of coupling may be changed by varying external conditions for the fish, such as the oxygenation of the breathing water. Similar relations exist in the intricate system of our movements when walking or working, *e.g.* the coordination of right and left, lower and upper extremities at walk (*cf.* BANGERT) as well as between voluntary movements and vegetative functions such as respiration and pulse (*cf.* ANDERS, HILDEBRANDT[23], PEIPER). Perhaps the tendency to form spontaneous patterns in tapping rhythms (6.14) is an example of interaction from other sources. HILDE-BRANDT has studied the coupling between heart rate and respiratory frequency (6.7). KOEPCHEN[1-2, 100] discusses this on a cybernetic basis. CLYNES builds the condition of rate sensitivity into the feedback formula, feeds it into a computer and then accurately predicts the reactions of the heart rate to respiration (pulmonary pressure receptor input into heart oscillator). FRANCK[100] made fascinating models of relative coordination by coupling oscillating electrodes (4.16), which imitate the fin curves of VON HOLST amazingly.

A remarkable biological model where all the relative coordination phenomena can be studied are the Medusae preparations of BETHE[1-2, 4-7, 101]. These have circular and radial musculature systems which contract rhythmically and which may interact through a variable coupling (*cf.* MAYNARD[1]).

19.34 – *Pacemaker* mechanisms are common in neuromuscular activity (*cf.* HOAGLAND, WELLS[1]). Especially well they have been studied in worms; and also in the heart, where the different parts show varying characteristic frequencies if decoupled (6.4,16). Frog heart preparations may show the same behaviour as demonstrated in Fig. 19.25b(1), LUCIANI's periods. In human heart block phase instabilities, locked frequency relations of various kinds, and extra interpolated or missed beats may occur. If the block is total, auricles and ventricles may beat absolutely independently of each other. An interesting ECG model has been built by VAN DER POL[4, 100-101]. It consists of three relaxation oscillators coupled in series and mimics rather well the various frequency relations in heart block. – Other muscular organs may also have pacemakers, *e.g.* the uterus (LARKS[100-101]).

Frequency demultiplication occurs in nerve fibres. It has also been advocated as one possible explanation for the accuracy and temperature independence (7.13) of circadian rhythms. The latter are then supposed to be generated through frequency demultiplication from high frequency oscillators on the molecular level. Actually, a remarkable precision is possible in this type of arrangement (SCHMITT[1]).

19.35 – *Aliasing. The Stroboscopic Effect.* The biological rhythms may be affected by our mode of observing them. A peculiar effect is obtained if the sampling period (or a multiple of it) deviates from the natural period of the variate. This may easily occur if we sample a circadian rhythm under the assumption of a 24-h rhythm. Some schematic examples are given in Fig. 19.35a. The phenomenon is called aliasing. It may also be regarded as an interference between a periodic impulse and a continuous cycle. A similar effect is obtained if we study a circular movement with the aid of a stroboscope. If the period of stroboscopic illumination is equal to that of the process we will observe no motion. In the same position is the physiologist who wants to exclude, say, the 24-h rhythm by always performing his experiments at a certain time of the day. The process will seem stationary to him and, which is worse, he cannot make any prediction as to the result of his experiment at any other time of the day. Perhaps, he would even achieve the opposite effect at another hour.

If we scan at slightly longer intervals than a multiple of the period the 'stroboscopic effect' will show a new 'forward' rhythm of lower frequency. If the scanning frequency deviates slightly in the other direction we will see a 'backward' rhythm. These phenomena are, in a way, a parallel to gear-shifts between wheels.

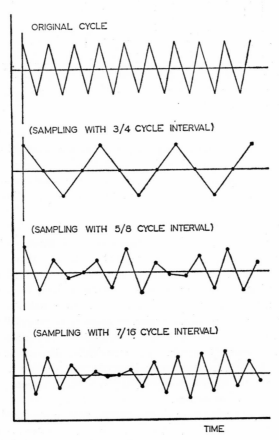

Fig. 19.35a. Aliasing.

At the ratio 1:1 a certain point on one wheel will always 'see' the same point on the other one, and so on. Obviously, our period of observation should be short as compared to the duration of the expected oscillation.

19.36 – One example of the stroboscopic effect may be that seen in the ordinary clinical temperature chart where we usually sample only twice a day. If, in certain diseases, circadian freerunning occurs the chart might look as in Fig. 19.36a. There are, of course, other possible explanations of this behaviour, *e.g.* some kind of amplitude-level dependency, and periodic interference between exogenous and endogenous rhythms. HALBERG[8] has demonstrated temperature freerunning in blinded mice and gross deviations from the 24-h schedule in human disease. Actually, the simple temperature charts in the hospitals hide a wealth of information about the patients and yet we are seldom interested in more than one bit of information: hyperpyrexia or not (*cf.* 19.13). More frequent recordings of the temperatures would also be valuable.

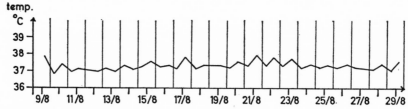

Fig. 19.36a. Typical temperature chart of a 44-year old diabetic. 9-29/8 1955. Insulin requirement 24 + 20 I.U.

PHILPOTT demonstrates another example of the stroboscopic effect in perception rhythms, where successive cycle durations would seem to increase logarithmically. If sampled at short regular arithmetic intervals, the series seems to exhibit a slowly increasing amplitude. The effect has otherwise been ascribed to fatigue.

19.37 – Another characteristic of the stroboscopic effect is that it makes essentially continuous data appear discontinuous, impulse-type. A similar effect is achieved if a rhythmic process is only perceived, or only calls forth certain effects, when its values exceed a certain level, a reaction level, as in Fig. 19.37a. In case of a constant reaction level we get the impression of regular pulses. The exacerbations of psychic diseases may sometimes be considered as the breakthrough of a cyclic metabolic process above a certain reaction level. Relaxation oscillations (4.13-14) may constitute another example if only one of their two phases (release and rebuilding) catches our attention. Mathematically, the distinction between pulses and waves implies continuous or discontinuous functions. In the physical and biological world, of course, any regular, repetitive action presupposes the continuous working of a mechanism.

If the continuous wave function slowly damps, with unchanged reaction level, another phenomenon appears, that of apparent irregular pulses, as pointed out by PHILPOTT. The same occurs with unchanged wave forms and rising reaction levels,

Fig. 19.37a. The examples of this illustration may also be regarded as a transformation effect on a rhythm by a transducer (*cf.* 19.16).

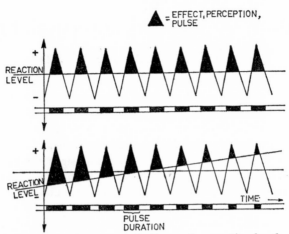

Fig. 19.37a. The interference between a rhythm and a reaction level.

19.38 – We have now seen that rhythmic models may interact or be influenced in the most varied manner. Many of these mechanisms probably occur in the living organism, with its innumerable avenues of intercommunication. If the research worker is faced with a biological rhythm which he has somehow recorded he usually knows nothing about the underlying mechanism. Before trying to decide among the wealth of possibilities, he must analyse his data in some suitable way. This entails the use of statistical and mathematical methods. After this he may wish to make an analog, a model for his biological periodicity and try it on the data.

In the analysis of rhythm data one may either try to adapt the conventional statistical methods used in biology, or the mathematical-statistical frequency analysis specially developed in economical statistics. The former alternative is the subject of the next chapter.

CHAPTER 20

Application of General Statistical Principles
to Biological Rhythms

20.1 – The previous chapter dealt with models of biological rhythms. Before we can apply any of these, we must, however, gain an insight into our own data by a careful analysis. One way of doing this, especially in short series is to use the same statistical tools as in other biological work; *e.g.* means, standard deviations, *t*-tests, the analysis of variance. This will be discussed here. The other way is to apply methods developed for the analysis of time series in mathematical and economical statistics, centering around the harmonic analysis. That will follow in the next chapter.

20.2 – The great variability of biological data often calls for a careful analysis in order to separate trends from errors of various kinds. In general, statistics is the problem of how to collect data, how to measure them, how to describe them, how to judge the reliability of the shapes found, how to evaluate differences in the shapes and, ultimately, the question of the relation between parts and of causation. Some textbooks are: AITKEN[1], BARTELS[2], CRAMÉR[1], FISHER[201, 300], GALLO, HERDAN, KENNEY, LINKE[100], MAINLAND, PEARSON[100], SAHLENAU, SIEGEL[200], SNEDECOR, TINTNER, WALLIS[100], YULE[100]; see also BLISS, McHUGH.

Biological rhythms often offer an almost too profuse wealth of data, since repeated assays in time are needed. Whatever we study, this necessity heavily multiplies our work, especially if we are not primarily interested in rhythms. Correlations between static measures may be difficult enough to study, especially if there are many variables. It must then be rather disheartening to realize that the relation may change from hour to hour, and that the problem now has to be met in terms of interactions between a series of variables which are all moving.

This probably explains the stubborn refusal of some disciplines to accept the existence of biological rhythms. The medical profession is only now reluctantly yielding to the fact that neither is the diseased person statically pathological nor is the normal subject an assemblage of static parts. What was earlier a problem of the transition from normality to disease by a set of well-defined functions is now a question of disturbed and oscillating servomechanisms, faulty transformation of rhythmic stimuli synchronizing the activity of bio-oscillators, and a patient who turns a new face towards the doctor at each different hour of the day or year.

The most remarkable lack of interest in biological rhythms has perhaps been demonstrated in pharmacology where publications on biological periodicity are still scarce. The action of drugs is difficult to evaluate and standardization must be accurate. Yet, it must also be realized that the response to drugs may differ considerably both with regard to the time of administration (5.20), and with the initial state of the body functions (*cf.* Chapter 11), also that drugs may act as synchronizers.

Biological statistics is getting increasingly important. Its high demand for repeated assays is met by rising funds for the life sciences and by automatic machinery. Most of the tedious statistical computations are rapidly performed by the modern computers.

20.3 – *Errors.* In biology, the errors of method are usually larger than in physics. Caution is therefore needed in choosing methods of assay so that the biological message is not drowned in noise. The rhythms need perhaps even more sensitive methods since the changes to be evaluated may be rather slight. It must not be forgotten, however, that here, as in general biology, a larger error may often be off-set by an increase in the number of assays. The error in a mean of N simultaneously recorded assays varies inversely with the square root of N (20.3a).

However, the errors of method are often insignificant as compared to the large interindividual variation and this can only be countered with a reasonable number of individuals. Here, however, the presence of a rhythm helps since consistent parallel curves of behaviour do not easily arise at random, not even in small groups of individuals. The consistency is, of course, enhanced and the interindividual variation reduced by a homogeneous material, both with regard to animals, times of assay and conditions of assay. HALBERG obtains remarkable results by using a carefully inbred, genetically pure strain of mice which is meticulously guarded against disturbance from without. Chickens are also easy to obtain in homogeneous batches.

20.3a N = number of variate values
x = single variate value
σ_x = error of method = error in a single variate value = standard deviation of the observed N values
$\bar{x}$ = arithmetic mean
$\varepsilon_{\bar{x}}$ = error of mean = $\sigma_x/N^{0.5}$

20.4 – *Sampling.* Recording of the rhythms is usually done by interval sampling. The observation period is important owing to the risk of aliasing (19.35-36). One should obviously be cautious when drawing inferences from such data. Mathematical methods are, however, available for a correct analysis of the values. Large observation intervals facilitate the scanning of very long records of individual cycles. If only short runs of rhythms are obtainable (which often happens in biology) a combination of relatively short sampling periods, and (instead of long series) a large number of individuals still permits more analysis than one may think (*cf.* BLUME, MENZEL[4-5, 9, 15-16, 100-102]). The amount of information required from a single curve also varies. If we only want the approximate location in time of the maximum of minimum, fewer observations are needed, than if a detailed study of the curve shape is required. One should remember, though, that the true peak may be anywhere within the range given by the two closest observed points

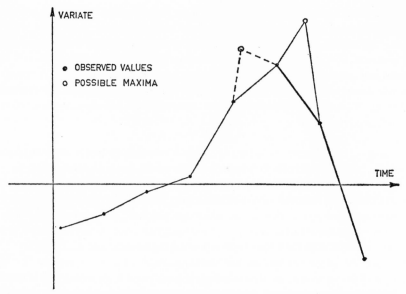

Fig. 20.4a. The location of a true maximum. Two possibilities are shown.

surrounding the nominal peak value (Fig. 20.4a).

In general, it may be said that the smaller the sampling interval the better for the biologist, and the easier the statistical analysis. Often, special conditions limit the number of observations which can be made, *e.g.* expenses, amount of distress tolerable to the subject, or interaction between the assay and the latter. Usually, it is a well-spent effort to push the recording technique towards this limit. Also, it is valuable to try as many different individuals as possible, since considerable differences in the shapes of the cycles occur. Long runs of records from a single subject may give a true picture of him, but the problem remains of how representative he is of the mother population from which he is derived. Notwithstanding this, very long single records may sometimes be explored with success (*cf.* BOCH-NIK[2-3]).

20.5 – The ideal case would be runs of continuously recorded cycles of some suitable continuous variable, from each subject in a homogeneous group of individuals. Modern telemetering techniques are becoming increasingly popular since they give continuous records and provide a minimum of interference with the animal. The latter is important since manual sampling may seriously disturb the animals and also act as a synchronizer. Telemetering techniques may be adapted to many types of assays, both physical and chemical. They should be used whenever possible. – Unfortunately, such ideal conditions cannot always be upheld. Some diseases, *e.g.*, are very scarce. Some methods of assay may be difficult, time consuming, or expensive. Telemetering may be impossible. In some cases, one has to kill the animal, *e.g.* in liver glycogen determinations, and continuous records are out of the question. Then, homogeneity of the material becomes important.

20.6 – *Variates*. Though our usual situation is discontinuous recording from continuous variates, some measurements are discontinuous in themselves, *e.g.* activity, since it is recorded as activity per time unit. In spite of this, activity rhythms have perhaps yielded more to the theory of rhythms than any other type of measurement. Some data are frequencies, *e.g.* seasonal variations in morbidity. Here, as in case of the killed animals, a certain distortion occurs, since individual differences in phase, range and shape of the curves cannot be evaluated. Often, however, the percentage is derived from a variate which is really continuous. One example constitutes the seasonal morbidity curves.

Morbidity, the catching of a disease, largely depends on continuous individual changes in the sensitivity to a disease. Let us assume that the susceptibilities of a group of persons are normally distributed (which is not necessarily true, especially if the sensitivity fluctuates) and that all persons superceding a certain susceptibility level catch the disease. The situation is depicted in Fig. 20.6a.

The true measure of susceptibility is not the percentage diseased persons, it is the deviation of the disease sensitivity limit from the mean susceptibility, *i.e.* the normal deviate. If the percentage fluctuates the deviate does so too, and may give a truer picture of the biological mechanisms. The deviates (in σ units) corresponding to each percentage may be read from tables; this transformation is the basis of the probit analysis. DeRudder[12, 16] has studied epidemic morbidity in this way. He shows that the fluctuations of the normal deviate are a function of the seasonal variations in solar radiation intensity. – The problem of what percentages really mean in biology is, however, rather complicated. The subject will return later.

The above illustrated one method of finding the true oscillating variate behind the actual data. One should always have this general problem in mind. The values

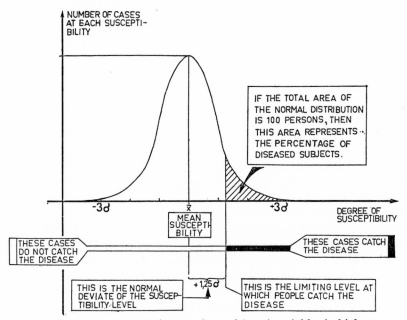

Fig. 20.6a. One relation between frequencies and 'true' variables in biology.

may only represent a transformation of the 'true' variate. The aliasing and similar phenomena (Figs. 19.35a and 19.37a) are conspicuous examples of such transformations.

It might also be well to remember that many of our biological variates have not been directly recorded, but are values calculated from several directly measured factors, as are e.g. quotients. Such measures have often embarrassing statistical properties with regard to frequency distributions and correlations. Actually, it is always possible to study each of the component variables separately, followed by a study of the interaction between their rhythms (cf. RUOSTEENOJA[100]). – Average curves also pose problems, to be discussed later.

20.7 – The variate assayed may be almost anything in biology which can be recorded, from pigments in the crustacean integument to the pain in phantom limbs. Some have been specially well studied, for the most varied reasons: body temperature because it was an early biological measure to be quantitatively measured; animal activity and plant leaf movements since they are relatively easy to record in large populations; liver glycogen owing to its impact on earlier concepts of metabolic physiology; basal metabolism in consequence of its conceptual fundamentality. An example of a group of variables exciting great interest today are the endocrine functions.

20.8 – *Methods of Assay.* The methods of assay are, of course, as varied as the things sampled. Automatism and relatively simple methods are advantageous owing to the large amounts of measurements necessary. An important type of recording device in biological rhythm research is the 'actograph'. All possible sizes and constructions exist: large wheel cages for mice; small fingerbowls for mud snails, suspended in spring-loaded levers; or wired cages for flies where two sets of wires, each containing every second wire, are connected to electric terminals and shortcircuits are recorded (cf. ASCHOFF[1], CLOUDSLEY-THOMPSON[16, 28], MANN[500], ROBERTS[3], SHIPTON[100], STEPHENS[1]).

Kymographic or electronic writers may be used; levers, mirrors, or electronic devices may be chosen for magnification of movements. An extremely sensitive actograph is the ballistocardiograph (6.17). – More remote measures related to activity are the counts of marked birds (18.9), various methods of recording action spectra (13.5) in unicellular animals, or the compass direction numbers used for studying animal orientation (18.11). – Time lapse photography is convenient for the recording of very slow movements in plants and animals (cf. OTT, TAYLOR[1]). – For telemetering methods see e.g. ESSLER[100], FOLK[6], MILES, SCHECHTER[100], SLATER, SULLIVAN[100].

If we want to maintain constant temperature in the experimental chamber, the thermostat sensor must not be too close to the animals, because their endogenous temperature rhythm will heat the room, especially if there are many animals. The control will then try to combat the endogenous rhythm. This is an interesting feedback situation but usually not what we want.

20.9 – *Definitions of Biological Rhythms. Terminology.* Before describing a biological rhythm, we must have a definition of it. Starting with the simple assumptions as given in Fig. 1.2a (cf. 1.8-9), we may define biological variate movement in time as chronobiological movement, and fluctuations of values between upper and lower limits as chronobiological variation. The latter may be irregular, with random timing or a variation between variable limits. This would more or less correspond to the statistician's stationary time series, random deviations from a trend level or line. The variation may also be regular, with a repetition of more or less identical waveforms. This would correspond to the statistician's non-stationary or evolutive time series. The biological rhythms might then be classified as a regular chronobiological variation.

20.10 – The word *rhythm* in itself is a broad term including most kinds of recurring phenomena, which in some loose usage may not even have to be regular. The same applies to *biological rhythm*. The early workers in the field sometimes felt a little uncomfortable when their work was confused with folk-songs and dances (though these *are* really biological rhythms). The same applies to the most natural condensation *biorhythm* which in Germany is helplessly tied-up with birth control. No wonder that many biologists even avoided the term rhythm altogether, using substitutes such as *period, cycle* or *oscillation*. Today, such considerations need not hamper us. The term *biological rhythms* has become accepted, though many persons unfortunately still strongly oppose the *biorhythm* version.

The biological rhythms are seldom very accurate. In this, they differ from the related physical and mathematical concepts, where terms such as period, cycle and oscillation seem to belong more properly. The philosopher KLAGES (cf. FRAUCHI-GER) strongly distinguished between meter and rhythm (Ge. Takt und Rhythmus). *Meter* would signify the recurrence of identical shapes at identical intervals in time or space, whereas *rhythm* would indicate the recurrence of similar shapes at similar intervals. If so, biological rhythms is again a correct term. Some mathematicians, however, find any biological variation far to irregular ever to be called even a rhythm and propose the term near-rhythms.

In general, the variability in the biological rhythm shapes together with our scant knowledge of their mode of action has made it well-nigh impossible for the biological rhythmologists to agree on an official nomenclature, though there exists a nomenclature board in the Society for Biological Rhythms. With the present rapid development of the field it is hoped that a firmer basis for this work will soon develop.

As it is, even *period, cycle, oscillation,* and *rhythm* are used as complete synonyms. Other stumbling blocks are *e.g.* the numerous names for endogenous rhythms (4.26) or the word *diurnal*. The latter in English also means the day-time as opposed to the night (nocturnal, nycthémérale). As synonyms are used: diel, dial, circadian, daily, 24-hour.

The word *amplitude* has a very exact meaning in mathematics but has been rather loosely used in biology, even signifying the total range of variation in any rhythm curve. The general problem is whether we should simply adopt terms from technology and reduce our demands for exactitude in biological rhythm research, or whether we should coin entirely new terms for everything (cf. 13.22). In the former case, the general scientist will be able to grasp what we mean without difficulty. In the latter case, biological rhythms will be even less intelligible to people than they are now, which is not too helpful.

One way would be to add the prefix *bio* or *biological* to the ordinary technical terms. Except for 'biorhythm', this would work; *e.g.* bioamplitude, bioperiod, biofrequency, biological phase angle, a biological power spectrum (or power biospectrum).

20.11 – *Biological Meaning.* When choosing statistical and mathematical tools in describing biological rhythms we should also demand that they have a definite biological meaning (*cf.* 20.6). This is, of course, a sensible proposition throughout biostatistics. One should go far in search of such methods. However, the goal is not always possible to achieve. The harmonic analysis, which utilizes all information in the data, presents them as an assemblage of superimposed sine curves which often do not exist at all as biological entities, though exceptions occur (19.11). Yet, the method is presently indispensable (*cf.* Chapter 21). This increases the responsibility of the statisticians and biologists who later interpret the results in biological terms. – Caution is also due with regard to the normal distribution. This is a law of random causes but not a biological law. True normal distributions are not so common in biology (*cf.* SOLLBERGER[2-3, 5, 100], TRELOAR).

20.12 – *Description of Rhythms. Graphs.* Given an assembly of rhythm curves, one has to describe them in some way. They contain a certain amount of information (trends), and of random variation (errors, noise). We want to eliminate the noise and extract as many bits of information as possible. The work of isolating this depends on the type of the rhythm. The perfectly regular sine rhythm is completely described by one formula containing three parameters; amplitude, phase and frequency. Other curves may present elaborate shapes which are impossible to catch mathematically, Figs. 1.30a (lower part) and 19.7a. A continuous rhythm graph may, under circumstances contain so much information that it seems almost impossible to save it all in the description. However, two methods are of value here: (1) the mathematical frequency analysis, conveniently performed with computers (see next section); and (2) graphical methods of computation and representation, which may save enormous amounts of labour.

Many examples concerning the use of graphs in representing and analyzing biological rhythms have already been given. Very common is the ordinary 'variate-time graph', where the values obtained are plotted on the Y-axis against time on the X-axis, depicting the variate as a function of time (19.6). Polar coordinates are, of course, well-suited to cyclic phenomena (*cf.* the clock graph, 5.22-23). Related are the compass direction charts used in animal orientation (18.11). The statistical properties of circular coordinates, including the circular normal distribution (*cf.* BARTON[300], BREITENBERGER, GUMBEL[100], KUIPER, WATERMAN[1], WATSON), pose many problems. We have also stressed the relation between the circle and the sine function, illustrating the phase angle concept (Figs. 1.31a-b).

Many other kinds of special graphs may, of course, be encountered, as when a cycle parameter (Fig. 7.10a) is plotted against day-number or light-intensity (ASCHOFF[16-17]). Cycle parameters may be correlated in graphs (amplitude-duration-phase-level graphs, *cf.* MENZEL[9]). Even three-dimensional graphs may be prepared.

On the mathematical side there are the gain-phase-frequency diagrams used for servomechanisms (3.30, Chapter 23); also the various frequency spectra (Chapter 21); and the phase-planes (velocity graphs, Chapter 22). Superposition of curve graphs is often used in the comparison and analysis of biological rhythms (cf. Fig. 19.29a, SOLLBERGER[7]).

20.13 – Often, it is actually difficult to utilize all the data in the rhythm curves. One may then wish to sacrifice some of the information (though it should always be done reluctantly) and to pick out some chosen bits of information, cycle parameters, such as bioamplitude, bioduration, peak-time, etc. as exemplified in Fig. 1.30a. Even the recording technique may be tailored to this. Interval sampling is, in itself, such a choice. Some parameters are fairly obvious, though their precise definition may sometimes be difficult. We shall now discuss them separately.

20.14 – Biolevels and Base-lines. Rhythmic variations occur around a certain central value which represents the general level of activity. It may be defined as the value we would get if the rhythm disappears, the noncyclic trend. Though its meaning is perfectly clear, its statistical definition is difficult, since we do not know the laws which govern the biological rhythms. In some cases the noncyclic trend may be constant and the level would be indicated by a horizontal straight line in our graphs, the base-line. In other cases, the trend may be non-horizontal or even nonlinear. The problem is discussed by PETRÉN[100], SOLLBERGER[3], [5-6]. Sometimes the noncyclic trend may be obtained directly by heavy damping of the recording system, as in intravascular blood pressure registrations.

If the noncyclic trend is constant, the horizontal level may conveniently be represented by some kind of statistical total average (arithmetic, harmonic or geometric mean, median, mode, middle value) of the whole cycle. Which parameter to choose would depend on the statistical distribution of the assay values.

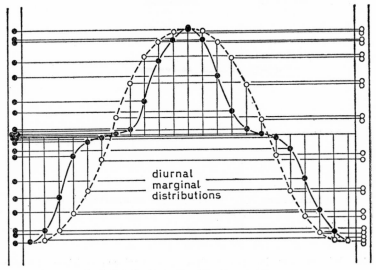

Fig. 20.14a. The marginal distribution of values in a cycle.

(of the 'hourly' averages, not of simultaneous values). We may start by asserting that this distribution will not be normal (Gaussian), Fig. 20.14a.

In a sine wave the distribution will be U-shaped. If a central tendency occurs, it will be combined with an accumulation of values in the middle. In both cases, the distribution will, however, be symmetrical, and any type of average may be used. The ordinary mean (arithmetic) is usually to be preferred owing to its mathematical properties. In large materials with many cycles the middle value may serve well. If the distribution of the hourly values around the level is skew, other types of averages could be used, or a transformation of the data tried, *e.g.* a logarithmic transformation (the mean of the logarithms is the logarithm of the geometric mean of the original values).

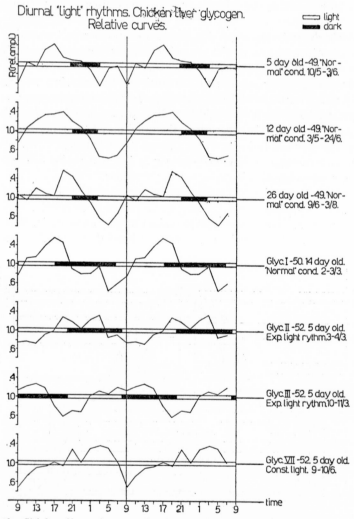

Fig. 20.14b. Chicken liver glycogen rhythms under various conditions, SOLLBERGER[3]. Each point represents 10-16 new animals. Relative variations.

Many biological rhythms display a central tendency, a kind of levelling off or an intermediate level (ELFVIN[100]), somewhere between the maximum and minimum. It appears in the 24-h glycogen rhythms in Fig. 20.14b. What it signifies is uncertain; an interference with a 12-h rhythm, or the reference value of the biological servosystem (3.2). Perhaps, it represents the true position of the cycle level.

20.15 – If the level is constant, the first and the last value of a cycle will be equal, otherwise not. The simplest approximation to a changing trend line is a sloping straight base-line, where the slope is given by the difference between the first and last value in the cycle. Such a line may also easily be made to pass through the centre of the cycle (*e.g.* represented by the total average placed at mid-time). This construction is simple and adequate enough for most practical purposes. Its use is illustrated in Figs. 20.15a-d.

Another way of finding the sloping line is to fit a straight regression line to the data. Of course, it may not necessarily show the slope indicated by the end points, unless this is given as a condition for its calculation. Regression lines may also be calculated with other conditions, *e.g.* that they must be logarithmic or sine-shaped (least squares method). Often the three types of resulting base-lines coincide fairly well, Fig. 20.15e. Unfortunately, the calculation of regression lines is very dependent on the statistical distribution of the cycle values and of the general

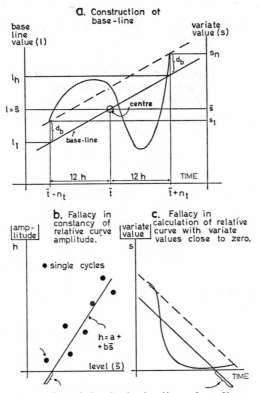

Fig. 20.15a-c. The construction of simple sloping linear base-lines **and relative** curves.

symmetry of the cycle curve along both coordinate axes. It may therefore under certain circumstances turn out quite erroneous. This risk is less if it can be calculated from several consecutive cycles. Then a baseline may also be drawn more or less by eye through the series of means of the cycles, as in Fig. 20.15f, or be obtained as a moving average covering a time period equal to the cycle length.

Diurnal rhythm of citric acid in diabetics.
Total output in the urine in mg/2 h
5 cases followed during 1—5 days.
Sloping baselines.

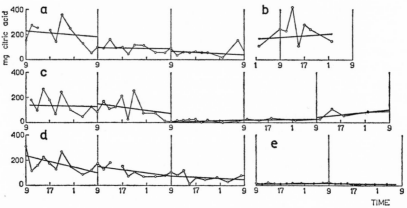

Fig. 20.15d. Linear sloping base-lines in 24-h rhythms of citric acid excretion in 5 cases of diabetes, a-e.

Fitting of various kinds of special baselines
to 5- 12- and 26-days old animals.
Diurnal chicken liver glycogen cycles.

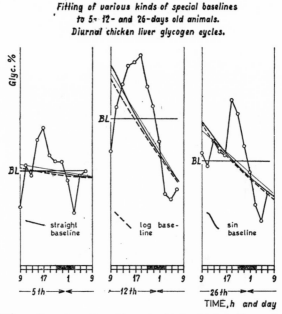

Fig. 20.15e. Fitting of various base-lines to 24-h chicken liver glycogen cycles, cf. Fig. 9.8a.

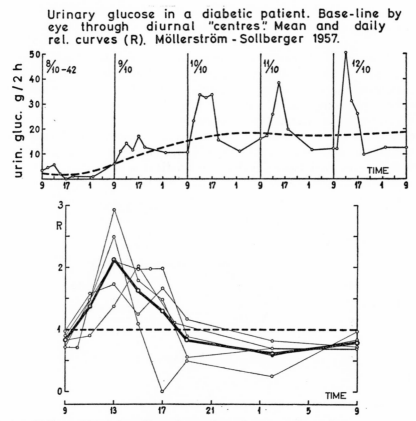

Fig. 20.15f. Several-cycle base-lines, drawn through consecutive cycle means. Glucosuria in one case of diabetes. Also corresponding relative curves.

20.16 – In some cases special assumptions may be made about the base-line, as in Fig. 9.8a. Here, total cycle averages are used for mature animals. The base-line in starvation is represented by a logarithmic formula ($\log l = a + b \log t$; $l =$ base-line value, $t =$ time). The base-line of the growing and feeding newborns is assumed to be S-shaped ($\log [(l\text{-}d)/(e\text{-}l)] = a + bt$, symbols as before, a, b, d and e are parameters). The same is assumed for the late embryos which are rapidly depleting their store of egg yolk. A straight sloping line represents the trend in the early embryos. In all cases the least squares method is used.

As can be seen, there are many methods for finding the base-line. It cannot be proven that any of them yields the true noncyclic trend. Neither can it be investigated by experimental obliteration of the rhythms, since such methods usually change the level, too.

The data used in calculations of the base-line constitute a temporal succession of values. If several assays are performed simultaneously they should enter the base-line calculations as one average, especially if the number of values changes from time to time in the cycle (even though the errors of the averages will vary somewhat owing to this). The assays should be equidistant in time. It should also be stressed that in calculations of this kind the cycle period must be known *a priori*. If not, we must resort to other types of analysis.

20.17 – *Bioamplitude. Amplitude Line.* Another parameter of the biological rhythm curve is its 'amplitude'. The term, though easy to understand intuitively, has been much discussed (20.10). As synonyms (for the double amplitude) there have been advocated expressions such as: height, cycle range, maximum-minimum difference, or peak-to-trough variation. The term amplitude will be difficult to avoid in practice. – The pathologist may talk about normal or non-normal bioamplitudes, *e.g.* with MENZEL[11] about hyperkymatia (too large bioamplitude), normokymatia, hypokymatia (too small bioamplitude) or akymatia (loss of bioamplitude).

The bioamplitude is easily measured. If a sloping base-line is present, this may be corrected for (*e.g.* as in Fig. 20.17a).

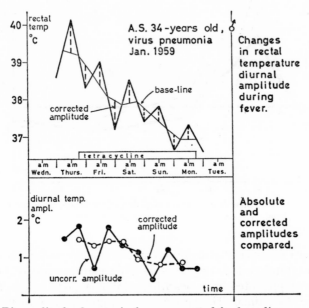

Fig. 20.17a. Bioamplitude changes in fever, corrected for base-line.

20.18 – The bioamplitude is often correlated to the other parameters, *e.g.* the biofrequency (MENZEL[9]) or the biolevel (MÖLLERSTRÖM[100], SOLLBERGER[1-5]). In the former case, the relation is often inverse, the higher the frequency the lower the biopeak. This may arise from energy considerations. If the bioamplitude represents the power of the cyclic function it is natural that more biological power should be available the longer the period of its turnover. This is seen in relaxation oscillators (Fig. 4.27b).

20.19 – Relationships between cycle amplitudes and levels may arise if a constantly turning system has a variable load (Fig. 4.6a and 27a). This may well be the case in diabetic blood sugar or glucosuria, liver glycogen storage, or other meta-

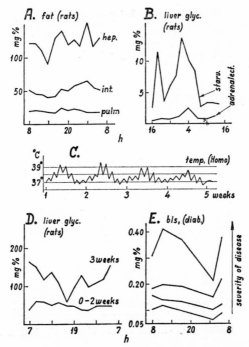

Fig. 20.19a-e. Relations between amplitude and level in biological rhythms, collected from literature; A. fat contents in rat organs (204 large white rats) with different capacity of storing and metabolizing fat, liver, intestines and lungs, mg/100 g body weight (HOLMGREN[4]); B. liver glycogen in 120 starving rats (ÅGREN) and 42 adrenal-ectomized rats, mg/100 g body weight (zero values put equal to 0.5 mg/100 g); C. clinical temperature chart in a case of periodic disease (ASK-UPMARK); D. liver glycogen in rats of different ages, 96 aged 0-2 weeks and 72 aged 3 weeks, mg/100 g body weight (SECKEL[100]); E. blood sugar in 4 cases of human diabetes of varying severity, starvation days (HOPMANN[2]). Cf. SOLLBERGER[5].

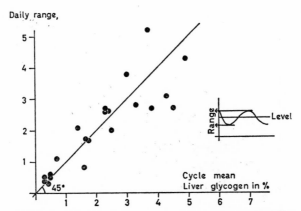

Fig. 20.19f. Amplitude–level relationship in 21 liver glycogen cycles of varying experimental conditions. This and Figs. 20.19 g-k illustrate amplitude lines.
Cf. SOLLBERGER[3].

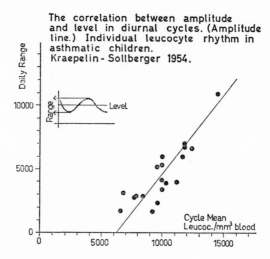

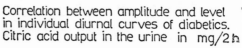

Fig. 20.19g.

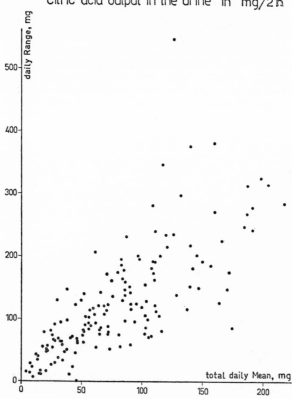

Fig. 20.19h.

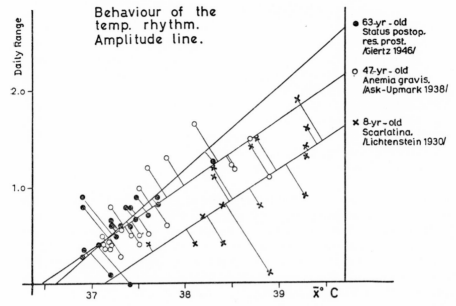

Fig. 20.19i.

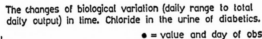

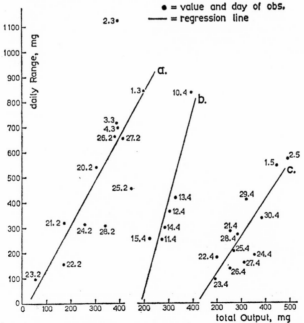

Fig. 20.19k.

bolites (*cf.* Figs. 20.15d,f, 20.17a and 20.19a-e). For a study of the relationship, daily ranges and levels may be plotted against each other. Usually, fairly linear relationships appear, the amplitude lines, Figs. 20.19f-k. They seem only to occur if some external factor brings about a variation in the total amount of available biological energy, whether between groups of animals (Fig. 20.19f), between individuals (Figs. 20.19e,g,h) or in one individual (Figs. 20.17a and 20.19c, i, k). In individuals or groups which only differ at random such correlations do not appear, *e.g.* in normal body temperatures (SOLLBERGER[3, 6]). If the available energy is very low, the rhythmic variations may be so small so as to be insignificant (Fig. 20.19b,d, lowermost). This does not necessarily mean that the rhythm has disappeared, only that the average level is small (SOLLBERGER[5]).

20.20 – The amplitude line may pass through the origin (Fig. 20.19f). This means that the variations disappear when the studied factor disappears. It does not necessarily mean that the causative biological rhythmic factor has stopped functioning. On the other hand, the variations may disappear at a certain level of the function. A theoretical estimate of this level may be obtained as the X-axis intercept of the amplitude line (Figs. 20.19g, i). One may well wonder about the significance of this intercept. Is it perhaps the normal (basal) value of the group or individual? May such relationships be used for finding individual normal values, yes, even while the subject in question is sick? To find the normal value of a single patient would be of importance in medicine.

20.21 – *Sigma Line.* Similar relationships sometimes exist between biological

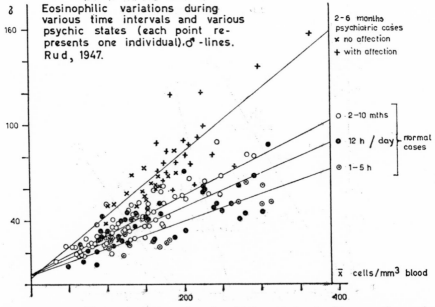

Fig. 20.21a. Temporal variation of eosinophil leucocytes in *Homo* under various conditions. Relationship between standard deviations and means of the various groups.

variations in general and corresponding group means (*cf.* Fig. 20.21a, SOLL-BERGER[1-3, 6, 100]), the sigma lines. They may also be nonlinear.

20.22 – *Relative Curve.* If the amplitude line represents one and the same cyclic system under different loads, the basic rhythm should be obtained by calculating relative variations around the levels, *i.e.* relative curves (PETRÉN[100], SOLLBER-GER[3, 5]). The resulting relative bioamplitudes are then simply represented by the coefficient of inclination of the amplitude line, and are theoretically constant. This will, however, only be true if the amplitude line passes through the origin, as in Fig. 20.19f. Else, a correction for the X-axis intercept must first be made; there may, unfortunately, arise fallacies in this procedure (as shown in Fig. 20.15b-c, lower part) especially if single cycles exist with a level smaller than that of the regression intercept (SOLLBERGER[3]). Relative curves and corresponding absolute curves are shown in Figs. 9.8c and 9.8a, 9.8d and 9.8a, 20.14b and 9.8a, 20.15f, 20.22a and 20.19b, 20.22b and 9.8a. In Fig. 20.22b the effects of several different base-lines are compared (*cf.* Fig. 20.15e). Fig. 20.22a, as compared to 20.19b, illustrates nicely that an apparent disappearance of a rhythm may only be due to a disappearance of the substrate forming it (glycogen) but not of the underlying rhythmic mechanism (*cf.* 20.20).

20.23 – *Duration, Frequency, Period.* It is inherent in the variability of biological rhythms that the duration of a rhythm may differ from cycle to cycle. This may arise from various kinds of errors, whether we are concerned with a natural frequency or a synchronized exogenous one. It may also signify an interference with other periodicities. This variability is often stressed by the biologist as a warning against a too energetic application of mathematical methods of analysis. The attitude is wrong. Particularly the mathematical frequency analysis includes such a variation as a normal component and enables the calculation of the average duration. This also means that the frequency (the inverse of the duration) is a statistical measure which either demands a long series of cycles for its determination or else an *a priori* assumption about the true value (as sometimes in exogenous rhythms).

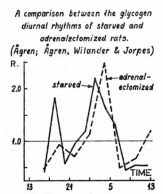

Fig. 20.22a. Relative 24-h glycogen curves in starved and adrenalectomized rats, *cf.* Fig. 20.19b.

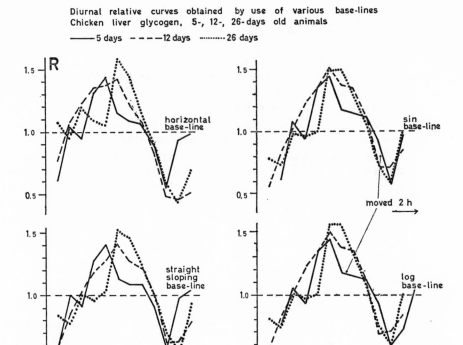

Fig. 20.22b. 24-h relative chicken liver glycogen curves, with varying base-lines. *Cf.* Fig. 20.15e.

An exception are cases where there is a continuous non-random shift in the period itself (*cf.* 6.26, 19.7,36, PHILPOTT). There is also a very slight shift of the period in damped oscillations (*cf.* 3.19). If the phenomenon is of large magnitude, it creates mathematical difficulties, unless some transformation of the time scale can yield a constant period.

20.24 – *Timing. Phasing.* The position in time of a cycle or its parameters is an important measure. This means a projection of a desired cycle point onto the time axis in our graphs. We ask *when* the desired phenomenon occurs. Often, this is the approach in practical applications of the rhythm research. The physician, *e.g.*, may want to know the optimal time to apply a drug. Prediction, whether in weather forecasts or economical cycles, aims at determining the future critical time points.

The timed event may be any parameter on the cycle curve: the maximum, (peak), primary or secondary; the minimum (trough), primary or secondary; base-line crossings; or any other irregularity of the contour. – Errors may arise from the interval of observation (19.35), the difficulty in defining the desired point, or biological variations in its time position.

The duration is a time measure. Partial durations may sometimes be calculated, the time distance between any two points; *e.g.* from minimum to maximum (the ascending limb); or the reverse (the descending limb). One example are the P-Q and S-T intervals of the ECG, *cf*. Fig. 6.16a.

20.25 – *Peaks*. The most often timed cycle measure is the peak, not least in the study of synchronization (*cf*. ASCHOFF[16-17]). This practice has contributed enormously to our knowledge of biological rhythms. There is a problem involved here, though. Even in a random time series (Chapter 21) peaks will appear and these will tend to occur at certain average intervals. Much depends on the definition of a peak and the observation interval. The problem has been treated by COLE[200-201] in connection with the animal population cycles.

If N random observations are made and if a simple peak is defined as a value surrounded by two smaller values, the average distance between peaks (cycle length) is $3N/(N-5)$ value intervals. If we want more clear-cut peaks we may define a dominant peak as a simple peak surrounded by two lower simple peaks and get an average 'cycle duration' of $9N/(N-17)$ value intervals. The theoretical durations become 3 and 9 intervals respectively if the number of observations (N) becomes infinite. The formulae are further modified if the number of possible variate values is restricted, if a certain minimum absolute value of a peak is required, or if serial correlation (Chapter 21) occurs. In practice, the random cycle lengths will always be somewhat larger than 3 or 9 years. Difficulties of this kind are lessened by using short recording intervals or mathematical frequency analysis.

A rhythm curve may have secondary peaks (or minima). It can be bimodal, indicating multiple control as in activity and glycogen 24-h rhythms, or even multimodal.

20.26 – *Shape*. The biological cycle shape varies extremely, from rather complex structures, such as the EEG or ECG (6.10-11,16) to the relative regularity of liver glycogen cycles. Compound indices describing the shape may, of course, be devised; from the assignment of appropriate models to the construction of quotients between the slopes of the ascending and descending limbs (SOLLBERGER[5]). Random variations in shape will also occur, and these may be used in statistical methods of analyzing exogenous rhythms (see the next sections).

20.27 – *Moving Variate. Rhythms in Frequency Distributions*. The dominating model for statistical frequency distributions is the normal (Gaussian) curve. It is, however, less common in biology than one would think. One might perhaps expect to find it in a group of values obtained simultaneously from a homogeneous population. If the latter belong to a temporally moving variate (SOLLBERGER[3, 7-9, 100]), the distribution is nevertheless usually not normal. It has been shown that both standard deviations and skewness change during the day in liver glycogen and rectal temperature data from chickens (SOLLBERGER[1, 3, 6, 100]). This is simply a general characteristic of the transformation and divergence phenomena, which will now be described.

20.28 – *Transformation Phenomenon*. This signifies that the distribution of variate values is a function of the variate path formula, the dispersion being roughly proportional to the velocity of the function (Fig. 20.28).

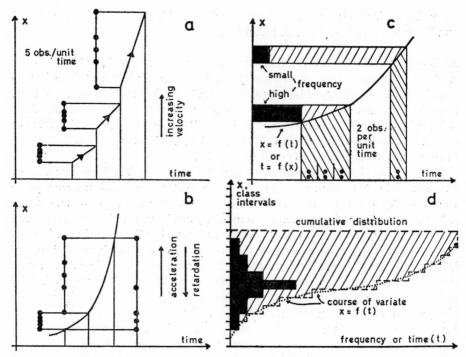

Fig. 20.28a-d. The transformation phenomenon. Equidistant sampling from one moving variate.

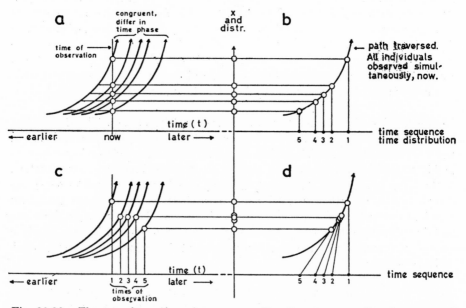

Fig. 20.28e. The transformation phenomenon. Simultaneous sampling from several phase-dispersed moving variate paths.

It is first assumed that equidistant sampling from one variate is made, without preservation of the time location (Fig. 20.28a). If the path accelerates, skew distributions should occur (Fig. 20.28b). If the variate values are collected into frequency distributions, the frequencies will be inversely proportional to the path velocity (Fig. 20.28c). Theoretically, the path could be reconstructed from the cumulative distribution (Fig. 20.28d).

If, instead, sampling is done at one single time point but from separate, congruent but phase-dispersed paths, essentially the same transformation effect occurs as before, Fig. 20.28e (a-b). The larger the dispersion of the paths in time, the larger the dispersion of the observed values. This is important since the transformation effect of Fig. 20.28a-b may be negligible in most relatively slow-moving biological rhythms, whereas the phase-displacement between individual rhythms is often considerable. Fig. 20.28e (c-d) shows that this effect can theoretically be offset by a suitable order of sampling.

20.29 – *Divergence Phenomenon.* This occurs if the variate paths are not congruent, and brings about a correlation between the average path values and the dispersions (Fig. 20.29a-b), *cf.* the σ-line (20.21). Fig. 20.29c shows that the effects of the transformation and divergence phenomena on the dispersion of observed values are roughly linearly additive. Fig. 20.29d shows the net result on a simple cycle model.

20.30 – *A Possible Method of Distinguishing Between External and Endogenous Components in Biological Rhythms.* Little is known about the distribution of

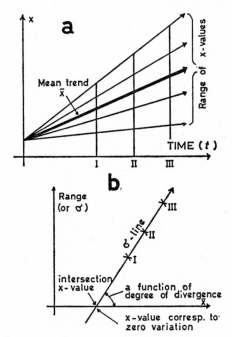

Fig. 20.29a-b. The divergence phenomenon.

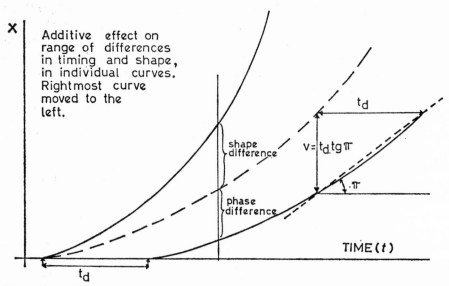

Fig. 20.29c. The linear additivity of the transformation and divergence phenomena.

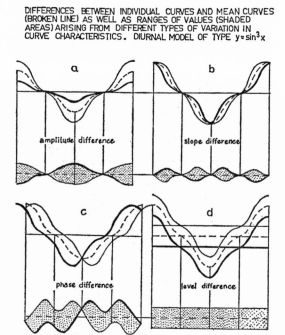

Fig. 20.29d. Rhythmic variations in vertical scatter on a cycle model.

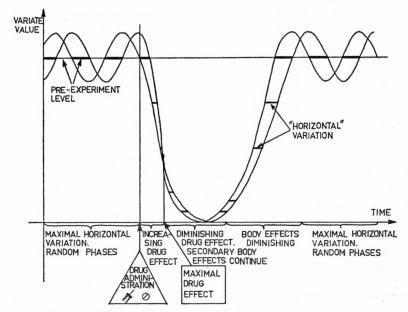

Fig. 20.30a. The possible action of drugs as synchronizers.

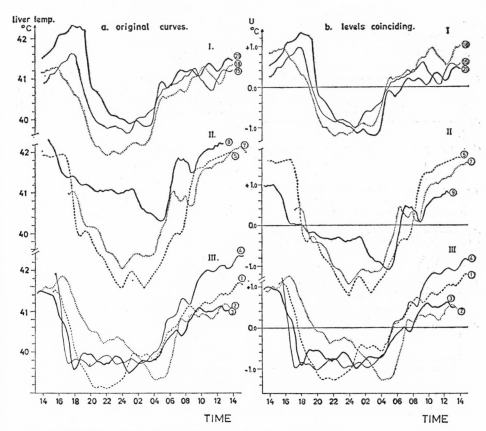

Fig. 20.30b. Ten 24-h chicken liver temperature rhythms.

individuals along the time axis. If no synchronizer is present no special time position should be preferable to any other, and one would expect a rectangular time distribution. Actually, all distributions of the recorded values along the variate axis (usually the Y-axis) may be transformed into time distributions along the time axis (usually the X-axis). In this case the errors of assay (probably often normal along the variate axis) and the divergence effects would turn up as non-normal errors in the rectangular time distribution. These problems have, however, not been investigated to any large extent.

Synchronizers act on the timing of the rhythms. Actually, they will tend to collect the individual cycle positions around certain time points, the time distribution probably approaching normality. It should be possible to use this for finding a method of demonstrating external influences on the exogenous rhythms (Fig. 1.38a). Thus changes in the *horizontal* (time axis) dispersion should be indicative of external influences, after elimination of amplitude differences and assay errors transformed through the cyclic path. Differences in cycle shapes may be regarded as random errors in timing. Fig. 20.30a demonstrates the possible action of a pharmacon as a synchronizer, an effect of drugs which is seldom heeded. A tentative example of how a moving variate analysis might work (SOLLBERGER[7]) is given in Figs. 20.30b-d. The amplitudes of the ten single curves are first equalized.

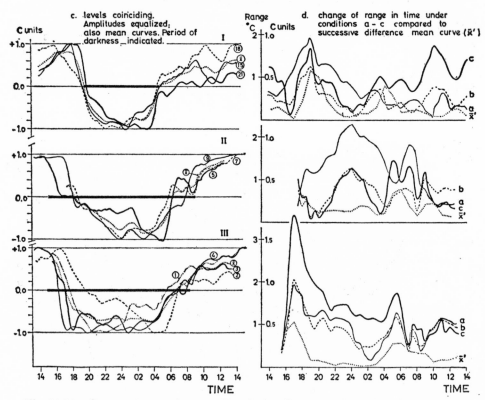

Fig. 20.30c. Same curves as in preceding figure. Ranges equalized, c. Variations in vertical ranges as compared to curve differential in d.

Changes in the horizontal range between curves should indicate synchronizer action.

20.31 – *Statistical Tests.* We have seen that the shape of a frequency distribution changes during a cycle. This must be of importance in the application of statistical tests to biological rhythm data. Most of the parametric tests are comparisons between group means (the *t*-test, the analysis of variance) and preassume that the dispersions are equal. These tests have been much used to prove the existence of a rhythm. Unfortunately, they are ill-fashioned for such usage, though a positive outcome (statistical significance) is proof that at least something occurs in the series of values; whether in the means, standard deviations or skewness values. It proves that the values do not represent a series of groups with equal means or dispersions, but does not specify what kind of changes occur. Neither does the analysis of variance, even if yielding significance, specify in which time sequence the deviating groups have to come.

Figs. 20.31a-b show the result of various parametric and nonparametric statistical tests on discontinuous liver glycogen and continuous temperature 24-h cycle

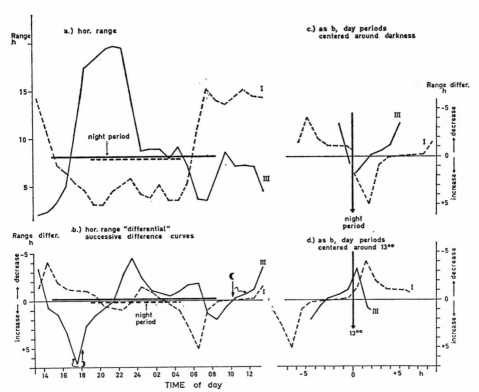

Fig. 20.30d. Analysis of horizontal ranges of groups I and III in preceding figure, a. Differential of this in b, expressing synchronizing influence. c and d amplify this.

data (*cf.* SOLLBERGER[3, 6]). It appears that some tests are more sensitive at the curve maxima, where means change less and dispersions (as expressions of acceleration in the curves) change more. Some tests react more on the limbs of the curves (large group mean changes and lesser acceleration). The *t*-test and the analysis of variance are more mean-difference sensitive, the *F*-test and the Bartlett test are dependent on changes in the standard deviations.

20.32 – In the earlier days of biological rhythm research, it was important to convince the sceptics that rhythms really exist, and statistics was the way to do it. Actually, this achieved more convincing than proving. Fortunately, the rhythms have become accepted and the real proofs have been obtained by the simplest statistical method possible, sheer repetition. This is actually an effective test. If we have only three or four individuals, congruent curves are proof enough since it would require quite a lot of chance to arrange all the values in the correct timing and sequences, if they were really random. A convincing demonstration is often achieved if one splits the material into two equal and independent groups of cycles. If the cyclic course of the two group means are fairly congruent little more statistics is necessary.

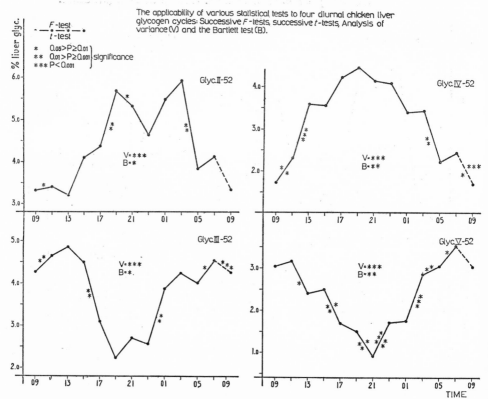

Fig. 20.31a. Parametric tests used on chicken liver glycogen 24-h rhythms. Each dot represents 15-16 animals.

The modern biological rhythm research worker thus has less the burden of proof but more the problem of analyzing the behaviour of the cycles. He can often start with the assumption that he is dealing with non-stationary time series (1.9).

Another approach is discussed in the next chapter (frequency analysis). A special test for the occurrence of peaks in serial data has been devised by SAVA-GE[100–101].

20.33 – *Average Cycles.* After reading the preceding sections it does perhaps not

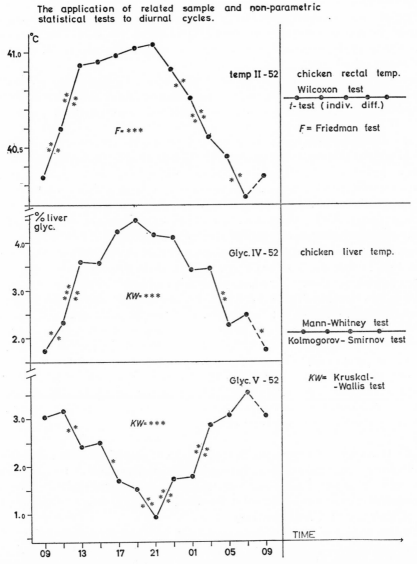

The application of related sample and non-parametric statistical tests to diurnal cycles.

Fig. 20.31b. Non-parametric tests used on chicken liver glycogen and rectal temperature 24-h rhythms. Each dot represents 15-19 animals. Significance marked as in preceding figure.

surprise the reader to learn that even the ordinary averages may fail in cycle research. The biological investigators often summarize their results in average curves. If a phase-dispersion occurs between the individual cycles, however, the mean curve will not be truly representative of the material. This is demonstrated on a simple model in Fig. 1.37a. In practice, thus, we must remember that the ordinary *vertical* average curves are always somewhat misleading. They are too shallow, more so the larger the phase differences of the components. Another possibility is to compute *horizontal* average curves; first, however, individual amplitude differences must be eliminated.

Another way is to align the curve phases (*cf.* Fig. 20.22b) before averaging, *e.g.* by minimizing the area between paired curves (BERGES, CLASING, KEL-LERSMANN). With too variable curve shapes, however, the concept of alignment becomes hazy.

Another type of average which is often used is the moving average (*cf.* Chapter 21). It is a valuable statistical tool for smoothing out small random variations in a curve (*cf.* LEONG, WALLIS[100]) but must be used with discrimination.

20.34 – *Biological Percentages*. In 20.6, one type of transformation of percentages in biology was discussed. The question of the biological significance of such measures is, however, more complicated and may differ from case to case. The probit transformation is built upon the assumption of a large variance in sensitivity between individuals. To the extent, however, that the percentages reflect the average course of the sensitivity changes, the transformation of Fig. 20.28d is more adequate, since morbidity and mortality percentages are cumulative. The values thus have a direct biological meaning as they stand, without transformation. How to combine these two interpretations of the percentages?

Another type of biological frequency values is the mitosis counts. We may regard them as measures of cell growth velocity if we assume the mitosis time to be constant. This percentage is not cumulative. It shows the effect *now*, and does not include cells from earlier mitoses, unless all cells stop at mitosis (as can be experimentally induced). Should the values, then, if depicting temporal changes, be cumulated (integrated)? The problem is important since a cumulation would tend to shift the theoretical peak-time of the functions a quarter cycle. Again the problem of individual phase lags arises. – If we count different stages of mitosis the situation changes (when we compare these *inter se*) because here the frequency is proportional to the duration of each stage.

20.35 – *Quantitative Comparisons Between Cycles*. A special problem arises in the quantitative comparison between rhythms of different variates. A transformation into common or non-dimensional units has to be made. The relative curves are one method. For instance, vertical differences between these may be constructed (*cf.* MÖLLERSTRÖM[100], SOLLBERGER[3]).

Another technique would be to recalculate all curves as far as possible into their energy equivalents. A simple try at this was made by SOLLBERGER[5], but it is really a complex subject, which would require the calculation of the free energy and also touches upon the problem of the applicability of the ordinary thermodynamical equations to the compartmentalization of living organisms. If possible, energy estimates would allow direct comparisons to be made of the bioamplitudes, vertical differences could be computed, and statistical tests of these fashioned.

In homogeneous cycle groups various parameters may be correlated (cf. 20. 18), e.g. amplitudes and levels, amplitudes and frequencies, or even peak-times and levels (BERGES, CLASING, KELLERSMANN, MENZEL[9], MÖLLERSTRÖM[100], SOLL-BERGER[1-5]).

20.36 – *In Vitro Creation of Rhythms.* A good test for any biological theory is the test-tube assembly of parts which mimics the behaviour of the living system. As to rhythms, this is easy for the physicist who can build oscillators from simple inert parts. It is more difficult for the biologist, though periodic chemical and biochemical reactions constitute a borderland. On the other hand it is sometimes claimed that an *in vitro* 24-h rhythm has been created by taking samples at different times of the day, 'freezing' and storing these and later reproducing the process by mixing the components. This is *in essence* an old technique. A true *in vitro* rhythm would, however, require that all components were non-rhythmic, but would form an oscillating system upon combination.

An interesting approach is the continued recording of circadian rhythms in isolated organs, such as hearts or adrenal glands (ANDREWS[100], THARP[100]).

20.37 – We have now discussed the application of conventional statistics to biological rhythms. Remarkably often they fail in the testing of rhythms. Another approach, which is more directly formulated for rhythm analysis, is the statistical-mathematical frequency analysis, based on harmonic analysis. This is the subject of the next chapter, to be followed by the mathematical formulae for periodic motion.

CHAPTER 21

Mathematical-Statistical Analysis of Time Series

21.1 – In the preceding chapter we have discussed the use of conventional biological statistics in our field. It was clear that there are many fallacies in their application. We need other types of analyses. One attempt to outline an alternative approach was made in sections 20.27-30. Another, well-established approach to time series is the harmonic analysis and the more general types of frequency analysis derived therefrom (*cf.* 1.35,39-40). They were mostly developed in theoretical economical statistics for the purpose of prediction. Whereas conventional statistics builds upon the Gaussian normal distribution, time series analysis has the stationary time series as a basis.

Frequency analysis is being used more and more in biology. As in general statistics its use poses two problems. One is how to use it for the description of any time series. The second is how to apply tests, *i.e.* to distinguish a trend, a non-stationary process (*e.g.* a rhythm), from the random stationary case. As a mathematical descriptive tool frequency analysis is very efficient. The real difficulty lies in the problem of testing the results, especially with rhythms. There exists as yet no direct statistical approach to and thus no clear-cut set of new tools for such time series. Also, the present methods are complicated and time-consuming, unless one is the happy owner of a computer.

21.2 – *Information in Rhythms*. The fundamental difference between ordinary and time-series statistics lies in the type of information handled. In the former case we are usually confronted with sets of values scattered around an average location. The fundamental units are the single values, which are rather independent entities. In time series we are less interested in the values themselves, but more in the interconnections between them, as illustrated in Fig. 21.2a. Here, the upper and lower sections contain exactly the same values, but the latter makes clearly much more sense, though even this may seem rather complicated to our eyes. The next step in processing the information would be attempts to construct an average cycle curve (*cf.* 20.33).

The dominating unit in non-temporal statistics is the frequency distribution of a set of values and the all-important model against which it is tested is the normal distribution. The dominating unit in temporal statistics is something evolving in time, the sine curve. The model for comparison is the random time series.

21.3 – *Stationary (Random) Time Series*. If we plot a sequence of random figures along a time axis the values will seem to 'oscillate' around an horizontal level

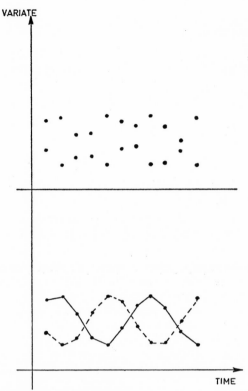

Fig. 21.2a. The information in a time series.

(which might be represented by some average of all the data). The oscillations will, however, be irregular (Fig. 21.3a). This is a random or stationary time series. Every second value might be above-level, alternating with below-level ones, though we may more often find one, two, three or even six successive points in either position. Let us make an analogy with ordinary coin-throwing. Let above-level values be heads and below-level values tails. We may easily throw the sequence illustrated in Fig. 21.3a.

Incidentally, this procedure of transforming time series values into two-valued data greatly facilitates the analysis of long records, often with little loss in information (cf. 19.13, 21.29, MERCER).

Random time series may give an impression of rhythmicity to the observer, especially if he is expecting it to occur. And he is not without reason, cycles do exist in the data. Unfortunately, any one period is theoretically as probable as any other. Let us analyze a long series of random values, picking out all cycles to be found (a tedious job well suited for the data machines), and record their strengths (amplitudes). We may then construct a frequency spectrum, by plotting the amplitudes against the corresponding frequencies. We will get the picture in the upper part of Fig. 21.3b, which is an example of random (white) noise. All wave lengths are equally probable and strong, at an average, within a certain range of wave lengths. In rhythm research we are less interested in white noise. We are

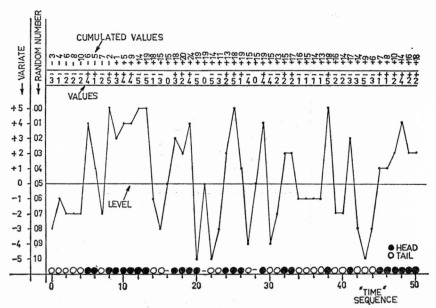

Fig. 21.3a. A random time series I. Figures from random number tables. A two-value transformation, heads and tails, included.

searching for cycle periods which are stronger than the others, for dominant frequencies. We want a frequency spectrum of the type shown in the lower half of Fig. 21.3b.

21.4 – *Serial Correlation*. If some frequencies dominate it means that there is some force which makes successive values in a time series follow each other in a certain pattern, bringing forth a correlation between them. If the causative agents disappear, only random variations would be left. However, pure random move-

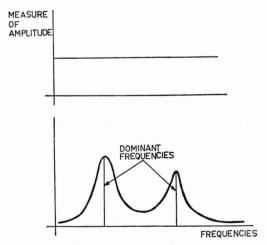

Fig. 21.3b. Frequency spectra. Upper = white noise. Lower = dominant frequencies.

ment does not really occur, except in theory. In practice there are always some kinds of physical links left, at least between adjacent values, causing serial correlation (Ge. Erhaltungsneigung). Inertia provides a good example. At war the best way of fooling the antiaircraft servorobots is absolutely random movements of the aircraft. Actually, this is impossible. It would require an infinite number of teleportations per second to random places in the sky. As it is, the direction and velocity of the aircraft at one instance determines fairly well where it will have to be an instant later. The same occurs in animal populations, since each animal has to exist from birth to death. He cannot appear and disappear erratically, barring migration.

Serial correlation may be positive or negative. In the former case high values tend to follow upon high ones and low values upon low ones. In the latter case, low values tend to follow upon high ones and *vice versa* (BARTELS[2]).

21.5 – Serial correlation may be introduced into the random series of Fig. 21.3a by assigning + and — signs to the values on each side of the level and then continuously adding them (Fig. 21.5a). The expected sum is zero but the values vary considerably around this. A true non-random shape has actually appeared, caused by the fact that successive values are now correlated. Being sums or differences they always have one factor in common. Furthermore, longer random runs of + or — values tend to determine the average level for long sequences of the curve.

This experiment was made by COLE[202] when showing how easily animal populations may be caused by random fluctuations and inertia. Let us, however, repeat the whole experiment once again (as COLE should have done), Fig. 21.5b and c.

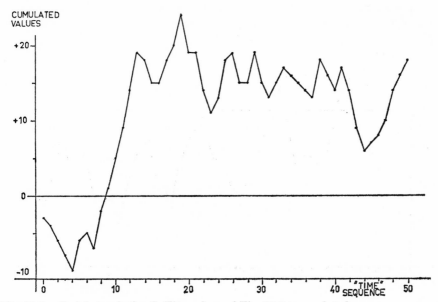

Fig. 21.5a. Serial correlation I. The values of Fig. 21.3a cumulated.

The new cumulative curve differs considerably from the former one (Fig. 21.5a) especially in shape and timing. – In long records, the correlating factor will determine a dominant frequency. The crucial test is not the detection of one wave shape in a series of data, but the recurrence of the same shape, period and some-

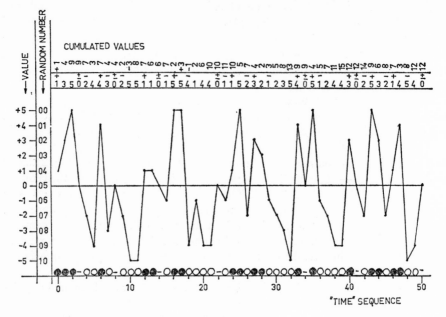

Fig. 21.5b. A random time series II; cf. Fig. 21.3a.

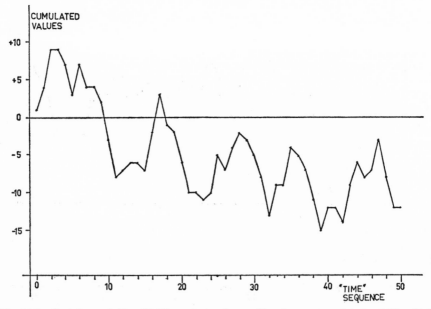

Fig. 21.5c. Serial correlation II. The values of preceding figure cumulated; cf. Fig. 21.5a.

times timing in long series, different individuals (uncorrelated), at widely different times or places, or by different investigators.

21.6 – *Statistical Treatment Causing Serial Correlation.* In biology true random time series do not exist since serial correlation can never be avoided. However, it may also arise during our statistical treatment of the data. One example is the too unsophisticated classification of peaks (*cf.* 20.25). Another is the calculation of moving averages, since each average includes several adjacent values (Fig. 21.6a).

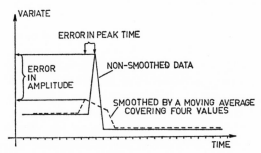

Fig. 21.6a. The effect of a moving average.

As can be seen, the serial correlation arising from the latter also causes errors in the peak height and peak time. They will be larger the narrower the peak and the fewer the observations during one cycle. The frequency of the induced cycles varies with the type of average (DODD, MORAN[1], SLUTZKY, WALD). Repeated averaging may under certain circumstances yield a sinusoidal limiting curve, whether the original time series is random or not.

Moving averages are obtained by summation. More generally, successive summation (integration) or differencing (differentiation) may give periodic artifacts (*cf.* 21.5). – Many methods of mathematical frequency analysis also contain calculations which may induce serial correlation into the data.

21.7 – *Tests for Non-randomness in Time Series.* One of the first problems in the analysis of a time series is whether it is random or not. Many tests for this are coupled to a harmonic analysis of the data. They will be referred to later. Simpler methods also exist, however, and may be useful as a first orientation in the data.

The simplest methods employ non-parametric statistics. The random model for comparison is here the so called random walk (SIEGEL[200], WALLIS[100]). It is known how many above-average or below-average values (heads or tails in Figs. 21.3a and 5b) may repeat themselves at random and against this the actual sequence of heads and tails is tested. Or, the number of successive increases or decreases is similarly tested.

21.8 – The *analysis of variance* (FISHER[201], SNEDECOR) may also be used, if the values are grouped along the time axis (each group containing n successive values). The variation of the group means is then tested against what is permitted by the basic scatter of the values within each group. Similar methods are used by

BARTELS[2]. The results must be viewed with caution owing to the non-normality of the statistical distributions and the problem of deciding upon the theoretical number of independent variate values (degrees of freedom). The latter depends on the degree of serial correlation (BARTELS[2]). The analysis of variance may also be combined with harmonic analysis (BLISS[1, 100]).

The mentioned methods of analysis cannot distinguish between true periodicity and serial correlation, though the former is more regular. In the latter case the dominating frequency (and its phasing) tends to change at random. The effect of serial correlation therefore lessens the longer the time series; the memory of the stationary time series is short (BARTELS).

21.9 – Sine Curve. Fourier Point. One of the simplest and most regular time series is the *sine* (or *cosine*) *curve*. It is the basic unit of harmonic analysis as well as a much-used and -abused model of rhythmic phenomena. It has a number of remarkable properties, most of which have already been discussed in connection with harmonic motion (1.31, 4.7, 19.9) together with a definition of its parameters, the phase angle concept and the congruity of its derivatives.

The sine and cosine functions are equal in shape but differ 90° in phase. They are the basis of the additive harmonic system of oscillations, found in sound waves or nonlinear transformation of rhythmic signals (19.11,16). Also, time series, whatever their shape, may be analyzed into an additive system of sine waves. This is the harmonic or Fourier analysis and here the sine function is called a *Fourier point*.

21.10 – Harmonic (Fourier) Analysis. Periodogram. The harmonic analysis is the key-stone of all frequency analysis. It analyzes the given time series into a harmonic set of sine waves, differing in phase and amplitude (*cf.* BARBER, SCHUSTER, SMITH[200], STUMPFF). Such a set is represented in formula 21.10a. We cannot fit this series to the actual data, however, since we do not know the phases $(\o_n)$. Therefore, we use the equivalent formula 21.10b (*cf.* 4.7d-e), where no *a priori* knowledge of the phase is necessary. Once 21.10b is obtained it may be transformed into 21.10a.

21.10a
$$y = A_0 + A_1 \sin(\omega t + \o_1) + A_2 \sin(2\omega t + \o_2) +$$
$$+ A_3 \sin(3\omega t + \o_3) + \ldots + A_m \sin(m\omega t + \o_m) =$$
$$= A_0 + \sum_{n=1}^{n=m} A_n \sin(n\omega t + \o_n)$$

21.10b
$$y = A_0 + (a_1 \cos \omega t + b_1 \sin \omega t) +$$
$$+ (a_2 \cos 2\omega t + b_2 \sin 2\omega t) + (a_3 \cos 3\omega t +$$
$$+ b_3 \sin 3\omega t) + \ldots + (a_m \cos m\omega t +$$
$$+ b_m \sin m\omega t) = A_0 + \sum_{n=1}^{n=m} a_n \cos n\omega t + \sum_{n=1}^{n=m} b_n \sin n\omega t$$

21.11 – Our problem is to estimate the parameters a_n and b_n from the data. This is achieved by the multiplication of each value of the actual time series (y_k) with the corresponding value of one of the expected cosine ($\cos N \omega t$) or sine ($\sin N \omega t$) functions (formula 21.11a) and by adding all these products together over the k range (formula 21.11b). The two formulae show the result upon multiplication with one of the cosine harmonics ($\cos N \omega t$).

21.11a $y_k \cos N \omega t = A_0 \cos N \omega t + (a_1 \cos \omega t \cos N \omega t +$
$+ b_1 \sin \omega t \cos N \omega t) + (a_2 \cos 2 \omega t \cos N \omega t +$
$+ b_2 \sin 2 \omega t \cos N \omega t) + \cdots\cdots +$
$+ (a_m \cos m \omega t \cos N \omega t + b_m \sin m \omega t \cos N \omega t)$

21.11b $\Sigma y_k \cos N \omega t = A_0 \Sigma \cos N \omega t + (a_1 \Sigma \cos \omega t \cos N \omega t +$
$+ b_1 \Sigma \sin \omega t \cos N \omega t) + (a_2 \Sigma \cos 2 \omega t \cos N \omega t +$
$+ b_2 \Sigma \sin 2 \omega t \cos N \omega t) + \cdots\cdots +$
$+ (a_m \Sigma \cos m \omega t \cos N \omega t + b_m \Sigma \sin m \omega t \cos N \omega t)$

Now, for time stretches of y with a whole number of periods many of the partial sums (Σ) in formula 21.11b add to approximately zero (formula 21.11c). The total sum (which we have calculated) equals approximately half the number of y_k values (K) times the coefficient a_N, according to formulae 21.11d, which enables us to calculate a_N. In this way the various coefficients a in formula 21.10b are obtained through multiplication with the proper cosine harmonic.

21.11c $\Sigma \cos N \omega t = 0$
$\Sigma \cos n \omega t \cos N \omega t = 0$; (if $n \neq N$)
$\Sigma \sin n \omega t \cos N \omega t = 0$

21.11d $2 \Sigma \cos n \omega t \cos N \omega t = K$; (if $n = N$)
$2 \Sigma y_k \cos N \omega t = K a_N$
$a_N = 2 (\Sigma y_k \cos N \omega t) / K$

21.12 – Similarly, the various coefficients b are obtained by an analogous multiplication with the various harmonics $\sin N \omega t$. The reader can work this out himself and with the additional conditions in formula 21.12a he will arrive at the approximate formulae 21.12b.

21.12a $\Sigma \sin N \omega t = 0$
$\Sigma \sin n \omega t \sin N \omega t = 0$; (if $n \neq N$)
$\Sigma \sin N \omega t \cos n \omega t = 0$
$2 \Sigma \sin n \omega t \sin N \omega t = K$; (if $n = N$)

21.12b $2 \Sigma y_k \sin N \omega t = K b_N$
$b_N = 2 (\Sigma y_k \sin N \omega t) / K$

From this, the various A_N and ϕ_n of 21.10a may be calculated. A_0 is simply the average level of the time series ($A_0 = K^{-1} \Sigma y_k$), or the average value of the time series corresponding to one period of the fundamental harmonic. a_N is twice the average value of $y_k \cos N \omega t$; b_N twice the average of $y_k \sin N \omega t$.

The various A values are the amplitudes of the harmonics. These may be plotted against the corresponding frequencies in an amplitude spectrum or periodogram (Fig. 21.3b). The phases (ϕ) may be recorded in a phase-frequency diagram.

21.13 – In contrast to some other types of frequency analysis the harmonic analysis yields both amplitudes and phases of the components. On the other hand, the results only comprise a small set out of all possible frequencies and may or may not, therefore, contain the true basic periodicity. The situation may be amended by the use of several sets with slightly different fundamental frequencies or by a kind of smoothing of the periodogram through moving averages. One may then obtain a continuous periodogram, the generalized harmonic analysis (WIENER[1]).

In any more comprehensive harmonic analysis, the computational work is very heavy. It is no match, however, for modern computers, which may perform instantaneous analysis, e.g. following the spectrum of the spoken sounds or nerve spikes continuously on a screen. There are also a large variety of mechanical, optical and electronic harmonic analyzers (cf. BARBER, NOGUCHI, OBERHOFFER).

For some applications of harmonic analysis in biology see ANDERSON[2], BLISS[1], [100], BLUME, HALBERG[10, 12, 116, 140, 146, 148], JORDAN[6], KAMIYA[2], KOEHLER[100], LARKS[100], MENZEL[4-5, 9, 15-16, 100-102], OBERHOFFER, OTTO[100], also ANDERSSON[300], CENKOVICH[100], ESSLER[100], KÜNKEL, WATERMAN.

21.14 – *Analysis on Single Cycles.* In principle, the classical harmonic analysis may be used on one single cycle of the fundamental harmonic (cf. BARTELS[1], BLISS[1, 100], BLUME) or on long runs of many cycles. In the former case we must know the period of the fundamental harmonic a priori. This we can reasonably do regarding seasonal cycles (BLISS[1, 100]). If, however, the fundamental cycle is not defined we have to try several, with different periods. For this we need longer runs of data. Of course, we can always repeat our single cycle as many times as we like in time but this just amounts to assuming that we already have the fundamental period. Furthermore, in the biological world there are always variations in shape from cycle to cycle. This makes our problem a statistical one; to bring out the average picture.

21.15 – Unfortunately, long runs are sometimes impossible to obtain in biology, e.g. in medical pathology. The pattern we analyze may also sometimes actually vary from cycle to cycle (e.g. during recovery) and it may be this we want to observe. There might, e.g., occur sudden phase jumps in one or another of the components. All this makes it imperative in biology to have a method for doing a complete harmonic analysis on a single cycle, without a priori assumptions about the fundamental period.

BLUME has managed to adapt the analysis to such conditions and tried them on biological data together with MENZEL[4-5, 9, 15-16, 100-102] (also JORDAN[6] and OTTO[100]) on pathological cases. When preparing periodograms, the ordinary run of cycles is, as it were, represented by a series of different patients. For instance, a three-dimensional diagram is given (MENZEL[9]), relating durations, levels and amplitudes of the various components in a number of recorded 24-h urea excretion curves in renal affliction. It shows an increase of amplitude with period length and with the level of excretion. In disease shorter periods than 24-h tend to be prominent. With BLUME's method it is also possible to interrelate the 24-h phasing of various metabolic factors in human subjects (MENZEL[101]). It is also useful in catching sudden phase jumps (BLUME[10-11]).

21.16 – Statistical Problems in Harmonic Analysis. The harmonic analysis, though employing averages, is essentially a mathematical method. Statistical problems arise, however, when we want to test the reliability of our results. We want to know the statistical significance of the dominant peaks in our periodogram (*cf.* Fig. 21.3b). Here we clearly need long runs of records. Nevertheless significance is a difficult problem in all types of frequency analyses. This will be discussed later.

21.17 – Harmonic analysis is also used for *curve-fitting* in single cycles. A harmonic pattern is established and the various components then superimposed and added, *cf.* Fig. 1.35a. However, any number of harmonics may be calculated and we would like to know how many of these are real, the rest constituting white noise (*cf.* 21.3). The latter can then be excluded, which saves considerable computational labour.

A method of testing how many harmonics to include in a given curve analysis has been developed by BLISS[1, 100], who has adopted the analysis of variance for use on biological time series (Fig. 1.35a). Here, the observed data (circles) deviate from the fitted curve and their variance around the latter is computed. With each new added harmonic in the analysis the calculated curve makes a better fit and the variance is reduced. This decrease is tested. As long as it is significant new harmonics are added. When it stops decreasing significantly only noise is supposed to be left and further harmonics are not needed. If necessary, several different fundamental periods may also be tried.

21.18 – Though we can test statistically how many harmonics have a descriptive meaning as opposed to the white noise, this does not mean that they have a biological meaning. Any curve can be described by a harmonic system, even an horizontal line, an impulse, or relaxation oscillations. In some cases, there is a rationale, though, *e.g.* in the analysis of sound, vibrations (BICKLEY[100], DEAN), turbulence (CORRSIN), or pulse waves (*cf.* 6.17, 19.11, GADERMANN[100], LOBEL).

21.19 – In synchronization studies (*cf.* Part II) we may calculate harmonic patterns both for the external agent and for the exogenous rhythm and then search these for common components. (Cross-correlation may also be used). Here new statistical problems are involved. However, we sometimes want to study the effect of a single or non-rhythmic stimulus upon an endogenous rhythm and here the harmonic analysis is difficult to apply. Compare with section 20.30, where the problem of analyzing the effect of any stimulus within one single biological cycle was outlined.

21.20 – General Frequency Analysis. As we have seen, any time series may be regarded as an additive assembly of sine curves. The parameters of these may vary: the frequencies (or durations), the phasing (timing), and the amplitudes. The last measure the amount of contribution of each sine component, its strength, or its power. The power is, however, usually recorded as the square of the amplitude. Since the amplitude is calculated from the central level upwards or downwards, the power is related to the variance estimate in statistics. If the amplitudes are plotted against the frequencies we get a periodogram (*cf.* Fig. 21.3b) or

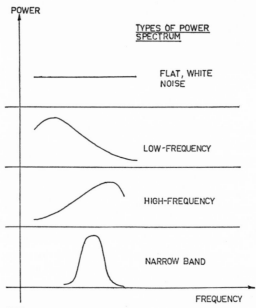

Fig. 21.20a. Some different power spectra.

amplitude spectrum. If the amplitudes are squared we get the power spectrum (Fig. 21.20a). The phases may also be plotted against the frequencies (*cf.* 21.12). The spectra of the ordinary Fourier analysis are discontinuous because they only comprise one set of harmonics. This may, however, be mended by using several fundamental frequencies and smoothing procedures (21.6,13).

21.21 – The stationary time series may be regarded as a conglomerate of all possible sine frequencies at random phases and amplitudes. Any non-stationary time series may be regarded as a combination of one or several true, dominating frequencies (hidden periodicities) and random components (noise, *cf.* 21.3). The way in which these are combined may perhaps differ (BENDAT). Either the amplitude and phase of the dominating frequency are varying at random, a kind of 'random amplitude and frequency modulation' (*cf.* 19.14), as shown in formula 21.21a. Or, the hidden periodicity and the noise are superimposed, formula 21.21b. There are all combinations, from complete randomness to pure cycles (*cf.* Fig. 21.28a). We have also the possibility that some of the component waveforms make sudden phase jumps, disturbed periodicities. YULE[3] gives the model of a pendulum which is disturbed by sudden blows. BLUME[10-11] finds such jumps in BÜNNING's botanical data (*cf.* 21.15). Most types of general frequency analysis are utterly unable to analyze such phenomena. – In other cases there are slow continuous shifts of the position of the frequency spectrum peaks, in time, *e.g.* with respiratory rhythms (GOODMAN).

21.21a $y = A(t) \sin [\omega t - \emptyset(t)]$

21.21b $y = A [\sin (\omega t - \emptyset)] + f(t)$

21.22 – Frequency analyses aim at finding the hidden periodicities (the information in the data) and eliminating the noise. There are several types: harmonic (Fourier, Schuster) analysis, autocorrelation (also called lag correlation), power spectrum analysis, and cross-correlation. The Fourier analysis is the basic procedure. The methods differ mostly with regard to which parameters of the hidden periodicity they emphasize, the mode of computation, and the statistical reliability of the results.

21.23 – One problem is the statistical reliability of the parameters yielded by the analyses (*cf.* 21.6,16). To a certain extent the errors may be calculated, *e.g.* in the power spectrum (*cf.* BARTLETT[1-2], BLACKMAN[100-101], PANOFSKY, TUKEY, WOLD[3]), but this involves difficult theoretical questions, such as the effect of smoothing procedures or distribution normality which does not always hold for evolutive time series. One basis for comparison is taken from the theory of the stationary time series, as for instance, the probability density function (Figs. 21.23a and 28a).

The probability density concept (*cf.* BENDAT, MERCER) is founded upon the same mode of reasoning as in the case of the transformation effect of the moving variate (20.28), though applied to the random time series. Here, the probability of finding a value within a certain range, y to $(y + \Delta y)$, is proportional to the fraction of the total time $(\Sigma \Delta t)$ spent within their limits. It is largest at zero level (base-line) and diminishes in a Gaussian manner upwards and downwards (Fig. 21.28a, bottom). – Another statistical approach is through correlational procedures, as in autocorrelation.

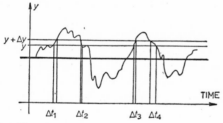

Fig. 21.23a. The probability density function.

It is usually stated that very long records are necessary for reliable results of frequency analyses and this is certainly true for the correlation procedures and the power spectrum analysis which mostly evolved in connection with such fields as information theory, electronics, sound analysis or turbulence. The harmonic analysis may, however, be adapted also to short records (*cf.* 21.15) which is important in the study of disturbed periodicities and in biology.

21.24 – One problem arises in the choice of the fundamental frequency. This should not be done from inspection of the graphs, instead a continuous spectrum should be aimed at. Sometimes, however, an *a priori* expectation of a certain period exists, *i.e.* seasonal, solar-day or lunar-day (*cf.* Chapter 17). It should, however, be accepted with caution as indicated in our previous discussions of endo- or exogeneity of biological rhythms. Generally, it is better to start without any assumptions at all; if our *a priori* expectation is correct, that frequency will turn up in the analysis anyhow. Sometimes, though, we may do it if we want to remove a clearly exogenous frequency and analyze a remaining nonperiodic component. We may, for instance, with BROWN[6-7, 9-10] want to eliminate the solar-day and lunar-day components and correlate the remainder with other variations in the environment (*cf.* Chapter 16).

21.25 – The theory of frequency analysis is developing rapidly and is beginning to penetrate into biology. This is a great step forward, since exact methods are badly needed in biological rhythm research. However, we know very little about the applicability of the methods used in the exact sciences to biological data. This will show in due time. There are *e.g.* the disturbed periodicities and the problem of the biological meaning of the periodogram (21.18). There may exist low-amplitude components which do not show up in the diagram but which still have a biological significance. Another source of error would arise if some components act on a logarithmic time scale (or then even interact), as suggested by PHILPOTT (*cf.* 6.26, 19.36).

The frequency analyses are, however, the most efficient tools we have today and we cannot do without them. There is no reason for the biologist either to become intimidated by the authority of mathematics and physics, or to reject them altogether as being too exact. On the other hand, we are yet far from the goal, a kind of analysis developed by the biologists and built upon the properties of biological matter. But this is not a special problem of biological rhythm research. It applies to the whole field of biostatistics and it is up to us to realize this goal. One thing which has to be developed is a general theory of evolutive time series.

21.26 – There is an enormous literature on time series and the various types of frequency analyses. See Conf. 1957i, BARBER, BARLOW[200], BARTELS[1], BARTLETT[1-2, 100], BENDAT, BLACKMAN[100-101], BLISS[1], BLUME, GOODMAN, HALBERG[125], HANNAN, HAVILL[100], KENDALL, KOEHLER[100], LAKATUA, LEE, McHUGH[100], MERCER, OBERHOFFER, PANOFSKY[1, 100], SCHUSTER, STUMPFF, TUKEY, WIENER[1], WOLD, YULE[1-3], ZEILON, Conf. 1963a.

21.27 – *Autocorrelation. Correlogram.* The Fourier analysis does not really distinguish between hidden periodicities and noise. For this, a statistical approach is needed. One such method is the autocorrelation developed by YULE[1-3], also called lag correlation. The aim is achieved by correlating the observed time series with itself. The curve is, as it were, duplicated and simultaneous values on the two curves correlated. Since the data are identical this correlation is always maximal ($r = +1$). One of the curves is then moved a step (the lag) and a new correlation calculated. The curve is then moved again and again, and each time a new correlation is obtained. When the two curves are out of phase, they will tend towards inverse values and the correlation coefficient (r) towards -1. In the process, all random components will cancel out. In the first step with zero lag they will contribute fully. In the following steps they will still add to the correlation coefficient owing to serial correlation (21.4) but at larger lags they will average out completely. The autocorrelation method tends to find the hidden periodicities and eliminates the noise, and it is therefore one of the most powerful tools in periodicity analysis.

21.28 – If the correlation coefficients (r) are plotted against the lags (phase displacement, τ) a correlogram is obtained. Fig. 21.28a gives three examples of correlograms. In case of the sine wave the r-value will, of course, vary regularly from $+ 1$ at a $0°$, $360°$, $720° \ldots n\ 360°$ displacement, to $- 1$ at a $180°$, $540° \ldots$ $(180 + n\ 360)°$ displacement. It simply reproduces the sine curve. Actually, the hidden periodicity curve shape is reappearing in the correlogram, whether symmetrical or not. If no hidden wave shape exists, the correlogram shows unity at zero lag and then rapidly peters out. On the other hand, the correlogram yields no analysis into various components of the hidden periodicity or their phasing.

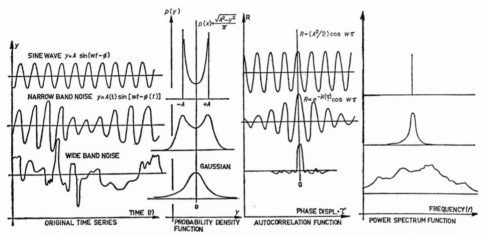

Fig. 21.28a. Three types of time series; their probability density functions, autocorrelation functions and power spectra. After BENDAT.

The correlogram has, however, many relations to the periodogram. At zero lag, the product sum which it represents obviously corresponds to the sums of the squared deviates from the average level of the time series, *i.e.* the variance. (In periodicity analysis the trends or base-lines are always eliminated first and the analysis performed on the deviations from these). The square root of the mean square (the variance divided by the effective number of deviates) is the standard deviation of the series. If each deviate is regarded as an instantaneous amplitude (another concept of amplitude than usually used) the variance will also represent the power of the series.

21.29 – Since the correlogram curve repeats the shape of the hidden periodicity it may be subjected to a harmonic analysis. The result of this will yield a series of sine curves, each with a height proportional to its power in the original time series, that is a power spectrum.

The correlograms are easily calculated with computers (*cf.* BARBER). The lag is simply represented by a built-in retardation. For instance, two pick-ups may be used and the computer tape looped between them, somewhat in the same way as echo effects may be obtained in electronic music instruments.

An ingenious simplification of the method consists of just recording above- and below-base-line values (MERCER), denoting them by $+ 1$ and $- 1$ (cf. 21.3). Long records are needed but the loss of information is less than one would think.

21.30 – *Power Spectrum.* As already indicated, the power spectrum (energy spectrum, spectral density) is obtained by a harmonic analysis of the correlogram. It yields a new type of periodogram; the squared amplitudes (variance, power) against the frequencies. The latter may become continuous after suitable smoothing. Yet another periodogram type is obtained if the power estimates are cumulated (WOLD[3]). Power spectra are shown in Figs. 21.20a and 28a.

Being built upon a statistical measure, the correlogram, power spectra lend themselves well to statistical tests of power dominance in the component frequencies (cf. 21.23).

21.31 – *Circadian Quotient.* HALBERG[125], in analyzing the power spectra of human temperature recordings, compares the power of different cyclic components by constructing quotients. The circadian quotient is thus the cumulated power in the circadian frequency band divided by the power of other periods. Like MENZEL[5, 15, 100-102] he finds an increase in power of high-frequency components as compared to the circadian one, in diseased subjects. Instead of power sums the latter uses amplitude sums.

21.32 – *Cross-correlation.* In autocorrelation two identical curves are correlated. If they are not identical, we have cross-correlation. Here, one curve is the time series to be investigated and the other is some suitable exploring function. It may be a sine wave. Then the procedure is nothing but a Fourier analysis. The exploring function may also be empirical, *e.g.* representing some environmental factor recorded together with the biological one. The resulting cross-power-spectrum will pick up frequencies common to both records, whether they are strong or weak or variable. Phase information is not lost. The simplest type is cross-correlation with a unit impulse (LEE, MERCER). This extracts periodicities equal to the exploring square wave but preserves wave form and phase.

For some reason cross-correlation methods are seldom applied to biological rhythm research, though they are well suited for this use. They should be used extensively.

21.33 – In the last chapters we have discussed the statistical approaches to the biological rhythms, both from the view of general statistics and theoretical statistics. There is, however, yet another approach, the purely mathematical one, the study of the differential equations for motion and their periodic solutions. This is the subject of the next chapter.

CHAPTER 22

Equations of Motion

22.1 – Throughout this book we have sometimes used mathematical formulae to describe rhythmic functions, *e.g.* in Chapters 4, 19 and 21, but no systematic presentation has been made. The statistical aspects were treated in the last two chapters, including the application of common statistical parameters and the various methods of frequency analysis.

The mathematical approach is to express a variate as a 'function of time' in as general terms as possible, and then to discuss all possible forms or solutions which such an equation might have. Some of these solutions are not periodic, others are. On the other hand, there may exist periodic phenomena which are difficult to describe mathematically, owing to a very complicated structure or to discontinuities. In this chapter we will, however, try to outline the mathematics for the equations of periodic motion. We will have to build up the concepts slowly, repeating a good deal about elementary and nonperiodic functions, even to the extent of studying complex numbers. The latter is necessary in order to understand the Fourier and Laplace transforms which are so important in all theoretical studies of periodic phenomena. *Cf.* textbooks on mathematics and servotheory, *e.g.* BOWER[100], KU, NICOLSON[100].

22.2 – *Differential Equations.* Motion in time is quite naturally described in terms of *position, velocity,* and *acceleration* (this involves the first two derivatives of the formula describing them): position, $x = f(t)$; velocity, $v = x' = f'(t)$; acceleration, $a = x'' = f''(t)$; *cf.* 19.6. In physics, this is natural since the application of a constant force theoretically gives constant acceleration. In more complicated motion patterns even further derivatives may turn up.

The formulae describing motion, $x = f(t)$, may be very complicated. They are often simplified and generalized if they are conceived as a function of a system of derivatives, from zero order and upwards (formula 22.2a). This is a general differential equation. The order of the equation is that of the highest differential. x itself (position) is of zero order. Equation 22.2a is of nth order. The degree of the equation is given by the exponential number of the highest differential. If the equation contains a term $(dx^n/dt^n)^m$ it is of mth degree. Another distinction is between linear and nonlinear differential equations. This is important, since general methods of solution only exist for the former. Unfortunately, biological phenomena are usually best described by nonlinear functions, though these may sometimes be approximated to linear differential functions.

Linearity, here, means that the motion is regarded as a linearly additive system of 1st degree differentials. Furthermore, the coefficients of each differential may be constants or functions of t but not functions of x. A linear differential equation may be described by formula 22.2b.

The various $f(t)$ are the coefficients of the differentials. $f_0(t)$ is the coefficient of the highest differential, which determines the order of the system. $f_n(t)$ is the coefficient of the zero order differential (x itself). $f_{n+1}(t)$ signifies an additional term which is independent of x but may be a function of t. If the coefficients are constant the equation reduces to formula 22.2c. The linear differential equation is 'homogeneous' if the $f_{n+1}(t)$ coefficient is zero, formula 22.2d, and 'inhomogeneous' otherwise (equation 22.2b). Equations describing forced oscillations are inhomogeneous, free oscillation formulae homogeneous (if linear).

22.2a $f(t, x, dx/dt, dx^2/dt^2, \ldots dx^n/dt^n) = 0$

22.2b $f_0(t)\,[dx^n/dt^n] + f_1(t)\,[dx^{n-1}/dt^{n-1}] + \ldots + f_n(t)\,[x] + f_{n+1}(t) = 0$

22.2c $a\,[dx^n/dt^n] + b\,[dx^{n-1}/dt^{n-1}] + \ldots + kx + l = 0$

22.2d $f_0(t)\,[dx^n/dt^n] + f_1(t)\,[dx^{n-1}/dt^{n-1}] + \ldots + f_n(t)\,x = 0$

22.3 – *Mathematical Solutions for Equations of Motion.* If one wants to study the detailed behaviour of the functions described by differential equations they have to be solved by integration, *i.e.* transformed into a form which does not contain differentials. Most of the solutions are difficult and there is no general method of integration. There are several types of solutions: straight-forward integration, trial solutions, transformation to various types of series or to special integrals, and graphical solutions. One differential equation may have many solutions. Some simple examples are given in formulae 22.3a-d (*cf.* 11.5a-b).

	Differential equation	*Solution*
22.3a	$x' + x = 0$	$x = Ae^{-t}$; exponential decay
22.3b	$x' + x^2 = 0$	$x = 1/(t + A)$
22.3c	$x'' + x = 0$	$x = A \sin (t + \emptyset)$; simple harmonic
22.3d	$dx^n/dt^n = 0$	polynomial of degree n-1

22.4 – For linear differential equations, whether with constant coefficients or coefficients which are functions of the independent time variable, the general method of solution by series is possible. Let us, as an example, take an exponential series, $y = a_0 + a_1 x + a_2 x^2 + \ldots + a_r x^r$, and solve the differential equation $y' - y = 0$. The steps of the computation are given in formulae 22.4a-c (*cf.* 22.3a).

The principle is to replace the integration of complicated expressions by an additive process, somewhat in the same way as we replace multiplication by addition when using logarithms. This is achieved by a transformation of our variate into another function with the desired properties. Many types of such transformations exist.

One transformation which is rather universally used in servomechanical theory is the Laplace transformation. This will, however, be described later, since it demands a knowledge of complex numbers. The transformation simplifies the solution of differential equations considerably, but it is only applicable to linear equations.

No general methods exist for the nonlinear differential equations. One of the main lines of their solution is therefore approximation to the linear case (BOGO-LIUBOV[100]), as is done in the derivation of the simple harmonic motion under the assumption of small deflection angles (*cf.* 4.7).

22.4a
$$y = a_0 + a_1 x + a_2 x^2 + \ldots + a_r x^r + \ldots$$
$$y' = a_1 + 2a_2 x + 3a_3 x^2 + \ldots + (r+1) a_{r+1} x^r + \ldots$$

$$y' - y = (a_1 - a_0) + (2a_2 - a_1)x + (3a_3 - a_2)x^2 + \ldots$$
$$\ldots + [(r+1)a_{r+1} - a_r]x^r + \ldots = 0$$

Now, we put all components equal to zero:

22.4b
$$
\begin{array}{ll}
a_1 - a_0 = 0 & a_1 = a_0 \;\; (= a_0/1!) \\
2a_2 - a_1 = 0 & a_2 = a_1/2 = a_0/2! \\
3a_3 - a_2 = 0 & a_3 = a_2/3 = a_0/3! \\
 & a_r = a_0/r!
\end{array}
$$

which gives:

22.4c
$$y = a_0 (1 + x + x^2/2! + x^3/3! + \ldots + x^r/r! + \ldots)$$
$$y = a_0 e^x$$

22.5 – Another quality which applies to homogeneous linear differential equations is the additivity (orthogonality) of the different solutions. If *e.g.* a given differential equation has the three solutions: $x_1 = f_1 (t)$, $x_2 = f_2 (t)$ and $x_3 = f_3 (t)$; then the linear combination: $x = A_1 f_1(t) + A_2 f_2(t) + A_3 f_3(t)$, is also a solution. The linear homogeneous differential equations thus satisfy the law of superposition. This does not hold for inhomogeneous linear differential equations, which differ from the homogeneous ones by containing one term, $f_{n+1}(t)$, which is a function of t but not of the dependent variable (*cf.* 22.2b). However, such expressions may be regarded as having a homogeneous counterpart which is obtained by putting $f_{n+1}(t) = 0$. Thus any solution of the inhomogeneous equation (a particular integral) and the solutions of the corresponding homogeneous expression (the complementary function) may be superimposed, whereby the new solution also satisfies the inhomogeneous expression. This is important in the theory of forced oscillations (Part IV, *cf.* BICKLEY[100], BOGOLIUBOV[100], NICOLSON[100]), where $f_{n+1}(t)$ represents the forcing function and the homogeneous part stands for the spontaneous oscillation. The particular integral needed to obtain a general solution of the inhomogeneous equation may be obtained by solving the latter under simplest possible conditions, *e.g.* at time zero ($t = 0$), or by trial and error.

Unfortunately, the law of additivity of solutions does not hold for nonlinear differential equations.

22.6 – *Graphical Solutions for Equations of Motion. Phase Plane.* It has been mentioned that no general methods of mathematical solution exist for nonlinear differential equations except in special instances. Great help may, however, be had by studying the interrelationship between the differentials graphically, without solving the equations. Such methods were used by V.D. POL[1-3] (*cf.* 4.13), when analyzing the relaxation oscillations; $x'' - (1-x^2) x' + \omega^2 x = 0$. One of the coefficients here, $(1-x^2)$, is itself a function of the dependent variable x, hence the equation is nonlinear.

In the phase plane (*cf.* BICKLEY[100], BOGOLIUBOV[100]), the first differential (the velocity function x', *cf.* 22.2) is plotted against the variate value itself (position, x). A number of examples are given in Figs. 22.6a-i. Take the linear differential equation $x'' + \omega^2 x = 0$. Integrated once, it yields a set of phase-plane ellipses: $(x')^2 + (\omega x)^2 = c$, *cf.* Fig. 22.6c. This represents the relation between velocity and position in a simple oscillation. The direction of the process in time is indicated by an arrow. The curves themselves are the 'phase trajectories'. One differential equation may be represented by a system of trajectories depending on the values of the constants which are introduced at integration. The characteristics of the phase plane curves may differ considerably. If a trajectory moves towards a terminal point on the x-axis (a focus, Figs. 22.6d,f,h) then the function always returns to standstill ($x' = 0$) after any disturbance which may change its position (Fig. 22.6f, lower curve) or impart velocity to it (Fig. 22.6f, upper curve).

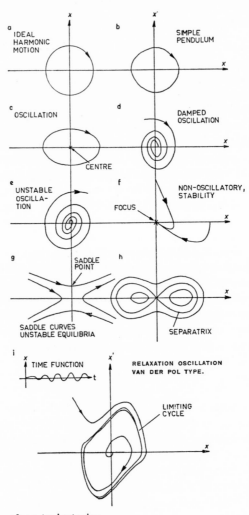

Fig. 22.6a-i. Phase plane trajectories.

22.7 – If the trajectory is closed around a centre (Fig. 22.6a-c, h-i) it represents
a stable, periodic motion, since velocity and position repeatedly return to a certain value. In Fig. 22.6c, starting from the left, we can follow the succession of
increasing velocity with advancing position (from the original curve minimum),
followed by decreasing velocity still with advancing position (towards the original
curve maximum), then increasing velocity in the other direction, followed by
decreasing velocity towards the original minimum.

The amplitude of the oscillation is represented by the range along the x-axis.
The duration of the cycle-period is represented by the surface of the enclosed area
(velocity integrated) which may be obtained mathematically or by some plani-
metric method.

If the trajectory is a spiral, it represents an oscillation with changing amplitude.
If it spirals inwards (Fig. 22.6d) the oscillation is stable and damped, going
towards a standstill (focus). If it spirals outwards (Fig. 22.6e) the oscillation is
unstable with increasing amplitude (cf. Fig 1.12d).

If the trajectory is saddle-shaped (Fig. 22.6g) it has an unstable equilibrium at
the saddle point. If the differential equation is represented by a group of curves,
these may all pass one singular point, the node. If the curve assembly comprises
different types of motion, each represented by a certain area or zone of the diagram, there may be a limiting function between these, the separatrix (Fig. 22.6h).
Sometimes all trajectories may tend asymptotically towards one single limit cycle
as in the relaxation oscillations of v.D. POL (Fig. 22.6i, the inset shows the original
curve). This system settles down to oscillations represented by the limit function.

The phase plane obviously gives important information about the movement at
one glance, telling whether it is non-periodic or periodic, damped or undamped,
stable or unstable.

22.8 – *The Multivariate Situation. General Equations of Growth.* The procedures
described above may be extended to several variables, either to several independent variables: $x = f(t, u_1 \ldots)$; or to several dependent ones: $x = f(t)$, $y = f(t)$,
etc. The former case is less important here since the independent variable is usually time. The other alternative is, however, common in biology where we can seldom
really isolate one single factor from the rest of the organism. Examples from physics are the pendulum which moves in a circle (Fig. 4.5a), or a double pendulum
(Fig. 22.8a) with two space coordinates and one time variable, or the problem
of how vibrations in the four springs of a car affect its balance (cf. BICKLEY[100]).

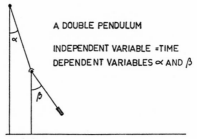

A DOUBLE PENDULUM

INDEPENDENT VARIABLE =TIME
DEPENDENT VARIABLES α AND β

Fig. 22.8a. The double pendulum.

In servomechanisms the problem is the interaction between several systems, *e.g.* coupled oscillators. This problem is, however, related to the theory of forced oscillations and will be discussed later.

A very general approach to the problem of interrelated moving systems is that of Ashby[1]. It is also well suited for the programming of digital computers.

22.9 – The multivariate system also turns up in 'growth' problems. Bertalanffy interprets the problem of interrelation between several species $(x_1, x_2, x_3 \ldots x_n)$ as a series of simultaneous first order differential equations, where the growth of each species $(x_1', x_2', x_3' \ldots x_n')$ is related to the instantaneous values of all populations, formula 22.9a (*cf.* Lotka[3]).

The general solution to this system of differential equations involves all possible results. All components may run towards a state with constant populations, an equilibrium. Or there may be unbalance with more or less irregular fluctuations and dissociation of the population numbers. Some may even vanish. There also exist solutions with periodic fluctuation in the proportions between the populations.

The two-variate example of this has already been discussed in connection with the predator-prey feedback (2.16) and animal populations (10.6). The set of equations may also represent the components in complex chemical equilibria, where periodic oscillations may occur (4.16-18).

22.9a
$$x_1' = f_1 (x_1, x_2 \ldots x_n)$$
$$x_2' = f_2 (x_1, x_2 \ldots x_n)$$

$$—$$
$$—$$

$$x_n' = f_n (x_1, x_2 \ldots x_n)$$

22.10 – The relation between several variates may, of course, be plotted in diagrams. If there are only two variables periodic fluctuations would be represented by a closed curve. Actually, Fig. 22.6a-i could also serve to represent some bivariate relationships if we let the x'-axis represent one of the variables and the x-axis the other. The closed trajectories, which would then represent cyclic variations in the predominance of one or the other variate, will now also be double-valued, *i.e.* for each value of one variable the other has two possible (but not simultaneous) values.

Another example would be the predator (N) – prey (F) problem. Let the populations be F and N. The number of N or F at time t may then depend on the immediately preceding values of the populations, formula 22.10a. The corresponding changes in N and F are represented in formula 22.10b, and (if we go towards very small changes, $\triangle$ F; $\triangle$ N) by 22.10c. If we let either of the changes approach zero we get formulae 22.10d.

We may now plot the various numbers of predators and prey in a N-F diagram, Fig. 22.10e. The formulae 22.10d would then be represented by two straight lines, one parallel to the N-axis and one sloping. Their intersection point, $F = 1/k$; $N = (m-1)/ck$, which is the focus, represents an equilibrium where both populations are constant. If any small change is forced in one of the variables the other will have to change, too. If the changes ($\triangle$ F; $\triangle$N) are plotted as small vector arrows, these will be seen to follow trajectories around the focus. Equations 22.10c give the signs of the changes, which depend on the starting point. It is easily seen that the vectors must behave as in Fig. 22.10e. The trajectories may spiral inwards or outwards. They may fail to reach an equilibrium, or may reach a stable focal point, or a closed limiting steady state cycle. This example derives from Levins. For other biological phase plane applications, see Dewan.

22.10a
$$N_t = k\ F_{(t-1)}\ N_{(t-1)}$$
$$F_t = m\ F_{(t-1)} - c\ N_{(t-1)}$$

22.10b
$$F_t - F_{(t-1)} = (m\text{-}1)\ F_{(t-1)} - c\ N_{(t-1)}$$
$$N_t - N_{(t-1)} = [k\ F_{(t-1)} - 1]\ N_{(t-1)}$$

22.10c
$$\triangle\ F = (m\text{-}1)\ F - cN$$
$$\triangle\ N = N\ (kF\text{-}1)$$

22.10d
$$F = cN/(m\text{-}1)$$
$$F = 1/k$$

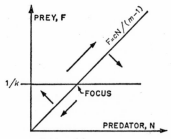

Fig. 22.10e. The predator-prey relationship.

22.11 – *Complex Variables. Phase-Amplitude Diagram.* Many calculations discussed in connection with the servotechnical, mathematical or statistical analysis of rhythms are considerably simplified by the introduction of complex notations and it is therefore necessary for us to understand this concept. It will help us in the evaluation of integration, power series, the Fourier and Laplace transformations, and of phase-amplitude analysis.

A complex number contains one real and one 'imaginary' number. Through this a complex variable may also be made to represent two real variables, where one is simply denoted as the 'imaginary' one and identified by always being multiplied by i ($= \sqrt{-1}$). Actually, there is nothing imaginary about the process. It was just the concept of the number i which caught the imagination of the mathematicians, until they started to deduct its properties in the same logical way as other mathematical concepts. It then proved to be very useful.

Let us, now, use a complex variable (z) to represent two real variables (x and y) as in formula 22.11a. Let us also introduce a second complex variable (ω) to represent another two real variables (u and v), formula 22.11a. We may now formulate complex equations which contain the two composite variables (z, ω). The equations will then, however, also describe the relations between the four real variables (x, y, u, v). When handling these expressions mathematically, we can perform all the usual operations such as addition, subtraction, multiplication, *etc*, remembering that $i^2 = -1$ (also $1/i = -i$). In the process, however, we always clearly distinguish between two sets of values, those containing an i-term and those which do not.

22.11a
$$z = x + iy$$
$$\omega = u + iv$$

22.12 – Let us take the complex equation $\omega = z^2$. In terms of real variables it represents the two equations $u = x^2 - y^2$ and $v = 2xy$, as shown in formulae 22.12a (*cf.* 22.11a).

22.12a
$$\omega = z^2$$
$$u + iv = (x + iy)^2$$
$$u + iv = x^2 - y^2 + i\,2xy$$

$$u = x^2 - y^2$$
$$v = 2xy$$

22.13 – A complex number may be represented by a point in the Argand diagram (Fig. 22.13a). This is an ordinary coordinate system where the value of the 'real' component (x) is marked on the x-axis and of the 'imaginary' part (y) on the y-axis (which may therefore be called the imaginary axis). The point z has in the ordinary system the coordinates (x; y), in complex notation $z = x + iy$ (*cf.* Fig. 22.13a:1).

The laws of addition, subtraction, multiplication, and division may be extended from real to complex numbers. Addition, *e.g.* of z_1 and z_2, will yield the result shown in formula 22.13b. Thus, if the complex numbers z_1 and z_2 represent two vectors (Fig. 22.13a:2) their sum $z_1 + z_2$ is simply the complex number of their resultant

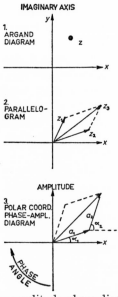

Fig. 22.13a. The Argand and the amplitude-phase-diagrams. The graphical representation of complex numbers.

(z_3) according to the parallelogram law, with the coordinates $(x_1 + x_2)$ and $(y_1 + y_2)$. Thus, the addition of complex numbers corresponds to 'vector addition' of real numbers.

Now, let us do the same with polar coordinates, with angles a and lengths a (Fig. 22.13a:3). Translating this to ordinary coordinates gives formulae 22.13c. The corresponding Argand diagram points are defined by formulae 22.13d. Actually, each z point may be taken to represent a sine wave, $y = A \sin(\omega t - \o)$, cf. 4.7. The length of the polar vector would represent the amplitude, the other polar coordinate the phase angle and the whole diagram may be termed a phase-amplitude diagram, whether we use complex notation or not (cf. Figs. 22.13a:2 and 13a:3).

Addition of the corresponding complex numbers would then mean a superposition of sine waves. It may under certain conditions be done graphically in a phase-amplitude diagram as illustrated in Fig. 22.13a:3. This also suggests that there is a relation between the parallelogram law and that of trigonometric superposition, furthermore that complex variables may be used in the Fourier series.

22.13b

$$z_1 = x_1 + iy_1$$
$$z_2 = x_2 + iy_2$$
$$\overline{z_3 = z_1 + z_2 = (x_1 + x_2) + i(y_1 + y_2)}$$

22.13c

$$x_1 = a_1 \cos a_1 \qquad\qquad x_2 = a_2 \cos a_2$$
$$y_1 = a_1 \sin a_1 \qquad\qquad y_2 = a_2 \sin a_2$$

22.13d

$$z_1 = x_1 + iy_1 = a_1 \cos a_1 + ia_1 \sin a_1$$
$$z_2 = x_2 + iy_2 = a_2 \cos a_2 + ia_2 \sin a_2$$

22.14 – If ordinary multiplication is extended to complex variates (z_1 and z_2) we get formulae 22.14a. The coordinates of the product ($z_3 = z_1 z_2$) are $(x_1 x_2 - y_1 y_2)$ and $(x_1 y_2 + y_1 x_2)$; or, in polar coordinates as shown by formula 22.14b (cf. 22.13c). Here, z_3 represents a new polar vector with the angle $(a_1 + a_2)$ and the length $a_1 a_2$. An extension of this result to the case of n variables of unit amplitudes ($a_1 = a_2 = a_3 = \ldots = a_n = 1$) and equal angles $a_1/n = a_2/n = a_3/n = \ldots = a_n/n = a/n$ yields an important corollary shown in formula 22.14c. Now, if n goes towards infinity ($n \to \infty$), a/n will tend towards zero, $\cos(a/n)$ will tend towards 1, $\sin(a/n)$ towards a/n, and the expression 22.14c to formula 22.14d. The latter is very similar to the definition of e^x (formula 22.14e) which has led to the establishment of the entity e^{ia}, as defined by formula 22.14f.

22.14a

$$z_1 = x_1 + iy_1;\ z_2 = x_2 + iy_2$$
$$z_3 = z_1 z_2 = (x_1 x_2 - y_1 y_2) + i(x_1 y_2 + y_1 x_2)$$

22.14b

$$z_3 = z_1 z_2 = (a_1 a_2 \cos a_1 \cos a_2 - a_1 a_2 \sin a_1 \sin a_2) +$$
$$+ i(a_1 a_2 \cos a_1 \sin a_2 + a_1 a_2 \sin a_1 \cos a_2) =$$
$$= a_1 a_2 [\cos(a_1 + a_2) + i \sin(a_1 + a_2)]$$

22.14c

$$[\cos(a/n) + i \sin(a/n)]^n = (\cos a + i \sin a)$$

22.14d

$$lim\ [1 + i(a/n)]^n = (\cos a + i \sin a);\ \text{when } n \to \infty$$

22.14e

$$lim\ [1 + x/n]^n = e^x;\ \text{when } n \to \infty$$

22.14f

$$e^{ia} = lim\ [1 + i(a/n)]^n = (\cos a + i \sin a)$$
$$ae^{ia} = a(\cos a + i \sin a) = z$$

22.15 – The complex number ae^{ia} would thus represent one point in the Argand diagram, or a sine wave (or vector) with polar coordinates $(a; a)$ in the phase-amplitude diagram. Formulae 22.14c and f may be rewritten as in formulae 22.15a. With the notations we now have learned, we may furthermore establish the identities in formulae 22.15b. The transformations from complex Cartesian to complex polar coordinates are summarized in formulae 22.15c.

Expression 22.15a may be used to explain the system of harmonic overtones found in the output from a nonlinear transducer with a pure sine input ($cf.$ 19.16). If we assume the transforming function to be approximated by a function of the type $y = c_0 + c_1 x + c_2 x^2 + c_3 x^3 + \ldots + c_m x^m$ and the sine input by $x = e^{ia}$, then the output will be an additive system of terms $c_n(e^{ia})^n = c_n e^{ina} = c_n (\cos na + i \sin na)$ where n only has integer values.

22.15a $\qquad z = a (\cos a + i \sin a)^p = a (\cos p\, a + i \sin p\, a) = a (e^{ia})^p = ae^{ipa}$

22.15b
$$ae^{ia} = a (\cos a + i \sin a)$$
$$ae^{-ia} = a (\cos a - i \sin a)$$
$$\cos a = 0.5 (e^{ia} + e^{-ia})$$
$$\sin a = -0.5i (e^{ia} - e^{-ia})$$
$$e^{ia} = 1 + i\, a + (ia)^2/2! + \ldots + (ia)^n/n!$$
$$e^{ia_1} e^{ia_2} = e^{i(a_1+a_2)}$$
$$(e^{ia})^n = e^{ina}$$
$$(e^{ia})^{m/n} = e^{ima/n}$$
$$(e^{ia})' = i\, e^{ia}$$
$$e^{i\pi/2} = i$$
$$e^{i\pi} = -1$$
$$e^{i2\pi} = +1$$
$$e^{ia_1} + e^{ia_2} = e^{ia_1} \left[1 + e^{i(a_2-a_1)}\right]$$

22.15c
$$z = x + iy = ae^{ia}$$
$$a = \sqrt{(x^2 + y^2)}$$
$$x = a \cos a$$
$$(x/y = \mathrm{tg}\, a)$$
$$y = a \sin a$$
$$\log z = \log a + i\, a$$

22.16 – *Fourier Transforms.* We may now also understand the complex Fourier series ($cf.$ 21.10-12). Let us start with any function of time, $y = f(t)$. It may be transformed into a series of harmonics according to formula 22.16a. After this transformation $f(t)$ is no more any function of t since the main harmonic covers the whole time region of observation. Instead it is rather a function of the phase angles $n\omega$. The coefficients a_n and b_n may (according to 21.11d and 12b) be expressed as in formulae 22.16b, summation being performed over the t-range. In complex notation this transforms into formulae 22.16c-d ($cf.$ 22.15b), summation being performed over the whole t-range. The $F(n\omega)$ and $F(-n\omega)$ are constants for each value of n, but if n varies, the expressions become functions of n. Then 22.16c-d give formulae 22.16e, and 22.16a yields formula 22.16f.

Now, if $F(n\omega)$ is regarded as a variable where n can assume positive values, $F(n\omega)$, or negative values $F(-n\omega)$, and since the constant $a_0 = F(0)$, then 22.16f transforms to formula 22.16g. This gives $f(t)$ for any value of t as a function of n. If we pass over from summation to integration and let the various pulsatances

$n\omega$ be represented by a series of ω-values, from $-\infty$ to $+\infty$, then 22.16d and 16g turn into the more general formulae 22.16h. $F(\omega)$ is the Fourier transform of $f(t)$. The first equation under 22.16h is a direct Fourier transformation, whereby one obtains one $F(\omega)$ value for each value of ω and where integration is performed over the whole time domain. Our original equation is now transformed into a harmonic system of sine waves with the pulsatances (ω) varying continuously from zero to infinity. The second equation is an inverse Fourier transformation, which yields the value of the original function $f(t)$ for any t-value in terms of its Fourier transforms, integrated over the whole ω-domain. The inverse transformation thus recovers the time function from its transform.

22.16a
$$f(t) = a_0 + 2 \sum_{n=1}^{n \to \infty} (a_n \cos n\omega t + b_n \sin n\omega t)$$

(for simplicity a_n and b_N here represent half the values of a_N and b_N in 21.10-12)

22.16b
$$a_n = \Sigma f(t) \cos n\omega t; \ b_n = \Sigma f(t) \sin n\omega t$$

22.16c
$$a_n \cos n\omega t + b_n \sin n\omega t = 0.5 \ a_n \ (e^{in\omega t} + e^{-in\omega t}) -$$
$$- i \ 0.5 \ b_n \ (e^{in\omega t} - e^{-in\omega t}) =$$
$$= 0.5 \ (a_n - ib_n) \ e^{in\omega t} + 0.5 \ (a_n + ib_n) \ e^{-in\omega t}$$

22.16d
$$a_n - ib_n = \Sigma f(t) \ e^{-in\omega t} = F(n\omega)$$
$$a_n + ib_n = \Sigma f(t) \ e^{in\omega t} = F(-n\omega)$$

22.16e
$$a_n \cos n\omega t + b_n \sin n\omega t = 0.5 \ F(n\omega) \ e^{in\omega t} +$$
$$+ 0.5 \ F(-n\omega) \ e^{-in\omega t}$$

22.16f
$$f(t) = a_0 + \sum_{n=1}^{n=\infty} F(n\omega) \ e^{in\omega t} + F(-n\omega) \ e^{-in\omega t}$$

22.16g
$$f(t) = \sum_{n=-\infty}^{n=+\infty} F(n\omega) \ e^{in\omega t}$$

22.16h
$$F(\omega) = \int_{-\infty}^{+\infty} f(t) \ e^{-i\omega t} \ dt$$

$$f(t) = (1/2\pi) \int_{-\infty}^{+\infty} F(\omega) \ e^{i\omega t} \ d\omega$$

22.17 – Laplace Transforms. Compare now, the Fourier transform with the Laplace transform which is simply a more generalized extension of the former, formulae 22.17a. If, in the Fourier transform the integral interval is cut into half and $f(t)$ further multiplied by $e^{-\sigma t}$ we get the Laplace transform. The factor $e^{-\sigma t}$ is to ensure a better convergence of the Laplace frequency transformation series than that of the Fourier frequency transformation.

The Laplace transform yields a general method for analyzing linear differential equations. These are multiplied by e^{-pt} and the product integrated over the whole t-range [or x-range, since x is a function of t, $x = f(t)$]. The integral now varies only with the value of p in the same way as the Fourier transform varied with the pulsatances ω in the harmonic system representing the function. An example is given in formulae 22.17b, which show the first step in the calculation. What we are searching for is, however, the Laplace transform of $x = f(t)$, which we may define as $\bar{x}$; $\bar{x} = \int_0^\infty e^{-pt}x\,dx = \bar{F}(p)$. Remember, $\bar{x}$ is a function of p. Once we have $\bar{x}$ we may use its inverse transform (*cf.* 22.16h) and recover $x = f(t)$ which is the solution we want.

Equation 22.17b must, therefore, first be solved in terms of $\bar{x}$ and p. These solutions can be found in tables of the Laplace transform. Formulae 22.17c demonstrate three important solutions taken from the tables. Formulae 22.17d show the full solution of the equation $x'' + \omega^2x = c$, which we started with in 22.17b. $\bar{x}$ is obtained as a function of p. This expression, sometimes after a certain rearrangement, is looked up in the Laplace transform tables and the corresponding function of t (inverse transform) is then the solution of the differential equation.

The advantage of the Laplace and Fourier transforms is that they change rather complicated differential equations into additive patterns of harmonic waves. A parallel is the logarithms by which we can transform the operation of multiplication into the much simpler process of addition.

The fact that the transformations give us any time series in terms of its harmonic pattern makes them very useful in the analysis of oscillating systems. Some examples of their use will follow later.

22.17a

Fourier transform.

$$F(\omega) = \int_{t = -\infty}^{t = +\infty} f(t)\, e^{-i\omega t}\, dt$$

Laplace transform

$$F(p) = \int_{t = 0}^{t = \infty} f(t)\, e^{-i\omega t}\, e^{-\sigma t}\, dt = \int_0^\infty f(t)\, e^{-(\sigma + i\omega)\, t}\, dt$$

$$p = \sigma + i\omega$$

$$F(p) = \int_0^\infty f(t)\, e^{-pt}\, dt$$

22.17b

Differential equation.
$$x'' + \omega^2x - c = 0$$
$$x = f(t)$$

Laplace transformation

$$F(x'' + \omega^2x - c) =$$

$$= \int_0^\infty e^{-pt} (x'' + \omega^2x - c)\, dt =$$

$$= \int_0^\infty e^{-pt}x''\, dt + \int_0^\infty e^{-pt} \omega^2x\, dt - \int_0^\infty e^{-pt}c\, dt$$

22.17c
$$F(x'') = \int_0^\infty e^{-pt}\, x''\, dt = p^2\, \bar{x} - p\, f(0) - f'(0)$$

$$F(x') = \int_0^\infty e^{-pt}\, x'\, dt = p\, \bar{x} - f(0)$$

$$F(ax) = \int_0^\infty e^{-pt}\, ax\, dt = a\, \bar{x}$$

$$F(x) = \int_0^\infty e^{-pt}x\, dt = \bar{x}$$

$f(0)$ and $f'(0)$ are constants, the value of $f(t)$ and $f'(t)$ if $t = 0$

22.17d
Differential equation: $x'' + \omega^2 x = c$
Conditions ($t = 0$, $x = 0$, $x' = 0$)
Some transforms (from tables):

Function	Laplace transform
$x = f(t)$	$\bar{x}$
ax	$a\bar{x}$
x''	$p^2\bar{x} - pf(0) - f'(0)$
a	a/p
$\cos \omega t$	$p/(p^2 + \omega^2)$

Under the conditions given $f(0) = f'(0) = 0$
Transformation; $p^2\bar{x} + \omega^2\bar{x} = c/p$

$\bar{x}\,(p^2 + \omega^2) = c/p$
$\bar{x} = c/p(p^2 + \omega^2) =$ by factorization $=$
$(c/\omega^2)\,[(1/p) - p/(p^2 + \omega^2)]$
Solution: $x = (c/\omega^2)\,(1 - \cos \omega t)$

The inverse transform of $1/p(p^2 + \omega^2)$ may also be read directly from larger tables $= (1/\omega^2)\,(1 - \cos \omega t)$

22.18 – We have now presented the basic statistical and mathematical concepts necessary to understand rhythm analysis. In biological rhythm research the statistical approach is important because our measurements usually contain great errors and because we often lack sufficient knowledge about the structure of our study objects to formulate the mathematical conditions for our systems clearly. We have, however, seen that difficulties are encountered when it comes to testing the statistical significance of our results. Without the mathematical background we cannot understand the rather complicated methods of analysis which have presently to be used if we want to approach our material without unnecessary and dangerous assumptions. Furthermore, feedback analysis will become increasingly important in biological rhythm research. The tools of the servo-mechanical analysis are, however, the general differential equations and the methods to solve them. We have seen that some solutions are non-periodic, others periodic. Unfortunately, only linear differential equations have general solutions, which may be obtained by aid of the Fourier and Laplace transformations. Most systems in nature are, however, nonlinear, particularly the biological ones, so there remains much mathematical and statistical work to be done, though non-linear approximation to the linear state may sometimes be used. The relaxation oscillations of v.d. POL are among the few nonlinear systems well investigated, hence their popularity in biological rhythm research. They represent, however, only one case out of an almost infinite range of differential equations which might be important in biological rhythm research.

There is one theoretical problem left to discuss; the control of and interaction between oscillators, or forced oscillations and coupled oscillators. This is also the basis for an analysis of the exogenous rhythms. We have hitherto discussed the sustained endogenous biological oscillations, the external physical periodicities, as well as the physical models and the statistical-mathematical methods for rhythm analysis. We will now turn to the exogenous rhythms and will start by continuing the mathematical analysis of the last chapter, extended to the problem of forced oscillations and coupling between oscillators. After that we will make a rather broad survey of the exogenous rhythms in different fields of the biological sciences and in different frequency domains.

PART IV

EXOGENOUS RHYTHMS

"To my mind the most interesting property of biorhythms is their faculty of getting synchronized with 'external' rhythms of a nonbiological nature ... Synchronization takes place when the 'natural' frequency of a biorhythm, for instance the change between activity and inertia, or the duration of a life cycle roughly corresponds with a powerful environmental rhythm such as the change between day and night or the change of the seasons. Most of the rhythms enforced by the environment can in the last instance be traced to the cosmic rhythms found in our solar system and especially to the periodic changes in the positions between the earth, the sun and the moon. Whether there are any biological effects attributable to the action of the planets or influences from outside the solar system is rather doubtful, except of course, that a hysterical outburst caused by the reading of a horoscope however stupid, is a biological event in some way connected with the 'stars'. If I felt called upon to isolate some planetary effect in organisms other than man I should perhaps look at the effect the light of Venus or Jupiter might have on the flight activity of nocturnal insects in moonless nights in a cloudless sky. However I should not recommend anyone to start such experiments yet. Diurnal, seasonal and similar rhythms may act upon a biorhythm by one or several special factors of which light and temperature are the most obvious and which must be explored in every case. Often the chain of causes is a very long one ..."

KALMUS – Repetition, autonomy and synchronization in the living world.

The three preceding parts have dealt with the endogenous and external rhythms as well as the physical and mathematical background to rhythmic phenomena. We will now link these aspects together in discussing the synchronized exogenous rhythms, that is the control of biological rhythms. The first chapter is a continuation of the theoretical considerations in Part III. It will treat the mathematical aspects of forced and coupled oscillations, as exemplified, *e.g.* in the theory of vibrations. This is followed by a discussion of the possible corresponding biological mechanisms. The third and fourth chapters review the literature on the various exogenous rhythm periods; the day, the month, the year. The last chapter outlines some particular aspects of the biological rhythms in the larger fields of the biological sciences, such as botany, zoology or medicine. The reading is facilitated if the introductory Chapter 1 is studied first, especially sections 1.3,14,22-27. The subject will be developed in five chapters:

CHAPTER 23

Oscillator Control and Interaction

23.1 – We started this book in Chapters 2 and 3 with the study of biological regulation and servomechanisms. We then left off to consider spontaneous oscillators, also the biological ones, and the external rhythmic agents. The preceding chapters have discussed the statistical and mathematical techniques for handling time series, including differential equations and their solution with the aid of complex variables. We are now ready to return to the problem of control and synchronization but we will first continue in the vein of the preceding chapter by applying our mathematical knowledge to the theory of forced oscillations and oscillator interaction. Our model will mainly be a physical one, vibrations, demonstrating the flow of energy in the operations. Biological rhythms have an energy background too, but more difficult for us to define. We will see how varied already this mechanical correlate of oscillations is and also how we rapidly approach the limits for the mathematical applications with increasing complexity of the systems. We will finally end up by looking at the transfer functions used in the analysis of servomechanisms.

Synchronization, forced oscillations and interaction have already been mentioned sporadically in 1.14,22-25, 3.29-31, 4.27-30, Chapter 12, 19.14-16, 20-30, 20.30, 21.19,32, 22.5,8. For further literature see textbooks on mathematics, physics and servotheory, e.g. BODE, BOGLIUBOV[100], BOWER[100], KU, LOTKA[3], NICOLSON[100], REICH, SEARS[100], STEWART[200], WAGNER[400]. A good textbook on vibrations is BICKLEY[100].

23.2 – *Energy Aspects*. We have talked a great deal about sustained oscillations in physical and biological rhythms. This does not mean, however, that the rhythms represent some kind of perpetuum mobile. Though they are closed systems they consume energy while going, as discussed in 2.25, 3.14 and 4.2. They are mobile and therefore the application of force may set them in motion. Sustained oscillations running in a steady state must receive as much new energy as is lost. If the energy dissipates they will stop. A wheel will spin when suddenly set in motion, then slow up. It can stop in any position. This does not necessarily mean that no forces are acting upon the wheel but rather that they balance each other in an equilibrium (*cf.* 3.13-16). Applied forces must upset this equilibrium if motion is to result and must be strong enough to overcome the resistance of the system.

Some systems, *e.g.* servosystems, or mechanical vibrating systems have certain positions of equilibrium which they seek when energy is lost. Forces which set the system in motion ('signals' in communication language) will therefore cause deviations (disturbances) from the equilibrium position. The return from this disturbed state to equilibrium depends on the characteristics of the system and the force applied. In some cases a more or less exponential return may occur. In oscillators oscillations may be set up. In the latter case we have three possibilities: too weak force, sustaining force and too strong force; with the possibilities of damped, sustained or wild oscillations. We have had many examples of this throughout the book (cf. Figs. 1.12a-d).

23.3 – It is not, however, sufficient that force is applied, it must also be supplied at the right place and time in an oscillation (cf. resonance, 4.3,30), else it may sometimes further the movement, sometimes brake it. The ideal case is that the oscillator itself regulates or triggers the delivery of energy, as in a clock, or in a relaxation oscillation (4.13), or in the way the KREBS cycle might regulate its own supply of acetate (2.15). In these cases the regulation may be regarded as a part of the system. The mechanism has so to say a built-in power supply. The energy packets are always delivered at the optimum times and their effects are therefore easily added. Since, theoretically, a system will keep moving at constant velocity after just one instant application of force, this summation will cause acceleration if the resistance is not too strong. The applied force does usually not have to be strong at all but the summation may give remarkable effects, that is how resonance works. The period stays constant but the amplitude increases.

23.4 – V.D. POL extended the problem a little further. His relaxation equation represents a system where the source of power increases with the amplitude up to a certain limit, when it is released from the system. Another example of intrinsic force control, though not necessarily in an oscillator is ASHBY's homeostat (3.16). Here the whole system changes itself if the applied force (disturbance) is too strong, so as to accomodate it.

23.5 – *Vibrations*. Mechanical vibrations are a good example of how forces interact in an oscillator (BICKLEY[100], ROCARD). The vibrating system has an equilibrium which is ensured by its stiffness. When a force sets it into motion, inertia keeps it going and this results in a deviation from the equilibrium, caused by the kinetic energy of the motion. The latter creates a tension (potential energy) in the material owing to its stiffness and builds up a restoring force which eventually causes a return to the equilibrium. Vibration may be regarded as a periodic transformation of energy from the kinetic to the potential state. Similar transformations are involved in the oscillation of the fine particles of matter.

Apart from the forces mentioned there will be a general resistance (3.21-22,28) which is independent of the direction of the process and causes energy loss. There are different kinds: (1) coulomb friction, which is constant; (2) viscous friction, at small speeds, which is approximately proportional to speed; (3) hydraulic friction at high speeds, proportional to the speed squared.

23.6 – Let us now build up a simple case. The position of the system is denoted by x. At equilibrium $x = 0$. The kinetic energy is proportional to mass (m) and velocity (x') squared, formula 23.6a.

The potential energy is slowly built up through the work performed by the motion. If the force of this is proportional to the displacement (x) and to the stiffness (s) at each position, then it cumulates during motion and creates the restoring potential force, formula 23.6b. Now, the total energy (E) of the system, kinetic + potential, should be constant throughout the movement. Equations 23.6a-b then give formula 23.6c. Differentiating with regard to time we get $mx'' + sx = 0$ or $mx'' = -sx$, which shows that mass and inertia are counteracted by the stiffness. There is, however, also a general resistance to the movement. Chosing viscous friction, we now add the term rx'. Like the stiffness it counteracts the motion; $mx'' = -sx-rx'$. We then arrive at a typical equation of motion, formula 23.6d (cf. 22.2). This is a differential equation of the second order and with constant coefficients. It is often written in another form (formula 23.6e, cf. 4.10b). The electrical analog was shown in 4.10a.

23.6a	kinetic energy $= 0.5\ m(x')^2$
23.6b	potential energy $= \int sx dx = 0.5\ sx^2$
23.6c	$E = 0.5\ m(x')^2 + 0.5\ sx^2$
	$mx'' + sx = 0$
23.6d	$mx'' + rx' + sx = 0$
23.6e	$x'' + 2\ a\ x' + \omega^2 x = 0$

23.7 – We have seen that the constants of the equation of motion may be thought of as representing the underlying force. a is sometimes called the resistance parameter (formula 23.6e). If a is zero, there is no damping force (or it is counteracted) and we get undamped sustained simple harmonic motion, formula 23.7a (cf. 4.7-8, 19.8-9, 21.9).–The introduction of the resistance term (a) causes damping. The solution is that of a damped oscillation, formula 23.7b (cf. 3.19-20), where the trigonometric term represents oscillation and the exponential one damping. We can see that the resistance (represented by a) has a rather direct effect on the damping. It also reduces the frequency of the oscillation through the ($\omega^2 - a^2$) term. However, the effect of a is less strong here than in the exponential term. If $a > \omega$ the oscillating part vanishes and the function represents a smooth asymptotic return to zero. There is a limiting condition where $a = \omega$ which is called critical damping.

23.7a	$x'' + \omega^2 x = 0$
	$x = a \sin \omega t + b \cos \omega t$
23.7b	$x = ae^{-at} \sin [\sqrt{(\omega^2 - a^2)}\ t + \emptyset]$

23.8 – The ω^2-term represents the frequency of the oscillation (ωt), which is primarily determined by the potential energy (stored 'endogenous' energy, mechanical stiffness) of the system, as distinguished from the kinetic energy which is usually imparted from without. It also helps to determine the velocity of the system (cf. 19.12) which is given by x'. We may further seek the maximum velocity ($\hat{x}'$). This is found at the baseline crossing and is, of course, proportional to the frequency and the amplitude of the oscillation.

23.9 – The theory of vibration is not only a theoretical aid in understanding biological rhythms. It has also a direct importance in such problems as sound perception and lesions; the effect of sonar and ultrasound (frequency > 18 kHz) on the body; as well as the mechanical stress resulting from contact with vibrating machinery (GOLDMAN).

A second order differential equation with constant coefficients would perhaps seem to suffice rather well in the description of rhythms, since it accounts for the basic expressions of the underlying physical forces. However, higher-order terms may arise in the interaction between oscillators, or variable forces may be acting. The coefficients may also be variable, either as functions of time, of each other, or as functions of the dependent variable (x), cf. 22.2. The latter is the case in the relaxation oscillation, $x'' - (1-x^2)x' + \omega^2 x = 0$ where the resistance term $(1-x^2)$ diminishes with increasing deviation from the equilibrium (position, x), cf. 4.13, 22.6.

If the oscillating system is not able to control the forces acting upon it they may instead conflict, with a resultant change in the characteristics of the oscillation. Then the movement may either be forced or there is a coupled oscillator situation.

23.10 – *Forced Oscillations.* If a system capable of oscillations is acted upon by a strong force which it cannot control, it must strike some kind of balance with it and a forced oscillation may result. Usually, equilibrium is not attained at once. Instead a series of transient oscillations occur first, ending in a steady state (cf. 4.29, 22.5). The forced oscillation may differ from the spontaneous sustained oscillation of the free system, with altered phasing, frequency, amplitudes or shape. The components of the new system are two, the forcing function and the spontaneous periodicity of the affected system.

23.11 – The *forcing function* may be of various kinds. It may be random or regular. The random case was discussed in connection with disturbed periodicity (21.21). This situation is difficult to describe and is essentially a statistical problem. Often, the random force may be regarded as noise which has to be reduced to an acceptable level. One example would be the rolling of a ship on the sea. Control is easier to perform in physics than in biology.

The forcing function may also consist of a single impulse or a change of level (switch function, step change). It may then trigger a series of spontaneous damped oscillations which may be regarded as transients. The force only controls one of the system parameters, the timing of the oscillation. This is, however, an important mechanism in biological rhythm research (cf. Fig. 1.12a-d, 7.7, 12.12, 19.13,15, 17-19, 24). Meteorological influences are often non-periodic.

23.12 – The forcing function may be periodic, *e.g.* a series of impulses or a sine wave. If the impulses are far between (*e.g.* dawn and dusk) they may simply generate a regularly recurring series of damped oscillations (cf. the ringing response, 19.24, 32) which may even interact (KENNETH[100]).

If the impulses have equal frequency with the free oscillation of the system they may set it going by resonance (23.3). The process may then even go on after cessation of the forcing function. This is about what happens in resuscitation with artificial breathing or heart massage.

We may also have the case of a periodic forcing function acting upon a purely passive system which transmits it with or without a transformation of it (19.16). As already mentioned such a transformation is, to a certain extent unavoidable and never really linear. There will for instance be random noise and harmonic overtones.

23.13 – The periodic forcing input may, of course, have any shape and may act upon oscillators possessing the most varied spontaneous wave types. In that case a wide range of possible interactions exists. The study of these is often highly complicated by the fact that most biological oscillators have clearly nonlinear functions. This is easily forgotten by the biological rhythm research workers who quite naturally seek relatively simple models for the exogenous rhythm. It also explains why so many models exist and why it is almost impossible to choose between them. Also, the natural synchronizers do not act with any appreciable force. Hence the organism may manipulate the input (19.14-15) before following them, even if it cannot alter them at their origin, and the process of synchronization is apt to become complicated.

23.14 – If the forcing function $F(t)$ and the spontaneous function are well known it should be possible to calculate the steady state and the transient solutions mathematically. This, unfortunately, is difficult or even impossible in some cases. As long as the equation is linear the Laplace transforms give one general method of solution (Chapter 22). It also helps to remember that the solution of the homogeneous part of the differential equation (the complementary function) represents the corresponding free oscillation (22.5). Thus, as soon as one particular integral has been found, by trial or systematical evaluation, the general solution is obtained by adding the complementary function. It helps considerably if some conditions are also given, e.g. the value of x at time zero. In the nonlinear case approximations to the linear state may be tried (BOGOLIUBOV[100]).

In the following we shall start with several examples of linear oscillating systems, of increasing complexity, and end with some comments on the behaviour of the nonlinear ones. Some simple forcing functions will be used as models, e.g. a suddenly applied constant force (relay) and the sine curve. The latter is important in testing servomechanisms (including biological ones). Furthermore, any periodic forcing function may be resolved into Fourier components, each of which can be separately treated. We will always consider the oscillator to be resting at zero position until the forcing function sets it into motion at time zero. Then the velocity of the function must be zero simultaneously and we get the initial conditions: $f(0) = f'(0) = 0$, $t = 0$. The methods of solution were discussed in 22.3-6,17.

The solutions may be complicated, but in essence they contain two parts. One is the transient function, which damps out. The other is the steady state function, which remains when the first part has disappeared. In the following β will signify the pulsatance of the forcing agent, ω that of the steady state solution, and μ that of the transient solution.

23.15 – *Constant Force Acting on Undamped Harmonic Oscillator.* Let a force F act upon a unit mass oscillator of type 23.7a, as in formulae 23.15a, which also show the solution. The function is plotted in Fig. 23.15b:1. It is seen that both amplitude and level are proportional to the force and that the amplitude equals the level (F/ω^2). This mimics remarkably the quantitative behaviour of 24-h liver glycogen rhythms (*cf.* the amplitude line, 20.19). Its behaviour would seem to be described by 23.15a where the homogeneous part is kept sustained from other sources and where F represents the glycogen.

23.15a
$$F = x'' + \omega^2 x$$
$$x = (F/\omega^2)\,(1 - \cos \omega t)$$
$$(cf.\ 22.17d)$$

23.16 – *Constant Force Acting on Oscillator with Resistance.* We now let the force act upon a unit mass oscillator of type 23.6d-e, as illustrated in formula 23.16a together with the solution. The latter represents a transient damped oscillation with the pulsatance μ. We recognize the damping term e^{-at}, *cf.* 23.7. The function

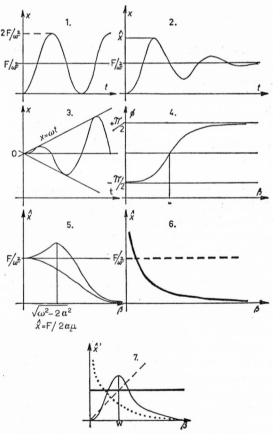

Fig. 23.15b. Types of forced oscillations and their characteristics.

peters out at a new steady state level, $x = F/\omega^2$, which is determined by the constant force and is lower the higher the frequency (or energy) of the free oscillation. Above critical damping (if $a^2 > \omega^2$) the function approaches the level asymptotically from below. The largest possible amplitude ($x_{max} = \hat{x}$) is given in formula 23.16b. This is always less than the amplitude in the undamped case (F/ω^2), Fig. 23.15b:2. It is the product of one transient and one steady state component.

Compare the function described here with the action of a relay on an oscillator (Figs. 1.12b, 19.24a), e.g. HILDEBRANDT's[21] theory of dawn acting on the 24-h rhythm, or FREEMAN's[5] damped oscillations in cortical behaviour.

23.16a
$$F = x'' + 2\,ax' + \omega^2 x$$
$$x = (F/\omega^2)\,[1 - e^{-at}\,(\cos \mu t + a\mu^{-1} \sin \mu t)]$$
$$\mu^2 = \omega^2 - a^2$$

23.16b
$$\hat{x} = (F/\omega^2)\,(1 + e^{-a\pi/\mu})$$

23.17 – *Periodic Force Acting on Undamped Oscillator.* Let us return to the situation in 23.15 and now apply a sinusoidally varying force ($F \sin \beta t$), formulae 23.17a. β represents the frequency of the forcing function. The solution is a complicated motion, though in principle it represents two superposed oscillations of different frequency and amplitude. If the driving frequency equals the free oscillation frequency ($\omega = \beta$), the expression turns into formula 23.17b, which illustrates the conditions at resonance (*cf.* 23.3). The term ($\omega t \cos \omega t$) shows that the amplitude will increase indefinitely with the 'envelope' $x = \pm\,\omega t$. In practice the increase will finally be checked by the resistance and nonlinearity of the system. Theoretically, we get wild oscillations as shown in Fig. 23.15b:3. *Cf.* the unbalanced feedback (Fig. 1.12d, 3.23).

23.17a
$$F \sin \beta t = x'' + \omega^2 x$$
$$x = (F/\omega)\,(\omega \sin \beta t - \beta \sin \omega t)/(\omega^2 - \beta^2)$$

23.17b
$$x = (F/2\omega^2)\,(\sin \omega t - \omega t \cos \omega t)$$

23.18 – *Periodic Force Acting on Oscillator with Resistance.* Now, let us go back to the situation in 23.16 and apply the sinusoidally varying force $F \sin \beta t$, as illustrated in formulae 23.18a. The result is complicated. In essence we can distinguish the two usual parts. One is the damped transient, characterized by e^{at}. The other is the steady state solution, represented by $\cos (\beta t - \phi)$, where ϕ is the phase lag between force and velocity.

23.18a
$$F \sin \beta t = x'' + 2\,ax' + \omega^2 x$$
$$x = (F/\mu)\,[e^{-at}\,(\mu \cos \phi \cos \mu t + \beta \sin \mu t \sin \phi +$$
$$+\,a \sin \mu t \cos \phi) - \mu \cos (\beta t - \phi)]\,/$$
$$[4\,a^2\beta^2 + (\beta^2 - \omega^2)^2]^{\,0.5}$$

23.19 – Let us look closer at the steady state solution. Its frequency is the same as that of the driving force (this is the linear case), but with a phase lag which is described by formula 23.19a. At resonance, forcing and free functions have equal frequencies ($\beta = \omega$ and $\phi = 0$). The driving force is then represented by $\sin \beta t$, the forced oscillation by $-\cos \beta t$ and the velocity by the 1st derivative of $-\cos \beta t = \sin$

βt. The driving force is thus not in phase with the forced oscillation, it leads with a quarter period ($\pi/2$). Instead the driving force and the generated velocity run parallel, as should be since the force determines the velocity. – If $\beta < \omega$ (larger driving period) velocity will lead the force with a phase lag which is maximally $\pi/2$ if β tends to zero (infinite period, constant force, 23.16). If $\beta > \omega$ (smaller driving period) velocity lags behind the force and at the limiting case ($\beta \rightarrow \infty$) the lag is $\pi/2$. The relation between β and lag is shown in Fig. 23.15b:4. The influence of resistance (measured by a) on this is to determine how pronounced the lag will be.

23.19a $$\operatorname{tg} \emptyset = (\beta^2 - \omega^2) / 2a\beta$$

23.20 – The *amplitude* response may be inferred by studying the maximal x-value ($\hat{x}$), formula 23.20a. If β tends to zero we approach the constant force case, $\hat{x} = F/\omega^2$, which is the steady state solution of 23.16b when the exponential transient response has vanished. If $\hat{x}$ is plotted against β (the amplitude response curve) one may study the behaviour closer. See Fig. 23.15b:5, where the upper curve represents cases with small resistance and the lower curve cases with large resistance. At the β-value ($\omega^2 - 2 a^2)^{0.5}$ the amplitude has the value $\hat{x} = F/2 a \mu = F/2 a$ ($\omega^2 - a^2)^{0.5}$, and may show a peak if the resistance or the frequency of the transient are not too large. A large resistance (a) may damp the response from the beginning, unless the free energy of the system (represented by ω) is very large.

The *velocity* of the forced oscillation may also be calculated. The maximal velocity ($\hat{x}'$) depends on the frequency and amplitude of the oscillations (*cf*. 23.8) and is a measure of the energy in the system, formula 23.20b. The graph, the velocity response curve, is shown in Fig. 23.15b:7, the peaked line. The peak occurs, of course, at resonance. In the undamped case ($a = 0$) the peak velocity then tends towards infinity (*cf*. Fig. 23.15b:3).

23.20a $$\hat{x} = F / [4a^2\beta^2 + (\beta^2 - \omega^2)^2]^{0.5}$$

23.20b $$\hat{x}' = F\beta / [4a^2\beta^2 + (\beta^2 - \omega^2)^2]^{0.5}$$

$$[4a^2\beta^2 + (\beta^2 - \omega^2)^2]^{0.5} / \beta = Z = \text{impedance}$$
$$= \text{(approx.)} = \text{peak force (amplitude)/peak velocity}$$

23.21 – *Periodic Force Acting on Oscillator with Dominant Stiffness*. Let us now study the effect of the sinusoidal driving force on some special cases of oscillators. In a system with high potential energy, *e.g.*, the ω term would tend to dominate (*cf*. 23.8) reducing the situation as in formulae 23.21a.

The amplitude-frequency diagram is given by the horizontal broken line in Fig. 23.15b:6 ($\hat{x} = F/\omega^2$). The amplitude is independent of the driving frequency, only determined by the high energy of the system. Thus, if we want a uniform amplitude response, stiffness should dominate over mass and friction. If we cannot achieve high stiffness we may get a similar amplitude stability by avoiding resonance as much as possible since the amplitude response is most labile in this region (Fig. 23.15b:5). This may be achieved by keeping the phase lag as large as possible.

This problem might perhaps have some bearing upon biological rhythms. Here, the forcing frequency is set. If the body wants amplitude stability it would do well to avoid having the same spontaneous frequency. Inheriting a free circadian frequency, *e.g.*, would not be advantageous for the stability of the 24-h rhythms. Rather, the body would profit from a high endogenous frequency, which simultaneously has a high energy (ω, 'stiffness'). Such reasoning agrees with the findings of MENZEL[5, 9, 15–16, 100–102] on diseased persons and of SOLLBERGER[3] on embryos, *viz.* 4-6-8 h endogenous rhythms (*cf.* 9.8-9).

Another point is that the biological external forcing function has, actually, very small energy. However, one must always think of it as triggering inner forces in the organisms. These forces, being ultimately chemical, are probably of the same order of magnitude as those of the endogenous oscillators; *i.e.* F would be relatively high for a biological system, and making ω large (in F/ω^2) would ensure stability by damping the amplitude. Thus two effects would be achieved, damping of the fluctuations and insensitivity at the resulting amplitude level. Of course, the circadian period may still be inherited, functioning as the force-releaser, triggered and timed by the weak external signal. But the body would then do well to counterbalance this with other high-frequency systems.

The peak velocity ($\hat{x}'$) of the system 23.21a increases linearly with the forcing frequency (Fig. 23.15b:7, broken line).

23.21a
$$F \sin \beta t = \omega^2 x$$
$$x = (F/\omega^2) \sin \beta t$$
$$\hat{x} = F/\omega^2$$
$$\hat{x}' = F\beta \, / \, \omega^2$$

23.22 – *Periodic Force Acting on Oscillator with Dominant Resistance.* Here, the term $2ax'$ would dominate (*cf.* 23.7), yielding formulae 23.22a. The amplitude-response curve ($\hat{x} = F/2a\beta$) is shown in Fig. 23.15b:6, the unbroken line. The velocity response curve is shown by the horizontal line in Fig. 23.15b:7. Thus the amplitude decreases with increasing frequency. The remarkable property of this system is that frequency and amplitude match each other so that the peak velocity is constant.

23.22a
$$F \sin \beta t = 2ax'$$
$$x = (-F/2a\beta) \cos \beta t$$
$$\hat{x} = F/ \, 2a\beta$$
$$\hat{x}' = F/2a$$

23.23 – *Periodic Force Acting on Oscillator with Dominant Inertia (Mass).* Here, the acceleration term x'' will dominate (*cf.* 23.6d-e), yielding formulae 23.23a. The amplitude and velocity response graphs are shown in respectively Fig. 23.15b:6 (unbroken line) and 23.15b:7 (dotted line). Thus both look similar to the high frequency ends of the corresponding complete response curves, Fig. 23.15b:5 and 7. In general, this tells us that at high driving frequencies inertia will always dominate.

23.23a
$$F \sin \beta t = x''$$
$$x = (-F/\beta^2) \sin \beta t$$
$$\hat{x} = F/\beta^2$$
$$\hat{x}' = F/\beta$$

23.24 – *Parametric Resonance.* We have now discussed two special cases of forcing functions, the constant and the sinusoidal force. In practice, any other periodic or nonperiodic shape may occur. The general forcing function case could be written (in the second order linear case) according to formula 23.24a. It can always be transformed into a set of harmonics, each component being treated as above.

However, the external influence may also act in other ways, *e.g.* directly on one or several of the parameters in the differential system (though still being, itself, dependent only on time), periodic coefficients, parametric resonance (*cf.* KLOTTER). This is illustrated in formula 23.24b. The expression is still linear. It is also well suited for analog studies. Take *e.g.* the electric analog of mechanical vibrations (formula 23.24c, *cf.* 4.10) where $C =$ capacitance, $R =$ resistance, $L =$ selfinductance and $q =$ charge. The capacitance, resistance or inductance may be forced separately to follow any desired function and the total output studied (WEVER).–Some examples of equations belonging here are LEGENDRE's equation (formula 23.24d) and BESSEL's equation (formula 23.24e).

23.24a $F(t) = x'' + 2\,a\,x' + \omega^2 x$

23.24b $f_1(t)\,x'' + f_2(t)\,x' + f_3(t)\,x = 0$

23.24c $Lq'' + Rq' + (1/C)\,q = 0$

23.24d $(1\text{-}t^2)\,x'' - 2tx' + n(n+1)\,x = 0$

23.24e $t^2 x'' + tx' + (t^2-n^2)\,x = 0$

23.25 – *Control in Nonlinear Oscillators.* The nonlinear types of oscillation functions are much more difficult to solve, and one has to use graphical aids such as the phase-plane (*cf.* ANDRONOW[100], v. D. POL[1-3]) or laborious approximations to the linear case (BOGOLIUBOV[100]). One simplified method which may be tried is to make an assumption about the solution, founded upon the fact that any function can be expressed as a Fourier series. If the nonlinearity is not too pronounced it might suffice to include only a few harmonics (*e.g.* $x = a_1 \sin \beta t + a_2 \sin 2\beta t + a_3 \sin 3\beta t$). This expression is then substituted in the differential equation which describes the oscillation. β is the driving frequency. We may also assume that $\beta = \omega$ if we want a steady state resonant solution.

23.26 – Whatever the type of oscillator function, we usually expect the driving frequency to take over, and our formulae are so constructed. We have a good analogy in the mechanical vibrating systems. We may always force a pendulum to assume any frequency we want by sheer brute force, but is easier the closer we come to resonance ($\beta = \omega$). If our manipulations are too feeble, the mechanism will rather not react at all. We may also easily observe the transients.

The solution of the forced oscillation equations is therefore rather to find out under which conditions (parameter values, driving frequencies) the system will react by entrainment, that is, follow the driving frequency. The chief condition is usually that the two frequencies should not be too different (the detuning must not be too large), because it is only at resonance that the energy of the systems is really built up.

The nonlinear systems are an exception here. We remember that if we force a frequency upon a passive system with nonlinear transformation response

(3.29, 19.16) harmonics will result in the output, *heteroperiodic oscillations*. The same will occur in a nonlinear oscillator, which may however, then make resonance with one of the harmonic overtones instead of the fundamental driving frequency, *synchronous oscillations*. Interaction may then occur in the system with the production of beats (19.22-23), *asynchronous oscillations*. Periodic changes in phasing may also occur. The overtone does not even have to be strong, owing to resonance, because then the energy of the successive inputs is added and stored in the system. It is typical of nonlinear oscillators that there are complicated relations between amplitude, phase and frequency (*cf.* 20.12). The nonlinear oscillators are more stable than the linear ones under parametric resonance, the latter easily build up the amplitude without limit. – Of course, beats may also arise if several driving inputs act upon one and the same oscillator.

23.27 – A well-instanced example of forced nonlinear systems occurs in the relaxation oscillations (4.13, 19.30). Fig. 19.30a demonstrates the mechanism. The driving frequency interacts with a subharmonic corresponding to the frequency of the free system (demultiplication), but the frequency range of possible resonance may be rather small. The amplitude of the system is rather dependent on small differences between the driving subharmonic (which does not have to be strong) and the free oscillations. Variations in the amplitude may easily appear (beats).

We may also have interaction between nonlinear systems with spontaneously varying parameters (amplitude and frequency), which are controlled by a driving frequency; or the driving frequency may, itself, vary periodically. Here, the maximum amplitude does not necessarily coincide with the time points of resonance between external and intrinsic frequencies.

23.28 — Beats in a nonlinear system form one basis for quite another possibility of forced oscillations, *viz.* frequency transformation. This domain is, however, of lesser interest in physics and has not been treated in such detail as the resonance case. In biology it may perhaps occur (*cf.* 1.23, 16.13). It also follows from the preceding sections that an analysis of the interaction between bioamplitudes, biofrequencies and biophases may give hints to the synchronization process.

23.29 – *Coupled Oscillators*. In forced oscillations the action is one-way ($F \rightarrow$ Oscillator). In physics F often delivers the maintaining energy (amplification) to the system and usually entrains the target completely. In biology, however, the amplifiers are often intrinsic and the forcing function only exerts a guiding influence, which may probably be transformed in many ways in the body (*cf.* 23.13).

Another situation appears if two oscillators are coupled together, mutually entraining each other (Oscillator I $\longleftrightarrow$ Oscillator II). This is a much more complicated problem. It differs from superimposition (19.22,28) where the effects of different systems are only added together. Here, the basic mechanisms interfere.

Coupled oscillators are common, both in physics and in biology. Especially in the latter case large numbers of them are probably interconnected.

A simple model would be two tuning forks or two pendulums suspended from the same base. Now, if one of them is set into vibration, the movement will slowly be transferred to the partner until the latter swings and the former is at standstill. The movement will then change periodically between the two oscillators (SCHMITT[3]). Other examples are the double pendulum or a system of springs, *e.g.* in a car (*cf.* 22.8). The effects of mechanical vibrations on the human body is another (GOLDMAN).

23.30 – The mathematical representation of coupled oscillators is necessarily complicated. Each oscillator will be represented by a differential equation, as described before, and the overall situation by a differential equation system. In principle, the Laplace transforms may be used to solve the linear case and approximations to the linear state may be tried in the nonlinear case. The mathematics tend, however, to become complicated. Standard solutions are of less value here, owing to the rich variety in possible interconnections and each case has to be solved as a new problem. Analog solutions are valuable owing to the complexity of the situation. Both mechanical, hydraulic, chemical and electronic analog computers are possible.

All kinds of interaction may occur in coupled oscillators, such as periodic fluctuations in amplitude (beats, 19.20-23), or in phasing (which may give the effect of a variable frequency, *cf.* 23.28, or disturbed periodicities, 21.21). There may also appear relative coordination phenomena (19.25-34) with locked or variable frequency relations. *Cf.* also what was said on the general action of forcing agents on nonlinear oscillators (23.25-27). In some parts or nodes of the system movements may cancel out completely causing a true dynamic equilibrium, antiresonance (*cf.* the shock hypothesis of RICHTER[5], 8.12).

23.31 – FRANCK[100] presents an interesting model by coupling several oscillating electrodes in different ways: galvanic (a resistor between the electrodes), capacitive (a capacitor between the electrodes), and through fluid currents (electrodes immersed in the same electrolyte). Inductive coupling (with one or two induction coils) is another possibility, though of less practical importance. If the single frequencies are similar the whole system assumes an intermediate frequency. A larger electrode dominates somewhat. If the single frequencies differ more, the typical picture of relative coordination occurs, with frequency coupling, intercalated beats or more subtle differences in shape (specially the capacitive coupling). The authors conclude that the whole mechanism aims at economizing with the total electric energy available, which has to pass through the coupling link. There is not always power enough for the superposition and beat phenomena displayed by other systems. A summation of energy from cycle to cycle actually goes on but as soon as a certain value is reached the system is forced to change its behaviour radically (extra beats or a relaxation reaction). A similar mechanism is assumed by BLUME[10-11] in leaf movements, where jumps in the harmonic components may occur (disturbed periodicities, 21.21).

More examples of biological coupled oscillators occur in 19.34 (*cf.* BANGERT, BETHE[1-2, 4-7, 101], CLYNES, HILDEBRANDT[3-5, 7-12, 14, 16, 20, 100, 104], v. HOLST, KOEPCHEN[1-2, 100]), on muscular coordination as well as the interaction between the respiratory and heart rates.

23.32 – Coupled oscillators may, of course, also be forced, but here the result is more variable than in the single oscillator case. Resonance with harmonics may occur in some parts, antiresonance in others. There may be several entraining forces, each acting upon its own oscillator. A two-oscillator model has for instance been proposed by PITTENDRIGH[100-102] and WENT[3] in explaining the entrainment of circadian rhythms by light and temperature (14.6). However, this entrainment may also act upon different parameters of one and the same oscillator (parametric resonance, *cf.* 23.24, KLOTTER). In mechanical vibrations acting upon the living body, the type of response varies with the frequency of vibrations (GOLDMAN). At frequencies < 3 c/sec the whole body reacts as one single unit. Up to 100 c/sec it behaves as a mechanical system of oscillators with inertia, resistance or elastic structures, and may show resonance. At $100 - 100,000$ c/sec the vibration energy travels through the medium as various types of physical wave forms (transverse, longitudinal, 19.10). Above 100,000 c/sec compression waves dominate. At very high frequencies, on the other hand, the penetration into the tissues is very poor with the surface effect dominating. The response to vibrations is largely nonlinear. *Cf.* COERMANN[100], LANGE[100], WHITE[100].

23.33 – *Nonlinearities. Transients. Entrainment.* A system at rest, in dynamic equilibrium, or in steady state movement may either be affected by disturbances which temporarily change its position, or by a resetting action, *i.e.* a change in parameters. In the first case, it will return to the initial state, in the second case it will usually seek a new equilibrium (*cf.* Fig. 1.12a-d). A combination of both is ASHBY's homeostat (3.16) where a disturbance is counteracted either by a persistence of the old conditions or by a change in parameters of the system so as to accomodate the disturbance without the destruction of the mechanism. This response is typical for living organisms. – The return to rest or to a new level of action occurs through a series of transient variations which depend on the spontaneous oscillation frequency of the system and the nature of the disturbance. Sometimes, a new equilibrium is not found and more or less irregular fluctuations occur.

23.34 – *Transients* (1.22, 4.29, 14.6, 23.10, 14) may occur after the onset or after the cessation of an external force, after a sudden short disturbance (shock), or after a change in internal parameters (*e.g.* disease). Usually, transients are of less interest in physics and mechanics since the aims of most constructions are stability and steady state operation. This is certainly important in biology, but biological rhythm research workers have also studied the transients, trying to extract information about the system from them (14.6). This is however, quite difficult since dissimilar systems may have similar transients. – Ordinary shock-induced damped oscillations may be regarded as transients. – Transients may be linear or nonlinear; *cf.* O'HARA[100].

23.35 – Another type of study is to register the steady state response to a rhythmic input after elimination of the transients, studying the relation between gain, phase lag and frequency of the system (3.29-30). This is a quite general method in systems analysis of transducers and feedback systems. Usually, there is then full synchronization (12.10), where the mechanism has adopted the driving frequency,

though with a change in amplitude and phase. This depends on pure energy requirements, as discussed in 23.3,26. The applied force must amplify, not counteract
the energy movements in the system. It is therefore equally understandable that
entrainment is usually only possible if the driving frequency (or its harmonic) and
the spontaneous frequency do not differ too much. In the mathematical treatment
of the problem entrainment is put in as a condition and the analysis shows under
which oscillatory conditions this is possible (cf. 23.26).

Biological entraining agents do, however, often represent extremely small
energies (cf. 23.13, 29). They may of course, trigger a release of stored energy,
thus ensuring entrainment, but theoretically any kind of transformation between the input control and the oscillator should be possible, even for instance a
frequency transformation. The mathematics would, however, tend to become very
complicated and the field has not been explored.

23.36 – The entrainment effect is naturally strongest at resonance, where the input
energies are maximally maintained and added in the systems. Actually, resonance
is dangerous because of this, since the ever-cumulating energy may cause wild
fluctuation with eventual disruption of the system. In practice, however, steady
state resonance is quite possible owing to energy loss or to nonlinearities which
diminish the response at high amplitudes. Actually, stable oscillators may even
contain deliberately introduced nonlinearities.

Unfortunately, the mathematics of nonlinear systems are complicated. One is
therefore tempted to approximate to the linear case. This is often possible with
quite satisfactory accuracy. The degree of linearity may also be tested. The
biologist must never forget, however, that the living mechanisms are essentially
nonlinear. Any true theoretical approach to biological rhythms should be based
on nonlinear systems but this has to await the development of new mathematical
and statistical techniques of handling them. Analog computers are, however,
already a good help.

23.37 – *Transfer Functions. Gain-Phase-Frequency Relations.* The last chapters gave
us some mathematical tools with which to analyze the behaviour of oscillators. However, their application demands a thorough knowledge about the component parts in a mechanism, as has *e.g.* the engineer who wants to construct a
complicated network out of an assembly of well-tested parts, or who studies the
behaviour of a machine with a detailed blue-print in hand. The biologist, unfortunately, knows relatively little about his object and never has the full picture.
He has to approach his experimental object as a partly specified transducer, as a
black box (cf. 2.3-4). He delivers information into it and measures the output. The
relation between output and input, the transfer function, tells him how the
transducer has handled the information and from this he tries to understand the
construction of the transducer.

It is typical of oscillators and servomechanisms, including their control, that
we are not concerned with simple interrelations between several variates, but with
changes in them; with changes affecting changes. This indicates that differential
equations and phase diagrams are a very proper way of handling the problems. It
is also here that the Laplace transforms (22.17) are superbly useful, transforming

an interaction between changes (convolutions) into a more easily handled form.

23.38 – Let us regard the input as a time function, the consecutive changes in which determine the response of a transducer. It may be described by a general differential equation of the type 22.2b. The transducer may be regarded as responding to a series of infinitesimally short changes, the effects of which appear after a certain time delay and which are superimposed upon each other, yielding a new time function embodied in another differential equation. This process is described by the transfer function and illustrated in Fig. 23.38c. The upper part of the figure shows the symbols used in working with transfer functions, as applied to a simple input-output diagram of a transducer (Fig. 23.38a) and to a feedback situation (Fig. 23.38b).

The expressions $E(p)$ and $C(p)$ are the Laplace transforms (indicated by the 'p'-notation), of the input and output functions (which may be simple or very complicated). The transfer function, $G(p)$, is given in formulae 23.38d-e (corresponding to Fig. 23.38a). Thus, the input Laplace transform multiplied by the transfer function gives the output transform. The multiplication of two transforms is called a convolution and represents a rather complicated process if viewed as a time function, *viz.* the integral of a product of two time functions (formula 23.38f, *cf.* 23.38e). Here, $C(t)$ represents the output at a certain time t_n. It may be regarded as the sum (integral) of the responses to a series of short duration input impulses e_1—e_n which occurred τ_n—τ_1 ($t_n = 0$) time units ago (Fig. 23.38c). The response to each input impulse is determined by the transfer function $g(t)$ which started to operate at the time of the impulse, *i.e.* from τ_1-τ_n time units ago, and which at time t_n has some value from $e_n g\ (\tau_1)$ to $e_1 g\ (\tau_n)$, all depending upon which impulse

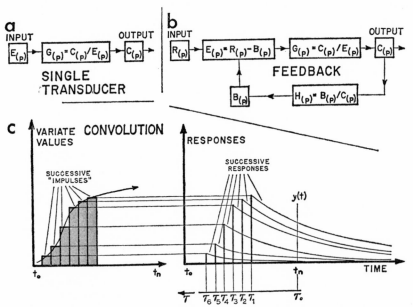

Fig. 23.38a-c. The input-output diagram, a, and a feedback, b, in transfer function notation. c demonstrates the convolution concept.

we are discussing. The summation of the *eg* (τ)-values intersected by the vertical line marked y (t) is made over the τ-range and represents one output value C(t).

For the biological experimenter equation 23.38d is more adequate than the form shown in 23.38e because he knows output and input but wants to know the transfer function G(p).

23.38d $$G(p) = C(p) / E(p)$$

23.38e $$C(p) = E(p)\ G(p)$$

23.38f $$C(t) = \int_0^{\cdot\infty} g\,(\tau)\ e\ (t - \tau)\ d\tau$$

23.39 – The feedback model in Fig. 23.38b may be regarded as containing the input and output Laplace functions R(p) and C(p), as well as two transfer functions, one in the forward loop, G(p) = C(p)/E(p), and one in the feedback loop H(p) = B(p)/C(p). The former is identical with formula 23.38d, and the latter is constructed in the same way, considering the direction of the information flow. B(p) is the correction of the input R(p) exerted by the feedback and resulting in E(p), *cf*. Fig. 3.2a. The conditions for feedback (still in Laplace transforms) are given by formulae 23.39a, which together yield formula 23.39b. Here, C(p)/R(p) is, again, the gain (output transform/input transform), or the transfer function of the total feedback system. It is expressed in terms of the transfer functions of the component loops, G(p) and H(p).

23.39a $$B(p) = C(p)\ H(p)$$
$$C(p) = E(p)\ G(p)$$
$$E(p) = R(p) - B(p)$$

23.39b $$C(p) / R(p) = G(p) / [1 + G(p)\ H(p)]$$

23.40 – The transfer function may vary with the type of the input. If investigating an unknown system one should therefore try a continuous series of inputs.

Two common types of experimental inputs are the single impulse and the sinusoid wave form. The former has been more used in biology than the latter. It will give rise to a series of transients and then return to quiescence, either at the initial level or some new operating level. Either the transients or the end result may be studied.

The sine input should, however, be more used in biology. It is common in systems analysis (3.29). The advantages are several: (1) Both input, output and transfer functions will contain the same basic sine functions, since all derivatives or integrals of it are still sine functions; (2) After a series of transients a steady state in the transfer function is reached where the gain shows up as easily measured changes in amplitude and phase from input to output; (3) The input may easily be varied over a large range of frequencies; (4) The Laplace transfer function has a simple meaning.

23.41 – *Harmonic Response Function. Nyquist Plot.* If the input is sinusoidal the transfer function represents the wave pattern in the output and is called the harmonic response function. This is a complex variable. If we plot the imaginary and real parts in an ARGAND diagram (*cf.* Fig. 22.13a : 1-2), this may simultaneously be interpreted as a polar amplitude-phase diagram (Fig. 22.13a :3). The amplitude part is here represented by the gain of the transfer function (= amplitude of dominant frequency/input amplitude), and the phase angle part by the phase shift between output and input. We thus have a gain phase diagram (the NYQUIST plot, *cf.* Fig. 3.30c). Since the phase angle varies regularly with the input frequency (and with the dominant output frequency at steady state and linear condition), the latter may also be plotted along the polar trajectory. – In the same way does the ordinary Fourier analysis and transformation describe a time series as a set of sine waves of different frequency, each characterized by an amplitude and a phase angle.

23.42 – A quite general method of testing a biological function is therefore to try a range of input sine frequencies and record the outputs. Both the gain and the phase shift may be read directly from the data and be plotted in a NYQUIST diagram. One may also plot the gain against the driving frequency (gain-frequency diagram, α-diagram, BODE plot, *cf.* Fig. 3.30b) or the phase lag against the frequency (phase frequency diagram, β-diagram, *cf.* Fig. 3.30a). By pure inspection of these plots inferences about the transfer mechanism can be made, *e.g.* regarding its degree of linearity. Nonlinear components also show up as series of superimposed harmonics in the output.

23.43 – We have now studied the general theory on the control of oscillators by forcing agents. This would correspond to the control of the endogenous rhythms in biological rhythm research. The next chapter will survey some of the theories which exist to explain the interaction between the surrounding world and the endogenous rhythms.

CHAPTER 24

Control in Biological Rhythms

24.1 – In Part II, on external rhythms, those factors were described which might control the biological rhythms. Their periods, and the effect of variations in their strength were discussed. In the subsequent theoretical discussion we have had many examples of control, especially Chapters 19 and 23 (cf. also Chapters 2 and 3). We may now appreciate the fact that there are innumerable ways in which rhythms may interact or be controlled. The models are rather exact; whereas the construction of the biological oscillators is largely unknown, they are 'black boxes' from which we try to extract information with great difficulties. We actually know so little that almost any possible model is being or has been used. The variety of models proposed does not, therefore, solve the enigma of biological rhythm control, but they are valuable as a help to understand the general properties of oscillating mechanisms, without which we will never get an answer to our biological problem. In the following, thus, the reader must not expect an explanation of biological rhythm control, but he may get some stimulating suggestions.

24.2 – The model-making has followed the general progress of sophistication. It started with the sine wave, which was mostly introduced to explain the concepts of amplitude, duration and frequency, but also because several external rhythms were more or less sinusoidal. The corresponding physical models were the pendulum or the tuning fork. Harmonic analysis was tried early but not extensively, owing to computational difficulties.

Later, the interest came to center around the relaxation oscillator and its mathematical definition by v.d. POL[1-4, 100-101]. As a model it has many advantages, *e.g.* the concept of an endogenous force source (amplification) triggered to periodic release spontaneously or by external influences. Its being the first nonlinear oscillator to be analyzed in detail was also decisive. As such it explained many peculiarities of behaviour which were otherwise enigmatic, *e.g.* the relative coordination studied by BETHE[4-7, 9, 101] and v. HOLST. For some time practically all biological rhythms were stamped as relaxation oscillators. Many of them certainly are, *e.g.* nerve impulses, heart beat or cell division, but an increased understanding of nonlinear functions is now widening the scope.

A new advance is the cybernetics approach, which allows us to treat the biological rhythm rationally as a black box which may be tested systematically without preconception (*e.g.* CLYNES, DRISCHEL, JENKINSON[1, 100], SCOTT[1-3, 100-101], STARK[2-5, 100-105], STEGEMAN, VOSSIUS, YOUNG[1, 100]). *Cf.* the analysis of transients by BRUCE[1], PITTENDRIGH[6, 100-102].

We have also the increasing application of mathematical-statistical frequency analyses to biological rhythms (e.g. BARLOW[200], BLISS[1, 100], BLUME, HALBERG[8, 10, 12, 110, 116, 125], MENZEL[4-5, 9, 15-16, 100-102], OBERHOFFER, PANOFSKY). One sometimes has the impression that the experimental techniques are reaching the limit of their power to elucidate biological control and that analytical techniques have to take over.

Other models, mathematical and physical, have been presented by ASHBY, BARLOW[201], BETHE[5-8], BÜNNING[29, 34, 103], CLYNES, EHRET[100], FRANCK[100], v. HOLST, KALMUS[100], KENNETH[100], KLOTTER, LOBEL, PITTENDRIGH[100-101], v. D. POL[1-4, 100-101], RICHTER[5], SCHMITT, WEVER. The homeostat of ASHBY might be controlled by rhythmic disturbances, as could be done with the coupled electrodes of FRANCK[100]. LOBEL's harmonic system of pulse waves reflected in the arterial wall could theoretically be driven, e.g. by changes in the elasticity of the vessel wall. KALMUS[100] constructed nonlinear hydrodynamic control models where the water level of one tank controls the in-or-outlet valves of another in various ways. This was also followed up by a mathematical description.

24.3 – *Peculiarities of Biological Rhythm Control.* The biological rhythms have several characteristics which must be accounted for in theories about their control. There are the nonlinear transducer characteristics (cf. Fig. 3.28b). We have seen that this induces a harmonic superstructure upon any rhythm, endogenous or exogenous. Actually, if there are pre-established nodes, even random disturbances may tend to set up a harmonic system (19.16). The nonlinear system furthermore may answer with complicated control response patterns (23.25) with varying amplitudes, phasing and relaxation-like interaction phenomena, as in relative coordination (19.25-34). It stabilizes the amplitude of an oscillation, especially if the frequency of the oscillator deviates from that of the driving agent. The nonlinearities also make possible harmonic synchronization. The relaxation oscillators are nonlinear and many biological phenomena perform like them, though perhaps not so much the circadian rhythm. The complicated patterns in the pathological ECG or in the EEG are better examples.

24.4 – The synchronizer energy reaching us is negligible, though on the other hand the organism cannot usually reach back and influence the source. This suggests on the other hand that the external signal is open to any kind of transformation in the body (cf. the autophasing theory, 1.23) and also that it has to trigger endogenous power sources. The latter is one reason for the interest in the relaxation oscillators. The low energy signal would seem to favour parametric resonance (23.24, cf. KLOTTER, WEVER). The body may be an active participant, picking up whatever information it wants for synchronization from the external data. It even needs energy to do this, not the reverse. The unfavourable energy relation may also disfavour most physical models of forced oscillations and corresponding mathematical solutions (23.5-23), though much depends upon how directly the synchronizer triggers the intrinsic energy. Also, the physical models usually apply better to rhythms which are fast, as compared to for instance the circadian rhythm.

24.5 – Some natural synchronizers (e.g. 24-h light and temperature changes) are rather variable. Though their average frequency is that of the day (24-h) many events within them continuously change position (*e.g.* dusk and dawn and tide) or intensity (*e.g.* solar radiation) from day to day. In such cases complete synchronization is not possible. The biological mechanisms must instead somehow be equipped so as to 'hunt' the synchronizer continuously. The circadian (near-but-not 24-h) rhythm may be one expression of this (12.17, DeCoursey[1-2], Pittendrigh[6], *cf.* the autophasing theory of Brown, 1.23). To such a 'hunting' mechanism environmental constancy may be quite unnatural.

One way in which the organism could follow a constant phase-change in the synchronizer is by sudden phase-jumps in the manner of disturbed periodicities. Blume[10-11] has shown that this possibility may exist if the natural and external period get out of phase; using his own method of analyzing single-cycle records. The jumps seem to be performed by harmonic components. We have here one example of how an intensive analysis of short single records may often yield as much information as the general analysis of large materials.

Apart from single disturbances causing damped oscillations, or random stimulation with rather complicated effects, we may distinguish between three main types of synchronizer conditions. It is important to realize the differences between them:

(1) *Constant conditions,* as regards dominant synchronizers. Freerunning then occurs, whether a true inherited spontaneity or a transformed weak synchronizer input.

(2) *Normal conditions.* Exposure to the surrounding day-night changes. Here, the average period may be regarded as constant and may be verified by observing the solar high-stand. However, the probable synchronizing events within it (such as dawn or dusk or tide) move at other frequencies. The synchronization must be a complex phenomenon.

(3) *Experimental entrainment,* with fixed LD-schemes. Here, true entrainment in the physical sense would seem possible.

24.6 – It is remarkable how easily the phasing of the biological rhythms is affected (*cf.* Bünning[29, 34], Brown[106], Bruce[102-103], Fingerman[103], Flink[100], Gunn[400, 500], Halberg[100], Pittendrigh[3], Strughold[2]). It is understandable that one single stimulus, for instance light, may start a dormant oscillator and simultaneously determine its timing. On the other hand, the phasing of an already existing rhythm may be radically changed by one single short stimulus.

While the phasing is easily upset, the frequency is much more stable. If one single stimulus is given then only the phasing can be changed. If repeated disturbances are used, the frequency may also be affected (*cf.* Aschoff[5-6, 11-12, 14-17, 104-106], Tribukait, who have set the example for innumerable experiments in entrainment). Synchronization takes some time during which transients appear, usually longer the higher the organization of the animal (Halberg[10]). The experiments share one characteristic with the usual examples of linear forced oscillations, *viz.* that entrainment is only possible if the synchronizing and spontaneous frequencies do not deviate too much (23.35), though harmonic entrainment may occur.

24.7 – The biological processes are mainly of biochemical nature and therefore the characteristics of such processes should be reflected in a model, *e.g.* chemical equilibria, catalytic action, diffusion, osmosis, mitochondrial structure, protoplasmic movements (*cf.* CLYNES, EHRET[5, 100], KAMIYA[2-4, 100-101], SEIFRITZ, WENT[6], 4.16-19, 6.29-30, 7.15). One might even guess that the use of chemical analog computers in the field should be stimulating.

24.8 – It is not altogether clear which signals (19.13-15) act upon the endogenous rhythms. Though we can record the external influence carefully, we cannot be sure how much of its informational contents is used by the body. This has again to do with the low energy contents of the synchronizers (24.4). Do we react to a continuous transformation of the stimulus or to discontinuous events in it, such as dawn or dusk? Do we record the rate of change, or the change in level, or do we favour one direction of change? *Cf.* ASCHOFF[16-17], CLYNES[2], HILDEBRANDT[20-21], [104], PITTENDRIGH[6], STARK[4], 12.14, 19.15. Are there several 'part' signals which each sets up its own response (*e.g.* as damped oscillations), the latter then interacting (KENNETH[100])?

24.9 – There is a considerable variability in the entrainment process with the variate, period and organism studied. It ranges from simple 'steering' (passive acceptance of synchronizer or pacemaker) to highly complex mechanisms, as in the cardiac and central nervous tissue reactions of relaxation oscillation character or the still more enigmatic circadian rhythms; from direct membrane or chemical influences in single cells to intermediate channelling through photoperiodic processes or nervous systems of varying development level (EHRET[100], HALBERG[10]); from fast rhythms as in the nervous system, which would be more apt to agree with the physical models of rhythms, to slow 24-h or seasonal rhythms, quite probably with other mechanisms of control. Thus many of our models may be realized in this vast field of oscillatory functions.

24.10 – In many types of experiments the approach consists in 'showing' the biooscillator an external rhythm and registering the exogenous rhythm response. By careful mathematical-statistical analysis the input rhythm is then searched for in the recorded data. The prime drawback of such methods is that it hinders a test of the results in a truly statistical manner, since a bias, the presumed knowledge of the external frequency, enters the test. This is avoided in systems analysis where a whole range of input frequencies is tried, and it would also be overcome in any type of statistical analysis which separates the endogenous and external influence by an analysis of the output data themselves. An attempt at formulating the latter possibility was given in connection with the moving variate (20.30).

The cybernetic approach has many avenues (*cf.* SCHMITT). One is to match the feedback continuously by coupling an analog computer into the loop, studying the response (CLYNES, YOUNG[1]). Birds have been trained to turn the illumination on and off themselves, thereby completing a feedback loop (WAHLSTRÖM). In man something similar can probably happen, on a subconscious level, and much would then depend on the psychological magnification of the artificial feedback. Or imagine that we let the movements of plant leaves control the intensity or spectral composition of the illumination. What would happen if we put a plant on wheels and let the leaf position direct the carriage (slowly) with respect to the position or movements of a light source?

With regard to the autocontrol of light it is not so easy to see what happens. Probably, the animals are in the same position as under constant conditions with freerunning. Actually, the underlying spontaneous rhythms must first wake them up before they can turn on the light. One may wonder, however, how the accuracy of the freerunning period is affected, whether enhanced or disturbed.

24.11 – As to the circadian rhythms one could easily imagine a process along the following lines: The true endogenous rhythm is relatively high-frequent with some 3-6 cycles a day. This may be a more or less random phenomenon, coupled to nonlinearities (24.3) and organ capacities. It may have an average frequency and variable phasing. A suitable subharmonic of it is somehow entrained by the environmental 24-h rhythm, the process involving frequency demultiplication (19.30). Under constant conditions the demultiplication mechanism may be retained (perhaps this is even what is inherited), creating a circadian rhythm. The external rhythm must trigger some mechanism in the organism strong enough to interfere with the endogenous rhythms. The events in the circadian cycle will slowly scan those of the external one. If they get too much out of phase, a phase-jump may occur from one peak to another in the high-frequency rhythm, in any direction; or there may be true random changes in the phasing which are utilized. Such a theory would incorporate the observations on developing organisms (9.4-10), the phase-jump theory of BLUME (24.5) and the autophasing concept (1.23). The mechanism would be adjustable, energy-saving and stable. It would allow for spontaneous changes in the circadian frequency, perhaps occurring in quantifiable jumps. It would account for the difference between morning and evening people, the question being which one of the high-frequency peaks is accentuated in the demultiplication.

24.12 – However, any deeper understanding of the entrainment process must include knowledge about the oscillator itself. It is typical for the state of biological rhythm research that we do not know which are the most basic oscillators (clocks) or where they may be found; whether in cell systems, cell parts or within the biochemical range. We do not know how many oscillators there are, nor how they interact. A basic issue in present research is simply how many oscillators there may be, and which one or which ones of them are controlled by the environment.

24.13 – *Multiple Oscillator Theories.* Such theories constitute an attempt to explain the fact that several rhythms of different timing may coexist in one individual, also that different entraining agents may have different effects, and that these may even interact in a complicated manner.

Most interest has centered around the dominant *light* and *temperature* synchronizers, which give clear effects on the body. PITTENDRIGH's[3, 6, 100-101] experiments are typical as well as unsurpassed in beauty (Fig. 24.13a-b). Animals previously entrained to a regular 24-h schedule were submitted to a single light-break during continuous darkness (Fig. 24.13a). The variable measured was the frequency of eclosion in *Drosophila* populations. The light-break was administered

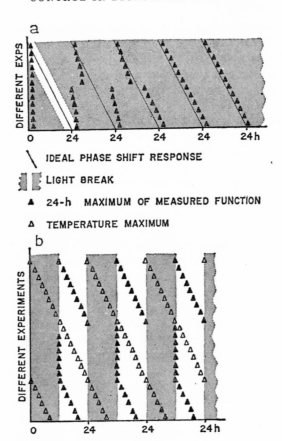

Fig. 24.13a-b. Transients in the entrainment of bio-oscillators with light and temperature stimuli. Idealized, after PITTENDRIGH.

at different times of the day throughout a 24-h period in different experiment batches. Some days after the light-break, the phasing of the eclosion rhythm was completely reset after having displayed some transient cycles with periods longer or shorter than 24 h. There is a certain economy in the resetting; the phase is either advanced or delayed according to which yields the shortest adjustment path (cf. DeCOURSEY[2], PITTENDRIGH[6]). An exception is strong radiation, e.g. UV light which always changes the phase in one direction only (EHRET[7], including discussion).

24.14 – In Fig. 24.13b a constant LD regimen is kept but simultaneously sinusoidal 24-h variations in external temperature are maintained. The phasing of the temperature is varied in relation to that of the light, in different experimental batches. The eclosion rhythm is now forced by two different synchronizers. Eclosion is favoured by low temperature and the two tend to be 180° out of phase, temperature-lows calling forth eclosion peaks. This entrainment holds as long as the temperature is advanced during lightness. During darkness, however, the relation is lost. The eclosion rhythm peak is completely entrained by the light, and jumps into a constant position at the artificial dawn, irrespective of the temperature phase. Sometimes, then, the light is the dominant synchronizer and sometimes the temperature. The results may, however, differ between animals, like *Drosophila,* hamsters and squirrels. Sometimes the experiments result in the appearance of higher-frequency rhythms (BRUCE[1]).

24.15 – The results of such entrainment experiments may be explained in different ways:
(1) The synchronizers may compete in the organism according to certain laws before entrainment.
(2) The synchronizers may entrain one oscillator each, the two oscillators being coupled and producing transients as observed.
(3) The synchronizers may act on different parameters of the same oscillator, producing the transients recorded.
(4) One endogenous rhythm exists which is completely entrained by the light. The effect of the temperature then depends upon which phase of this rhythm in which it (*e.g.* the temperature low) hits. It also depends upon how the organism perceives its own endogenous rhythm (subjective rhythm), *cf.* the behaviour of nocturnal and diurnal, as well as of long- and short-day organisms.

24.16 – PITTENDRIGH favours a two-oscillator theory; one oscillator is supposed to be temperature-sensitive and the other light-sensitive (14.6). They are coupled in such a way that the latter controls the former, rather as a pacemaker, whereas the feedback in the reverse direction is only slight. KLOTTER has shown, however, that the eclosion results could also be explained by one oscillator under multiple parametric control (23.24). He also stresses that many different models can be constructed which show similar patterns of behaviour (*cf.* BARLOW[201]).
    WENT[3-6] considers two-oscillator mechanisms in plant growth (14.6), as does HARKER[2-9] in cockroaches (13.12). The latter envisages two light-sensitive oscillators, one of which, the optical one, is immediately reset through the ocelli by any light-stimulus; whereas the other, the neurosecretory one (suboesophageal ganglion), is entrained by the normal environmental LD-changes. They are coupled so that the optical oscillator can only control the neurosecretory one at certain values of the latter. This would make it possible for an animal to follow the slow inter-24-h shifts in dawn or dusk time but would prevent a resetting by random light flashes (*e.g.* moonlight or transitions from shade into sunshine). – A too strong conflict between the setting of the two oscillators may produce tumors in the animals. – The rhythm could be transplanted to another animal with the oesophageal ganglion.
    In locusts, EIDMANN found that extirpation of the corpora allata or of the lobi optici alone did not abolish the rhythm, whereas cutting the connection to the suboesophageal gland or extirpation of the whole brain did so (*cf.* also LEES[7]). FINGERMAN[1, 101] found a persistence of rhythms in allatectomized and brainless grasshoppers, but not if the suboesophageal ganglion was extirpated. The removal of the eye-stalks in crabs did not abolish the rhythms.

24.17 – RICHTER[3-5] in his *shock-phase theory* (8.12) postulates a multitude of oscillators in the body, with different periods, phasing and localization. They are all normally supposed to be functionally synchronized so as to cancel out, yielding a nonperiodic resultant. A sudden shock may, however, bring them out of phase (perhaps by trying to align them or by disturbing one component so that the balance is upset), unmasking the rhythms. One example was the sudden appearance of periodic arthritis, with different phasing and frequency in different joints. Other *multiple clock* theories have been proposed by BROWN[9-10, 12], CLOUDS-LEY-THOMPSON[10], FINGERMAN[100], KAMIYA[2], NAYLOR[2].

24.18 – If there are a large number of oscillators controlling different body variates there must be some interaction between them (*cf.* 19.25-27, 23.29-32) resulting in a more or less organized steady state pattern, especially under synchronization. For 24-h rhythms this has been explored by HALBERG[7-8, 10, 103, 114] and MENZEL[15-16]. The former aims at charting all the various rhythms and their phasing, *circadian charts*. Apart from the valuable information about the rhythms themselves, this is necessary if we ever want to establish true normal values for experimentation and in medicine. HALBERG also distinguishes between several developmentally determined levels of activity; the cellular, endocrine and central nervous system levels. These are interacting. The cellular and nervous levels may perhaps be controlled independently from without. Perhaps the dominant synchronizers act through the higher level and the weak ones on the lower. *Cf.* 8.12,16 and Fig. 24.18a.

The reason for the normal phase-dispersal of the various biological rhythms is not well understood. It may depend on variations in synchronizer or synchronizer action. There may be natural relations between metabolites and their formation, such as glucose being formed from or forming glycogen, demanding a differential-integral relationship (*cf.* 7.8). Another reason may be the variates chosen, one being a transformation of a true variate (*cf.* 20.34). An interesting suggestion was made in 9.3, *viz.* the avoidance of dangerous combinations of factors. For instance, the calcium and phosphate turnovers show inverse rhythms (SCHAAF, personal communication).

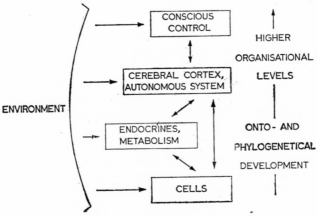

Fig. 24.18a. The organizational levels and their rhythm control.

Actually, in this way the study of rhythms could tell us much about the general relations between variates in the organism, not to mention the fact that this relationship may vary radically during one day. It may even be dangerous to study a metabolic problem only at one single time of *e.g.* the day (*cf.* 27.13).

24.19 – *Transients*. If the control is not periodic (single influences, random), or before steady state synchronization with a periodic influence has been attained, there appear transients (1.22, 4.29, 14.6, 23.10,14,34). A close study of them should yield important information as to how the biological control works (PITTEN-DRIGH[102]). However, they are complicated phenomena. – One may, with PITTEN-DRIGH (24.13-14) select only a part of the information for study (20.13), *viz.* the peaks. Or one may try building models to mimic the observed biological behaviour (*cf.* KLOTTER, BARLOW). If we attempt a mathematical-statistical analysis we will have to use methods which are applicable to single cycles (21.15). BLUME has already scored considerable success with his modification (24.5), tracing sudden phase-jumps. Another possible way of analysis was hinted at in connection with the moving variate (20.30).

24.20 – *Circadian Phase-Synchronization*. As already pointed out (24.6) the circa-dian rhythm phase is easily shifted, even by single stimuli. PITTENDRIGH's multi-ple oscillator experiments (24.13-14) used phase shifts as indicators of the tran-sient response. The *sensitivity* to timing influences also varies throughout the single circadian cycle in a similar manner as does the general sensitivity, even if the cycle is simultaneously entrained by another synchronizer (5.20). It is important to distinguish between the circadian changes in general sensitivity to light, tempera-ture or drugs (5.16, Chapter 25), and in sensitivity to phase-setting by such agents. The latter has been well illustrated by WILKINS[2-5] on the circadian rhythm of CO_2 output in plants. He applied light or a high-temperature stimulus at different positions in this rhythm. If coinciding with a peak, the disturbance does not cause any phase shift, if hitting a low on the endogenous rhythm it induces a shift. The mechanism will give swift internal phase synchronization. It means that the degree of shift is graded so as to bring different curves together. Or, as a simplified example: if half of the curves are not affected at all, the other half will be moved to meet them.

The different effects of blue and red light agreed with the general rules for photoperiodism in plants. Low temperature acts only around the peaks. The phase-setting is proportional to the intensity and duration of the stimulus within a cer-tain range of illumination, and also dependent upon the end time of the stimulus. WILKINS stresses the similarity between the light and temperature effects, which suggests that there could be only one oscillator involved, for instance a relaxation oscillator (*cf.* 4.13 and Fig. 19.30a).

24.21 – A relaxation oscillator may be triggered during its ascending phase. There will then be a phase shift if the stimulus is strong enough to lift it towards the discharge level. This technique is used in electronics to zero a function at command. A strong signal is applied to a relaxation oscillator, which then immediately resets itself into the resting position.

24.22 – In biology there tends to be a time lag between the forcing function and the physiological response. The lag-time may differ from individual to individual. It may perhaps sometimes become very long. One may imagine an intermediate process which is entrained first and which after a certain time excites the variate assayed (WILKINS[2]). This is one way in which several functions may run inverse courses, or by which the organism may display both positive and negative reactions to a certain stimulus. The various functions found in circadian charts (24.18) may differ in phasing considerably, though the entraining influence is probably the same.

At steady state there may also be a lead, the oscillator anticipating the synchronizer (23.19). Compare also the synchronization between driving force and generated velocity in mechanical vibrators.

24.23 – One type of phasing experiments which has been done repeatedly, especially in older studies, is the total reversal of the 24-h regimen, exchanging the times of light and darkness (APPEL[1, 100], BENEDICT[1, 100], CAMPBELL[100], ECHAVE[100], ELFVIN[100], FLINK[100], FOLK[1, 3], GALBRAITH[100], HALBERG[7, 107, 134], HINMAN, HOLMGREN[101], KLEITMAN[6], KURCZ[1, 3], LAIDLAW[100], MIGEON[100], NORN, SHARP[1-5, 100], SOLLBERGER[3], STRUGHOLD[2]). In some cases night-workers were studied, other experiments were performed on animals. Earlier investigators sometimes failed to demonstrate an inversal of the exogenous rhythm, which may be due to a competition between synchronizers. In general, however, the phase-adjustment takes place though it may require about a week. Individual variations in response are great. How complete the process can sometimes be is shown by ELFVIN[100] and SOLLBERGER[3], where there is an almost complete congruence between the chicken liver glycogen curves before and after the shift. Heavy phase displacements are also experienced in modern travelling and it takes about a week to readjust, as most transatlantic travelers know (NOHARA, STRUGHOLD). Compare with experiments on migration (5.23, 18.10, MARSHALL[201]). If the travel is slow, however, continuous resynchronization occurs. On a boat-trip to India, JOSLINGS (Conf. 1939a, p. 43) found a diuresis maximum constantly at about 16 o'clock local time.

The resynchronization time varies with the synchronizers, the phase lag and the complexity of the species (HALBERG[10]).

24.24 – *Phase-Comparator*. If there are several coexistent phase-dispersed rhythms, either inside (HALBERG[116]) or outside (BARLOW[201]) the organisms, the latter might profit by comparing the phases in order to decide how to react. See PITTENDRIGH's experiment (24.14) where the phase-relationship between light and temperature determined whether there should be an entrainment or not. We have already mentioned two models to account for these findings, the two-oscillator theory of PITTENDRIGH and the linear parametric monoscillator one of KLOTTER. A third nonlinear model based on a relaxation oscillator and a phase comparator has been proposed by BARLOW[201]. The oscillator is immediately reset to zero by light stimuli (as described in 24.21). The temperature input is projected with the same average level as the oscillator trace, and each time the relaxation phase (flyback) of the latter crosses the temperature line (equal amplitudes) the apparatus delivers an output signal (the exogenous rhythm). If, now, the temperature varies this will cause a modification in the output.

24.25 – In BARLOW's model the temperature may also act back upon the oscillator by modifying its threshold. This will cause a change in the frequency (*cf.* Fig. 4.27b). A step-change (change in temperature level) causes a permanent change in frequency. An impulse causes a short stretch of frequency change, then a return to the old frequency. The net result is a phase shift.

Comparisons show that the model may mimic PITTENDRIGH's experimental transients fairly well. It suggests that the light may act primarily by changes of threshold, temperature by changes in rates. BARLOW's model had initially been fashioned to explain some phenomena in the EEG, but proved to work as a model of circadian rhythms as well.

24.26 – *Circadian Frequency Synchronization.* We have now discussed phase shifts, which may be caused by single stimuli. Frequency synchronization, however, requires rhythmic stimuli. We know that entrainment is usually possible if the forcing frequency does not deviate too much from the circadian one (*cf.* 4.29, 7.3, ASCHOFF[2, 11-12, 14-17, 104-106], BROWMAN[3], BRUCE[1], CLAES[100], CLAUS[100-101], EIFF[1], HAUTY[1-3, 100], KLEITMAN[6, 14], KLEINHOLZ[100], LEWIS[100-104], MILLER[200], MILLS[300], [302], TRIBUKAIT), as is also the case in linear oscillator theory. The limits seem to lie between about 19-29 h, though BROWMAN managed even with a 16-h entrainment in rat activity (*cf.* HIEBEL[100]). If the forcing frequency is too rapid, the circadian periodicity takes over or there may occasionally appear higher-frequency rhythms (BRUCE[1]). Harmonic entrainment can also occur. There is even a considerable individual variability in the type of response (HAUTY).

24.27 – There also occur examples of mixed entrainment, as was already discussed in connection with the multiple oscillator and phase control theories (24.13-25). Another example is found in rats which have two activity maxima, one during day-time and one at night, shortly after dusk. TRIBUKAIT, in classical experiments, found an advance of the night peak of activity if the entrainment day is shortened and a delay if it is prolonged as compared to the new dusk time. When the night maximum is delayed or advanced so as to meet the day peak (which always follows the external dawn time) the limit of entrainability is reached. Actually, it seems as if the day peak rhythm can only be entrained if the stimulus occurs during a certain phase of the night-peak rhythm (however controlled), preferably the low of that period. This agrees rather with WILKINS findings on plants. Double peaks have also been observed in glycogen rhythms of rabbits and chickens. One of the peaks may be abolished by starvation but not the other. *Cf.* ÅGREN[100], ELFVIN[100], FORSGREN[6], HOLMGREN[8], HOLMQUIST[1], SJÖGREN[100], SOLLBERGER[3, 15].

24.28 – One may extrapolate from here. It would seem that the double-peak curves may represent an interference between several synchronizers or oscillators. Light could be a dominant synchronizer with regard to the day peak but weak with respect to the night peak. Perhaps the day-peak action inhibits the sensitivity of the other mechanism to light, so that new synchronizers may take over and direct the endodiurnal rhythm. The mechanism may be the same as proposed by HARKER (24.16), to permit a slow phase adjustment towards changes in the environment but to avoid random entrainment to light. On the other hand, the night-peak mechanism sometimes inhibits an entrainment of the dawn peak. This would constitute a kind of feedback which is only stable at certain frequencies. Thus entrainment is impossible to still longer or shorter forcing periods. At very short periods, however, synchronization may be possible with a theoretical high-frequency endogenous oscillation.

24.29 – The exogenous rhythms may also show beats at entrainment to non-24-h schemes. The circadian rhythm always persists, but superimposed upon this is often the new frequency (cf. EIFF[1], HAUTY[1-3, 100], KLEITMAN[6, 14], LEWIS[101-102, 104], LOBBAN[2], MILLS[300-302], SHARP[6]). Under these circumstances the new frequency may differ considerably from the circadian (e.g. 4 and 8 h in HAUTY's experiments). Maybe this means a synchronization to the high-frequency 'hour' rhythms. However, there are great individual differences in the capacity for such adaptation, even in highly intelligent and healthy people (HAUTY[1-3, 100], KLEITMAN[6]).

The extra frequency component may be quite hidden and may have to be found by careful frequency analysis, as in HAUTY's[3, 100] data, or in BLUME's analysis of KLEITMAN's old temperature curves (see MENZEL[17]), where both the remembered 24-h component, the actual entrained 28-h period, and the preceding experimental period (21 h) coexist. Cf. also beats between lunar and 24-h rhythms (BÜNNING, BLUME).

For some reason these linear systems of beats have been demonstrated in human subjects, whereas most animal experiments seem to agree well with a number of nonlinear oscillator models. On the other hand, the latter experiments only utilize one bit of all the information available (the peak-time). Either there is a different entrainment mechanism in Homo, or else these different results must be integrated.

It may well be that metabolic control on lower organizational levels (food, drugs, temperature) may be more like true forcing, causing linear reactions; whereas the more complicated light control is nonlinear in character. LINDAN, controlling the metabolic activity of paretic patients observes linear interaction (personal communication).

There may be a differential entrainment to non-24-hour synchronizers in one single subject, with regard to different variates. In LEWIS and LOBBAN's experiments the order of entrainability was: heart rate, blood pressure, PO_4-excretion, body temperature, water diuresis, Cl-excretion, Na-excretion and K-excretion. The last-mentioned was very resistant (cf. PRUNTY[100]).

In spite of many excellent experiments and fascinating models we cannot really tell, however, which kind of oscillator the circadian rhythm possesses, or how it is controlled.

24.30 – *Circadian Synchronizer Parameters*. We should also with ASCHOFF[12, 14-17] and WEVER like to know what it is in the synchronizer which constitutes the controlling function (1.24, 12.12-15, 19.15,18-19). Is it the whole external shape as in models of forced oscillations (23.10-23)? Or does the body extract some part of the available information during the sensory channeling and transformation of the external data, before applying control of the rhythms (24.4)? Does it follow the dawn or dusk (differential Zeitgeber, a step or switch function); the lengths of either of the constant conditions in the environment, L or D (proportional Zeitgeber); the rate of change, or something else? Apart from the already-described effects of constant conditions (*cf.* 13.18-22), ASCHOFF has worked with constant external periods, varying the LD ratio, and also with constant LD ratio, varying the period. He has recorded the phase shift in peak activity. It would seem from this, that the Zeitgeber acts both with its proportional and differential parameters. Here, the activity peak tends towards the middle of the light period when different LD schemes are used at constant period (differential effect), but simultaneously the phase-advance is relatively largest the shorter the light period (proportional effect).–The quality of the light is also of importance (Chapter 13). *Cf.* EHRET's[1-7] studies of action spectra in chlorella-less *Paramecium* and of the strong phase-shifting action with UV-light, perhaps acting on the nucleic acid metabolism.

24.31 – WEVER has built an electronic sinusoidal oscillator and simulated ASCHOFF's investigations, by parametric control (23.24) of this single oscillator, manipulating either the inductance, capacity or grid bias with rhythmic inputs of variable periods and LD-schemes. Inductance and capacitance mainly determine the frequency of the system, the grid bias its energy level. The model could mimic the behaviour of biological systems fairly well if both inductivity and grid bias were forced simultaneously. Capacity forcing did not produce comparable results. It may be mentioned that amplitude changes can also be forced with this model by control of the resistance. – It is interesting to see how both sinusoidal and relaxation oscillation models can describe the biological rhythms very well.

24.32 – *Frequency Transformation*. We have seen that the peculiar energy relations in biological rhythm control (24.4) give the organism great freedom. Instead of being dominated by sheer force from the synchronizer it may perhaps even hunt the input actively. We may imagine our body recording the external stimuli, searching them for rhythmic information by some kind of phase and frequency comparisons, deciding whether it would be profitable to follow these rhythms, and then, in the end, changing itself so as to facilitate synchronization. We can also build models which do all this.

24.33 – In BROWN's[6-12, 109, 111] autophasing theory it is assumed that the body is always informed about the 24-h period somehow and that it modifies itself to approach this frequency (frequency transformation), but not to adopt it fully. The latter is to make possible a synchronization with an external change in phasing of events within the period. This indirect synchronization, instead of direct control by some fixed parameter (*e.g.* time of maximal sun altitude), depends on the need for adaptation to the actual surrounding conditions of visibility, temperature and dangers, as well as for judging the daylength as a means of assessing the seasons. Or, the circadicity may simply be the first rough saccadic (*cf.* 3.7) step in a complicated synchronization mechanism.

There are similar problems in the tides, the timing of which travels slowly through the day. Shore animals must follow this phase-changing lunar rhythm within the 24-h one. Of course this could also be done in a more direct way, synchronizing to both the 24-h and the lunar rhythms, letting them interact within the body.

24.34 – The autophasing theory in general gives a convenient explanation of some phenomena. It is quite natural that the so-called endogenous rhythm frequency should be independent of temperature or chemical influence since it is controlled from without (*cf.* temperature independence). It would also be expected that only biological rhythms with external correlates should show such independence. The transformed frequencies would be expected to collect around the external one, like the circadians do. One might also, with STEPHENS[5], get an average 24-h spontaneous rhythm in a population of animals but circadian rhythms in the individual subjects. One problem is, however, to identify the synchronizers, since the circadian rhythm persists even if most controllable factors are kept constant. Thus, the existence of the autophasing phenomenon requires the existence of subtle synchronizers (Chapter 16).

24.35 – Another problem is how the frequency transformation takes place. A physical model is easy to conceive; two equal transmission wheels, where one is driven at a determined frequency and the other is constantly slipping somewhat. The process involves a phase lag, but not an ordinary constant lag between oscillators of equal frequency. It is rather a lag which changes progressively within the cycle. In order to obtain this as a steady state operation, the mechanism must be able to measure time within one cycle, *i.e.* in smaller time units than the driving frequency. Mathematically, the problem may look something like formulae 24.35a-d.

The organism must be able to calculate the phase angle (ωt) which is proportional to time. The time-measuring in question may be possible since various random or nonlinear disturbances in the system are apt to set up harmonics (19.16). The harmonics may split the cycle period into smaller parts. Another possibility is that the organism has a high-frequency spontaneous oscillation, which it uses as a clock. – The alternative 24.35d is interesting since exponential transformations are common in the living organism.

24.35a-d.   Frequency transformation. Driving
                        function $= y$. Transformed function
                        $= z$.

a $y = \sin \omega t$
      $z = \sin [f(\omega t)]$

b $z = \sin (\omega t - r \omega t) =$
      $\sin [(1-r) \, \omega t]$

c $z = \sin (\omega t \, \delta \, t)$

d $z = \sin (\omega t)^r$

24.36 – There are other possibilities of obtaining a frequency transformation. Phase-variability may occur in nonlinear oscillators (23.25-28), and beats in linear ones (19.22). Two relaxation oscillators with a strong coupling may strike an intermediate frequency. KENNETH[100] gives another example, *viz.* the interaction between rhythms set up by different stimuli. They let two sets of rhythmic impulses (*e.g.* dawn and dusk) both generate response rhythms which then interfere, producing an exogenous rhythm of another frequency than that of the driving one.

Remarkably enough this is a linear system. It is not operating at steady state which would demand complete entrainment, but may be regarded as a continued undamped transient (23.14), which responds only to certain parts of the input.

24.37 – *Ultradian Rhythms.* Rhythms of higher frequency than the circadian have been discussed on several occasions (6.9-37, 7.13, 8.5, 9.6,8,10, 21.31, 23.21, 24.11) as time-keepers, as possible circadian frequency stabilizers, and in a long range of endogenous microrhythms. – Of some interest are the hour-rhythms, which are approximately harmonics of the 24-h period, and might be generated in this way through biological nonlinearities and random disturbances. In some cases there have even been experiments with entrainment to such cycles (*e.g.* HAUTY[1-3, 100]). Another explanation would be that the high-frequency rhythms may be true spontaneous oscillations and that the circadian period is that subharmonic (obtained by submultiplication) which is closest to 24-h, being re-enforced by resonance at entrainment.

In disease, the circadian component seems to weaken and the high-frequency ones to increase in power (DISSMAN[3], HALBERG[16], HEIDE, HILDEBRANDT[20-21, 104], MENZEL[5, 9, 15-16, 100-102]). In the early embryo only the latter seem to exist (ELFVIN[100], PETRÉN[2, 100], SOLLBERGER[3, 5]). This would point towards their character as natural frequencies. On the other hand, the capacities of the biological tissues for energy storage in early life or following the energy loss in disease may be such that only short periods are possible and that therefore the harmonics of the entraining external 24-h rhythm are favoured. Important is the analysis made by BLUME[10-11], on some of BÜNNING's records of circadian plant leaf movements (21.15, 21, 23.31, 24.5), using his method for the harmonic analysis of single cycles. Here, he could observe a phenomenon which would go unnoticed if many other of the currently used methods had been applied, namely phase-jumps in the high-frequency component generated so as to economize with the plant's energy expenditure. The coincidence of two maxima or two minima is avoided. If it is necessary the plant may even introduce several new harmonics to offset such an effect. If the mechanism does not succeed in avoiding too extreme energy expenditure the whole level of activity (base line) may, instead, be changed. JORDAN[6] using BLUME's method on cardiac beat intervals in so-called arhythmia, found several frequencies superimposed and phase-jumps as well as amplitude jumps in the higher frequency.

24.38 – *Circadian Control in Pathology.* We have seen in the preceding paragraph that shorter rhythms tend to dominate in disease, *e.g.* shown by MENZEL[5, 9, 15-16, 100-102] as a proportional change in amplitude sums, and by HALBERG as a lowering of the circadian quotient in the power spectrum analysis. This appears in the complete rhythm curve usually as a decrease in amplitude, something which has been observed by physicians for a long time. The reaction seems to come early in the disease and may therefore be used as a diagnostic. ARBORELIUS uses this in the differential analysis between gastric cancer (with lowered amplitude of the urinary sodium chloride rhythm) and gastric ulcer (with little change in amplitude). Compare this with HARKER's findings of cockroach tumours in cases of conflicting rhythm control, when transplanting suboesophageal ganglia.

HILDEBRANDT[20-21, 104], during the treatment of vegetatively labile patients, observed damped frequencies of 6-8-12-h periods in the pulse and respiratory rate, which are initiated each morning and superimposed upon a supposedly sinusoidal 24-h rhythm (ringing response, 19.24,32).

24.39 – The explanation for the high-frequency dominance is uncertain. Anyhow, it indicates that the 24-h control is weakened. Another sign of this is that freerunning circadian periods may be observed in patients, *e.g.* in the temperature records of cancer cases, and also in blinded animals (HALBERG[7]). In higher organisms the control of rhythms is chiefly exerted by light and transferred by neural pathways. This puts some emphasis on the connection of the eye with the hypothalamus and the possible hook-up with the endocrine system through the pituitary and the melanophore hormone (13.16-17).

In disease, the different variates may also dissociate, the normal phase and frequency relations being lost (*cf.* FORSGREN[100], MENZEL[101]).

24.40 – *Control in Non-Circadian Periodicity.* The bulk of investigations on external control refers to the 24-h rhythms. However, all periodicities with external correlates, lunar and seasonal rhythms, pose similar problems. The existence of endogenous counterparts to these is less certain but they have been proposed (circummonthly, -lunar, -annual, -seasonal, *cf.* 7.20). And even endogenous rhythms with no correlates at all could be controlled.

One example is the control of periodic growth (*cf.* 10.7), such as cell populations where each cell has its own phasing, *e.g.* mitosis rate or accumulation time of secretion in some gland cells (HIRSCH[1-3, 100], JÄRVI, KRIJGSMAN, PRESCOTT). These can be synchronized by an external stimulus, *e.g.* by cooling or mitotic poisons, retardation synchronization (SCHERBAUM[100]), or also by an autonomous nerve signal. Something similar happens in wars, where certain age groups are decimated and replaced by newborns, usually at an increased rate.

Metamorphosis is another example of a single occurrence which may be synchronized by external rhythms (*cf.* the eclosion rhythm studies of LEES[1-3] and PITTENDRIGH[3, 6, 100-101]). JOHNSON[1, 100-102] studied the 24-h flight rhythms in aphids, which fly a certain time after eclosion (tenereal period), depending on the amount of heat available. In their model, they assume the moulting rate to be constant, external temperature to vary sinusoidally, total heat to be represented by the area under that curve, and also that the total heat necessary for development is constant (thermal constant). From this, the flight rate is calculated. However, the animals do not fly at night which gives a peak of activity in the morning (retardation synchronization) and makes the 24-h curve bimodal. It may also be regarded statistically as a case of mixed populations (10.6). *Cf.* SCOTT[400].

24.41 – In sexual activity both spontaneous and exogenous rhythms appear. Oestrus cycles in many animals seem to be spontaneous (6.39-40, 7.21-26), though it may be debated in *Homo*. Other animals show, however, seasonal reproduction cycles, *e.g.* invertebrates, fish, reptiles, migratory birds and wild mammals (*e.g.* BARTHOLOMEW[2-3], BROWMAN[4, 100], BULLOUGH[1, 2, 5, 7], GIESE[1], GRIESER[100], HARRINGTON, LEES[4, 6-7], PARIS[100]). Light (the length of the day) seems to be the dominant synchronizer, but other external factors seem to be active, too. In birds gonadal function and morphology vary throughout the year (BENOIT[1-4], [100-106], BRADEN, FARNER[1-3], [100-102], HILL[300], MARSHALL[1-6], [100-103], [200-202], THREADGOLD, WOLFSON[1-10], [100]). The seasonal change in gonadal growth is controlled by the variation in the length of the daylight period. The prevailing LD-scheme may even determine if sexual or asexual aphids are to be developed (LEES[7], MARCOVITCH).

Such influences may well be transmitted through the retino-hypothalamic system (13.16-17). JÖCHLE[2-4], [101] has studied the effect of light and of the melanophore hormone on the normal sexual cycle in mice and rats (6-7-day periods). Constant light shortens the period but lengthens the oestrus until a state of continuous oestrus is reached. In continuous darkness the period and the interoestrus time lengthen. The melanophore hormone had a similar effect.

24.42 – Increased daylight is supposed to promote growth and bring more rapid sexual maturity, even in man. Children grow faster in summer than in winter (NYLIN, OTTO[2]). Human birth rates show annual variations (OTTO[3], [100]). On the other hand, continuous light throughout the day is probably detrimental in the long run. The *egg-laying* in hens may be increased by additional light, especially in winter, but only up to a certain limit. However, the total amount of light needed to sustain a maximum egg production may be drastically reduced if substituted by a series of short light flashes, *e.g.* six evenly spaced one-minute photoperiods in 24-h (FRAPS[1-3], [100], WILSON[500-503]). It may be that each light stimulus causes the release of some substance which acts for a certain time during the ensuing darkness before being exhausted (*cf.* 5.17, 24.22, GIESE[100]).

24.43 – In plants, the picture is similar. Usually there is an optimum light regimen for growth (WENT[3-6]). In DICKSON's[100] plants extremely short LD periods (0.0045: 0.0045 sec) were as effective in promoting growth as the LD 12:12 h, and both better than LD 2:2 min.

Mushrooms grow periodically outwards, giving rise to zones of fruit bodies, zonation. The light-dependency of this process is less clear and varies from species to species (JEREBZOFF, PIRSON[1], [100-103], SAGROMSKY). Some mushrooms have purely endogenous rhythms with about 15-20-h periods. The frequency depends on the chemical milieu and on the light intensity. Some varieties grow best in continuous light, others in certain, not too short, LD schemes. The oscillations may be damped or sustained, 24-h entrainment occurs. The type of response to light and the part of the organism that is sensitive (mycelial growth, konidiae, fruit bodies or spore formation) may vary with the degree of morphological development of the particular mushroom. Here is really a rich field for the study of the mechanism for entrainment by light and by chemical factors, *e.g.* drugs.

DeRUDDER's theory of the sinusoidal seasonal variations in light intensity affecting the limiting level of susceptibility to disease in populations of subjects has been mentioned earlier (20.6).

24.44 – Lunar periodicity is very pronounced in some water life, especially the lower animals living on the shore. This was mentioned in connection with animal migration. Well known is the behaviour of the Palolo worm which appears once a year in October or November and only in the third moon quarter at sunrise (BURROWS, CASPERS[1, 3, 5-6], McKAY[1], WHITMEE). All of a sudden the water is swarming with edible worms during some few hours. The natives predict the appearance with such accuracy that they can prepare for large Palolo feasts in advance.

24.45 – Eels appear periodically in the North Sea with a strong lunar periodicity, which is important to the fishing industry. The daily percentage of eel catches within the lunar month shows a peculiar skew, one-peaked curve with its maximum at the end of the third quarter-phase (JENS[1-2]). The curve can be remarkably well derived from an ellipse (cf. 19.7). This points to some astronomical influence though no direct relationship with the lunar light or the water levels can be proved to exist. On the other hand, 'lunar' periodicities may be experimentally induced by periodic changes in the 24-h LD-scheme over a month (HAUENSCHILD). – The herring catches may also show lunarmonthly variations (JENS[3]), though less well defined and with the maximum earlier than that of the eels.

24.46 – It is more uncertain, however, if lunar periodicities occur in *Homo* (cf. 7.21-26). The female menstrual cycle of 28 (or perhaps 29.5 days) suggests a connection, though the individual cycles are not synchronized. There is the possibility of a genetical memory (caused by selection) from our ancestral shore life, though it is remarkable in that case that the other mammals do not show this cycle (according to some observers, however, their periods tend to be harmonics of the 28-day period, containing 7-day units). Reports keep appearing on *Homo*, from the statements of a mother that the children (or maybe herself) are unruly at new moon to large statistics showing probable lunar peaks of menstruation, birth rate (MENAKER[200]), mortality or cancer. Even in such materials, however, the information is usually very noisy and statistical proof difficult (HECKERT).

24.47 – We have seen that the theories regarding the causation of exogenous rhythms are legion and that we actually know very little about it. Almost all experimental evidence can be interpreted in diametrically opposite ways. Much more data are needed before we can begin to outline a general theory of rhythm causation and control.

We shall now turn our attention to the exogenous rhythms as such, discussing the data accumulated on the different exogenous periods and then the main points of interest in the various fields of science. In connection with the latter, the development of the biological rhythm study and its application to practical problems will be outlined.

CHAPTER 25

Twenty-four Hour Rhythms

25.1 – In the previous chapters we have dealt mainly with the theories of rhythm control. It remains to survey the various synchronized exogenous rhythms and the various biological fields in which periodicity research is applied. Now, the 24-h rhythms will be discussed. Though the emphasis is on the entrained rhythm, the surveys of the literature on different biological variates will include all circadian contributions. First, however, follows a discussion of some theoretical and practical considerations.

By far the largest part of the biological rhythm literature is concerned with 24-h rhythms. Though the circadian phenomenon of near 24-h periods under 'constant' external conditions has dominated our discussions up to now, the bulk of the material is, nevertheless, concerned with the entrained, 'diurnal' rhythms. This is especially true of the older literature since at that time recordings were usually made throughout the normal day without manipulation of the environment, perhaps apart from some attempts to reverse the rhythms (24.23).

The literature on 24-h rhythms is enormous. As an introduction one may study various conferences on biological rhythms (References, sections one and two), also AJELLO[100], ASCHOFF[14-15], BÜNNING[29], BYKOW[1], CLOUDSLEY-THOMPSON[28], HALBERG[6, 10, 121], HARKER[5], HILDEBRANDT[20-21], JORES[5-7, 9, 12, 14], KALMUS[4-5], KLEITMAN[6, 9], MENZEL[8, 11, 14, 17], REINBERG[100], WELSH[5].

25.2 – As regards general activity, the 24-h rhythm has been self-evident throughout mankind's history. Man had to sleep during the dark periods before artificial lighting existed and he had to follow the daily habits of the prey carefully if he wanted to survive. The profound consequences of this were already realized by HUFELAND in 1797, but it is only very late that the phenomenon was scientifically studied. This had to be preceded by the slow development in biology from static morphological thinking to the acceptance of dynamic physiology. For a long time only such periodicities were acknowledged which had unavoidably to be accepted, e.g. in the heart rate, respiration, bowel movements and body temperature (after the introduction of the clinical thermometer in the 18th century). All other measures were regarded as static.

Plant 24-h rhythms were the first to be studied scientifically, already at the beginning of the 18th century (5.22). In physiology and medicine, however, the real breakthrough came very late, first with KLEITMAN's[1-6, 101] studies on the sleep-wakefulness mechanism, VÖLKER's[1] recordings of physiological 24-h rhythms in man, and FORSGREN's[3-8] description of the 24-h liver glycogen rhythm in the 1920s.

It was then realized that the whole metabolism displayed a periodicity. Around the same time came, with BÜNNING[1], [105-106], the realization that all these rhythms were perhaps not necessarily exogenous.

25.3 – There are actually few biological variates which do not display 24-h rhythms. This was only gradually realized. Early papers are abundant where the investigator tried to prove that there was not a 24-h factor in his field of study. The rhythms were supposed to be caused simply by the need for intermittent periods of sleep and feeding. Sleep naturally occurred at night and that was the sole reason for the periodicity. Eliminate this factor and distribute the food evenly, and the rhythm must disappear. The investigators often made the error of using negative statistical proof, sometimes on rather scant and badly controlled material. Actually, only the presence of statistical significance means anything. The absence of it proves nothing.

25.4 – *Theoretical Aspects on Twenty-four Hour Rhythms.* The importance of the 24-h rhythm as a clock has been repeatedly stressed. Clearly, it should be completely synchronized in order to function well. If circadian, the clock would soon err seriously though it would be reasonably accurate for a while, for instance in keeping the old time when travelling. The role of the circadian rhythm with regard to the time sense and orientation capacity of the animals has already been discussed (Chapters 5 and 18).

The 24-h rhythm has also been extensively used as a tool for the study of the mechanism behind biological rhythms. This was exposed in connection with the biological oscillator theories and freerunning experiments (5.16-24, 7.3-18; Chapters 9, 13, 14, 18, 24). Another use is in the search for the site of the mechanism in the organism, by straight-forward elimination of different parts of the body. It is remarkable to see how the rhythm is sometimes retained even after heavy surgery, and in higher animals. (Of course, some of the 24-h rhythms may disappear if they are too closely connected with the organ in question.) Neither hepatectomy, splenectomy, adrenalectomy, hypophysectomy, starvation, blinding, blocking of the ear, sleep deprivation, electric shocks and brain ablation, nor similar pathological afflictions, such as adrenal insufficiency, blindness or diabetes do necessarily abolish the rhythm. *Cf.* ÅGREN[1], ALBRECHT[100], BOCHNIK[4], BROWMAN[1], BROWN[200], [300], BRUSS[100], CHAUDRY[103], FERGUSON[100], FLEESON[100], GALICHICH[1-2, 100], HALBERG[1, 3, 7, 9, 14, 101, 112, 115, 121, 124, 128, 131, 135, 152, 155], HILL[300], JARDETSKY[100], JORES[13], KLEITMAN[1], MENZEL[17], MÖLLERSTRÖM[4-10, 12-15, 18-22, 100-103], OSBORN, PAYNE[100], PONUGAJEWA, RADNOT[1-3], SHOLITON[100], ZANDER[100]. Sometimes phase reversals may occur (*cf.* PAYNE[100]), though it would have to be differentiated from freerunning. Certainly, the central nervous system is an important link in the 24-h informational flow in higher animals, but it is difficult to pin down a certain place as the center (*cf.* EIDMANN, FINGERMAN[1, 101], HARKER[2-9], LEES[7], 24.16).

Other examples of the persistence of these rhythms, which have been mentioned (24.26-29), are the temperature independence of the circadian freerunning, the fact that entrainment to artificial LD-schemes is usually only possible around the 24-h day, the persistence of the 24-h period as a component in such experiments.

25.5 – HALBERG[7-8, 10, 103, 114] (*cf.* 24.18) describes different levels of organization and draws circadian maps, a systematic recording of 24-hour rhythms in all possible aspects of body function, such as DNA, liver glycogen, body temperature, sensitivity to toxins, *etc.* The single rhythms may differ in shape and above all, in phasing. This is obvious since the various body variates are coupled *inter se*; circulatory changes precede renal excretion variation and some metabolites turn into other metabolites.

Obviously all the possible variates cannot be assayed simultaneously and on the same individuals. This would, of course, be desirable, but on the other hand different subjects can be used if there is a careful control of the experimental conditions, such as a fixed LD-entrainment, and homogeneous materials. The simultaneous recording of a few variates is common in the literature. Some larger investigations on *Homo* are BOCHNIK[8], LEWIS[100-105], MENZEL[2], THEDERING, TRÄNKLE, VÖLKER[1].

The ease of phase synchronization (24.20) contrasts with the difficulty of frequency synchronization. On the other hand, the possibility of a differential synchronization, with some variates behaving in another way than others in the same organism, shows the difficulty of assuming that only one single central rhythm site exists.

The 24-h rhythms do not necessarily have to be pure. In lower animals subjected to the tides there is a marked lunarday component (BENNETT[100-102], BROWN[6-7, 9-10, 101, 103, 107, 109, 113, 115-118], FINGERMAN[2-6, 103]). Some activity rhythms have two peaks (*cf.* 24.27).

25.6 – The formation of biological rhythms may be studied on the 24-h periodicity (*cf.* 9.1-9). This is also of interest in pediatrics (Conf. 1961a). Usually, the curves start at birth with very low amplitudes, which subsequently increase. This has been studied in *Homo* and in rats with such factors as activity (BÜHLER[100], GESELL, HELLBRÜGGE[1, 101], KLEITMAN[6, 10-12, 102-103], LANGE[200]), body temperature (GOFFERJÉ, GYLLENSWÄRD, HELLBRÜGGE[1], JUNDELL, KLEITMAN[106], LANGE[200], SEIDL), heart rate (BIERSACK, HELLBRÜGGE[100], LANGE[200]), liver glycogen (SECKEL[100]), bile (COSSEL), electrical skin resistance (NIGGESCHMIDT, RUTENFRANZ[1-2, 100]) and various aspects of the diuresis (FRÖBA, FUNCK, HELLBRÜGGE[1], HOHAUS, KATHAN). Studies in some birds indicate a dominance of high frequency rhythms in the embryo (a low circadian quotient, *cf.* 24.38) and a rather abrupt appearance of a nearly mature rhythm on the first day after hatching (BARNWELL[1], ELFVIN[100], PETRÉN[100], SOLLBERGER[3]). Similarly, there is a high-frequency dominance in the sleep-wakefulness pattern of infants which is only slowly converted into the adult pattern. An analogous break-down of the 24-h rhythm is seen in many diseases (*cf.* 24.38, ARBORELIUS, HILDEBRANDT[20-21, 104], MENZEL[5, 9, 15-16, 100-102]).

25.7 – The sleeping period is an important part of the 24-h pattern and its physiology (marked by a lowering of the energy expenditure) has received much attention. The many problems here are not specially of interest in connection with biological rhythms. The literature on sleep is enormous, a few examples are ASERINSKY[100-101], BLANKENHORN[100], BOND, BORING[100], BRAINES, BRINKMANN, BRUSH, DEMENT[1, 100-102], FORSGREN[13, 19], FROBENIUS, GANS, GOLLWITZER-MEIER[100], GOODENOUGH[100], HELLBRÜGGE[1, 101], HERZ, HESS[400], HOLMQUIST[2],

HOWELL, KATSCH[100], KLEITMAN[1-6, 11, 101-103], LANDIS, LANGE[100, 200], LESSE, LEWIS[700], LÜDERITZ[2], MONNIER, MORUZZI, OHLMAYER[100], OSWALD[200], PIERACH[3], RANSON, REED[100], RUTENFRANZ[2], SCHULTE, SHAPIRO, SIMON[100], SIMPSON[2], STRAUB[1], TATAI[1], WILLIAMS[400]. However, it is interesting to see that the higher frequency rhythm found in newborns seems to stay in the adult sleep, appearing as a periodic variation in the frequency of eye movements, dreaming and EEG changes. The proneness to dream thus varies rhythmically during sleep at about 70-100-min intervals, a variation between two kinds of sleep (ASERINSKY[100-101], DEMENT[1, 100-102]) with different functions, under the control of the reticular system in the brain stem. – A very special kind of sleep is hibernation (cf. 26.7) which appears in the seasonal activity patterns of some animals.

25.8 – The terminology of the 24-h rhythms is mixed, cf. 20.10. A hemerography (BARKER[100]) is a detailed psychological description of a person's behaviour during one day. Diurnal, though widely accepted, means really day-time as contrasted to the night, and the French nycthéméral the opposite. To say 24-h rhythms is not quite exact; and circadian indicates freerunning.

25.9 – *Practical Aspects on Twenty-four Hour Rhythms.* Our synchronization to the surrounding daily regimen (24.20-31) is a very smooth process which seldom gives us any trouble as long as we comply with the external commands. It offers problems, however, in some diseases and when we try to tamper with it, in shift work and travelling.

We have already seen that the phasing of our rhythms is easily changed (24.20-24). However, it requires about a week and during that time the organism is deeply affected, as anyone knows who has flown over the Atlantic (FLINK[100], GERRITZEN[8], RUTENFRANZ[102]). The required neurovegetative adaptation stresses the body considerably, with pronounced tiredness. This feels similar to what one experiences when adjusting to a new climate, e.g. high up in the mountains or at the sea. It is remarkable that we can gladly transfer from the indoor heat to winter cold without much discomfort, if adequately protected, but that we find it difficult to adjust to a change in the temporal pattern even if the range of the variation involved is negligible (STRUGHOLD[2]). The 24-h variation in temperature is scarcely 1 degree Celsius. No doubt the slow travelling of older days was much more physiological. Nowadays, we are usually pressed for time and can do little to remedy the situation. This is already a professional problem for flight personnel and the military. Maybe, we could start several days before the flight by changing our living regimen artificially and helping the adjustment along with the judicious use of sedatives and sleeping pills. As to animals, we know very little how they feel, but they do lose their orientation which should be rather upsetting (cf. Chapter 18).

25.10 – Similar problems are met with in shift work and night work, where the change between regimens is constantly repeated, sometimes rather too often. Nervous disorders, such as gastric ulcer and sleeplessness are not infrequent. This is one of the problems in industrial medicine and hygiene, studied by e.g. ANDLAUER[100], BJERNER[100-101], BROWNE, ERÄNKÖ, GRAF[202-205], KLEITMAN[13], LAURELL[2],

LEHMANN, MARGOLINA[100], MENZEL[6, 17, 26-27, 33], MONGELLI-SCIANNAMEO, PHILIPS-BORN[3], PIERACH[1, 3-4], PIRTKIEN, THIIS-EVENSEN, VERING[1-5], WALDOW. The error-proneness varies throughout the day, probably being highest in the night. The individual capacity to follow shift regimens varies strongly. It decreases with increasing age. Some people simply keep the old rhythm indefinitely, others develop nervous disorders. Probably, some kind of medical screening should be used to prevent such people from doing shift work. Also, adequate quiet living-quarters are necessary, allowing an undisturbed sleep. The unrestricted diurnal sleep is shorter than the nocturnal one (MENZEL[17]). Various schemes for the rotation of shifts have been devised but they do not remove the cause of the evil.

Apart from the 24-h rhythm the factories may also try to make the rhythm of the work follow some of the body's natural high-frequency rhythms (cf. tapping rhythms, 6.14) or to stimulate with music (LEHMANN). Such a scheme must not be too rigid, however.

25.11 – A screening of synchronization-sensitive people becomes still more important if we have to drop the usual 24-h period completely, as may be required, e.g. in astronautics (cf. HALBERG[8], HAUTY[1-3, 100], KLEITMAN[6, 100]). HALBERG's circadian quotient may perhaps be used as an indicator of the individual's entrainability. Another situation is the sensory deprivation which may be encountered in space or in modern long-range submarines where the normal synchronization with the environment is impaired (HALBERG[15], KLEITMAN[14]). Here, the whole problem of circadian frequency synchronization appears; with synchronization to near-24-h periods, possibly to harmonics of the 24-h one, beats, or freerunning (24.26-29, 32-36).

25.12 – Many diseases show a disturbed 24-h rhythm. The tendency towards high-frequency rhythms with a diminished circadian amplitude and quotient has already been mentioned (25.6). ARBORELIUS uses this phenomenon to distinguish between gastric cancer and ulcer. In some diseases, the 24-h rhythm is, instead, rather enhanced (feedback instability?) as in diabetes with its high-amplitude blood sugar variations and 24-h shift of acidosis, or in psychic disease. The rhythm may be inversed, as in nycturia (JORES[1-4, 8]). Since, normally, the general activity level and sensitivity of the organism varies rhythmically, this affects the sensitivity to drugs or to pathological influences (HALBERG[7-8, 106, 111, 117, 120-123, 127, 129-130], MENZEL[8-9, 11]). Usually, the highest sensitivity is about 4 o'clock in the morning, when cardiac and asthmatic attacks, as well as death and birth, tend to be most frequent. The cardiac patient is about 40 times as sensitive to digitalis in the night as compared to the day and the diabetic subject is most sensitive to insulin around 4 o'clock. In balneotherapy a slow and cautious re-intrainment to a normal 24-h rhythm is aimed at (HILDEBRANDT[4-5, 9-14, 16, 20-21, 100, 102]). In the hospital the rigid schedule of sleep, food, visits and treatments constitutes a strong synchronizer.

The involvement of the 24-h rhythm in various diseases, such as cardiac insufficiency and infarct, hypertension, asthma, gastric ulcer, renal disturbances, diabetes, tuberculosis, cancer, epilepsy and psychic disorders has been described by AJELLO[100], ARBORELIUS, ARNDT, BINGEL, DISSMAN, FÉRÉ, FORSGREN[5, 14-18],

20-21, 23, 27, 30, 32-33, 35-36, HALBERG[2, 7-8, 111-112, 116-117, 121, 124-125, 137], HEGGLIN, JORES[1-4, 8-9, 100], KARNELL, LANGDON-DOWN[100], LÜDERITZ[1], MASTER, MENZEL[1-11, 14-17, 100-103], MÖLLERSTRÖM[2, 4, 7-10, 12-22, 100-103], PATRY, SOLLBERGER[3-4, 12], WEBER.

25.13 – Rather remarkable is the morning sickness which may occur in early pregnancy and, so pronounced, in renal insufficiency. Even the healthy individual is rather sensitive in the morning. Few people can eat heavily at that time. There has also been much discussion about 'morning' and 'evening' types; some people being most active in the morning and others late at night, though little has been done to corroborate this scientifically. BINGEL perceives this difference in psychiatric disease and compares the morning type to the schizoid psyche and the evening type to the cyclothyme psyche. Actually, there are day-active and night-active animals; why not people? Of course, other factors may be of importance. The late hours are quiet and allow the intellectual worker to concentrate on his problem.

Actually, the mood varies more than that during the day as some introspection may show. Most people probably feel a little sluggish around 4, 12, 18 and 24 o'clock after which they get more alert again. The noonday nap is universal and certainly very healthy. Food at these times also helps. It is difficult to tell what this approximate 6 hour periodicity may signify. Maybe it is just determined by our need for food. Maybe it is a harmonic of the 24-h period. Maybe it is the high-frequency rhythm found in embryos and diseases. Perhaps the 'morning' and 'evening' types differ in that they synchronize with different of these peaks, about the same way as the mature chicken liver glycogen rhythm was formed from one of the embryonic peaks (9.8).

25.14 – *Activity Rhythms in Vertebrates.* Activity is one of the most studied 24-h factors owing to the comparative ease of registration (1.34, 20.6,8). In *Homo* it is usually represented by the sleep-wakefulness pattern in children and adults (*cf.* 25.6-7). The 24-h activity rhythm of many animals may be of practical importance to us, *e.g.* the sleep habits of our prey, the stinging hours of mosquitos, or the feeding hours of cockroaches.

25.15 – Activity rhythms in *Homo* have been studied by ASCHOFF[108], BARKER[100], BÜHLER[100], GESELL, HELLBRÜGGE[1, 101], KLEITMAN[6, 10-12, 102-103], LANGE[200]; in monkeys by STSCHERBAKOWA, TSCHERKOWITSCH.

Activity rhythms in dogs, foxes, jackasses and dingoes were recorded by BASSET[100] and STSCHERBAKOWA[1]; in squirrels, bats and hedgehogs by DECOURSEY, GRIFFIN[100], PITTENDRIGH[6], PONUGAJEWA, RAWSON[3-4] and STSCHERBAKOWA[1]. Activity rhythms in rats and mice have been one of the most popular activity subjects, studied by ASCHOFF[1, 3, 11, 102, 104, 106], BROWN[7, 9, 110], CALHOUN, FILATOWA, FOLK[1-3], HALBERG[9, 104, 139], HOLMGREN[101], KURCZ[1, 3], MAISELIS[100], MEYER-LOHMAN, NOTHDURFT, PITTENDRIGH[6], RAWSON[4], STSCHERBAKOWA[1], SZYMANSKY, TRIBUKAIT, VOGEL[100], WOLF[2]. Activity rhythms in guinea-pigs, rabbits, and hamsters were observed by FILATOWA, RAWSON[4], STSCHERBAKOWA; and in kangaroo rats by JUSTICE.

25.16 – Activity rhythms in birds have been studied by ASCHOFF[5, 100, 103, 105, 107]

BARTHOLOMEW[1], EMLEN, HOFFMANN[1-3], [7-9], KRAMER[1-8], [100-103], LEHTONEN, MATTHEWS[1-5], MERKEL, PALMGREN[1-3], [5-7], PRATT[200], [300-301], RAWSON[1], SAUER[1-4], [100-102], SIEGEL[100]; but this also includes innumerable further studies on bird migration (*cf.* Chapter 18).

25.17 – Activity rhythms in reptiles and amphibians were studied by BENNETT[103], HOFFMANN[4-6], [9], McINTOSH, TAYLOR[1], in fishes by BRAEMER, DAVIS[800] (light shock activity reaction), HASLER[1-3], [100-102], HOAR[1-2], [100], KASSIMOW, SCHWASSMANN, SPENCER, including the orientation problem in fishes (*cf.* Chapter 18).

25.18 – *Activity Rhythms in Invertebrates.* 24-h activity rhythms in higher invertebrates have been discussed in detail by CLOUDSLEY-THOMPSON[3-15], [17], [19-21], [24-28], *e.g.* in spiders, scorpions and centipedes (*cf.* PAPI[3-4], [101-102]). In crustaceans they were studied by BENNETT[100-102], BROWN[6], [9], CUSHING, FINGERMAN[5], [100], GUYSELMAN, KIKUCHI[1], NAYLOR, PARK[103].

25.19 – 24-h activity rhythms in insects have been studied in mayflies (HARKER[1]), grasshoppers (CLOUDSLEY-THOMPSON[10], [13], FINGERMAN[101]), cockroaches (CLOUDS-LEY-THOMPSON[4], [15], GUNN[400], HARKER[2-9], MELLANBY, RALPH[2], ROBERTS[2-3], SCHECHTER[100]), beetles (BIRUKOW[1-2], [5], BODENHEIMER[1], CLOUDSLEY-THOMPSON[5], HEMPEL[100], PARK[2]), *Drosophila* (BRETT[1], DYSON-HUDSON, KALMUS[8], MITCHELL[300], MORI[10-12], PAVAN[100], PITTENDRIGH[1], [3], [6], [100-101], ROBERTS[1], TAYLOR[300]), other flies and mosquitos, *e.g.* as regards biting and swarming (DUKE, CORBET, EASTROP, HADDOW, PARK[1-2], [100], RAU[1], WILLIAMS[200]). Activity rhythms in ants and bees are closely connected with the problem of orientation in invertebrates, as are the studies on pond skaters and beach fleas. These things were discussed in detail in 18.12. Many insect activities, *e.g.* biting or swarming are coupled to their 24-h metamorphosis and sexual rhythms (eclosion, nuptial flights). *Cf.* BREMER, BRETT[1], DUNNING, GAUL, HARKER[1], JOHNSON[100-102], KALMUS[10], KENNEDY, LEES, LEWIS[300], McCLELLAND[200], McCLUSKEY, NOWOSIELSKI[100-101], PALMÉN, PATTON, PAULIAN[100], PITTENDRIGH[1], [3], [6], [100-101], REMMERT, ROBERTSON. The time of activity varies with many factors, and may even be genetically determined (KALMUS[10]).

25.20 – 24-h activity rhythms have also been studied in snails (STEPHENS[1]), oysters (BENNETT[1], BROWN[2], [103]), worms (BALDWIN[200], RALPH[1], WELLS[1]), coelenterates (BOHN[2-4], [100], MORI[1-3], [101], PIERON), plankton (CLARKE[1], CUSHING, KIKU-CHI[1], ROSE, RUSSELL[200], vertical movements and organic drift in the sea, *cf.* FOX[3]), and unicellular organisms (*e.g.* BRUCE[101-102], [104], EHRET[1-7], HASTINGS[1], [102-106], SWEENEY[1], [100-101]). *Cf.* also MÜLLER[200], WELSH[100].

Activity rhythms in starfish were studied by MORI[100]. Parasites of various kinds (in *e.g.* malaria and filariasis) assume the 24-h rhythm of their host (BELDING, ENGEL[300-301], HALBERG[121], HARKER[5], HAWKING[1-2], [100], HINMAN, McFADZEAN[100], MANSON, STAUBER).

25.21 – *Various Rhythms in Invertebrates and Plants.* Studies of 24-h rhythms in invertebrates have been made *e.g.* on color changes (classical studies of crab chromatophore movements); BROWN[7], [9], FINGERMAN[2], [4], [103], KLEINHOLZ[1], [100],

KLEITMAN[7], STEPHENS[2-5], WEBB[1]. Other factors recorded are the optic pigments and neurosecretion (BENNITT, FINGERMAN[102], KLUG, WELSH[1-5]); oxygen consumption (BROWN[7, 10, 101, 117, 121], FINGERMAN[1, 100-101], MORI[8], RALPH[1], WEBB[100]); further aspects of metabolism in sea-pens (MORI[8]: pH, CO_2, NH_3, glycogen); and mitosis in sea urchins (ZEUTHEN). The learning process in earthworms was studied by ARBIT.

25.22 – 24-h rhythm study in botany started with the observation of rhythmic patterns in flower and leaf activity (cf. LINNAEUS, BÜNNING[1-3, 20, 23, 29, 105-106], BROUWER, BÜNSOW, KELLER[200], KLEINHOONTE, PARKER[300-301], PFEFFER, ROYER, SACHS[1-2, 200-201], SCHMITZ[1, 200], SCHWEMMLE[1-4, 100-102], SEMON, SNYDER[1], STOPPEL [1-3, 5-6, 11-13, 100-101], VIRZI). It got considerable impetus from BÜNNING's[1-5, 8-36, 100-104] theory of the endodiurnal rhythm. The literature is very extensive.

25.23 – Some examples of the studied variates in plants are: mushroom growth (BRANDT[200], GALLEMAERTS, HAFITZ, HEDGECOCK, JEREBZOFF, SAGROMSKY); plant growth and nutation (BALL[300-304], BARANETZKY, FRIESNER, GODLEWSKI, KELLICOTT, WENT); spores (BRUCE[103], BÜHNEMANN[1-2], RICH[100], VERING[6]); cell division and mitosis (BÜHNEMANN[5], BÜNNING[16, 104], KELLICOTT, SWEENEY[102]); leaf structure (FOGG); electric potentials (BURR); root pressure (GROSSENBACHER[1]); activity in unicellular organisms (EHRET[1-6, 101], HASTINGS[1-3, 100-106], SWEENEY[1, 100-101]); protoplasmic parameters and metabolism in plants (BROWN[6-7, 9, 108], MEYER[100], RAU[200], SIDERIS[100], STÅLFELDT[1, 3], URSPRUNG[100], VENTER, WILKINS). For further literature cf. 5.16-22, 7.3-19, Chapter 13 (especially 13.24-25) and BÜNNING[29] (also CARR[200-201], FLÜGEL, GARDNER[100], HUSSEY, LEINWEBER, WASSERMAN, ROMELL, SLATYER).

25.24 – Throughout the rest of the chapter various 24-h rhythms in higher animals will be discussed. The emphasis is on Homo with some exceptions, such as body temperature and liver glycogen in other mammals and in birds, blood sugar in chickens. An extensive review of 24-h rhythms in Homo has been made by MENZEL[17].

25.25 – *Temperature Rhythms in Higher Animals.* Twenty-four hour temperature rhythms have been studied mostly in Homo but also in monkeys (GALBRAITH[100], STSCHERBAKOWA[1-2], TSCHERKOWITSCH), birds (GALBRAITH[101], HILDEN[100], SIMPSON[300], SOLLBERGER[3, 6]), hamsters (CHAUDRY[101], FOLK[104]), rats and mice (FERGUSON[300], HALBERG[138, 150, 155], HOLMGREN[101], MAISELIS[100]), bats (MENAKER[1], PONUGAJEWA), and armadillos (JOHANSEN[1]). – They have been recorded in different sites such as the rectum, mouth, liver (GRAF[400, 500-502], SOLLBERGER[3, 6]), skin (HILDEBRANDT[101]), forehead, finger and foot. Even the contralateral asymetry in temperature has been followed (HILDEBRANDT[101]). All temperature curves are not parallel; the cycles in the core and the surface tend, for physiological reasons, to be inverse. Careful 24-h studies have also shown that the liver temperature is lower than the rectal one (GRAF[400, 500], SOLLBERGER[3]). Actually, the rectal temperature is, for some reason, about the highest in the body.

The 24-h temperature rhythm has also been recorded under various functional conditions; *e.g.* in infants (GOFFERJÉ, GYLLENSVÄRD, HELLBRÜGGE[1], JUNDELL, KLEITMAN[106], LANGE[200], SEIDL) where it is of low amplitude though increasing with age; in pregnancy (MALEK[3-4, 104]); and in disease (BÜTTNER, MENZEL[4-5, 15], MÖLLERSTRÖM[14, 102-103], OLNJANSKAJA). – The temperature has been used as an indicator of rhythm behaviour in experimental work, *e.g.* entrainment, inversal, cold, exercise and neural shock (BENEDICT[1, 100], FLEESON[100], FOLK[2], GIBSON, HALBERG[7-8, 115], KLEITMAN[100, 104-106], SHARP[7], SLONIM[100], TIMMERMAN[100]). – In earlier days recordings were of course made with the mercury thermometer, but later continuous measurement has been facilitated by the use of thermocouples, thermistors and telemetering (FOLK[5-6], GRAF[400, 500-502], SOLLBERGER[3]). – Further references to 24-h temperature rhythms are ASCHOFF[8], BARTTER[1], BÄNDER[1], FORSGREN[19, 25, 100], GESSLER, HALBERG[9, 13, 121, 140], HILDEBRANDT[1-2, 10-11, 18, 102], HOLMGREN[3, 11], HOWE, JOHANSEN[100], JOHANSSON, JORES[9], KLEITMAN[1, 5, 6, 101, 105], LÜDERITZ[1, 3], MARGOLINA[100], MENZEL[9], MÜHLMANN, OGATA[100], PETERSEN[1], DERUDDER[101], SIMPSON[300], TRÄNKLE, TROJAN, VÖLKER, WAGNER[1, 100].

25.26 – *Metabolic Rhythms in Higher Animals.* The classical studies were on liver glycogen, starting with FORSGREN's[2-8, 10, 13-15, 18-19, 22-24, 29-31, 34, 36, 100-101] discovery (1927) of the 24-h bile and glycogen rhythms. The latter is, however, also found in other organs such as the blood (MÖLLERSTRÖM[14]), the heart, skeletal musculature, spleen and pancreas (KÖHLER[400], SOLLBERGER[3, 100], ÅGREN[100]). Since continuous determinations are difficult almost all glycogen studies have been made in animals by sacrifice, *e.g.* in chickens (ELFVIN[100], PETRÉN[2, 100], SOLLBERGER[1, 3, 5-6, 15, 100], WIJK[100]), guinea-pigs (HOLMGREN[8], PETRÉN[1]), rabbits (BERINGER, EULER[100], FORSGREN[3], SJÖGREN[100], STAHLE), rats and mice (ÅGREN[1, 100], DEUEL[100], EDLUND[102], HALBERG[7-8, 17, 100, 103], HIGGINS[100], HOLMGREN[1-3, 5, 8-12, 14, 100], HOLMQUIST[1], JORES[13], KÖHLER[400], SECKEL[100]). BERINGER has, however, studied the liver glycogen in *Homo* by liver biopsy. *Cf.* also MAYERSBACH[100].

The various glycogen curves differ considerably in shape and in timing. Often they are fairly symmetrical (*cf.* Figs. 9.8a, 20.14b). The peak-time varies with the investigator and the animal, with day or night activity, but seems to cluster around 14-19 o'clock and 01-07 o'clock. Sometimes both times are represented, through the introduction of a secondary peak (in rats, mice, rabbits, guinea pigs and chickens, *cf.* Fig. 20.14b). Either one of the two peaks may disappear (or almost so) in starvation, whereas the other stays, indicating that also the neo-glycogenesis is under circadian control. The double-peaked shape may correspond to that found in animal activity, being an indicator of a two-oscillator system (*cf.* 24.27, TRIBUKAIT). In chickens, the secondary peak may be preceded by an intermediate level' on the curve limbs (*cf.* Fig. 20.14b). In *Homo*, and in chickens, the glycogen metabolism seems to have two turning points, at around 16 and 04 o'clock. *Cf.* SOLLBERGER[15].

25.27 – Many 24-h metabolites related to the carbohydrate and fatty metabolism have been assayed. The blood sugar variation has, of course, mostly been recorded in diabetes, where the bioamplitude is large. The latter is also proportional to the sugar level (HOPMAN[2], SOLLBERGER[3]). Actually, the relative variations around the level (relative curves) are more or less constant (*cf.* 20.19-20, 22). The literature on diabetic hyperglycemia is large. Some further examples are Möllerström[2], [4], [7-10], [12], [14], [16] (with two different methods) and Seyderholm[100]. The blood sugar has also been recorded in healthy persons by Möllerström[4] (after exercise), Schiessl (in children) and Seyderholm[100]. It has been assayed in animals like monkeys (Kanfor), chickens (Sollberger[3], [100]), rabbits (Eadie) and rats (Pitts). The effect on the 24-h sugar rhythm of phenamin (Kanfor), glucose tolerance tests (Unger) and psychosis (Holmgren[6], [103]) has also been studied. The blood sugar curve follows the differential of the liver glycogen one (Sollberger[3], [100]). Further studies are: Bänder[1], Bochnik[8], Forsgren[17], Halberg[103], Holmgren[9], Jores[5], [9], Krasnjansky, Lange[100], Menzel[105], Sachse, Sweeney[200], Trimble[100], Vogel[1].

25.28 – In diabetes the glucosuria rhythm is conspicuous, as is the excretion of citric acid, pyruvic acid, acetone, β-hydroxybutyric acid and ammonia; Möller-ström[4], [9-10], [12], [14], [100-103] (also in the blood), Sollberger[3-4]. Diabetic acidosis seems to be most active around 4 o'clock in the morning and 16 o'clock in the afternoon, which are the turning points in the glycogen metabolism, between assimilation and dissimilation; it tends to recede spontaneously between these times even without insulin. – Other recordings of the carbohydrate metabolism rhythm are: Dell'Acqua[1], Edlund[102], Frajola, Glick[1], [100], Jores[9], Magaro[100]. Rhythms in alcohol metabolism were studied by Dell'Acqua[1], Möllerström[14], [16], Pansini[100], Wilson[300].

25.29 – 24-h lipid metabolism rhythms include chylomicrons (Bohm[100], Möller-ström[14]); suprarenal cholesterol (Mödlinger[100]) and serum cholesterol (Dell' Acqua[1], [100], Berenstein[100], Bruger[100], Georgi[3], Lippi[1], [100], Pansini[101], Peter-son[100]); tissue fat (Holmgren[3-5]). Other studies of lipid metabolism are: Bar-num[102], Beringer[1], Boyd[1], Georgi[1-2], Halberg[9], [13], [103], Ohlsson[100], Pincus[100], Vermund[100]. Sulfhydryl groups and protein metabolism have also been investigat-ed (Beck, Linneweh).

25.30 – The O_2 and CO_2 metabolism was studied by Bänder[1], Barnwell[1], (chick embryos), Barrot[100], Bornstein[100], Burckhard[300] (in chickens), Fila-towa (in mammals), Heusner (in rats), Hiebel[100] (in chickens and chick em-bryos), Hildebrandt[18], Johansson, Jores[9], Mödlinger[100] (in mice), Sondén[100], Völker[1].

25.31 – The 24-h formation of bile was described by Forsgren[3-4], [6], [12], [19], who found that the accumulation of bile and glycogen in the liver ran inverse courses; also by Josephson[100], in a patient with a biliary fistula, and by Pfaff[100]. – There are rhythms of bilirubine and urobiline in serum and urine (Balzer[1], Brüschke[100], Forsgren[16], [19], Friedrich[100]); of coproporphyrin excretion (Galambos[100]); urea excretion (Campbell[100], Gerritzen[3], Menzel[4-5], [9], [100-101], Simpson[1]); urinary amino acids (Kleinbaum); 5-hydroxytryptamine metabolism in blood and brain (Albrecht[101], Berendes[100]); and hepatic phospholipids (Vermund[100]). Twenty-four hour rhythms are also found in the liver detoxification capacity (Georgi[2]); creatine and creatinine excretion (Addis[100], Bochnik[8], Jores[9],

KATHAN in children, MAGEE in children and muscular atrophy, MENZEL[4]); pyridine derivatives (MÖLLERSTRÖM[13-14]); choline (MÖLLERSTRÖM[14]); uric acid excretion (LEATHES, SIMPSON[1]); non-protein nitrogen (FORSGREN[9, 11], SIEBER in chickens), and urinary nitrogen (CAMPBELL[100], FORSGREN[19, 100], KURCZ[2] in rats, VÖLKER[1]). Cf. the NH₃-excretion in diabetes studied by MÖLLERSTRÖM[12, 14, 22, 101-102], also CAMPBELL[100].

As to metabolism in man the general picture emerges of a day period with dominating utilization of muscular fuel and storage of carbohydrates for the night, especially in the liver. At night the utilization of the stored energy with a depletion of liver glycogen dominates, but also the use of such energy for synthesis, e.g. in the formation of bile or protein. The turning points would be around 4 and 16 o'clock, when the body seems to be fully occupied with the change. It is then most labile and sensitive to external disturbing influences. In diabetes, e.g., the formation of ketone bodies starts twice a day, at these time points. The common feeding practice with predominantly cereals in the morning and meat in the evening is also understandable. Some people have a definite craving for protein food late in the evening, before going to bed.

25.32 – *Rhythms of Body Electrolytes in Higher Animals.* The sodium and potassium excretion is most studied of electrolyte 24-h rhythms. Apart from healthy adults, the rhythm has been studied in small children (FUNCK, HELLBRÜGGE[1], HOHAUS) and in disease; e.g. adrenal insufficiency (AZERAD[100]), diabetes (GHATA[1], MÖLLERSTRÖM[14]), epilepsy (MERTENS), or as a tool in cancer diagnosis (ARBORELIUS). It has been observed in mammals (STSCHERBAKOWA[1]) and rats (KURCZ[2]). It has been used as an indicator in entrainment and inversal studies (LEWIS[100-104], LOBBAN, SHARP[1-2, 5]). Other descriptions are AZERAD[101], BARTTER[1] (in women), BELKE, FOLK[5], GERRITZEN[1, 3], GHATA[100], LEWIS[103], (in exercise), MILLS[200, 300-302], MONGELLI-SCIANNAMEO, NORN, STANBURY[100].

25.33 – The serum calcium rhythm was also recorded (BELKE, BUCK[1], HOLMQUIST[3] in men and rabbits, MÖLLERSTRÖM[14] in diabetes); as well as serum iron (HALBERG[121], HAMILTON[100], MAHIEU[100], WETZEL); serum phosphate (PELLEGRINI[101]) and copper (MUNCH-PETERSEN). – Urinary chloride was assayed by CAMPBELL[101], GERRITZEN[1-4], KURCZ[2] (in rats), Menzel[4-5, 101-102] (including renal insufficiency), MERTENS, MILLS[301], MÖLLERSTRÖM[14] (also in blood), NORN, SIMPSON[1-2]; and magnesium by DOE[100], MOURS-LAROCHE. – Urinary phosphate was recorded by CAMPBELL[100], KATHAN (in children), KURCZ[2] (in rats), LUBELL, MILLS[301], MÖLLERSTRÖM[14] (also in blood). – Urine acidity was described by HARDERECK, MERTENS, MILLS[301], MONGELLI-SCIANNAMEO, MÖLLERSTRÖM[14, 103], SHARP[2] (reversal experiment), SIMPSON[1] and STSCHERBAKOWA[1-2] (in mammals), cf. CULLEN[100].

25.34 – *Rhythms of Enzymes and Hormones in Higher Animals.* A number of enzymes and hormones also describe 24-h variations, as regards their formation (they may even be used as a measure of vegetative nervous function), blood values and secretion. Gastric secretion rhythms have been studied by FORSGREN[32-33, 35], HEGGLIN[1], HELLEBRANDT[100], KREITNER[100], SCHUNK[100] and THIES in normal and diseased subjects. Gastric malfunction caused by stress and a dysrhythmic living

seriously aggravates the course of a tuberculous infection. The salivary pH was
recorded by GROSSMAN[100], the exocrine pancreatic secretion by BALZER[100]. The
urinary excretion of urokathepsin and uropepsin was followed by MERTEN;
glycolytic enzymes by GLICK[1, 100], and MOORE, properdin by DRESSLER, transaminidase by PILSUM. – The 24-h rhythm of the adreno-cortical hormones has
been studied by DELL' ACQUA[1], BARTTER[1] (in women), DOE[100], LUETSCHER[100],
CANIGGIA[100] (including cardiac patients), CARROZZINI, FRANK[1] HALBERG[7, 9, 13,
103, 105, 113, 131 139, 141, 149, 151], HAUS[3, 102], MIGEON[100] (including blind subjects),
MULLER[100], PERKOFF[100], PINCUS[2, 100], REINBERG[100], SHARP[100], SHOLITON[100], TA-
KEBE[100], UNGAR[100]. Rhythms also appear in the melanophore hormone (JORES[9],
cf. RAHN[100]) and the catecholamines (DELL'ACQUA[1], EULER[100] in rabbits, JORES[9],
(PELLEGRINI[100], cf. APOR, NIEBROJ); in the prolactin production (CLARK[500]), the
pregnandiol excretion (MALEK[3-4]) and the sexual parameters, such as ovulation,
oestrus or activity (BEACH[100], BOUGHTON[100] in birds, EVERETT[100], FRAPS[1-3, 100]
in birds, HEMMINGSEN[100] in rats, LARSSON in rats).

25.35 – Rhythms of Blood Constituents in Higher Animals. The eosinophil leukocytes are very useful as an indicator of adrenal function and have also been extensively studied with regard to their 24-h rhythm. As in all studies on white blood
cells large materials or pure animal strains are needed. Owing to the impressive
work on adrenal rhythmicity performed by HALBERG and his group in Minneapolis
it is one of the best documented of all biological rhythms. The 24-hour eosinophil
rhythm has been studied in man, in dogs (HALBERG[118]), rats (HALBERG[101, 138]),
mice (ALBRECHT[100], HALBERG[13, 114, 126, 132, 135-136, 152, 154], LOUCH[100]), and hamsters
(CHAUDRY[102]). It has been recorded in health and in disease, e.g. hemidecortication
and adrenal insufficiency (HALBERG[112, 115, 124, 137]); after experimental manipula-
tion such as stress (LOUCH[100]), cortisone administration (ENGEL[300]), adrenalectomy
(HALBERG[135]), hepatectomy (JARDETZKY[100]), splenectomy (ALBRECHT[100], HAL-
BERG[101]), and seizures (FLEESON[100], ENGEL[303], HALBERG[111, 144]). Other studies are
APPEL[1, 100], BARTTER[1] (in women), BROWN[200], DJAVID, FLINK[101], HALBERG[109],
HILDEBRANDT[11], KAINE[100], LANDAU[100], RADNOT[100, 103, 106], RUD, TATAI[101],
VISSCHER[100].

25.36 – The other leukocytes in the blood have also been recorded. Here, the discussion raged long and heavily as to the existence of a true 24-h rhythm. Some
data are: BARTTER[1] (in women), BROWN[200, 300] (normal and adrenalectomized
mice), ELMADJIAN[100] (including psychoses), HALBERG[7], JORES[5, 9], MALEK[3-4,
102-104] (in pregnancy), PHILIPSBORN[1], SABIN[100], SHARP[1, 3-4] (reversal experiments),
SHAW, WEIL (in TB). – The erythrocytes also vary with regard to the count or the
hematocrit (DELL'ACQUA[1], JORES[5, 9], LASCH[100], LEAKE[100], MENZEL[1-2], RABINO-
WITSCH, TATAI[101], WARD); mean corpuscular diameter (PRICE-JONES); reticulocyte
count (GOLDECK[1-2, 100, 102]); sedimentation rate (JORES[5, 9]); hemoglobin (DREYER
[100], JORES[9], WARD); as well as their distribution in different organs such as the
liver, adrenals and thyroid (ENGSTRÖM[100]). – The thrombocyte 24-h rhythm has
been described by GOLDECK[101], JORES[9] and KRANZFELD. – Some other 24-h blood
variates are the serum proteins (DÖRING[105], FRANCAVIGLIA[100], LANG[400], PELLE-
GRINI[102]), and the coagulation mechanism (BUCKEL[100], EVERSON in rodents).

25.37 – *Rhythms in the Circulation and Respiration of Higher Animals.* Twenty-four hour variability in the circulation dynamics have specially been recorded in the heart rate and the blood pressure. The heart rate variations have been studied in children (BIERSACK, HELLBRÜGGE[1, 100], LANGE[200]), in pregnancy (MALEK[3-4, 104]), in cold stress (FOLK[2, 5-6] with telemetered data), in exercise (TIMMERMAN[100]), under arctic conditions (FOLK[6], SLONIM[100]), and in hypertension (MASONI). HILDEBRANDT[3, 5, 7-9, 12, 17-18, 20-21, 104, 109] studied their coordination with the respiratory frequency and the changes of this during balneotherapy. Other descriptions of the heart rate are: BOAS[100], BOCHNIK[8], JORES[9], KLEITMAN[105], MARGOLINA[100], MENZEL[9], PIRTKIEN, TRÄNKLE, VÖLKER[1]. The heart rate can be read accurately from the ECG, which can nowadays be recorded continuously and telemetered during full activity. Other 24-h changes in the normal and pathological ECG were described by BÖCKH, ENGELBERTZ[100], FRANKE[1-2], GROSS[100], HILDEBRANDT[17, 108], KELLERSMANN, KENEDI[100], KLEITMAN[105], MASONI.

25.38 – Twenty-four hour blood pressure variations were discussed by BOCHNIK[8], JORES[9], GÖNCZY[100] (venous pressure), KARNELL (in aortic coarctation), KROETZ, MALEK[3-4, 104] (in pregnancy), MENZEL[9, 103] (in hypertension), MUELLER[100], SACHSE, TRÄNKLE, VÖLKER[1], WEYSSE[100]. A knowledge of the 24-h variations is valuable in determining the physiological changes of the blood pressure and in early diagnosis of hypertension. – Other 24-h circulatory variations have been recorded in the cardiac output (BROD[100], HILDEBRANDT[18], KAISER[300], KROETZ), in the capillary resistance (DÖRING[102]), in the peripheral vascular tonus (HILDEBRANDT[106-107], KORÖSY[100]), and the blood volume (MENZEL[18-20, 104]).

25.39 – The respiratory frequency varies during the day. HILDEBRANDT[3, 5, 7-9, 12, 17-18, 20-21, 104, 109] recorded its coupling to the heart rate. Other studies are BÄNDER[1], JORES[9], STSCHERBAKOWA[1-2] (in mammals), TRÄNKLE. The pulmonary ventilation changes were recorded by BOCHNIK[8], DISSMANN[3], HILDEBRANDT[18-19], OECHSLER, VÖLKER[1].

25.40 – *Rhythms in the Urine of Higher Animals.* Numerous investigations on 24-h rhythms, especially in *Homo*, have been performed on the urine and its constituents. Many examples have already been given (25.28,31-34). The urine, like the blood, is easily obtainable in large quantities. Furthermore, whatever variate was the aim of the study, the urinary volume was always obtained as a by-product. Its variations may be affected in cardiac insufficiency, when the peak production is changed from the day to the night (nycturia) owing to the increased efficiency of the circulation at night when its working load is reduced, JORES[1-4, 7-8, 100]. The 24-h urinary volume changes were recorded in children (FRÖBA, HELLBRÜGGE[1], MAGEE); in many animals (FOLK[2], KURCZ[2], STSCHERBAKOWA[1]); after stress (FOLK[2], LEWIS[103]); and in arctic entrainment experiments (LOBBAN, LEWIS[100-102, 104], SHARP[1-2, 5]), where low 24-h bioamplitudes were found under constant conditions, as well as beats in entrainment. Reversal is easily effected. The urinary volume rhythm has been recorded in various diseases (ARBORELIUS, AZERAD[100], JORES[1-2, 4, 8, 100], MAGEE, MENZEL[1-5, 9, 101], MERTENS, MÖLLERSTRÖM[9]). Other investigations are: BAZETT[100], CAMPBELL[101], FOLK[5], FORSGREN[15, 100],

GERRITZEN[1-4, 6], GHATA[100], HAUFF, HOESCH, LÜDERITZ[1], MONGELLI-SCIANNAMEO, QUINCKE, RHODIN, ROSENBAUM[100], SIMPSON[1], TRÄNKLE, VÖLKER[1], WILSON[1].

25.41 – Other 24-h renal excretion rhythms are displayed in the urinary specific gravity (BOCHNIK[8], SHARP[2], STSCHERBAKOWA[1]), the effect of the water tolerance test (FORSGREN[15], MÖLLERSTRÖM[105]), and the renal circulation (EBBECKE, SIROTA [100]). Cf. also rhythms in the excretion of body electrolytes (25.32-33).

25.42 – *Rhythms in the Nervous System of Higher Animals.* The central nervous system also displays 24-h rhythms, being a receptor and coordinator of external influences. Rhythms are found in the sensory threshold and pain perception (BOCHNIK[1-3] in phantom limb pain, GRABFIELD[100], JORES[101], SLAVINA); in the psyche (HAMPP) and memory (GATES[1], LAY); in the flicker fusion test (PIRTKIEN); in performance, errors and accidents, as discussed in connection with industrial medicine (25.10, ANDLAUER[100], ANKERMÜLLER, BJERNER[101], BROWNE, FREE-MAN[300], GATES[2], JORES[9], KLEITMAN[5], KRIS[1], MARSH, RUTENFRANZ[101]); in the tapping rate and the neuromuscular function (BOCHNIK[6-8], TRÄNKLE); in the EEG (ENGEL[200, 302-303], FRANK[1, 100], HALBERG[144], RICHTER[400]); and in the composition of the liquor cerebrospinalis (DOBREFF[100], JORES[9]). – The vegetative nervous system is said to fluctuate between sympathicotonia in the day and parasympathico(vago)-tonia at night. This can be seen in the ECG and other circulatory responses, the exocrine gland secretion, body temperature and other variates already described (PIRTKIEN). It also appears in the sweat glands (HILDEBRANDT[103], JORES[9]) and the electric skin resistance (BOCHNIK[8], GRAF[200], HELLBRÜGGE[1], NIGGESCHMIDT, PIRTKIEN, REGELSBERGER[1-2], RUTENFRANZ[1, 100]). – Intestinal resorption varies rhythmically, HAMAR. The intramuscular pressure has a 24-h rhythm (KÜCH-MEISTER[100]).

25.43 – The eye displays pronounced rhythms, not least in the intra-ocular pressure, which must be carefully followed in the diagnosis of glaucoma; BOYD[200], ERICSON, JORES[9], KÖLLNER, MASLENIKOW, RADNOT[4, 103]. The position of the eye in the orbita, the degree of exophtalmus, also varies (HINTSCHE[100], WIESINGER); as well as the pupillary area (DÖRING[103], WIESINGER); and the eye potentials (BOGOSLOWSKY, KRIS[2-3]).

25.44 – *Sensitivity Rhythms in Higher Animals.* Important to medicine are the variations of the general sensitivity of the body during the day (cf. 25.12), both to pathological influences and to drugs. The greatest sensitivity seems to lie around 4 o'clock in the morning. Then the acidosis starts anew in diabetes and the insulin reaction is strongest. The probability of cardiac and asthmatic attacks is largest (MASTER, WEBER). Mortality similarly varies throughout the day (CRAMER[200] in infants, FISHER[400], FREY[1], JENNY[1], JUSATZ[100], OPPENHEIM[100], SCHNEIDER[1], SIEMS, WIGAND). – HALBERG and coworkers have done much to demonstrate the 24-h changes in sensitivity to hormones, noxic stimuli and drugs, mostly in mice. Examples of such periodicity are: the sensitivity to insulin (EDLUND[101], FORS-GREN[5, 7, 10, 14, 18, 20-21, 101], HOLMGREN[13], MÖLLERSTRÖM[12, 14]), neurohormones (HAUS[4], HOLMGREN[3, 13], MÖLLERSTRÖM[12, 14]), gonadotropin (LAMOND[100]), narcotic agents (EDLUND[100]), ethanol (HALBERG[9], HAUS[4, 100-101]), librium (MARTE[1, 100]), strophantine (HALBERG[9, 120, 130]), bacterial toxins (HALBERG[7, 9, 121, 123, 127-129]), carcinogens (HALBERG[13]); even to audiogenic convulsions (HALBERG[7, 9, 106, 117, 121-122, 130, 142], HARNER[1, 100]). Rhythmicity in epilepsy is a long-observed phenomenon: BERCEL, ENGEL[303], GRIFFITH[100], HALBERG[144], LANGDON-DOWN[100], PATRY, SCHULTE, STAUDER. 24-h rhythms in sensitivity to nembutal were found by EMLEN[300].

The sensitivity rhythms are almost never heeded in the treatment of patients. Though the physician often splits the medicine into several doses, he wants to achieve a constant dosage, rather than follow any rhythm. Yet, he is sometimes forced to accept this periodicity when he notices that the sensitivity to cardiac drugs is highest in the evening, or when he has a diabetic patient who needs perhaps 40+40 I.U. of insulin at 8 and 16 o'clock but may get a heavy insulin shock if given 20 units around 4 o'clock in the morning. Nevertheless, the hesitation of the medical profession to accept these things has been strong and is only slowly yielding now, latest of all in pharmacology.

25.45 – *Rhythms in Obstetrics and Gynaecology.* 24-h rhythms appear in lactation, in the onset of menstruation (MALEK[3-4, 101]) and of labour (CHARLES, GUTHMAN[100], HORN, KAISER[100], MALEK[1-4, 100-101], WURSTER). The time of birth likewise varies rhythmically (CHARLES, GUTHMAN[100], HORN, JENNY[1], JORES[9], KAISER[1, 100], DePORTE). These materials are enormous and corroborated all over the world. It is an old experience at obstetric wards that births tend to occur in the early morning hours. Incidentally, it has been pointed out philosophically, this makes us tend to live a whole number of days. – The mating behaviour varies throughout the day in rats (BEACH[100], LARSSON); also in *Paramecium* (*cf.* EHRET[1-7]).

25.46 – *Rhythms of Morphology and Mitosis in Higher Animals.* Even in the morphology 24-h variations appear; in the body weight (SIMPSON[1]), owing to changes in the water balance, or in the size of the liver, lungs or spleen (FORSGREN[34], HOLMGREN[7], HAGBERG) and cell cultures (ENDERLE). Cell sizes, nuclear sizes, and the nucleic acid metabolism show 24-h rhythms (BARNUM[1, 100-102], CASPERSSON[100], EHRET[101], HALBERG[7, 9, 13, 103], JARDETSKY[101], MÖDLINGER[100]). Even dental tissue characteristics and hairgrowth fluctuate (FRIEDERICH, HIMMEL[100], MÜHLEMANN[101], SCHOUR[100]).

25.47 – A widely studied 24-h rhythm is that of the mitosis frequency (*cf.* 10.8). It may perhaps serve to synchronize the different cells in an organ. The rhythm is often assayed in the easily accessible skin (BLUMENFELD[2-5], BRODERS[100], BROGI[101], BULLOUGH[4, 8], CHAUDRY[100-104], COOPER[1, 100-101], ECHAVE[100], GOLOLOBOVA[3], HALBERG[107], MÖLLERBERG, PICON, VINOGRADOVA); but also in oral and oesophageal epithelium (DOBROKHOTOV[100], MÜHLEMANN[100-101], RATEITSCHAK[100]); the cornea (GOLOLOBOVA[2], VASAMA[1, 100], VINOGRADOVA); the liver (BARNUM[102], BROGI[100], JAFFE, JARDETSKY[101]); the kidney (BLUMENFELD[1, 3]); the adrenal (DOBROKHOTOV[102], HALBERG[114, 149], MÜHLEMANN[100]); the thyroid (MÜHLEMANN[100]); the submaxillary gland (BLUMENFELD[3]); and in cancer (DUBLIN[100], HALBERG[108]).

The mitotic rhythms have been studied in *Homo* and in frogs (MÖLLERBERG), cats (LEYDEN[1]), mice (BARNUM[102], BROGI[100-101], BULLOUGH[3-4], CHAUDRY[100], COOPER[300], GOLOLOBOVA[2], HALBERG[103, 107-108, 114], PICON, VASAMA[1, 100]), in rats (BLUMENFELD[1-3], DOBROKHOTOV[100-102], GOLOLOBOVA[1, 3], HALBERG[107, 138], JAFFE[1], MÜHLEMANN[100], RATEITSCHAK[100], VINOGRADOVA), in hamsters (CHAUDRY[101]), and in rabbits (BLUMENFELD[5]). – The 24-h mitotic rhythms have also been studied in regeneration experiments (DOBROKHOTOV[1, 101], GOLOLOBOVA[2-3], JAFFE[1], VINOGRADOVA). Further references are: BLUMENTHAL, BULLOUGH[6], CARLETON, HALBERG[7, 9, 13, 121], KARSTEN[2], LEYDEN[2].

25.48 – We have now reviewed some of the many studies on 24-h or near-24-h rhythms, including a discussion of their general properties. Next come the lunar and seasonal exogenous rhythms.

CHAPTER 26

Lunar and Seasonal Rhythms

26.1 – We have, in Part IV, hitherto discussed possible mechanisms for external control and also the 24-h rhythms, with emphasis on their exogenous aspects. Now, we will discuss the lunar-day, lunar-monthly, and seasonal rhythms. They are clearly exogenous, though they may very well be founded on an endogenous base (cf. 5.21, 7.20,27, 24.40-46) along similar principles as discussed for the 24-h rhythm in the two preceding chapters (lunar and seasonal clocks). However, the forces of the tide and the seasonal changes in light, weather and temperature are very strong influences, indeed, perhaps even more imperative for many animals and plants than the day-night changes. An adaptation to them has a large survival value.

The actual external agent in lunar control is not really known; whether the moonlight, the gravitational changes or other factors. As to the seasonal adaptation we have already seen that the day-light period (as compared to the synchronized 24-h period) is used by plants and animals to judge the time of the year as an aid in assessing the proper season for renewed growth or migration (cf. 5.14-23, 13.8-12).

26.2 – *Lunar-day Periodicity*. The influence of the moon makes itself felt in two different ways; the interference with terrestrial gravitation generating the tides and the lunar-day periodicity (17.3), and the phases of the moon which may give rise to lunar-monthly cycles.

The lunar-day (24.8-h) periodicity is well documented, especially by BROWN[6-7, 9-12, 101, 103, 107-110, 113, 115-118] and coworkers. It appears clearly in marine and shore animals. The latter have to anticipate the tides in order to move up and down the beach (FINGERMAN[4-6], TURNER[300]) in search of shelter and food, or to catch food so moving. Their movement also includes the problem of orientation which may probably be done with the aid of sun or moon (cf. 18.5,8,12-13) since the animals are far too small to perceive the large morphology of the beach or the advancing flood. The tidal influence shows up as an interference with the 24-h rhythm, making the daily peak advance about one hour a day. There are actually two tides a day but one may dominate. After one month, the peaks have travelled through one 24-h cycle. This phenomenon has been described in tidal activity rhythms for different animals, like clams (BENNETT[1], BROWN[10, 103], RAO, TURNER[300]), snails (STEPHENS[1, 100]), worms (RALPH[1]), crabs (BENNETT[100-102], BROWN[6, 9], GUYSELMAN, NAYLOR[1, 3]), salamanders (BENNETT[103]), rats and mice (BROWN[10, 109-110]). The tidal rhythm of color changes in crabs is another example (BROWN[107],

FINGERMAN[2-5, 103]). Lunar-day variations in O_2-metabolism were found in sea-weeds, carrots and potatoes (BROWN[7, 10, 108]), worms (RALPH[1]), snails (BROWN[117], SANDEEN[100]) and crabs (BRETT[100], BROWN[9-10, 101]). *Cf.* also BLUME[100], BÜNNING[109].

26.3 – *Lunar-monthly Periodicity*. The lunar-day phenomenon actually contains a true lunar component. Obviously, it appears chiefly in marine animals owing to the tidal mechanism, but one may wonder about its meaning in other animals, *e.g.* rats. Many statistics even report lunar rhythms in man. One possibility is a confusion with the 27-day solar rotation cycle (*cf.* 17.8, HOSEMANN) and the corresponding fluctuations in the strong solar radiation. A definite answer cannot yet be made owing to the large scatter in the data, the limitations of the present-day statistical methods of analysis, and the difficulty of collecting records long enough for classical frequency analysis (*cf.* Chapters 20, 21).

26.4 – In many lower animals the lunar cycles are also sexual cycles; such as the mass-production of sperm and eggs by the Palolo worm at the last quarter of the moon in October or November (24.44), the swarming of mayflies some days after full moon (HARTLAND-ROWE), or of marine mosquitos in Heligoland some days after full and new moon (CASPERS[1-2, 4], OKA[100]). The time of day and year chosen is constant and depending on the local geography, dryness, temperature, *etc.* This sexual coordination probably increases the probability of offspring production and survival. – Other studies of animal tidal and lunar rhythms are: BOHN[1-4, 100], DRZEWINA, FOX[1-2, 4], HARRISON, HAUENSCHILD, KORRINGA, RAMANATHAN, RAY[100], WILLIAMS[100-101]. – Even in algae lunar rhythms may appear (BAILLAUD[7], BÜNNING [23], GESSNER).

Migration and sexual activity likewise have a lunar periodicity in fishes, *e.g.* herrings (peak shortly after full moon), and eels (peak at the end of the first moon quarter, JENS, *cf.* 24.45).

26.5 – In man the lunar influence is uncertain (7.21-27), at least difficult to prove statistically. It is also, unfortunately, full of mysticism, from the bible to the word lunatic, which simply means moon-mad. Some mothers keep reporting that their children are unusually unruly at new moon. Of course, one might imagine many subtle lunar synchronizers such as the length of the moon-lit daily period, variation in the spectral composition of the light, terrestrial and atmospheric tides with accompanying general influence upon the atmosphere. How these influences would act is difficult to tell.

Neither do we know whether the menstrual rhythm of the women (and its supposed counterpart in men) is a genetic memory of an earlier entrainment to the lunar period, though not, any more, phase-locked, or whether it is purely coincidental. The oestrus cycles in animals with completely different cycle durations speaks against the theory. However, some authors claim that there is a common weekly base, a harmonic of the month (RIEBOLD, TIETZE). Huge statistics (though with a large scatter in the data) even exist, claiming that menstruation is actually more common at new and full moon (*cf.* ARRHENIUS, BRAAMSON, GUNN[1, 300], HECKERT[4], HOSEMANN, KIRCHHOFF[1], LAURELL[4], OSWALD[1]).

Lunar rhythms have also been reported in the birth rate (ARRHENIUS, BÜHLER

[200], GÜNTHER, HECKERT[1, 4], HOSEMANN, JENNY[2], KIRCHHOFF[2, 100], MENAKER[200], NIELAND), in the death rate and epidemics (HECKERT[1-2, 4]), and in the spectral sensitivity of the eye (DRESLER).

Careful studies of the physiology of the menstrual cycle have been performed by DÖRING and many other authors (cf. 7.23-25).

One may, of course, also speculate upon whether our own pronounced weekly period of general activity may not be a harmonic of the monthly one, or a spontaneous rhy*hm entrained by a harmonic of the lunar cycle.

26.6 – *Seasonal Rhythms*. The seasonal variations in nature are so strong that most living phenomena have to follow them, especially at higher latitudes. This holds certainly for poikilothermic animals which have an activity proportional to the ambient temperature and go into forced hibernation in winter. Invertebrates usually spend this time in special stages of metamorphosis. Some amphibians exhibit a relatively dormant stage called aestivation during the driest part of the year. Less dependent on the environment are the homoiothermic vertebrates, however they may have difficulties finding food. Some prefer therefore to migrate or to submit to voluntary hibernation. Migration is, of course, easiest for the birds. However, even coldblooded animals do migrate, cf. fishes. Least dependent is man who nowadays creates his own environment, though he does not escape completely. One example is the seasonal incidence of diseases, which may of course, depend on the strength of the invaders in parasitic disease but also on the resistance of the body. For instance, children may be more apt to react. Also (at least earlier) a vitamin deficiency state developed during winter and culminated in early spring. Various climatic factors may be active, creating meteorotropic diseases, some of which will appear seasonally.

In general, one might expect to find a higher physiological and metabolic activity in summer and lower in winter.

26.7 – The physiological processes involved in hibernation are complex: cf. EISENTRAUT, FOLK[2, 4, 100-102], FONTAINE[4], JUVENELLE[100], KAYSER[1-5, 100-101], LACHIVER, LYMAN, MENAKER[1], POPOVIC, SLONIM[102], SUOMALAINEN[1-4, 100].

26.8 – Photoperiodism (Chapters 5, 7, 13) is important in the control of seasonal cycles, since both plants and animals judge the time of the year by the duration of the daylight period as compared to the length of the correctly entrained endodiurnal rhythm. In this connection it is important how the organisms react to the light signal, whether they are long- or short-day plants, day- or night-active animals. The seasonal rhythm in plants is regulated in this way, as well as the timing of metamorphosis changes in invertebrates, eclosion or nuptial flights.

The seasonal migration in vertebrates includes the problems of hibernation and of navigation (Chapter 18). It is however, also followed by gonadal involution changes, creating a sexual breeding rhythm (cf. 24.41). Changes also occur in other endocrine glands such as the thyroid or hypophysis. Whereas the sexual rhythms in invertebrates are mainly controlled by lunar influences, they are seasonal in many vertebrates, e.g. birds, fish and amphibians. The purpose may, again, be that of increasing the probability of breeding and survival. The photoperiodic control is probably exerted over the retino-hypothalamic connections (*cf.* 13.16).

26.9. – The exogenous influence would seem to be obvious in seasonal rhythm. Nevertheless it has been suggested that this also is really an endogenous rhythm, a circum-seasonal or circ-annual rhythm, entrained by the physical seasons (MARSHALL[1-6, 100-103]). Actually, BÜNNING gives an example of seasonal rhythms in trees which were desynchronized *inter se* and with the environment. A possible freerunning of the rhythms (with change in period) is more difficult to investigate in seasonal rhythms than in the circadian ones, owing to the 365-fold time-span.

26.10 – *Seasonal Rhythms in Plants and Their Photoperiodic Control.* As mentioned, the seasonal control is intimately connected with the endodiurnal photoperiodism. The material to be cited here therefore contains numerous examples of experimental manipulation of the light in order to study the general mechanism of the process. These problems are of importance in agriculture and horticulture, from the harvest of grass and cereals to the production of tomatoes. The practical application of this knowledge is now spreading rapidly, resulting in valuable gains in yield.

The seasonal variations in plant growth are discussed by ALLEWELDT, DOWNS[1, 100-101], GARNER[1, 101], HENDRICKS[1-2], IKEMOTO, JOZEFACIUK, LANGE[600], LEWIS[500], LOCKHART, NITSCH[1-2, 101], POHYAKALLIO, RAPPE, TAMIYA[100], TOOLE, VAARTAJA, WARBURG[100]. Flowering has been studied by ARNOLD[2], BÜNSOW[2, 4], GARNER[1, 100], HAMNER[1, 3, 100], HARDER[100], HENDRICKS[1], KÖNITZ, MANN[1], NITSCH[100], OVERLAND, PARKER[300-301], SACHS[200], SCHMITZ[200], SCHWEMMLE[2-3], SNYDER, STROUN[100], TAKIMOTO, VEEN[100], ZEEUW. Seasonal rhythms occur in plant metabolism; including O_2 and carbohydrate turn-over, as well as phenolic compounds and freezing resistance (BROWN[7, 9], HUGON, PARKER[1]); also in seed germination, seed production, leaf coloration, leaf fall, bud dormancy, plant shape and plant sex (HENDRICKS[1], TASHIMA).

Other studies are: BAKER[100], BÜNNING[13], DAVIDSON[100], HERRICK, JACOB, KERLING, KLEBS, LANG[1, 100], McCLELLAND[1], MELCHERS, PERRY[100], PIRINGER[100-101], SCURFIELD; *cf.* BOYD[500].

Another aspect is the agriculturist's endeavour to follow the seasonal rhythms in plant pests, seeking the optimal times for insecticide spraying, harvest and fertilizing, *cf.* BOSCH[100], McCOY, OATMAN[100], PIENKOWSKI[100], PITRE[100], WALLIS[200].

26.11 – *Seasonal Rhythms in Invertebrates.* The most varied factors have been observed: for instance the activity of millipedes and beetles (BARLOW[1], BODENHEIMER[1], PERTTUNEN); insect biting (LUMSDEN, KENNEDY, MATTINGLY); mating and breeding in squids (KALMUS[10]) and in locusts (WALOFF); sex of aphids (LEES[5], MARCOVITCH) and shapes of *Daphnia* (KALMUS[10]); metamorphosis and diapause of insects (BLAKE, DANILYEVSKY[100-101], FUZEAU-BRAESCH, HENDRICKS[1]); aphid wing production (SHULL); leech respiration (MANN[200], using a polarographic respirometer). Plankton display a seasonal rhythm, varying with latitude (BOGOROV, CLARKE[100]). This is important to the animals feeding on them. Other examples from the vast literature are: BECKWITH, BELLAMY[100], BURDICK[100], BURRAGE,

CORBET, GILLIES[100], HOFFMAN[400], HUBERT[100], JAMNBACK[100], LOAN, RABB, SELHIME [100].

26.12 – *Seasonal Rhythms in Vertebrates*. Seasonal endocrine-gonadal rhythms in fish occur concomitantly with migration: BULLOUGH[1-2] (minnows), BURGER[1-2], CRAIG-BENNETT (stickle-backs), EVANS (eel pituitary), FONTAINE[1-3, 5, 100-103] (salmon, migration, hypophysis, iodemia), HARRINGTON (bridled shiner), HICKLING (hake ovary), HOAR[1-3, 100] (thyroid, goldfish, salmon), HOOVER[100] (trout), MATTHEWS[200] (killifish), POLDER (herring gonads), ROWAN[2], SCRUGGS (carp and goldfish pituitary), SWIFT (thyroid in trout), TURNER[1] (perch). The seasonal variation of visual pigments in fish was studied by DARTNALL[100].

26.13 – The photoperiodism in frogs is discussed by OORDT, and in reptiles by BARTHOLOMEW[3]. The O_2 and CO_2 capacity as well as blood sugar in alligators was investigated by HOPPING.

26.14 – Best studied of the sexual involution rhythms are those in birds *e.g.* finches, sparrows, pigeons, starlings, ducks, turkeys, geese and chickens. In the domestic animals, though, the seasonal aspect is more or less lost. Instead, experimental manipulation of the light cycles aim at achieving continuous growth and high-level egg-laying (*cf.* 24.42). Strongly coupled to the sexual rhythm are all the activities of the birds: including the preparation for migration, the Zugunruhe (LOFTS[100], PALMGREN[1, 7], SCHILDMACHER[1, 100]); the migration itself (*cf.* Chapter 18); moulting (HENDRICKS[1], WOLFSON[6]); weight (RICHDALE, in penguins); and metabolism (DAVIS[400], SCHILDMACHER[3]).

Studies of the seasonal endocrine rhythm in the birds and experiments on its photoperiodic control are: ASCHOFF[10, 100, 105, 107], BAKER[1] (egg-seasons), BARRINGTON[100] (thyroid), BARTHOLOMEW[2], BAUMGARTNER, BENOIT[1-6, 100-107] (hypophyseo-gonadal system), BISSONNETTE[1, 3-4, 6-8, 10], BURGER[3-6, 100], CLARK[100], COOMBS [100], DAMSTE, ENGELS, EYSTER, FARNER[1-3, 100-102], FRANZ[2], GREELY[100] (hypophysis), HAUKER (thyroid), HANN (castration), HAWKINS, HIATT[100], JENNER[100], KENDEIGH, MARSHALL[1-6, 100-103], MARTIN[100], MERKEL, MILLER[1-3], NALBANDOV, RILEY[1, 100], RINGOEN, ROWAN[1-6], SCHILDMACHER[2, 4], SCOTT[300], SPEIRS, THREADGOLD, WAGNER[200-201], WOLFSON[1-5, 7-10, 100].

26.15 – Seasonal endocrine rhythmicity in mammals and its experimental control have been studied both in cattle and in wild animals. Of domesticated animals sheep (HART[1], YEATES), goats (BISSONETTE[9]), bulls (ERB[100]), and horses (JÖCHLE[4]) were chosen; some objects of study being semen (ERB[100]), fertility (MERCIER[100]), sex ratio and gestation period (JÖCHLE[4]).

Other mammals studied were mice (WHITAKER), rabbits (BISSONNETTE[101]), hamsters (KAYSER[100-101], PETROVIC[100]), ferrets (BISSONNETTE[3], LeGROS-CLARK[100], HART[2], HILL[300-301] in hypophysectomy), foxes (BASSETT[100]), deer (BROWMAN[4, 100], GRIESER[100]) and monkeys (STSCHERBAKOWA[3]). Some variates studied are; breeding (BEDFORD[100] after change of latitude, WELLS[200]), moulting (HENDRICKS[1]), thyroid and thymus (BROWMAN[4, 100], LACHIVER), gonadotropins (GRIESER[100]), length of night-sleep (SLONIM[101]). Other studies are: ASCHOFF[10], BISSONNETTE[2],

[5-6, 10, 100], BULLOUGH[5, 7], JÖCHLE[6], MCKEEVER, ORTAVANT[100], SAINT-GIRONS.

26.16 – *Seasonal Rhythms in Homo*. The seasonal sexual cycles are not so pronounced in *Homo* but some signs remain in the birth rate (HUNTINGTON[2], KATZ, OTTO[3, 100], SONESON) with a maximum in March, also in the birth weight (ABELS). Otherwise, the seasonal influence is rather general and manifests itself in the growth, metabolism, hematology, circulation, neural activity and, not least, in the susceptibility to diseases.

Children grow rhythmically with a peak in spring: BACKMAN, BLEYER, EMERSON, FRANK[200], GRIPENBERG, HERTZBERG[100], NYLIN, OREL, OTTO[1-2], PORTER, SCHMID-MONNRAD, VEEDER[100]. Other seasonal variations in *Homo* occur in the basal metabolism (GUSTAVSSON[100], HOOGENHUYZE[100], LINDHARD), blood CO_2 (STRAUB[100]), body temperature (KLEITMAN[105], RENBOURN, DERUDDER[101], WAGNER[2]) and the light sensitivity of the skin (KNUDSEN[100]). The same applies to the circulation; including the heart rate (KLEITMAN[105], PAUL[1], RENBOURN), the hemoglobin (FINSEN), the blood platelets (TOCANTINS), the serum calcium and phosphate (BAKWIN[100], BRUUN, GRASSHEIM[100], HESS[100]), the uropepsin production (HIROKAWA[100]). Nervous system rhythms are found with respect to the mental activity in general (HUNTINGTON[2]), pain perception (BOCHNIK[2-3]), spectral sensitivity of the eye (DRESLER), accidents (OTTO[4], with a maximum in summer), psychosis, suicide and crime (HUNTINGTON[2]). – Other studies are HENROTTE, LIESE, TAKAGI, THOMPSON[100], WATANABE; including BMR, Iodine, cholesterol, uropepsin, ketosteroids and cutaneous circulation.

26.17 – *Seasonal Rhythms in Pathology*. Many diseases vary in frequency throughout the year, such as cancer, circulatory, respiratory and gastrointestinal disorders, central and peripheral nervous afflictions, dermatographismus, eczema, rheumatic disease, vitamin deficiences (rachitis, night blindness), infections and allergies: HOPMAN[1], HUNTINGTON[2], HUTTER, KIRSCH, LEDERER, MARTINI[1], MEMMESHEIMER, OTTO[1, 4], DERUDDER[2-4, 11, 13, 17], RUSZNYAK, TISDALL[100-101]). The net result of this is perhaps a seasonal mortality rhythm: GUGGENHEIM, HUNTINGTON[2], PIRQUET, RIETSCHEL, WIGAND.

26.18 – Especially many infectious diseases show pronounced peaks at certain times of the year. The phenomenon has always been wellknown to the medical profession. It is intimately linked with the more general problem of meteorotropic diseases (Ref. J.e., BERG[1], MENGER, PETERSEN[200-201], DERUDDER[1-2, 5, 7-8, 10-11, 14]). Tables of the epidemic seasons are given by DERUDDER[3, 8]. In his investigations of the infectious diseases, DERUDDER[3, 9, 15-16, 100] distinguishes between true, and secondary seasonal epidemics. In the first case there is a more or less direct coupling to the solar radiation. In the second case (*e.g.* german measles, whooping cough and chicken pox) the morbidity is rather randomly distributed whereas, still, the complications and mortality may peak at certain times of the year. Remarkable is the high and thin peak of the true epidemic cycles. If logarithmated, they become fairly sinusoidal in shape (BLISS[1, 100], DERUDDER[16]). Alternative explanations are those of DERUDDER[12], envisaging a change of susceptibility in a population of people with the sinusoidal variation in solar light intensity

(20.6). Another approximation is the logarithmic function $x = n^{\sin t}$ (DeRUDDER[16], 19.7).

26.19 – Seasonal periodicities have been described for scarlet fever (DONLE, DeRUDDER[3, 8]) and diphtheria (DONLE, GALLENKAMP, DeRUDDER[3, 8, 100]), both with peaks in winter; typhus and typhoid (DONLE); tuberculosis, with a peak in spring (ALBINGER, BURNS, HAMBURGER, OREL, ORSZAG, PEYRER, DeRUDDER[8-9], STRANDGAARD); polio, with a peak in late summer (DONLE, DeRUDDER[15-17]); measles (BLISS[100], SCHADE); chicken pox (RIVERS[100], TISDALL[101]); and the common cold (TISDALL[100]).

26.20 – Allergies against plant products is also a typical seasonal disease, either with summer-long durations, as in hay-fever, or only lasting a few days, when some exotic plant dispels its pollen. Actually, the blood eosinophils show seasonal variations even in normal people (ROMEYKE, DeRUDDER[6], TONACK), The incidence of tetany (MORO) and the serum sensitivity also varies (MAKAI). – For further literature on seasonal morbidity rhythms see: AHMED[100], ANDREWES, BEUNDERS, BOSTOCK, CHASSAGNE[100], COUVREUR[100], DAQUET, DÖMÖK, FUJIKURA, GOLDSMITH[100], HOLMES[100], JUSATZ, KIKUCHI, LIMAN[100], LOOSLI, MAGNUS[209], MOGABGAB, MOMIYAMA, REISINGER, SCHULMAN[100].

26.21 – *Further Observations on Exogenous Periods.* Of course, 24-h, lunar, and seasonal rhythms often coexist in the same individual. An example is the Palolo worm, which appears in certain months of the year, in conjunction with a certain moon quarter and at a certain time of the day (24.44, 26.4).

26.22 – There are also other periods which might have external correlates. Several possible astronomical periods (17.8-11) have been reported in biology. Especially the 11-year cycle has been identified everywhere; in social crises, business, tree ring width, crop yields and insect pests (*cf.* Ref. J.c-d., BELAK, BERG[2-4], HUNTINGTON[2], LAURELL[1, 3-4], PETERSEN[200-201], DeRUDDER[13], SCHULTZ[1-5], TCHIJEWSKY, WEBSTER[1, 4]). It remains to be proven statistically-mathematically whether or not the various cycles really exist in the biological data (*cf.* 6.41-43).

26.23 – If one tabulates the durations of all biological periods reported, one will get a rather broad period spectrum ranging from milliseconds to many years, with obvious maxima at the exogenous periods of 24 h, 28 days and one year. This has been done for *Homo* by HILDEBRANDT[20-21, 104].

26.24 – We have now discussed all the endogenous and exogenous biological rhythms as well as the various theories for their function. There remains, however, to be given a short review with regard to another way of classifying the biological rhythms, according to the scientific field.

CHAPTER 27

Rhythms in Botany, Zoology, Physiology and Medicine

27.1 – We have now discussed the biological rhythms from all angles of viewpoint except one, *viz.* the fields of science, where they appear. This shall be done here, though the presentation will be incomplete. Botany and zoology which have hitherto dominated our discussions will be only briefly mentioned. The emphasis is on human physiology and medicine. The latter is, together with botany, important as one of the few fields of applied biological rhythm science. It is also a region of biology where rhythm research started late and where the full impact of its application has still to be realized.

27.2 – *Biological Rhythms in Botany.* Biological rhythms were observed very early in botany, already in the 18th century (DUHAMEL, LINNAEUS, DEMAIRAN, ZINN, 5.22). Periodic flower and leaf movements were well visible. The study progressed slowly but unimpeded by the resistance which met biological rhythm studies in some other fields. BÜNNING's theories in the 1930s, about the endogeneity of the 24-h rhythm was a major advance though the concept took a long time to become recognized.

The dominant topic is the adaptation to light; starting with the photosynthesis by chlorophyll and ending with the realization that quite other pigments and wave lengths of light are active in connection with rhythms, separating photoperiodism clearly from photosynthesis (13.7-11). – The distinction between long- and short-day plants and the capacity to 'judge' the time of season, based on the relative daylength as estimated with the endodiurnal clock are important (5.14). Our mastering of the underlying principles is now beginning to pay off with increased crop yields in horticulture and agriculture, also in terms of increased control in forestry.

27.3 – Several characteristics of the plants and of unicellular organisms affect the recording techniques. The simple expedient of tying a thread between the moving leaf and a kymograph yields beautiful curves. The plant is also easily accessible to drugs and various manipulations, as seen in some experiments on mushroom periodicity (24.43) or on protoplasmic movements in plasmodia (6.29). The enormous age of some trees permits long-range studies, *e.g.* the sun-spot cycles in tree rings (6.42). The action spectrum (13.5), where different kinds of reactions are correlated to the wave lengths of light, is also a typical tool. Very special are the nutation movements in tendrils (6.36) or the spatial rhythmicity in tree-branching. Mitosis rhythms are easily studied in the relatively large plant cells and are related to the general growth (25.46-47).

Spontaneous oscillations in the diffusion through yeast cell membranes (6.36) and the elicitation of electric potentials from plant roots (6.30) are other examples of the wide variety of studies which can be made on botanical rhythms. – Obviously a nervous system is no prerequisite for biological rhythms or their control, though it may be an important channel of communication in higher animals.

27.4 – *Biological Rhythms in Zoology.* As in botany, zoological rhythm research has developed slowly and relatively undisturbed. There were many obvious rhythmic phenomena inciting to investigation, such as migration of birds and fishes (Chapter 18), insect metamorphosis or animal activity rhythms (25.14-20). KALMUS' studies of insects, BROWN's and coworkers' discovery of the temperature independence of crab melanophore rhythms (13.14), and PITTENDRIGH's and coworkers' experiments with the circadian *Drosophila* eclosion rhythm (24.13) parallel BÜNNING's work in botany. There has developed an interesting debate concerning the endogeneity or exogeneity of the circadian rhythm and the possible mechanisms of external control. The latter has been chiefly explored by ASCHOFF and coworkers, introducing the Zeitgeber concept (13.18-23).

27.5 – A major difference between plants and animals is the development of a nervous system, which has taken over the task of receiving and channeling the external entraining influences. Contrary to the situation in medical physiology which has to cope with a highly integrated nervous system, the zoologist can often isolate all the developmental stages. He is also free to manipulate these rather drastically, extirpating and transplanting great parts of an organism.

Photoperiodism is as pronounced in animals as in plants, the length of the day being used as information to the time of the year; controlling migration of birds and fishes, metamorphosis, moulting. There is also the question of the circadian chronometer needed for orientation by all kinds of animals, from beach fleas to birds.

It is interesting to note that the basic receptor mechanism with photosensitive pigments is found both in plants and animals, and also that there always seems to be several such systems in one individual; *e.g.* the ordinary eyes, ocelli, photosensitive neurosecretory cells reached directly through a translucent body, and the retino-hypothalamic connection, with the melanophore hormone. The possibilities exist for a balance between the mechanisms, generating a photoperiodism, apart from the purely visual sensory information.

27.6 – Interesting is also the close connection between photoperiodism and sexual activity (26.4,8,12-15), probably enhancing the probability of offspring production and survival, *e.g.* the periodic testicular involution in birds. This periodism seems to be tied up with lunar phenomena in lower animals, especially littoral tide-dependent creatures, and with seasonal changes in higher animals.

27.7 – Another phenomenon is the intense fight for accomodation and survival which takes so many expressions among the enormous variety of animals (9.12-13). CLOUDSLEY-THOMPSON gives a vivid example of this when showing how dependent the primitive animals are on the surrounding humidity in order to avoid water-evaporation and dessication in desert climates. Here the 24-h activity pattern serves to avoid the dryest conditions. Also, after emerging, the insects cannot fly before the integument has hardened, a process much dependent upon air humidity and temperature, which makes it profitable for the animals to emerge at a suitable time of the day. – It is also typical of metamorphosis data that they represent trends in populations. Each animal actually only appears once.

Population cycles are another branch where much work and vivid discussions have been going on (Chapter 10). It is of considerable interest in wild-life management. Other practical connections are the knowledge of plankton and fish migration in the fishing industry, the study of mosquito and parasite behaviour, and the possibility of photocontrol of cattle breeding and egg-laying, in animal husbandry.

27.8 – Common objects of study are the activity rhythms, which has led to a variety of very ingenious actographs (20.8). – The dissociation of the embryo from the maternal organism which occurs in some animals (as in plants) offers unique possibilities for the study of embryonic rhythms (9.8-10).

Much of the biological rhythm research going on in zoology, notably on mammals, particularly primates, merges into the realms of general physiology and medicine.

27.9 – *Biological Rhythms in General Physiology and Medicine.* The history in this branch of biological rhythm research has been more fraught with difficulties. For one, the rhythms tend to become more obscured and the dependency on the environment less. This, together with a peculiar static thinking of the medical mind (in spite of the clear recognition of such dynamic functions as the heart-beat, the respiratory rhythm or bowel movements by the physiologists) caused a solid reaction against the concept of biological rhythms. The medical profession was strongly opposed and more prepared to regard the 24-h variations as simple reflexes and effects of the feeding habits. This resistance has continued more or less up to the present day. In no field has the lack of interest been stronger than in pharmacology.

Nevertheless, rhythms were accepted in some fields, as mentioned. There were also the epidemic cycles as studied by DeRudder, or the 24-h temperature rhythm which was soon definitely established after the introduction of the clinical thermometer in the 18th century. Kleitman's studies of temperature rhythms (25.25) and their control, as well as of the sleep-wakefulness rhythm and Völker's recording of several physiological variates (in the 1920s) are beautiful examples of early rhythm studies in physiology.

27.10 – There were, of course, some early students, who realized the importance of meteorotropic influences and of rhythmicity in all living processes, *e.g.* Hufeland (in 1797) or Petersen with his fascinating collection of meteorotropic data. The major break-through came, however, with Forsgren (in 1927) when he realized that rhythms occurred even in the metabolism. This came simultaneously with Möllerström's findings of rapid variations in the plasma peroxydase and the erythrocyte sedimentation rate, as well as (later) periodic fluctuation in the whole diabetes metabolism.

In 1937 these two scientists met together with JORES (who was studying the melanophore hormone mechanism as well as rhythms in pathology, *e.g.* nycturia), with HOLMGREN (who as an anatomist and histologist was continuing FORSGREN's work and who was also closely associated with MÖLLERSTRÖM during the latters' early years as a sanatorium doctor and later at the Swedish diabetic hospital), with ARBORELIUS (studying the deranged 24-h rhythm in disease), with GERRITZEN (renal excretion rhythms) and with KLEINHOONTE (the botanist) at the Ronneby health resort in Sweden, where MÖLLERSTRÖM and HOLMGREN were in charge of the medical care. During happy and very rhythmic sessions, partly executed in the water, these scientists constituted the International Society for Biological Rhythms. Through JORES, the proceedings appeared in the *Deutsche medizinische Wochenschrift.*

Later conferences of the Society were held at Utrecht, the Netherlands (1939), Hamburg (1949), Basle (1953), Stockholm (1955), Semmering, Austria (1957), Siena, Italy (1960) and Hamburg (1963).

The second, Dutch conference was unfortunately heavily shadowed by the second world war which caused a break in the meetings for ten years. During that time a small internordic conference was held at Stockholm in 1941. The focal points of the Society's activity were for many years Germany and Scandinavia. Later, through the increasing interest of the English-speaking world and lastly, the Roman-speaking world, biological rhythm research has finally become recognized as an important interdisciplinary branch of science. Especially the very last years have seen a tremendous development in the field through the American interest, represented by such men as BROWN, HALBERG, KLEITMAN, PITTENDRIGH and WENT. A not unimportant impetus was derived from space medicine, with the problem of how the body rhythms are controlled from without and what happens if this influence vanishes.

27.11 – Many physiological problems arise in biological rhythm research. There are the evasive mechanisms for rhythm control (Chapters 12 to 16, 19, 24) and for interaction between rhythms, as well as the attempts to find the site of the biological clock. Earlier physiologists demanded the presence of a morphologically distinct receptor organ for each acceptable external stimulus. This does not hold today. Many influences may act directly upon the cells, *e.g.* gravity, or electrostatic and magnetic fields.

In higher organisms the nervous system is important, especially for the control of the rhythms. Photoperiodicity, perhaps directed through the retino-hypothalamic connection, is important even in man, as shown by cases of lessened control, *e.g.* blindness, where circadian freerunning may occur. Other synchronizers may however take over, *e.g.* the hospital routine, a less clearly recognized form of therapy.

Photoperiodicity in man chiefly gives rise to seasonal variations in body functions and diseases, less to sexual cycles, though birth frequencies vary both seasonally and throughout the day. – We definitely use the circadian rhythm as a clock, as shown by experiments on the human time sense (CLAUSER, 5.24). In travel drastic changes of the external milieu may occur, especially during trans-longitudinal passage, when the body has to resynchronize with the new phasing of events (24.23).

HALBERG distinguishes between different levels of rhythm organization: neural, endocrine, and cellular (24.18); where the neural may be entrained chiefly by dominant synchronizers, the cellular perhaps by weaker synchronizers, and where there is a feedback between the levels. – In man there is perhaps a fourth, psychological level with more or less conscious attempts to modify the rhythmic control, creating new complicated feedback channels. Since our understanding of the rhythmic phenomena is scant this might lead to difficult situations, with an artificial non-rhythmic pace of life, or somatic and nervous disorders. Take the way the insulin dosage is often adjusted according to the patient's blood sugar curve. This is very much the same as if a house owner would change the setting of his thermostat each time he notices a deviation from the desired temperature. This soon causes instability in the servosystem, with still higher fluctuations.

The interaction and synchronization between biological rhythms is another most difficult problem. The phenomenon ranges from pure beats to relative coordination and pacemaker systems (19.14-34). Mathematical and physical models may be used but they are complicated, especially in the nonlinear case, which unfortunately is characteristic of the numerous biological oscillators.

There is a peculiar difference in the animal and human multiple frequency synchronization experiments. In the former case long runs are obtainable. Yet, most of the information in the data is sacrificed and only one bit, the peak-time, is followed through the transients. These data usually fit a series of complicated nonlinear oscillator models. In *Homo*, on the other hand, longterm experiments are more difficult to obtain. Instead a short but careful, more or less continuous recording is made. One then often observes beats between several frequencies, typical of interaction between linear oscillators.

The question of the 'rhythmic center' is also most elusive. Rhythms and their entrainment occur at all levels of biological organization. Even in the basic parts of cellular protoplasm the oscillatory capacity still rests (6.29). Perhaps the question is unnecessary, since all biological systems capable of survival must be adaptable, that is act as servomechanisms. And therefore, they may oscillate. It is rather the questions of pathways, interaction and control which are important.

27.12 – There are several ways of approaching the problem of biological rhythms. One is by experimentation, chiefly on animals. Another is the theoretical model making (Chapter 19), which however mostly shows that many different models may fit the same set of data. The adaptation of the engineers' systems analysis is, perhaps, a less biased approach (Chapter 3). Still another method is pure observation and mathematical analysis which is best suited for the study of rhythms in man (Chapters 20-21). It interferes least with the subject studied and his delicate servomechanisms. However, it requires advanced statistical and mathematical methods of analysis, which have hitherto been only partially developed. Most methods are built upon classical mathematics and statistics. Special methods, founded upon the properties of the biological rhythmic systems, remain to be constructed.

Some variates may, of course, be difficult to record in *Homo, e.g.* liver glycogen. However, drastic examples exist. Both liver glycogen (by biopsy, 25.26, BERINGER) and liver temperature (25.25, GRAF) have been measured in human subjects.

27.13 – Biological Rhythms in Diagnosis. Normal Values. Basal State. The long-standing hesitation of the medical world to accept the rhythmic phenomena may be understood from practical reasons. It would have increased the already heavy diagnostic work manyfold. The doctor would have to keep in mind the changes of normal values throughout the day and the year. He would have to examine the patient many times more, prescribe different medicines at different times of the day, keeping in mind the changing resistance of the body. The pharmacologist, already taxed with the investigation and standardization of innumerable drugs would have to repeat his standardization at different times of the day. The medical profession had neither the techniques nor the time to add this responsibility to their burden of work.

When the inevitability of biological rhythmicity began to dawn upon the doctors the medical research naturally took the easy way out. It became modern to do all experiments, still only once, but at a certain time of the day. This peculiar attitude resembles the study of a periodic process with a stroboscope, turning a dynamic process into a static picture. The attitude is dangerous. We know by now much about normal and pathological processes before noon and something about what happens during sleep, but less about the other times. Unfortunately 'evening man' may differ altogether from 'morning man'. Actually, some chemical equilibriae, some physiological processes, some pathological behaviour may even be reversed during the day. Many of the so common instances where different investigators have diametrically opposite opinions about a process may have arisen just from a neglect to state when the experiments were made. – Furthermore, if pathological influences cause the circadian rhythms to free-run, the use of fixed day-times may cause serious errors, as pointed out by HALBERG[116] (*cf.* 19.35).

27.14 – What is now slowly forcing medicine to accept the rhythms is the steadily increasing quest for early diagnosis. The doctor is faced with the problem of establishing precise limits of normal values for man. Now, biological variation in the normal data includes the influences of interindividual differences in size, age and sex, body constitution, *etc.* Apart from this there are errors in the methods of assay (random or systematic), unrecognized diseases in the subjects as well as other random errors, day-to-day, 24-h and seasonal fluctuations. There are also difficulties in defining a basal state with minimum activity and therefore less scatter. All this tends to make the normal limits large and therefore the chance of judging the value from a single patient small. The primary problem of early and preventive medicine is to reduce the limits of normal variation, *e.g.* by considering different ages and sexes separately and by recording in a basal state.

27.15 – However, the basal state may give a false impression of equilibrium in the body, at least the way the concept is sometimes used by the clinicians, namely an uncritical withdrawal of food, medicines and activity. This is no normal state and may even, in a diseased subject be dangerous. A diabetic patient, *e.g.*, who is perfectly well regulated may in a short time turn into an almost precomatose state if he is not allowed to take food or insulin and furthermore has to wait for hours at the hospital for a test to be made. By that time his blood sugar will be high, which is the organism's way to combat the danger. It may even happen that the doctor upon seeing the high blood sugar increases the insulin dosage, whereafter the patient goes home waiting for insulin shocks. By now, the sensitive blood sugar servomechanism has lost its normal setting (determined by the insulin) and begins to oscillate. The next time, the insulin and food deprivation (caused by the so-called basal state) therefore causes a heavy disturbance and a still higher blood sugar than the preceding time. This may induce the physician to raise the insulin dosage still more and so on, establishing a vicious cycle. There is nothing basal about withdrawing adequate medical treatment. Neither is food deprivation in healthy persons, who may actually develop a severe ketosis and feel quite sick after a one day fast (recent experiments at the hospital of the Swedish Diabetic Foundation).

The basal condition problem actually reminds one of the experiments with constant conditions in rhythm research. This state is certainly not normal and may interfere with the equilibrium of the living system.

27.16 – As to the normal values, there is a considerable variation left, even after age, sex and individual equilibrium have been considered. Contrary to popular belief a refinement in the method of assay does not always reduce the interindividual scatter so much. More important is often the elimination of individual differences in constitution, for instance the size of the individuals. This is usually done by interrelating body variates, e.g. by plotting the heart volume against the body surface. The interindividual range of heart volumes at a certain body size is considerably smaller than that of all normal heart volumes. By increasing the number of comparisons some further reduction in normal scatter may be achieved but at the cost of a rapidly increasing complexity.

After all these attempts have been made to reduce the normal limits, the data still contain the 24-h and seasonal trends. Only by eliminating these can a further refinement in our definitions of health be achieved. We need circadian maps (25.5, HALBERG), where the ranges of instantaneous and 24-h variations as well as the phase relationships between different variates be recorded. The so popular tolerance tests, which often force the body into quite abnormal states, might perhaps partly be replaced by Nature's own physiological tolerance test, the 24-h variation. – Quite apart from this the results of tolerance tests may vary rhythmically too.

27.17 – *Biological Rhythms in Pathology and Treatment.* One thing which clearly separates the general biologist and the physician is the observation of those peculiar experiments made by Nature herself, which we call disease. One may say that almost all possible experiments have been or are being performed by Nature. It is the close observation of the diseases which gives the medical mind so many clues as to the workings of the normal subject. This also applies in the biological rhythm research. We have seen how complicated the delicate servomechanisms in the body are; the position and direction controls in the motor system, the endocrine feedback, as well as the interplay between lower reticular-hypothalamic centers and the cortex. Disturbances easily occur, e.g. vicious circles and oscillations, caused by overload, changed sensitivity or disarranged loops. The variety of chronopathological periodicities generated, as discussed by GJESSING, MENNINGER-

LERCHENTHAL, REIMANN and RICHTER, are astounding (Chapter 8). They have given rise to several multiple oscillator theories.

The physician should also realize that even single traumata may call forth rhythmic events, *viz.* a series of damped oscillations. The traumata may be accidents, operations, radiation exposure or drug administration (8.6, DERER, HILDE-BRANDT[21], LANGENDORFF[100]).

27.18 – The first, often very slight, pathological changes in disease usually start at the functional level, that is the realm of disturbed or wrongly controlled servo-mechanisms. This would tend to show up as subtle modification in the rhythm. Such early changes in the 24-h bioamplitude or in the biofrequency may occur in disease (24.37-39, ARBORELIUS, MENZEL). A study of the quantitative relations between amplitudes, levels and frequencies may become important (MENZEL, SOLLBERGER). The reduction in bioamplitude may be due to a diminished energy turnover (often followed by decreasing levels) or a disintegration into higher frequencies as observed by BLUME and MENZEL. We still know very little about the latter phenomena, whether they are primary rhythms comparable to those found in embryos, or secondary and arising in the impaired servosystems. BLUME's studies of phase-jumps in plant data may prove to be highly significant for what happens in the diseased human subject.

27.19 – Rhythmic disturbances in preexisting rhythms have been observed in many diseases (*cf.* ARBORELIUS, FORSGREN, HILDEBRANDT, JORES, MENZEL, MÖLLERSTRÖM). Well studied are diabetes (where disturbances of the basic biochemical servosystems cause heavy fluctuations in the metabolism), renal and hepatic disorders (affecting the liver glycogen), ulcer (in connection with tuberculosis, shift work and in the differential diagnosis against ventricular cancer). Other examples occur in circulatory diseases where the analysis of cardiac arrhythmia and disrhythmia (JORDAN, V.D. POL) and the patterns of reflected pulse waves may be mentioned (6.16-17). Other pathological rhythms are the 24-h parasite cycles and the seasonal epidemics (26.18-19, DERUDDER).

In industrial medicine 24-h changes in the accuracy, error-proneness and accidents occur. Shift work may upset the body's servosystems, causing ulcer and nervous disorders (25.10-11). Night workers complain about a 'dead point' around 4 o'clock at night (MENZEL[17]). In balneotherapy the importance of a regular regimen as an entraining agent has long been realized; it may help to heal.

27.20 – *Circadian Sensitivity Changes.* An important factor in therapy is the changing sensitivity to disease and drugs throughout the day and the year (25.44). It starts with the pharmacological assessment and standardization of drugs. The test animals need a regular environment. In one insulin laboratory at least, standardization was impossible on holidays, until music was played at the times of ordinary activity. Also, the tolerance of the animals to the drugs varies; as does the tolerance of the human patients. The ignorance of such things may well cause the pharmacologist to miss the more subtle effects of new pharmaca. Furthermore, test-animal and human rhythms do not always run parallel courses. It might therefore be difficult to perform delicate tests concerning drug action and dosology on laboratory animals only. This aspect adds some emphasis to the importance of clinical trials.

27.21 – The 24-h variations in the patient's sensitivity are, in some cases, well-known to the clinician. In many diseases complications tend to occur at certain times of the day. Asthmatic attacks, acute heart insufficiency or infarcts are most common around 4 o'clock in the morning. The onset of labour and births show 24-h preferences. HALBERG[10, 116] has introduced the concept of 'horae minoris resistentiae', a parallel to the 'loci minoris resistentiae'.

Variations in the sensitivity to drugs have also been observed by the clinicians and have now been corroborated by experimental work on mice by HALBERG (25.44). Some drug houses even make special day and night medicines. The heart patient responds better to diuretics in the evening than in the morning. Even the sensitivity to narcotic agents varies. The diabetic subject is very sensitive to insulin in the evening. The morning insulin dose has also a stronger effect the earlier it is given, maximally at around 4 o'clock in the morning. This may be helpful to know in critical conditions. It may seem as if the times when the metabolism shifts between storage (in the day) and utilization (in the night) are the danger points, when the organism is fully occupied by its internal affairs and highly sensitive to disturbances from without. In diabetes this occurs at about 16 o'clock in the afternoon and 4 o'clock in the morning, when the spontaneous tendency to produce keto-acids seems to be highest. These times would then tend to be ideal for the administration of insulin. If given later, the hormone would have a double work to perform: (1) to protect the organism during the most sensitive time of the day when acid formation may easily start and (2) to aid in the re-metabolization of keto-acids accumulated in increasing amounts after this time.

27.22 – In view of the above, the modern production of longacting depot drugs (e.g. insulin) with an alleged constancy of action throughout the day may seem peculiar. Here belongs also the principle of prescribing some drugs three or four times a day, because it is typical that the physician is more concerned with constant drug levels or with giving the medicine at the meals, than in preferring certain times of the day. Is it so certain that the body really wants a constant dosage throughout the day? In diabetes the physician is often prompted to use single daily depot insulin doses by the patient's reluctance to double the number of injections. However, he often has to split them up into two doses if the patient gets worse or if much insulin is needed, whether longacting insulin is used or not. In general, double injections yield a more stable balance in the patient's well-being and in his resistance to sudden disturbances. When seeing series of patients turn up after many years of untroubled diabetes and two equal daily doses of standard insulin, one may even sometimes wonder whether all the long-acting types are really so necessary.

27.23 – If we visualize the metabolism as a system of biochemical servomechanisms, then drug administration may be regarded as an effort to establish external control (Chapters 19, 24). Conceivably, the medicine may act in different ways, as a blocking or as an amplifying agent acting on the feedback loop or on other places in the closed system. In other instances, the drug may change the reference of the mechanisms or act as a synchronizer. Perhaps it may set up a series of damped oscillations. Since the sensitivity of the patient may vary, drugs could also be introduced at a certain time point in the oscillation, *e.g.* on its ascending or descending limb. One of these phases may be suitable for interaction with the drug, the other not. The phase-setting and the frequency-synchronizing effects of a drug must be distinguished between (12.17).

Another aspect of pharmacology is the elimination of the drugs from the body. This function also changes rhythmically. Then, the time of administration may be decisive for the risk of drug accumulation. Furthermore, different diseases may affect the fundamental servosystems or the rhythms differently. It is therefore even possible that the action of a drug may change from one disorder to another.

27.24 – We have touched upon the behaviour of biological rhythms in disease on several occasions (*e.g.* Chapter 8, 25.10-13, 27.17-21). Let us summarize some possible types of reaction:
1. Shock-induced spontaneous natural damped transient oscillations.
2. Oscillator instability causing appearance of new sustained pathological rhythms.
3. Effect upon oscillator parameters causing change in natural frequency of a biooscillator.
4. Oscillator instability causing increased amplitudes, or wild oscillations with crises.
5. Blocking of normal control with return to freerunning.
6. The creation of or break-up into harmonics.
7. Shift in rhythm phasing.
8. Various disturbances and interactions creating beats in the biological system.

27.25 – With this, we have finished our exposition of biological rhythms. As can be seen, it is a young science of pronounced interdiciplinary character. It leans heavily upon the physical sciences. It offers many unsolved problems and thus a healthy challenge to the young and unprejudiced mind. It is a rapidly advancing science. The final goal is to predict accurately from the *a priori* knowledge about the construction of a biological system, under which conditions the latter will oscillate, how it will oscillate and how these oscillations may be controlled.

Bibliography

Sᴇᴄᴛɪᴏɴs ᴡɪᴛʜɪɴ ᴛʜᴇ ʙɪʙʟɪᴏɢʀᴀᴘʜʏ

The bibliography contains four sections, *viz.*:

I. *Conferences of the Society for Biological Rhythm* (*SBR*)
   Referred to as: Ref. + year (*e.g.* Ref. 1960a).

II. *Other Conferences*
   Relating to conferences on rhythms and/or related subjects. Referred to as under I. Section IV may contain references to I and II (*e.g.* Aɴᴏɴʏᴍᴏᴜs, A., Rhythms, Ref. 1948c, p. 45).

III. *Journals*
   Journals on rhythms or related subjects are referred to as: Ref. + J. + letter of alphabet (*e.g.* Ref. J.c.).

IV. *General References*
   The bulk of the references may be found under this heading. The ordinary papers are referred to by: name of author(s) – title of contribution – journal + volume/number, fascicle or supplement–year–page (*e.g.* Aɴᴏɴʏᴍᴏᴜs, A., – Teɪres-trial cycles – *J. Biol. Cycl.* 3/16–1958–4; or Aɴᴜɴʏᴍᴏᴜs, A. – Biological cycles – *J. Biol. Cycl.* 3b/suppl. 6–1960–68).

   Books are referred to as follows: name of author(s) – title of book (or title of part of book) – publisher + year + page(s), (*e.g.* Aɴᴏᴜɴʏᴍᴏᴜs, A. – *Rhythm Control*, in *Principles of Rhythms* – Metropolis 1961, p. 100), etc.

Rᴇғᴇʀᴇɴᴄᴇ sʏsᴛᴇᴍ

In the text the references refer either to a conference (*e.g.* Ref. 1961c), a journal (*e.g.* Ref. J.e.) or (an) author(s) (*e.g.* Aɴᴏɴʏᴍᴏᴜs [15]). In the latter case the numbering starts anew for each author according to the following code:

	(numbers)
author alone	1 – 99
author with co-authors.	100 – 199
second author with the same name, alone	200 – 299

[315]

second author with co-authors. . . . . 300 – 399
third author with the same name, alone. . . . . 400 – 499
third author with co-authors . . . . 500 – 599
etc.

INTRODUCTORY LITERATURE

Apart from the various conferences and journals to be quoted below under sections
I to III, there are some more comprehensive publications on biological rhythms,
which might serve as introductions to the field. They are found under the general
references in section IV. These are:

in English: BULLOUGH[5], CALHOUN[1], CLOUDSLEY-THOMPSON[28], FOLK[102], HAL-
                BERG[6,10, 19-21, 121], HARKER[5], HUNTINGTON[2], KLEITMAN[6,9], REIMANN
                [9], TROMP[1], WELSH[5], WENT[3,5].
in German: ASCHOFF[11-12,14-15], BÜNNING[29], BYKOW[1], CLAUSER[1], JORES[9,14-15],
                KALMUS[4], MENNINGER-LERCHENTHAL[3], MENZEL[8,11,17], MÖLLER-
                STRÖM[14], DERUDDER[13-14].
in French: REINBERG[100].
in Italian: AJELLO[100].
in Russian: EMME[1], LOBASHOV[100].
in Japanese: REINBERG[100].

I. Conferences of the Society for Biological Rhythm (SBR)

1937a *1st Conf.*, Ronneby, Sweden, August 13-14th.
       D. Med. Wschr. 64/(21, 28)-1938-737, 989.
       Ed: A. Jores
1939a *2nd Conf.*, Utrecht, Holland, August 25-26th.
       Verh. 2. Konf. Internat. Ges. Biol. Rhythmusfrschg.
       Acta Med. Scand. 1940, Suppl. 108
       Ed: H. Holmgren
1941a *Scandinavian Conf.*, Stockholm, Sweden, August 22nd. [In Swedish]
       Med. Fören. Tidskr. (Sweden) 1941, No. 9-10, and 1942, No. 1
       Ed: H. Holmgren
1949a *3rd Conf.*, Hamburg, Germany, September 30th-October 1st.
       Verh. 3. Konf. Internat. Ges. Biol. Rhythmusfrschg.
       Acta Med. Scand. 1953, Suppl. 278
       Eds: H. Holmgren, J. Möllerström and Å. Swensson
       (May be ordered from the secretary of the Soc. Biol. Rhythm)
1953a *4th Conf.*, Basle, Switzerland, September 18-19th.
       Verh. 4. Konf. Internat. Ges. Biol. Rhythmusfrschg.
       Acta Med. Scand. 1955, Suppl. 307
       Eds: W. Menzel, J. Möllerström and T. Petrén
       (May be ordered from the secretary of the Soc. Biol. Rhythm)
1955a *5th Conf.*, Stockholm, Sweden, September 15-17th.
       Rep. 5th Internat. Conf. Soc. Biol. Rhythm
       ACO-Print, Stockholm 1961

Dedicated to J. Möllerström
Eds: T. Petrén and A. Sollberger
(Includes one supplement: A. Sollberger, Studies of temporal variations in biological variates. The Reports may be ordered from the secretary of the Soc. Biol. Rhythm)

1957a *6th Conf.,* Semmering, Austria, August 26-28th.
Duplicated summaries (out)
(Will not appear in print)

1960a *7th Conf.,* Siena, Italy, September 5-7th.
Rep. 7th Internat. Conf. Soc. Biol. Rhythm
Panminerva Medica, Turin 1962
Eds: G. Dell'Acqua, A. Jores, A. Canniggia and A. Sollberger

1963a *8th Conf.,* Hamburg, Germany, September 9-11th.

II. Other Conferences

1930a *Lyon Conference,* Lyon, France.
Group Lyonnais d'Etudes médicales, philosophiques et biologiques
Les rythmes et la vie
Lavandier, Lyon 1931

1949b *Symp. on Application of Autocorrelation,* Woods Hole, U.S.A., June.

1954a *1st Internat. Photobiol. Congr.,* Amsterdam, Holland.
Internat. Committee of Photobiology
Proc. 1st internat. photobiol. congr.
Weenman and Zonen, Wageningen 1954

1954b *Symp. on Cycles in Animal Populations,* U.S.A.
J. Wildlife Manag. 18/1-1954
Ed: O.H. Hewitt

1954c *Koll. über den Einfluss atmosphärischer und kosmischer Phänomene auf physikalisch-biochemische und biologische Prozesse,* Oct.
Max-Planck-Inst. Biophysik
Arch. Meteorol. Geophys. Bioklimatol. 7B/1-1955

1956a *15th Symp. on Growth and Development,* Providence, U.S.A.
Soc. Study of Growth and Development
Rhythmic and synthetic processes in growth
Princeton Univ. Press, Princeton 1957
Ed: D. Rudnick

1956b *Symp. on Biological Chronometry,* Storrs, U.S.A., Aug. 29th.
Am. Naturalist 91/858-1957-129

1957b *Colloque International sur le Photo-Thermo-Périodisme,* Parma, Italy.
Union Internat. Sci. Biol. (U.I.S.B.)
U.I.S.B. (Paris), serie B (Colloques), No. 34, 1957

1957c *Symp. on Biol. Rhythms,* U.S.A., April 24.
National Acad. Sci. U.S.A.

1957d *22nd Cold Spring Harbor Symp. Quant. Biol.,* Cold Spring Harbor, U.S.A., June 3-12th.
Long Island Biol. Assoc.

Symp. on population studies
C.S.H. Symp. Quant. Biol. 22, New York 1957
Eds: K. Brehme-Warren and M. Demerec

1957e *1st Internat. Bioclimatol. Conf.*, Vienna, Austria, Sept. 23-27th.
Int. Soc. Biometeorol.
Int. J. Biometeorol. 2-1958
Ed: S.W. Tromp

1957f *Conf. on Photoperiodism,* Gatlinburg, U.S.A., Oct. 29th-Nov. 2nd.
National Acad. Sci. U.S.A.
Photoperiodism and related phenomena in plants and animals
Am. Ass. Adv. Sci., publ. 55, Washington 1959
Ed: R.B. Withrow

1957g *12. Kongr. für Arbeitsmedizin,* Helsinki, Finland.
Helsinki 1957

1957h *2nd Internat. Photobiol. Congr.,* Turin, Italy.
Internat. Committee of Photobiology
Ediz. Minerva Medica, Turin 1958

1957i *Symp. of Spectral Approach to Time Series.*
Proc. Roy. Stat. Soc. 19B-1957-1

1958a *Perspectives in Marine Biol.*
Union Internat. Sci. Biol. (U.I.S.B.)
U.I.S.B. Ser B, No. 27, Univ. Calif. Press, Los Angeles 1958
Ed: A.A. Buzzatti-Traverso

1958b *Colloque sur les Méchanismes Physiologiques de la Périodicité chez les Plantes,*
Besançon, France, May 31st-June 1st.
Soc. Franc. Physiol. Veget.
Ann. Sci. Univ. Besançon 2 Bot/12-1958-1
Ed: L. Baillaud

1958c *Symp. Internat. sur les Relations entre Phénomènes Solaires et Terrestres en Chimie-Physique et en Biologie,* Brussels, Belgium, Oct. 8-10th.
Comm. l'Etude Tests Chim. Internat. Soc. Biometeorol.
Presses Acad. Europ., Brussels 6, 1960

1960b *3rd Internat. Photobiol. Congr.,* Copenhagen, Denmark.
(The Finsen Memorial Congress)
Internat. Committee of Photobiology
Progress in photobiology
Elsevier, Amsterdam 1961
Eds: B.C. Christensen and B. Buchmann

1960c *25th Cold Spring Harbor Symp. Quant. Biol.,* Cold Spring Harbor, U.S.A., June 5-14th.
Long Island Biol. Assoc.
Biological clocks
C.S.H. Symp. Quant. Biol. 25, New York 1960
Eds: L. Frisch and A. Chownik

1960d *2nd Internat. Bioclimatol. Conf.,* London, England, Sept. 4-10th.
Int. Soc. Biometeorol.
Biometeorology

Pergamon Press, London 1962
Ed: S.W. Tromp

1961a *39th Ross Conf. Ped. Res.,* Minneapolis, U.S.A., June 4th.
Ross Lab., Columbus 16, Ohio, U.S.A.
Circadian Systems
Rep. 39th Ross Conf. Ped. Res., Ross Lab., Ohio 1961
Ed: S.J. Fomon

1961b *Symp. on Orientation and Migration,* Cambridge, England July 11-13th.
cf. New Scientist 11/245-1961-232

1961c *Symp. on Rhythmic Functions in the Living System,* New York, U.S.A.,
Oct. 8-11th.
New York Acad. Sci.
Ann. N.Y. Acad. Sci. 98/4-1962-753

1961d *Symp. on High Magnetic Fields,* Cambridge, U.S.A., Nov.
Mass. Inst. Technol.
Section on biological effects of magnetism
cf. New Scientist 13/273-1962-316

1961e *26th Cold Spring Harbor Symp. Quant. Biol.,* Cold Spring Harbor, U.S.A.,
June 4-12th.
Long Island Biol. Assoc.
Cellular regulatory mechanisms.
C.S.H. Symp. Quant. Biol. 26, New York 1961
Eds: L. Frisch and A. Chownik

1961f *Symp. on Solar Variations, Climatic Change and Related Geophysical Problems,*
Boston, U.S.A., January 24-28th.
New York Acad. Sci. and Am. Meteorol. Soc.
Ann. N.Y. Acad. Sci. 95/1-1961-740
Ed. R.W. FAIRBRIDGE

1962a *Ve Congr. Internat. Méd. Neo-Hippocratique,* Montpellier, France, Sept.
3-9th.
Soc. Internat. Méd. Neo-Hippocratique

1962b *Symp. on Time Series Analysis.*
Brown Univ. and Office Naval Res.
Time series analysis
Wiley, New York 1963
Ed: M. Rosenblatt

1962c *Meeting on Circadian Rhythms in Experimental Medicine,* June 5th.
Royal Soc. of Medicine, London
Proc. Roy. Soc. Med. 56/4-253

1962d *Symp. on Animal Orientation,* Garmisch-Partenkirchen, Germany
September 17-21th.
Animal orientation
Ergebn. Biol., 26
Ed: H. Autrum, Springer, Berlin 1963.

1962e *Symp. on Biological Rhythms in Relation to Climate,* April 11th.
Japanese Soc. of Biometeorology
Int. J. Biometeorol. 7/1-1963-76

1963b *Symp. on Photo-Neuro-Endocrine Effects in Circadian Systems with Particular Reference to the Eye*, New York, U.S.A., June 6-8th.
New York Acad. Sci.
Ann. N.Y. Acad. Sci. 117/1-1964-1
1963c 3rd Internat. Biometeorological Congr., Pau, September 1-7th.
Internat. Soc. Biometeorol.
1963d *Symp. on the Mechanism of Cytoplasmic Streaming, Cell Movement, and the Saltatory Motion of Subcellular Particles*, Princeton, April 1963
Primitive mobile systems in embryology
Academic Press, New York 1964
Eds: A.D. Allen and N. Kamiya
1965a *Symp. on Time*, New York, U.S.A., December 1965
New York Acad. Sci.

III. Journals

J.a. *Annales Françaises de Chronométrie*
Besançon, France
J.b. *Basimetry*
Information bull.
International Basimetric Society
Editor: J. Wilder; 1199 Park Ave., New York 28, N.Y.
J.c. *Cycles,* and
J.d. *Journal of Cycle Research*
Foundation for the study of cycles
Editor: E.R. Dewey; East Brady, Penna., U.S.A.
J.e. *International Journal of Biometeorology*
Internat. Society for Biometeorology
Editor: S.W. Tromp; Hofbrouckerlaan, Oegstgeest (Leiden), Holland

IV. General References

1 ABBOT, C. G. – Twenty-five years of solar radiation – *Ann. Rept. Smithson. Inst.* 1931–175.

1 ABELS, H. – Jahreszeitliche Geburtsgewichtsschwankungen – *Mschr. Kinderhlk.* 37–1927–33.

100 ADDERLEY, E. E. and E. G. BOWEN – Lunar component in precipitation data – *Science* 137/3532–1962–749.

100 ADDIS, T., E. BARRETT, L. J. POO and R. W. LIPPEMAN – Relation between protein consumption and diurnal variations of the endogenous creatinine clearance in normal individuals – *J. Clin. Invest.* 30–1951–206.

1 ADER, R. – Gastric erosions in the rat: effects of immobilization at different points in the activity cycle – *Science* 145/3630–1964–406.

1 ADEY, W.R. – Data acquisition and analysis techniques in a brain research institute – *Ann. N.Y. Acad. Sci.* 115/9–1964–844.

1 ADLER, H. E. – *Psychophysical Limits of Celestial Navigation Hypotheses* – Ref. 1962 d, p. 235.

1 *Admiralty Manual of Navigation I-III* – H.M.S.O., London 1958–1960.

1 ÅGREN, G. – Die zyklischen Veränderungen im Leberglykogen von Ratten nach Nebennieren-Extirpation – *Biochem. Z.* 281–1935–367.

100 ÅGREN, G., O. WILANDER and E. JORPES – Cyclic changes in the glycogen content of the liver and the

muscles of rats and mice, *Biochem. J.* – 25–1931–777.

100 AHMED, S. Z., M. LEVINE and R. B. FINKBINER – The seasonal incidence of complications of peptic ulcer – *Ann. Intern. Med.* 59/2–1963–165.

1 AITKEN, A. C. – *Statistical Mathematics* – 6th ed., Oliver and Boyd, London 1949.

100 AITKEN, R. S., E. N. ABBOTT, L. I. M. CASTLEDEN, and M. WALKER – Observations on a case of familial periodic analysis – *Clin. Sci.* 3–1937–47.

1 AJELLO, L. – Über die Biorhythmen und ihre anatomischen Äquivalente – *Wien. Med. Wschr.* 99–1949–214.

100 AJELLO, L. and F. FEA – *J. Bioritmi* – Ed. Minerva Medica, Genova 1959.

1 ALBERTS, W. W. – *Negative Resistance and Bistable Properties of Nerves and other Excitable Cells* – Univ. California Thesis, Berkeley 1956.

1 ALBINGER – Zur Frage des Frühjahrsgipfels der Meningitis tuberculosa im Kindesalter, *Brauers Beitr. Klin. Tuberk.* 51–1922–223.

100 ALBRECHT, P., M. B. VISSCHER, J. J. BITTNER and F. HALBERG – Eosinophil rhythm in splenectomized Mice – *Proc. Soc. Exp. Biol. and Med.* 90–1955–397.

101 ALBRECHT, P., M. B. VISSCHER, J. J. BITTNER and F. HALBERG – Daily changes in 5-hydroxytryptamine concentration in mouse brain – *Proc. Soc. Exp. Biol. and Med.* 92–1956–703.

1 ALEXANDROWICZ, J. S. – A pulsating ganglion in the Octopoda – *Proc. Roy. Soc. (Engl.)*, 157 (Ser. B) / 969–1963–562.

1 ALLARD, H. A. – The photoperiodism of the fire-fly – *Proc. Entomol. Soc. Wash.* 33–1931–49.

100 ALLEN, M. B., L. H. PIETTE and J. C. MURCHIO – *Studies of the Function of Photosynthetic Pigments* – Ref. 1960b, p. 170.

1 ALLEWELDT, G. – Der Einfluss von Photoperiode und Temperatur auf Wachstum und Entwicklung von Holzpflanzen unter besonderer Berücksichtigung der Gattung – *Vitis* 1–1957–159.

1 ALTMAN, J – Diurnal activity rhythm of rats with lesions of superior colliculus and visual cortex – *Am. J. Physiol.* 202–1962–1205.

1 AMEN, R. D. – The concept of seed dormancy – *Am. Sci.* 51/4–1963–408.

1 ANDERS, P. – Über den individuellen Eigenrhythmus beim menschlichen Gange und seine Beziehungen zum Rhythmus der Herz- und Atemtätigkeit – *Pflügers Arch.* 220–1928–287.

1 ANDERSON, J. A. – *Clinical and Research Considerations in Pediatrics* – Ref. 1961a, p. 16.

2 ANDERSON, J. A. – *Thermovariance Spectra in Children* – Ref. 1963b:354.

400 ANDERSON, A.Y. – *Solar-terrestrial climatic patterns in varved sediments* – Ref. 1961e, p. 424.

300 ANDERSSON, B. and I. G. PORJE – Study of Ph. Broemsers manometer theory for oscillations in the aorta – *Acta Physiol. Scand.* 12/1–1946–3.

100 ANDLAUER, P., and METZ – *Variations Nychthémérales de la Fréquence Horaire des Accidents du Travail* – Ref. 1953a, p. 86.

100 ANDRÉN, L. and K. PALMÉN – Seasonal variation of birth dates of infants with congenital dislocation of the hip – *Acta Orthoped. Scand.* 33/2–1963–127.

1 ANDREWES, C. – *Climate, Weather and Season in Relation to Respiratory Infection* – Ref. 1963c.

100 ANDREWS, R.V. and G.E. FOLK, JR. – Circadion metabolic patterns in cultured hamster adrenal glands – *Comp. Biochem. Physiol.* 11–1964–393.

100 ANDRONOW, A. and A. WITT – Zur Theorie des Mitnehmens von Van der Pol – *Arch. Elektrotechn.* 24–930–99.

1 ANKERMÜLLER, F. M. – *Biologische Rhythmus-Beeinflussung durch das Wettergeschehen* – Ref. 1955a, p. 36.

1 APOR, L. – Untersuchungen über den Tagesrhythmus in der Hypophyse der Tauben – *Z. Zellforsch.* 33–1943–40.

1 APPEL, W. – Über die Tagesschwankungen der Eosinophilen – *Z. Ges. Exp. Med.* 104–1939–15.

100 APPEL, W. and K. J. HANSEN – Lichteinwirkung, Tagesrhythmik

der eosinophilen Leukocyten und Hypophysennebennierenrindensystem – *D. Arch. Klin. Med.* 199–1952 –530.

1 ARBIT, J. – Diurnal cycles and learning in earthworms – *Science* 126–1957–654.

1 ARBORELIUS, M. – *Die klinische Bedeutung der menschlichen Rhythmik* – Ref. 1937a, p. 993.

2 ARBORELIUS, M. – *Klinische Versuche über Tagesrhythmusstörungen* – Ref. 1939a, p. 178.

3 ARBORELIUS, M. – *Om dygnsrytmen vid sjukdomstillstånd* – Ref. 1941a, p. 23.

4 ARBORELIUS, M. – *Rhythmusstörungen bei Tumoren* – Ref. 1949a, p. 115.

5 ARBORELIUS, M. – *Cancer or Peptic Ulcer, a Biorhythmic Differential Diagnosis* – Ref. 1955a, p. 42.

100 ARMSTRONG, N. E. and H. T. ODUM – Photoelectric ecosystem – *Science* 1943/3603–1964–256.

1 ARNDT, M. – Über täglichen (24-stündigen) Wechsel psychischer Krankheitszustände – *Allg. Z. Psychiatr.* 92–1929–128.

1 ARNOLD, C. G. – Die Blütenöffnung bei Oenothera in Abhängigkeit vom Licht-Dunkelrhythmus – *Planta* 53 –1959–198.

200 ARNOLD, W. – *Rhythmische Vorgänge im Erleben des Menschen unter besonderer Berücksichtigung der Pauli-Tests* – Ref. 1963a.

1 ARRHENIUS, S. – Die Einwirkung kosmischer Einflüsse auf physiologische Verhältnisse – *Skand. Arch. Physiol.* 8–1898–367.

100 ARTHUR, J. M. and E. K. HARVILL – Plant growth under continuous illumination from sodium vapor lamps, supplemented by mercury arc lamps – *Contrib. Boyce Thompson Inst.* 8–1937–433.

100 ASANO, M., K. YOSHIDA and K. TATAI – Influence of high environmental temperature on the microcirculation in the rabbits' ear – *Int. J. Biometeorol.* 7/1–1963–80.

1 ASCHOFF, J. – Messung der lokomotorischen Aktivität von Mäusen mittels mechanischer Gleichrichter – *Pflüger's Arch.* 254–1951–262.

2 ASCHOFF, J. – Die 24-Stunden-Periodik der Maus unter konstanten Umgebungsbedingungen – *Naturwiss.* 38/21–1951–506.

3 ASCHOFF, J. – Frequenzänderung der Aktivitätsperiodik bei Mäusen im Dauerdunkel and Dauerlicht – *Pflüger's Arch.* 255–1952–197.

4 ASCHOFF, J. – *Zeitgeber der 24-Stunden-Periodik* – Ref. 1953a, p. 50.

5 ASCHOFF, J. – Aktivitätsperiodik bei Gimpeln unter natürlichen und künstlichen Beleuchtungsverhältnissen – *Z. Vergl. Physiol.* 35–1953–159.

6 ASCHOFF, J. – Zeitgeber der tierischen Tagesperiodik – *Naturwiss.* 41–1954 –49.

7 ASCHOFF, J. – Tagesperiodik bei Mäusestämmen unter konstanten Umgebungsbedingungen – *Pflüger's Arch.* 262–1955–51.

8 ASCHOFF, J. – Der Tagesgang der Körpertemperatur beim Menschen – *Klin. Wschr.* 1955–545.

9 ASCHOFF, J. – Exogene und endogene Komponente der 24-Stunden-Periodik bei Tier und Mensch – *Naturwiss.* 42–1955–569.

10 ASCHOFF, J. – Jahresperiodik der Fortpflanzung bei Warmblütern – *Stud. Gen.* 8–1955–742.

11 ASCHOFF, J. – Aktivitätsmuster der Tagesperiodik – *Naturwiss.* 44/13–1957–361.

12 ASCHOFF, J. – Tierische Periodik unter dem Einfluss von Zeitgebern – *Z. Z. Tierpsychol.* 15/1–1958–1.

13 ASCHOFF, J. – Periodik licht- und dunkelaktiver Tiere unter konstanten Umgebungsbedingungen –*Pflüger's Arch.* 270–1959–9.

14 ASCHOFF, J. – Zeitliche Strukturen biologischer Vorgänge – *Novo Acta Leopoldina* 21NF/143–1959–147.

15 ASCHOFF, J. – Der biologische Tag – *Mitt. Max-Planck-Ges.* 6–1959–381.

16 ASCHOFF, J. – *Biologische Uhren* – Ref. 1960b, p. 50.

17 ASCHOFF, J. – *Exogenous and Endogenous Components in Circadian Rhythms* – Ref. 1960c, p. 11.

18 ASCHOFF, J. – Aktivitätsperiodik von Mäusen im Dauerdunkel – *Pflüger's Arch.* 255–1952–189.

19 ASCHOFF, J. – Comparative physiology: diurnal rhythms – *Ann. Rev. Physiol.* 25–1963–581.

100 ASCHOFF, J. and D. v. HOLST – *Schlafplatzflüge der Dohle* – Proc. 12th. Intern. Ornithol. Congr. Helsinki 1960, p. 55.

101 ASCHOFF, J. and K. HONMA – Art- und Individual-Muster der Tagesperiodik – *Z. Vergl. Physiol.* 42–1959–383.

102 ASCHOFF, J. and J. MEYER-LOHMANN – Die Schubfolge der lokomotorischen Aktivität bei Nagern – *Pflüger's Arch.* 260–1954–81.

103 ASCHOFF, J. and J. MEYER-LOHMANN – Angeborene 24-Stunden-Periodik beim Kücken – *Pflüger's Arch.* 260–1954–170.

104 ASCHOFF, J. and J. MEYER-LOHMANN – Die 24-Stunden-Periodik von Nagern im natürlichen und künstlichen Belichtungswechsel – *Z. Tierpsychol,* 11/3–1954–476..

105 ASCHOFF, J. and J. MEYER-LOHMANN – Die Aktivität gekäfigter Grünfinken im 24-Stunden-Tag bei unterschiedlich langer Lichtzeit mit und ohne Dämmerung – *Z. Tierpsychol.* 12/2–1955–254.

106 ASCHOFF, J. and J. MEYER-LOHMANN – Die Aktivitätsperiodik von Nagern im künstlichen 24-Stunden-Tag mit 6-20 Stunden Lichtzeit – *Z. Vergl. Physiol.* 37–1955–107.

107 ASCHOFF, J. and R. WEVER – Beginn und Ende der täglichen Aktivität freilebender Vögel – *J. Ornithol.* 103/1–1962–2.

108 ASCHOFF, J. and R. WEVER – Spontanperiodik des Menschen bei Ausschluss aller Zeitgeber – *Naturwiss.* 49/15–1962–337.

109 ASCHOFF, J. and R. WEVER – *Biologische Rhythmen und Regelung* – Bad Oeynhausener Gespräche (V) über Probleme der zentralnervösen Regulation, Springer, Berlin 1962. p. 1.

100 ASERINSKY, E. and N. KLEITMANN – Regularly occurring periods of eye motility and concomitant phenomena during sleep – *Science* 118–1953–273.

101 ASERINSKY, E. and N. KLEITMANN – Two types of ocular motility occurring in sleep – *J. Appl. Physiol.* 8–1955–1.

1 ASHBEL, D. – *Comparison of Solar Radiation in the Northern and Southern Subtropics with Condition in the Temperate Climates* – Ref. 1960b, p. 92.

1 ASHBY, W. R. – *An Introduction to Cybernetics* – Chapman & Hall, London 1958.

2 ASHBY, W. R. – *Design for a Brain* – 2nd ed. Chapman & Hall, London 1960.

1 ASIMOV, I. – Round and round and . . . *Fantasy and Science Fiction* 26/1–1964–104.

1 ASK-UPMARK, E. – On periodic fever – *Acta Soc. Med. Suec.* 64–1938–1.

1 ASSMAN, D. – *Die Wetterfühligkeit des Menschen* – Jena 1955.

2 ASSMAN, D. – *Physiochemical State of the Blood* – Ref. 1960d, p. 510.

100 AUTRUM, H. and H. STUMPF – Das Bienenauge als Analysator für polarisiertes Licht – *Z. Naturforsch.* 5b–1950–116.

100 AZÉRAD, E., J. GHATA et A. REINBERG – Disparition du rhythme nycthéméral de la diurese et de la kaliurie dans 8 cas d'insuffisance surrenales – *Ann. d'Endocrinol.* 18/4–1957–484.

101 AZÉRAD, E., H. LESTRADET, A. REINBERG and J. GHATA – Variations nychthémérales de l'élimination urinaire du potassium, du sodium et du chlore chez l'homme normal – *Ann. Med.* 54/5–1953–431.

100 D'AZZO, J. J. and C. H. HOUPIS – *Feed-back Control System Analysis and Synthesis* – Mc Graw-Hill, New York 1960.

100 BACH, E. and L. SCHLUCK – Untersuchung über den Einfluss von meteorologischen, ionosphärischen und solaren Faktoren sowie der Mondphasen auf die Auslösung von Eklampsie und Praeeklampsie – *Zentr. Gynäkol.* 1942–196.

1 BACKMAN, G. – Körperlänge und Tageszeit – *Proc. Upsala Med. Soc.* 29NF–1924–255.

100 BADE, E.G. and J.M. ECHAVE-LLANOS – Variation in the mitotic activity of the liver during the second day of post hepatectomy regeneration – *Naturwiss.* 50/22–1963–693.

1 BAGGERMAN, B. – An experimental study on the timing of breeding and migration in the three-spined stickleback – *Arch. Néerl. Zool.* 12–1957–105.

1 BAILLAUD, L. – Action de la temperature sur la période de nutation des tiges volubiles de Cuscute – *C.R. Acad. Sci.* 236–1953–1986.

2 BAILLAUD, L. – Action de l'acide iodo-acétique sur le mouvement des tiges volubiles – *C.R. Acad. Sci.* 242–1956–164.

3 BAILLAUD, L. – Recherches sur les mouvements spontanés des plantes grimpantes – *Ann. Sci. Univ. (Besançon)*, 2 Bot/11–1957–1.

4 BAILLAUD, L. – Zirkumnutationsbewegungen nach einigen neuen Arbeiten – *Phyton* 7/1–3–1957–32.

5 BAILLAUD, L. – *Les Gradients morphologiques et physiologiques latéraux et longitudinaux et la Circumnutation chez les Tiges volubiles* – Ref. 1958b, p. 81.

6 BAILLAUD, L. – La circumnutation des tiges volubiles et des urilles – *Ann. Biol.* 34/(1–2)–1958–17.

7 BAILLAUD, L. – Rythmes endogènes et rythmes exogènes, notamment chez les végétaux – *Ann. Biol.* 34–1958–299.

8 BAILLAUD, L. – Introduction à la notion de rythme endogène – *Bull. Bim. Soc. Hist. Nat. Doubs* 18–1958–185.

9 BAILLAUD, L. – *Les Mouvements périodiques du Zinnia elegans et l'Acide gibbérellique* – Ref. 1960a p. 5.

10 BAILLAUD, L. – *Les Mouvements périodiques spontanés des Feuilles du Haricot* – Ref. 1960a, p. 6.

11 BAILLAUD, L. – *Les Recherches sur les Rhythmes chez les Plantes* – Ref. 1963a.

12 BAILLAUD, L. – *Significance of the Study of Biological Rhythms for Phytological Biometeorology* – Ref. 1963c.

100 BAILLAUD, L. and Y. COURTOT – Corrélations et polarités dans la morphologie d'un Cyprés – *Ann. Sci. Univ. (Besançon)* 6/2–1955–83.

101 BAILLAUD, L. et Y. COURTOT – Temps et rythmes chez les végétaux – *Ann. Franc. (Chronométrie)* 2/2–1955–87; *Ann. Sci. Univ. (Besançon)* (4–5) Ser. 2–1955–87.

102 BAILLAUD, L. and Y. COURTOT – *Observations sur le Rythme de la Ramification du Chamaecyparis nootkatensis* – Ref. 1960a, p. 7.

103 BAILLAUD, L, and Y. MONNIER – *Le Rythme de l'Allongement de la Tige d'un Haricot nain rendu volubile par l'Acide gibberellique* – Ref. 1960a, p. 5.

1 BAKER, J. R. – Latitude and egg-seasons in old world birds – *Proc. Zool. Soc. (London)* 108A–1938–557.

2 BAKER, J. R. The seasons in a tropical rain-forest (New Hebrides) VII – *J. Linn. Soc. (Zool.)* 41–1947–248.

100 BAKER, J. R. and J. – The seasons in a tropical rain-forest (New Hebrides) II – *J. Linn. Soc. (Lond.)* 39–1936–507.

101 BAKER, J. R. and Z. – The seasons in a tropical rain-forest (New Hebrides) III – *J. Linn. Soc. (Zool.)* 39–1936–123.

102 BAKER, J. R. and T. F. BIRD – The seasons in a tropical rain-forest (New Hebrides), IV – *J. Linn. Soc. (Zool.)* 40–1936–143.

103 BAKER, J. R., A. J. MARSHALL and T. H. HARRISON – The seasons in a tropical rain-forest (New Hebrides), V – *J. Linn. Soc. (Zool.)* 41–1940–50.

100 BAKWIN, H. and R. – Seasonal variation in the calcium content of infants serum – *Am. J. Dis. Child.* 34–1927–994.

1 BALDWIN, E. – *Dynamic Aspects of Biochemistry* – 3rd ed., Univ. Press, Cambridge 1957.

200 BALDWIN, F. M. – Diurnal activity of the earthworm – *J. Anim. Behav.* 7–1917–187.

1 BALL, J. – The female sex cycle as a factor in learning in the rat – *Am. J. Physiol.* 78–1926–533.

300 BALL, N. G. and I. J. DYKE – An endogenous 24-hour rhythm in the growth rate of the Avena coleoptile – *J. Exp. Bot.* 5/15–1954–421.

301 BALL, N. G. and I. J. DYKE – The effects of indole-3-acetic acid and 2:4-dichloro-phenoxyacetic acid on the growth rate and endogenous rhythm of intact Avena coleoptiles – *J. Exp. Bot.* 7/19–1956–25.

302 BALL, N. G. and I. J. DYKE – The effects of decapitation, lack of oxygen, and low temperature on the endogenous 24-hour rhythm in the growth rate of the Avena coleoptile – *J. Exp. Bot.* 8/24–1957–323.

303 BALL, N. G., I. J. DYKE and M. B. WILKINS – The occurence of endogenous rhythms in the coleoptiles in various cereal genera – *J. Exp. Bot.* 8/24–1957–339.

304 BALL, N. G. and NEWCOMBE, G. B. – The relationship between the growth of the primary leaf and of the coleoptile in seedlings of Avena and Triticum – *J. Exp. Biol.* 12/34–1961–114.

1 BALZER, E. – *24-Stunden-Rhythmus des Serumbilirubins* – Ref. 1949a, p. 67.

100 BALZER, E. and K. WERNER – *Zur Rhythmik der Fermentsekretion des exokrinen Pankreas* – Ref. 1953a, p. 124.

1 BÄNDER, A. – *Über den 24-Stunden-Rhythmus einiger vegetativer Funktionen und die Änderungen im histologischen Funktionsbild endokriner Drüsen und vegetativer Ganglien* – Ref. 1949a, p. 86.

2 BÄNDER, A. – Die Beziehungen des 24-Stunden-Rhythmus vegetativer Funktionen zum histologischen Funktionsbild endokriner Drüsen – *Z. Ges. Exp. Med.* 115–1950–229.

1 BANGERT, H. – Untersuchungen zur Koordination der Kopf- und Beinbewegungen beim Haushuhn – *Z. Tierpsychol.* 17/2–1960–143.

1 BARANETZKY, J. – Die tägliche Periodizität im Längenwachstum der Stengel – *Mém. Acad. Sci. (St. Petersburg)* 27 VII Ser.–1879–1.

2 BARANETZKY, J. – Die kreisförmige Nutation und das Winden der Stengel – *Mém. Acad. Sci. (St. Petersburg)* 31 VII Ser./8–1883–1.

1 BARBER, N. F. – *Experimental Correlograms and Fourier Transforms* – Pergamon Press, London, 1961.

1 BARE, J.K. – Hunger, deprivation and the day-night cycle – *J. Comp. Physiol Psychol.* 52–1959–129.

100 BARKER, R. G., M. F. SCHOGGEN and L. S. BARKER – Hemerography of Mary Ennis, in *Clinical Studies of Personality* – Burton and Harris Eds., Harker, 1955.

300 BARKER, R. J., A. MAYER and C. F. COHEN – Photoperiod effects in Pieris raphe – *Ann. Entomol. Soc. Am.* 56/3–1963–292.

302 BARKER, R.J., C.F. COHEN and A. MAYER – Photoflashes: A potential new tool for control of insect populations – *Science* 145/3637–1964–1195.

1 BARLOW, G. A. – Distribution and seasonal activity in three species of diplopods – *Arch. Neerl. Zool.* 13/1–1958–108.

200 BARLOW, J. S. – Autocorrelation and cross correlation analysis in electroencephalography – *Trans. Med. Electr.* M.E.6–1959–179.

201 BARLOW, J. S. – *A Phase-Comparator Model for the Diurnal Rhythm of Emergence of Drosophila* – Ref. 1961 c, p. 788.

202 BARLOW, J. S. – *Possible Physiological Bases for Animal Navigation with Special Reference to Inertial Guidance Navigation Systems* – 1st Intern. Biophysics Congress, Stockholm 1961.

1 BARNES, G. E. – The behaviour of Anodonta cygnea L. and its neurophysiological basis – *J. Exp. Biol.* 32/1–1955–158.

2 BARNES, G. E. – The behaviour of unrestrained Andonta – *Animal Behaviour* 10–1962–174.

1 BARNOTHY, J. M. – *Biomagnetic Experiments* – 1st Intern. Biophysics Congr., Stockholm 1961.

2 BARNOTHY, J. M. – *Compensation of Radiation Syndromes through Treatment in Magnetic Field* – 1st Intern. Biophysics Congr. Stockholm 1961.

1 BARNUM, C. P. – *Relative Specific Activity of RNA and DNA in Liver* – Ref. 1961a, p. 79.

100 BARNUM, C. P. and F. HALBERG – A 24-hour periodicity in relative specific activity of phosphorus fractions from liver microsomes of mice – *Metabolism* 2–1953–271.

101 BARNUM, C. P., C. D. JARDETZKY and F. HALBERG – Nucleic acid synthesis in regenerating liver – *Texas Rept. Biol. Med.* 15/1–1957–134.

102 BARNUM, C. P., C. D. JARDETSKY, and F. HALBERG – Time relation among metabolic and morphologic 24-hour changes in mouse liver – *Am. J. Physiol.* 195/2–1958–301.

1 BARNWELL, F. H. – A solar daily variation in oxygen consumption of

the embryonated egg – *Proc. Soc. Exp. Biol. Med.* 105/2–1960–312.

100 BARNWELL, F. H. and F. A. BROWN Jr. – Magnetic and photic responses in snails – *Experientia* 17–1961–513.

100 BAROYAN, O. V. – The incidence of diseases caused by respiratory viruses in the USSR and Czechoslovakia – *Am. Rev. Resp. Dis.* 88/3(2)–1963–22.

100 BARRINGTON, E. J. W. and A. J. MATTY, – Seasonal variation in the thyroid gland of the Minnow – *Proc. Zool. Soc. (London)* 129–1954–89.

100 BARROT, H. G., J. C. FRITZ, E. M. PRINGLE and H. W. TITUS – Heat production and gaseous metabolism of young male chickens – *J. Nutr.* 15–1938–145.

101 BARROT, H. G. and E. M. PRINGLE, – Effect of environment on growth, and feeding and water consumption of chicks (IV)–*J. Nutr.* 45–1951–265.

1 BARTA, G. – *Connections between the secular variations of the earth's magnetic field and other phenomena* – Ref. 1961e, p. 351.

100 BARTAWICK, H. A., S. NAKAYAMA and S. B. HENDRICKS – *Failure of Reversibility of the Photoreaction Controlling Plant Growth* – Ref. 1960 b, p. 394.

1 BARTELS, J. – Harmonic analysis of diurnal variations for single days – *Terrest. Magn.* 44/2–1939–137.

2 BARTELS, J. – Gesetz und Zufall in der Geophysik – *Naturwiss.* 31/(37–38)–1943–421.

3 BARTELS, J. – *Erfahrungen beim Studium geophysikalischer Rhythmen* – Ref. 1953a, p. 65.

200 BARTELS, M. – Über Orientierung und Ortsgedächtnis der Netzspinne – *Rev. Suisse Zool.* 35–1928–247.

1 BARTHOLOMEW, G. A. – The daily movements of Cormorants on San Francisco Bay – *Condor* 45–1943–3.

2 BARTHOLOMEW, G. A. – The effect of light intensity and day length on reproduction in the English sparrow – *Bull. Mus. Comp. Zool.* 101–1949–431.

3 BARTHOLOMEW, G. A. – *Photoperiodism in Reptiles* – Ref. 1957 F, p. 669.

1 BARTLETT, M. S. – Smoothing periodograms from time series with con-

tinuous spectra – *Nature* 161–1948–686.

2 BARTLETT, M. S. – Periodogram analysis and continuous spectra – *Biometrica* 37–1950–1.

100 BARTLETT, M. S. and D. V. RAJA-LAKSHMAN – Goodness of fit tests for simultaneous autoregressive series – *J. Roy. Stat. Soc.* 15B–1953–107.

1 BARTON, D. S. – Study of temperature and electric potentials in the menstrual cycle – *Yale J. Biol. Med.* 8–1940–503.

300 BARTON, D. E., F. N. DAVID and E. FIX – Random points in a circle and the analysis of chromosome patterns – *Biometrika,* 50/(1–2)–1963.

500 BARTON, G. W. and S. H. BARTON – Forms of sounds on an oscilloscope by roulette figures – *Science* 142/3598–1963–1455.

1 BARTTER, F. C. – *Map of Variables in Human Female*–Ref. 1961a, p. 60.

100 BARTTER, F. C., C. S. DELEA and F. HALBERG – *A Map of Blood and Urinary Changes related to Circadian Variations in Adrenal Cortical Function in Normal Subjects* – Ref. 1961c, p. 969.

101 BARTTER, F. C. and C. S. DELEA – *Circadian Aspects of Human Adrenal Functions* – Ref. 1962c, p. 257.

100 BASSETT, P., and N. LEWELLIN – The effect of increased or decreased length of day light on pett primeness in growing foxes – *Can. Silver Fox and Fur* 13–1947–10.

100 BASTIAN J. W. and M. X. ZARROW – A new hypothesis for the asynchronous ovulatory cycle of the domestic hen – *Poultry Sci.* 34–1955–776.

1 BATEMAN, M. A. – The effect of light and temperature on the rhythm of pupal ecdysis in the Queensland fruitfly – *Austr. J. Zool.* 3–1955–22.

1 BAUMGARTNER, A. M. – Seasonal variations in the tree sparrow – *Auk* 55–1938–603.

1 BAUTZMANN, H. – *Über rhythmische Bewegungsvorgänge innerhalb der Eihüllen von Tieren* – Ref. 1955a, p. 44.

2 BAUTZMANN, H. – Natur und Bedeutung einer Fruchthüllenmotorik bei Amnioten (Film description) –

Verh. D. Zool. Ges. Hamburg 1956.

3　BAUTZMANN, H. – Fruchthüllenmotorik und Embryokinese – *Arch. Gyn.* 187–1956–519.

100　BAUTZMANN, H., E. DUNKER and R. SCHRÖDER – Registrierung der Motorik des Amnions und des embryonalen Herzens beim Hünchen mittels des Kathodenstrahl-Oscillographen – *Verh. Vers. Anat. Ges.* 52–1954–317.

101　BAUTZMANN, H. and R. SCHRÖDER – Das Amnionschaukeln des Hühnchens im Ei – Inst. Wiss. Film, Göttingen, Film 385.

102　BAUTZMANN, H., R. SCHRÖDER and E. DUNKER – Amnionmotoric and rocking movements of the embryo in the hens egg – *Anat. Anz.* 108–1960.

100　BAXTER, C.H. and P.E. PICKENS – Control of luminescence in hemichordates and some properties of a nerve net system – *J. Exp. Biol.* 41/1–1964–1.

100　BAZETT, H. C., S. THURLOW, C. CROWELL and W. STEWART – The diuresis caused by warm baths together with some observations on urinary tides – *Am. J. Physiol.* 70–1924–430.

100　BEACH, F. A. and G. LEVINSON – Diurnal variations in the mating behaviour of male rats – *Proc. Soc. Exp. Biol. Med.* 72–1949–78.

1　BECK, L. V. – Diurnal variation in mouse and rat liver sulfhydryl – *Proc. Soc. exp. Biol. Med.* 97 –1958–229.

1　BECKER, L. – Untersuchungen über das Heimfindevermögen der Bienen – *Z. Vergl. Physiol.* 41–1958–1.

300　BECKER, R. O. and C. H. BACHMAN, – 4th Intern. Conf. Med. Electronics, New York 1961.

400　BECKER, U. – *Sonnenaktivität und chemische Tests* – Ref. 1958c, p. 113.

1　BECKWITH R. C. – American oak leaf tier in Connecticut – *Ann. Entomol. Soc. Am.* 56/6–1963–741.

100　BEDFORD, D. and F. H. A. MARSHALL – On the incidence of the breeding season in mammals after transference to a new latitude – *Proc. Roy. Soc.* 130B–1942–396.

1　BELAK, S. – Weitere Beiträge zur Beziehung zwischen Sonnenflecken und Diphterie – *Mschr. Kinderhlk.* 77–1939–190.

1　BELDING, D. L. – *Textbook of Clinical Parasitology* – Appleton-Century, New York, 1942.

1　BELING, J. – Über das Zeitgedächtnis der Bienen – *Z. Vergl. Physiol.* 9–1929–259.

1　BELKE, J. – *Beitrag zur Frage rhythmischer Vorgänge des Mineralstoffwechsel nach Untersuchungen im Serum und Urin gesunder Menschen* – Diss. Freiburg i.B. 1945.

100　BELL, R.A. and P.L. ADKISSON – Photoperiodic reversibility of diapause induction in an insect – *Science* 144/3622–1964–1149.

100　BELLAMY R. E. and W. C. REEVES – The winter biology of *Culex tarsalis* in Kern County, California – *Ann. Entomol. Soc. Am.* 56/3–1963–314.

1　BELLROSE, F. C. – Celestial orientation by wild mallards – *Bird-Band* 29–1958–75.

1　BENDAT, J. S. – *Principles and Applications of Random Noise Theory* – Wiley, New York 1958.

2　BENDAT, J. S. – Interpretation and application of statistical analysis for random physical phenomena – Lect. Univ. Calif. Med. Center, July 1961.

1　BENEDICT, F. G. – Studies in body temperature. I. Influence of the inversion of daily routine, the temperature of night-workers – *Am. J. Physiol.* 11–(1904–1905)–145.

100　BENEDICT, F. G. and J. F. SNELL – Körpertemperatur-Schwankungen mit besonderer Rücksicht auf den Einfluss, welchen Umkehrung der täglichen Lebensgewohnheit beim Menschen hat – *Pflüger's Arch.* 90–1902–33.

300　BENEDICT, H.M., R. SWIDLER, and J.N. SIMONS – Chlorophyll content and growth of soybean plants; possible interaction of iron availability and day length – *Science* 144/3622–1964–1134.

1　BENNETT, M. F. – The rhythmic activity of the quahog, Venus mercenaria, and its modification by light – *Biol. Bull.* 107/2–1954–174.

2　BENNETT, M.F. – The phasing of the cycle of motor activity in the fiddler crab–*Z. Vergl. Physiol.* 47–1963–431.

100 BENNETT, M. F. and F. A. BROWN JR.
– Experimental modification of the
lunar rhythm of running activity
of the fiddler crab, *Uca pugnax* –
Biol. Bull. 117/2–1959–404.

101 BENNETT, M. F. and F. A. BROWN
Jr. – Phasing of the rhythm of
running activity of the fiddler crab
– *Biol. Bull.* 117/2–1959–404.

102 BENNETT, M. F., J. SHRINER and
R. A. BROWN – Persistent tidal
cycles of motor activity in the
fiddler crab, *Uca pugnax* – *Biol.
Bull.* 112/3–1957–267.

103 BENNETT, M. and F. J. STALEY –
Cycles of motor activity in the newt,
Triturus viridescens – *Anat. Rec.*
137/3–960–339.

1 BENNITT, R. – Diurnal rhythm in the
proximal pigment cells of the crayfish retina – *Physiol. Zool.* 5–1932–
65.

1 BENOIT, J. – Activation sexuelle ob-
tenue chez le canard par l'éclairement artificiel pendant la période
de repos génital – *C.R. Acad. Sci.*
199–1934–1671.

2 BENOIT, J. – Stimulation du déve-
loppement testiculaire par l'éclairement artificiel – *C.R. Soc. Biol.*
118–1935–664.

3 BENOIT, J. – Hypophysectomie et
éclairement artificiel chez le canard
mâle – *C.R. Soc. Biol.* 120–1935–
1326.

4 BENOIT, J. – Contribution à l'étude
du réflexe opto-hypophysaire gona-
dostimulant chez le canard soumis à
des radiations lumineuses de diverses longeurs d'ondes – *J. Physiol.*
42–1950–537.

5 BENOIT, J. – *Structural Components
of the Pathway concerned with
Photo-Sexual Stimulation in Birds* –
Ref. 1963b.

6 BENOIT, J. – *The Role of the Eye and
of the Hypothalamus in the Photo-
stimulation of the Gonads of the Drake*
– Ref. 1963b.

100 BENOIT, J. and J. ASSENMACHER –
Rôle des photo-récepteurs superficial et profond dans la gonadostimulation par la lumière chez les
oiseaux – *J. Physiol.* 45–1953–34.

101 BENOIT, J. and J. ASSENMACHER –
Rapport entre la stimulation sexuelle préhypophysaire et la neurosécré-

tion chez l'oiseau – *Arch. Anat.
Microsc. Morph. Exp.* 42–1953–334.

102 BENOIT, J. and J. ASSENMACHER –
Le contrôle hypothalamique de l'ac-
tivité préhypophysaire gonadotrope
– *J. Physiol.* 47–1955–427.

103 BENOIT, J. J. ASSENMACHER, and
F. X. WALTER – Responses du mécanisme gonado-stimulant à l'éclairement artificiel et de la préhypo-
physe aux castrations bilatérales et
unilatérales – *C. R. Soc. Biol.*
144–1950–573.

104 BENOIT, J. and R. KEHL – Nouvelles recherches sur les voies nerveu-
ses photoréceptrices et hypophyso-
stimulant chez le canard domestique – *C.R. Soc. Biol.* 131–1939–89.

105 BENOIT, J., P. MANDEL, F. X. WAL-
TER and J. ASSENMACHER – Sensibi-
lité testiculaire aux hormones gona-
dotropes hypophysaires chez le
canard domestique au cours de la
période de régression testiculaire
saisonnière – *C.R. Soc. Biol.* 144–
1950–1400.

106 BENOIT, J. et L. OTT – Actions de
lumières de differentes longeurs
d'onde sur la gonadostimulation
chez le canard mâle impubère –
C.R. Soc. Biol. 127–1938–906.

107 BENOIT, J. and J. ASSENMACHER –
The control by visible radiations of
the gonadotropic activity of the
duck hypophysis – *Rec. Progr. Horm.
Res.* 15–1959–143.

100 BENTLEY, E. W., D. L. GUNN and
D. W. EWER – The biological behaviour of Ptinus, a pest of stored
products. I. The daily rhythm of
locomotor activity especially in
relation to light and temperature –
J. Exp. Biol. 18–1942–182.

1 BERCEL, N. – *The Periodic Features
of some Seizure States* – Ref. 1963b.

100 BERENDES, H. W., E. MARTE, R. J.
ERTEL, J. A. McCARTHY, J. A.
ANDERSON and F. HALBERG – Circadian physiologic rhythms and
lowered blood 5-hydroxytrypta-
mine in human subjects with
defective mentality – *The Physiologist* 3–1960–20.

100 BERENSTEIN, S. and F. GEORGI –
Les variations rhythmiques du cho-
lésterol sérique – *J. Suisse Med.*
74/21–1944–582.

1 BERG, H. – *Wetter und Krankheiten* – Bonn 1948.

2 BERG, H. – *Der Rhythmus der Sonnenflecken im biologischen Geschehen* – Ref. 1949a p. 40.

3 BERG, H. – *Solar-terrestrische Beziehungen in Meteorologie und Biologie* – Leipzig 1957.

4 BERG, H. – *Relations entre Phenomènes solaires et terrestres en Biologie* – Ref. 1958c, p. 161.

5 BERG, H. – Exogener oder endogener 24-Stunden-Rhythmus – *Grenzgeb. Med.* 2–1949–386.

1 BERGES, D. – *Elektromyographische Untersuchungen an Sportlern zur Frage einer Tagesrhythmik der Muskelaktivität* – Diss. Münster 1957.

1 BERGMAN, P. – Om det praktiska värdet av basaltemperaturmätningar i menstruationscykeln – *Hormoner* 11/5–1947–57.

2 BERGMAN, P. – Sexual cycle, time of ovulation and time of optimal fertility in women – *Acta Obst. Gyn. Scand.* 29/suppl. 4–1950.

3 BERGMAN, P. – Anovulationens klinik och behandling – *Hormoner* 20/4 –1956–61.

1 BERINGER, A. – *Über die rhythmischen Schwankungen im Fett- und Glykogengehalt der Leber, ihre Beeinflussung sowie ihre Ursache* – Ref. 1953a, p. 172.

2 BERINGER, A. – *Der Leberrhythmus, seine Beeinflussung und Ursache* – Ref. 1955a, p. 49.

3 BERINGER, A. – Über das Glykogen und seinen Einfluss auf den Stoffwechsel der Leber beim Gesunden und Diabetikern – *D. Med. Wschr.* 75–1950–1715.

1 BERLAGE, H.P. – *Variations in the general athmospheric and hydrospheric circulation of periods of a few years duration, affected by variations of solar activity* – Ref. 1961e, p. 354.

1 BERNARD, C. – *Les Phénomènes de la Vie* – Paris 1878.

1 BERTALANFFY, L. v. – *Theoretische Biologie* – Francke, Bern 1951.

1 BERTSCH, W. F. – *The Promotion of Photosensitivity Growth by Sugars and Cobalt in Etiolated Pea Stem Sections* – Ref. 1960b, p. 398.

1 BETHE, A. – Die Bedeutung der Elektrolyten für die rhythmischen Bewegungen der Medusen (I-II) – *Pflüger's Arch.* 124–1908–541; 127–1909–219.

2 BETHE, A. – Versuche an Medusen als Beispiel eines primitiven neuromuskulären Reaktionssystems – *Pflüger's Arch.* 235–1934–288.

3 BETHE, A. – Die Latenzzeit des Froschmuskels in Abhängigkeit vom Reizinterfall – *Pflüger's Arch.* 239 –1937.

4 BETHE, A. – Rhythmik und Periodik besonders im Hinblick auf die Bewegungen des Herzens und der Meduse – *Pflüger's Arch.* 239–1937–41.

5 BETHE, A. – Experimentelle Erzeugung von Störungen der Erregungstätigkeit und von Alternanz und Periodenbildung bei Medusen im Vergleich zu ähnlichen Erscheinungen am Wirbeltierherzen – *Z. Vergl. Physiol.* 24–1937–613.

6 BETHE, A. – Die biologischen Rhythmusphänomene als selbständige bzw. erzwungene Kippvorgänge betrachtet – *Pflüger's Arch.* 244–1940–1.

7 BETHE, A. – Teilrhythmus, Alternans, Amplitude und die Grenzen des Alles-oder-Nichts-Gesetzes – *Pflüger's Arch.* 244–1940–43.

8 BETHE, A. – Wie kann man sich die Transformierung eines kontinuierlichen Lichtreizes in eine Reihe rhythmische Aktionsströme vorstellen – *Pflüger's Arch.* 244–1941–583.

9 BETHE, A. – Irritabilität, Rhythmik und Periodik – *Naturwiss.* 33–1946–86.

10 BETHE, A. – Rhythmus und Periodik in der belebten Natur – *Stud. Gen.* 2–1949–67.

100 BETHE, A. and A. SALMONSON – Beziehungen zwischen Bewegungsfrequenz und Grösse des Ausbreitungsgebietes der Erregungen – *Pflüger's Arch.* 226–1931–749.

101 BETHE, A. und H. SCHAEFER – Erregungsgesetze einen Blinkschaltung im Vergleich zu denen biologischer Objekte – *Pflüger's Arch.* 249–1947–313.

1 BETHUNE, A. J. DE – Child spacing: The mathematical probabilities – *Science* 142/3600–1963–1629.

1 BEUNDERS, B. – Les infections à

adéno-virus chez les recrues de l'armée néerlandaise – *Arch. Ges. Virusforsch.* 131–(1–3)–1963–302.

1 BIALE, J. B. – Periodicity in transpiration of lemon cuttings under constant environmental conditions – *Proc. Am. Hort. Sci.* 38–1940–70.

100 BICKLEY, W. G. and A. TALBOT, – *An Introduction to the Theory of Vibrating Systems* – Oxford Univ. Press, Oxford 1961.

1 BIERSACK, G. – *Über die Pulsfrequenz des Kindes während und nach der Geburt* – Diss. Univ. München 1958.

100 BILEK, O., Z. KALAB, and M. KONECNY – *The influence of the opticothalamic system on the deposition of iron in the brain of rats* – Ref. 1963b.

1 BINAGHI, G. – Il ritmo biologico del sangue nelle 24 ore – *Minerva Med.* 41–1950–355.

1 BINGEL, F. – Über die Tagesperiodik Geisteskranker dargestellt am Elektrodermatogramm – *Z. Ges. Neur. Phychiatr.* 170–1940–404.

1 BIRUKOW, G. – Menotaxis im polarisierten Licht bei *Geotrupes silvaticus* Panz – *Naturwiss.* 40–1953–611.

2 BIRUKOW, G. – Photogeomenotaxis bei *Geotrupes silvaticus* Panz und ihre Zentralnervöse Koordination – *Z. Vergl. Physiol.* 36–1954–176.

3 BIRUKOW, G. – Lichtkompassorientierung beim Wasserläufer *Velia currens* am Tage und zur Nachtzeit (I) – *Z. Tierpsychol.* 13/3–1956–463.

4 BIRUKOW, G. – Tages und jahreszeitliche Orientierungsrhythmus beim Wasserläufer *Velia currens* F. – *Naturwiss.* 44–1957–358.

5 BIRUKOW, G. – *Innate Types of Chronometry in Insect Orientation* – Ref. 1960c, p. 403.

100 BIRUKOW, G. and E. BUSCH – Lichtkompassorientierung beim Wasserläufer, *Velia currens* P. am Tage und zur Nachzeit, II – *Z. Tierpsychol.* 14/2–1957–184.

101 BIRUKOW, G. and D. EMEIS – Zweisinnige Steuerung bei der Orientierungsrhythmik des Wasserläufers *Velia currens* F. – *Naturwiss.* 17–1957–474.

102 BIRUKOW, G. and H. OBERDORFER – Schwerkraftorientierung beim Was-

serläufer *Velia currens* F. (*Heteroptera*) am Tage und zur Nachtzeit – *Z. Tierpsychol.* 16/6–1959–693.

103 BIRUKOW, G., K. FISCHER and H. BÖTTCHER – *Die Sonnenkompassorientierung der Eidechsen* – Ref. 1962 d, p. 216.

1 BISBY, G. R. – Zonation in cultures of *Fusarium discolor sulphureum* – *Mycologia* 17–1925–89.

BISHOP D. W. – Spermatozoan motility – Publ. 72 of the AAAS, Washington D.C., 1962.

1 BISSONETTE, T. H. – Studies on the sexual cycle in birds. IV – *J. Exp. Zool.* 58–1931–281.

2 BISSONETTE, T. H. – Modification of mammalian sexual cycles – *Proc. Roy. Soc.* 110B–1932–322.

3 BISSONETTE, T. H. – Light and sexual cycles in starlings and ferrets – *Quart. Rev. Biol.* 8–1933–201.

4 BISSONETTE, T. H. – Inhibition of the stimulating effect of red light on testis activity in *Sturnus vulgaris* by a restricted diet – *Biol. Bull.* 65–1933–452.

5 BISONETTE, T. H. – Modification of mammalian sexual cycles – *J. Comp. Physiol.* 22–1936–93.

6 BISSONETTE, T. H. – Sexual photoperiodicity – *Quart. Rev. Biol.* 11–1936–371.

7 BISSONETTE, T. H. – Photoperiodicity in birds – *Wilson Bull.* 49–1937 –241.

8 BISSONETTE, T. H. – Sexual photoperiodicity in the Blue Jay – *Wilson Bull.* 51–1939–227.

9 BISSONETTE, T. H. – Experimental modification of the breeding cycles in goats – *Physiol. Zool.* 14–1941–379.

10 BISSONETTE, T. H. – Some recent studies on photoperiodicity in animals – *Trans. N.Y. Acad. Sci.* 5 II–1943–43.

11 BISSONNETTE, T. H. – Studies on the sexual cycles in birds – *Amer. J. Anat.* 45–1930–289.

100 BISSONETTE, T. H. and A. G. CSECH – Modification of mammalian sexual cycles – *Proc. Roy. Soc.* 122B–1937–246.

101 BISSONETTE, T. H. and A. G. CSECH – Modified sexual photoperiodicity in cotton tail rabbits – *Biol. Bull.* 77–1939–3.

100 BJERNER, B., A. HOLM, and Å.
SWENSSON – *Om Natt och Skiftarbete*
– Stockholm 1948.

101 BJERNER, B., and Å. SWENSSON –
Schichtarbeit und Rhythmus – Ref.
1949a, p. 102.

1 BLAAUW, A. – Licht und Wachstum
(III) – *Meded. Landbouwhoogeschool*
15–1918.

100 BLACKMAN, R. B. and J. W. TUKEY
– *The Measurements of Power Spectra* – Dover Publications, New York
1958.

101 BLACKMAN, R. B. and J. W. TUKEY
– Measurement of power spectra –
Bell Syst. Tech. J. 37–1958–185, 485.

1 BLAKE, G. M. – Shortening of a dia-
pause-controlled life-cycle by means
of increasing photoperiodism – *Nature* 198–1963–462.

100 BLANEY, L. T. and K. C. HAMNER –
Interrelations among effects of temperature, photoperiod, and dark
period on floral initiation of soy-
beans – *Bot. Gaz.* 119–1957–10.

100 BLANKENHORN, M. A. and H. E.
CAMPBELL – The effect of sleep on
blood pressure – *Am. J. Physiol.*
74–1925–115.

1 BLEYER, A. – Periodic variation in
the rate of growth of infants – *Arch.
Ped.* 34–1917–366.

1 BLISS, C. I. – Periodic regression in
biology and climatology – *Conn.
Agr. exp. Station, Bull.* 615, New
Haven, 1958.

2 BLISS, C. I. – *Statistics for Biologists*
– McGraw-Hill, in press.

100 BLISS, C. I. and D. L. BLEVINS –
The analysis of seasonal variations
in measles – *Am. J. Hyg.* 70/3 –
1959–328.

1 BLUM, H. F. – On the origin and
evolution of living machines – *Am.
Sci.* 49/4–1961–474.

1 BLUME, H. – Über die Analyse kurzer Kurvenzüge – *Z. Angew. Math.
Mechan.* 23–1943–346.

2 BLUME, H. – Nachweis der Eindeu-
tigkeit der Schwingweg- und Be-
schleunigungsaufzeichnungen stoss-
artig verlaufender Vorgänge durch
geeignete Analyse – *Z. Angew. Math.
Mechan.* (25-27)/(5-6)–1947.

3 BLUME, J. – *Über den Nachweis von
Periodizitäten in Kurven, dargestellt an der Analyse von Herzschallkurven* – Ref. 1949a, p. 92.

4 BLUME, J. – *Grundsätze und Erfahrungen der Periodenbestimmung me-
dizinischer Kurven* – Ref. 1953a,
p. 83.

5 BLUME, J. – *Ergebnisse der Perioden-
forschung von Herzschallkurven einer
Serie von Kindern bei mechanischer
Belastung* – Ref. 1955a, p. 54.

6 BLUME, J. – Das Auffinden und der
mathematische Nachweis der Existenz von Perioden in komplizierten
Kurvenschreiben – *Z. Kreislaufforsch.* 44–1955–461.

7 BLUME, J. – Zusammenfassung der
Ergebnisse der mathematischen A-
nalyse von Herzschallschrieben bei
Kindern – *Z. Kreislaufforsch.* 44–
1955–821.

8 BLUME, J. – Über die Beeinflussung
des Grundrhythmus der Körpertemperatur durch rhythmische Änderungen der Wach- und Schlaf-
zeiten – *Z. Ges. Exp. Med.* 128–
1957–452.

9 BLUME, J. – Rhythmische Arbeits-
weise von Patienten im Paulitest
und klinische Diagnose – *Z. Ges.
Exp. Med.* 132–1959–247.

10 BLUME, J. – *Folgen die Blattbewegungen einer Pflanze unter Einwirkung eines künstlichen periodischen
Lichtdunkelwechsels einem ökonomischen Prinzip?*–Ref. 1960a, p. 12.

11 BLUME, J. – Folgen die Blattbewegungen einer Pflanze unter Einwirkung eines künstlichen periodischen Licht-Dunkelwechsels einen
ökonomischen Prinzip? – *Z. Bot.*
49/3–1961–253.

12 BLUME, J. – Erste Ergebnisse der
Auswertung von Herzschallkurven
mit Hilfe einer neuen Analysier-
methode – *Z. Kreislaufforsch.* 38–
1949–533.

13 BLUME, J. – Nachweis von Perioden
durch Phasen- und Amplituden-
diagramm mit Anwendungen aus
der Biologie, Medizin und Psychologie (Polycop. 1964) – Address:
Prof. J. Blume, Schürkesfeld 39,
Strümp (Post Osterath), Germany.

100 BLUME, J., E. BÜNNING and D. MÜL-
LER – Periodenanalyse von Aktivi-
tätsrhythmen bei *Carcinus maenas* –
Biol. Zbl. 81–1962–569.

1 BLUMENFELD, C. M. – Periodic and rhythmic mitotic activity in the kidney of the albino rat – *Anat. Rec.* 72–1938–435.

2 BLUMENFELD, C. M. – Periodic mitotic activity in epidermis of albino rat – *Science* 90–1939–446.

3 BLUMENFELD, C. M. – Normal and abnormal mitotic activity; comparison of periodic mitotic activity in epidermis, renal cortex, and submaxillary gland of the albino rat – *Arch. Pathol.* 33–1942–770.

4 BLUMENFELD, C. M. – Studies of normal and of abnormal mitotic activity (II) – *Arch. Pathol.* 35–1943–667.

5 BLUMENFELD, C. M. – Rate and periodicity of mitotic activity in regenerating epidermis of healing wounds in rabbits – *Arch. Pathol.* 36–1943–493.

1 BLUMENTHAL, H. T. – The nature of cyclic variations in mitotic activity – *Growth* 14–1950–231.

100 BOAS, E. and E. T. GOLDSCHMIDT – *The Heart Rate* – Springfield, 1932.

1 BOCH, R. – Die Tänze der Bienen bei nahen und fernen Trachtquellen – *Z. Vergl. Physiol.* 38–1956–136.

1 BOCHNIK, H. J. – *Über Tagesschwankungen zentral-nervöser und autonomer Funktionen*–Ref.1949a, p.122.

2 BOCHNIK, H. J. – *Schmerz und Tagesrhythmik* – Ref. 1953a, p. 142.

3 BOCHNIK, H. J. – *Komponenten spontaner Tagesschwankungen dargestellt am Beispiel einer statistischen Analyse von Phantomschmerzen* – Ref. 1955a, p. 55.

4 BOCHNIK, H. J. – "Tagesrhythmen" nach halbseitiger präfrontaler Leukotomie – *D.Z. Nervenhlk.* 168–1952–95.

5 BOCHNIK, H. J. – Tagesschwankungen der Hautsensibilität – *Arch. Psychiat. Nervenkr.* 197–1958–223.

6 BOCHNIK, H. J. – Spontane Tagesschwankungen der neuromuskulären elektrischen Erregbarkeit – *D.Z. Nervenhlk.* 178–1958–254.

7 BOCHNIK, H. J. – Tagesschwankungen der muskulären Leistungsfähigkeit – *D. Z. Nervenhlk.* 178–1958–270.

8 BOCHNIK, H. J. – Mehrgleisig simultane Untersuchungen spontaner Tagesschwankungen sensibeler, motorischer und vegetativer Funktionen – *Nervenarzt* 29-1958-307.

100 BOCHNIK H. J. and LEGEWIE – *Faktorenanalysen der Spontanschwankungen physischer und psychischer Funktionen im Ermüdungsversuch* – Ref. 1963a.

1 BODE, H. W. – *Network Analysis and Feedback Amplifier Design* – v. Nostrand, New York, 1959.

100 BODEN, B. P., E. M. KAMPA and B. C. ABBOTT – *Photoreception of a Planktonic Crustacean in Relation to Light Penetration in the Sea* – Ref. 1960b, p. 189.

1 BODENHEIMER, F. S. – Studies on the ecology of Palestinian *Coleoptera*. II – *Bull. Soc. Ent. Egypt* 1934 (1–2)–1934–1.

100 BODENHEIMER, F. S. and H. J. KLEIN – Über die Temperaturabhängigkeiten von Insekten. II. – *Z. Vergl. Physiol.* 11–1930–345.

1 BÖCKH, E. M. – Ein Beitrag zur Frage der Tagesschwankungen im EKG der Standard-Extremitätenableitungen – *Z. Kreislaufforsch.* 42–1953–420.

1 BÖHM, H. – Vom lebendigen Rhythmus – *Stud. Gen.* 4/1–1951.

100 BOGOLIUBOV, N. N. and Y. A. MITROPOLSKY – *Asymptotic Methods in the Theory of Non-Linear Oscillations* – Hindustan Publ., Delhi, 1961.

100 BOGORAD, L. and W. J. MACILRATH – *A Correlation of Photoperiodic Response of Xanthium and Germination of Implanted Lettuce Seed* – Ref. 1957 f, p. 301.

1 BOGOROV, B. G. – *Perspectives in the Study of Seasonal Changes in Plankton and of the Number of Generations at Different Latitudes* – Ref. 1958a p. 145.

1 BOGOSLOVSKY, A. J. – Diurnal changes in the electrical sensitivity of the eye – *Bull. Biol. Med. Exp. USSR* 3–1957–127.

100 BOHM, E., G. GERNANT and H. HOLMGREN – Rytmiska variationer i blodets halt av chylomicron – *Nord. Med. (Swed.)* 8–1940–2389.

1 BOHN, G. – Sur les mouvements oscillatoires des Convoluta roscoffensis – *C.R. Acad. Sci.* 37–1903–573.

2 Bohn, G. – Periodicité vitale des animaux soumis aux oscillations du niveaux des hautes mers – *Acad. Sci.* 139–1904–610.

3 Bohn, G. – La persistance du rythme des marées chez l'*Actinia equina* – *C.R. Soc. Biol.* 61–1906–420.

4 Bohn, G. – Le rythme nychtéméral chez les Actinenes – *C.R. Soc. Biol.* 62–1907–473.

100 Bohn, G. and H. Pieron – Le rythme des marées et la phénomène de l'anticipation réflexe – *C.R. Soc. Biol.* 61–1906–660.

1 Bond, N. B. – The psychology of waking – *J. Abnorm. Soc. Psychol.* –1920–226.

1 Bonde, E. K. – The effect of various cycles of light and darkness on the growth of tomato and cocklebur plants – *Physiol. Plant.* 8–1955–913.

1 Bonhoeffer, K. F. – Activation of passive iron as a model for the excitation of nerve – *J. Gen. Physiol.* 32–1948–69.

100 Bonhoeffer, K. F. and K. Vetter – Zur Aktivierung und Repassivierung von passivem Eisen in Salpetersäure – *Z. Physik. Chem.* 196–1950–127.

101 Bonhoeffer, K. F. and G. Vollheim, – Über die Wechselwirkung von Aktivitätswellen auf passiven Eisendrähten – *Z. Naturforsch.* 8b–1953–406.

1 Bonner, J. – *The Photoperiodic Process* – Ref. 1957f, p. 245.

2 Bonner, J. – *Chemical Nature of the Inductive Processes* – Ref. 1957f, p. 441.
Booz, K. H. – Experimentelle Untersuchungen zum Problem der kontraktil aktiven v. portae des Meerschweinchens – *Anat. Anz.* 113–1963–68.

100 Boring, E. F. and L. D. – Temporal judgements after sleep – *Titchener Commem.* 1917–225.

100 Bornstein, A. and H. Völker – Über die Schwankungen des Grundumsatzes – *Z. Exp. Med.* 53–1926–439.

1 Bortels, H. – Das Gefrieren unterkühlten Wassers in Beziehung zu interdiurnen Luftdruckänderungen und zur Solaraktivität – *Arch. Meteorol. Geophys. Bioklimatol.* 7B/2–1956–269.

2 Bortels, H. – Die hypothetische Wetterstrahlung als vermutliches Agens kosmo-meteoro-biologischer Reaktionen – *Wiss. Z. Humbolt-Univ. (Berlin)* 6/2–(1956–1957)–115.

3 Bortels, H. – Ungeklärte Umgebungseinflüsse auf die Vermehrungsfähigkeit aerober Bakterienzellen – *Zbl. Bakt. Parasitenkde. Infekt. krkh. Hyg.* 2–1958–218.

1 Borthwick, H. A. – *Photoperiodic Control of Flowering* – Ref. 1957f p. 275.

100 Bosch, A. v. d., E. I. Schlinger and K. S. Hagen – Initial field observations in California on *Trionys pallidus* – *J. Econ. Entomol.* 55/6–1962–857.

1 Bostock, J. – Case of a periodical affection of the eyes and chest – *Ann. Allergy,* 21/6–1963–344.

100 Boughton, D. C., F. O. Atchley and L. C. Eskridge – Experimental modification of the diurnal oocyst-production of the sparrow *Coccidium* – *J. Exp. Zool.* 70–1935–55.

1 Boute, C. C. – *Wirkungen elektrischer Felder und Strahlungen atmosphärischen und kosmischen Ursprungs auf das Wasser* – Ref. 1954c.

2 Boute, C. C. – *Observations sur les Tests Chimiques de Piccardi effectues à Bruxelles de 1950 à 1958* – Ref. 1958c, p. 51.

100 Bower, J. L. and P. M. Schultheiss, *Introduction to the Design of Servomechanisms* – Wiley. New York, 1958.

100 Bowie, E. J. W., W. N. Tauxe, W. E. Sjoberg and M. Y. Yamaguchi – Daily variation in the concentration of iron in serum – *Am. J. Clin. Pathol.* 40/5–1963–491.

1 Boyd, E. M. – Diurnal variations in plasma lipids – *J. Biol. Chem.* 110–1935–61.

200 Boyd, T. A. S. – *Plasma Corticoid Levels and Diurnal Variations of Intraocular Pressure in Glaucomatous Eyes* – Ref. 1963b.

500 Boyd, W. L. and J. W. – Soil micro-organisms of the McMurdo Sound area, Antarctica – *Appl. Microbiol.* 11/2–1963–116.

1 Boyer, R.F. – Coal mine disaster: Frequency by month – *Science* 144/3625–1964–1447.

1   BRACHER, R. – The light relations of
    Euglena limosa Gard. (I); The influ-
    ence of intensity and quality of
    light on phototaxy – *J. Linn. Soc.
    Bot.* 51–1932–23.
100 BRACKETT, S. and A. HOLLAENDER –
    *Remarks on the Significance of
    Action Spectra* – Ref. 1957f, p. 41.
1   BRADEN, A. W. H. – The relation-
    ship between the diurnal light cycle
    and the time of ovulation in mice –
    J. Exp. Biol. 34/2–1957–177.
    BRADLEY, D. A. and M. A. WOOD-
    BURY – Lunar synodical period and
    widespread precipitation – *Science*
    137/3532–1962–748.
1   BRAEMER, W. – *Versuche zu der im
    Richtungsgehen der Fische enthal-
    tenen Zeitschätzung* – Verh. D. Zool.
    Ges. (Münster) 1959, p. 276.
2   BRAEMER, W. – *A Critical Review of
    the Sun-Azimuth Hypothesis* – Ref.
    1960c p. 413.
100 BRAEMER, W. and H. G. SCHWASS-
    MANN – *Vom Rhythmus der Sonnen-
    orientierung am Aequator* – Ref. 1962
    d, p. 182.
1   BRAINES, S. N. – Erfahrungen mit
    künstlichem Schlaf im biologischen
    Experiment – *Pavlovz. Höhere Ner-
    ventätigkeit* 2–1952–505.
1   BRAMSON, J. – Onderzoek naar de
    correlatie tusschen maanphase en
    menstruatie bij 10,000 vrouwen –
    Psychiatr. Neurol. Bl. – /(1–2)–
    1929.
1   BRANDAN, R. A. – La electricidad
    ionica del aire en Cordoba – *Bol.
    Acad. Nacional (Córdoba)* 35–1940–
    1.
1   BRANDT, H. – Untersuchungen über
    die Änderung der photo- und geo-
    taktischen Reaktionen der Nonnen-
    raupe *Lymantria monacha* L. im Ver-
    laufe des Raupenlebens – *Z. Vergl.
    Physiol.* 24/2–1936–188.
200 BRANDT, W. H. – Zonation in a pro-
    lineless strain of Neurospora – *My-
    cologia* 45–1953–194.
100 BREHM, E. and G. HEMPEL – Unter-
    suchung tagesperiodischer Aktivi-
    tätsschwankungen bei Käfern – *Na-
    turwiss.* 39–1957–265.
1   BREITENBERGER, E. – Analogues of
    the normal distribution on the
    circle and the sphere – *Biometrika*
    50/1–2)–1913.

1   BREMER, H. – Über die tageszeitliche
    Konstanz im Schlüpftermine der
    Imagines einiger Insekten – *Z. Wiss.
    Insektenbiol.* 21–1926–209.
100 BRENNAN, E. G., I. A. LEONE and
    R. H. DAINES – Atmospheric alde-
    hydes related to Petunia leaf
    damage – *Science* 143/3608 –1964–
    818.
1   BRETT, W. J. – Persistant diurnal
    rhythmicity in *Drosophila* emer-
    gence – *Ann. Entomol. Soc. Am.*
    48–1955–119.
100 BRETT, W. J., H. M. WEBB and F. A.
    BROWN Jr. – Contribution of loco-
    motion to the oxygen-consumption
    rhythm in *Uca pugnax* – *Biol. Bull.*
    117–1959–405.
1   BRICK, I. B. – Periodic disease; a
    case of intermittent fever, spleno-
    megaly and leukopenia of eleven
    years duration – *Bull. Georgetown
    Univ. Med. Center* 2/6–1949–232.
100 BRICK, I. B. and M. CAJIGAS,
    Benign paroxysmal peritonitis –
    N. Engl. J. Med. 244–1951–786.
1   BRINKMANN, A. – *Untersuchungen ü-
    ber den zeitlichen Ablauf und das
    Ausmass tagesrhythmisch schwan-
    kender Körperfunktionen bei an
    Schlafstörungen leidenden Personen* –
    J.-D. Hamburg, 1954.
100 BRITTIN, W. and G. GAMOW, –
    Negative entropy and photosynthe-
    sis – *Proc. Nat. Acad. Sci.*, 57/5–
    1961–724.
100 BROD, J. and V. FENCL – *Diurnal
    Variations of the Cardiac Output and
    Peripheral Vascular Resistance* –
    2nd Eur. Congr. Card. Stockholm
    1956.
100 BRODERS, A. C. and W. B. DUBLIN –
    Rhythmicity of mitosis in epider-
    mis of human beings – *Proc. Staff.
    Meet. Mayo Clin.* 19–1939–423.
100 BROGI, G., G. MARINI and L. COM-
    PARINI – *Daily Mitotic Rate in Nor-
    mal and Regenerating Liver of Albi-
    no Rat* – Ref. 1960a, p. 13.
101 BROGI, G., G. MARINI and L. COM-
    PARINI – *Daily Mitotic Rate in the
    Epidermis of White Mice* – Ref.
    1960a, p. 16.
1   Brookhaven National Laboratory –
    Homeostatic mechanisms – *Brook-
    haven Symp. Biol.* (BNL 474, C-25)
    no. 10, New York 1958.

1   BROOKS, C. E. P. – Periodicities in the Nile floods – *Mem. Roy. Meteorol. Soc.* 2/12–(1927–28)–9.

1   BROUWER, G. – *De Periodieke Bewegingen van de Primaire Bladeren bij de Kiemplanten van Canavalia ensiformis* – Diss. Univ. Utrecht, Amsterdam 1926.

1   BROWMAN, L. G. – The effect of optic enucleation upon the activity rhythms of the albino rat – *J. Comp. Psychol.* 36–1943–33.

2   BROWMAN, L. G. – The effect of controlled temperatures upon the spontaneous activity rhythms of the albino rat – *J. Exp. Zool.* 94–1943–477.

3   BROWMAN, L. G. – Artificial 16-hour day activity rhythms in the white rat – *Am. J. Physiol.* 168/3–1952–694.

4   BROWMAN, L. G. – Seasonal variations in the mule deer thyroid – *Anat. Rec.* 128/3–1957–528.

100   BROWMAN, L. G. and H. S. SEARS – Cyclic variation in the mule deer thymus – *Proc. Soc. Exp. Biol. Med.* 93–1956–161.

1   BROWN JR., F. A. – A simple automatic continuous-recording respirometer – *Rev. Sci. Instr.* 25–1954–415.

2   BROWN JR., F. A. – Persistent activity rhythms in the oyster – *Am. J. Physiol.* 178–1954–510.

3   BROWN JR., F. A. – *Biological Chronometry* – Ref. 1956b, p. 129.

4   BROWN JR., F. A. – The rhythmic nature of life in *"Rec. Advances Invert. Physiol"*. – Univ. Oregon Publ. 1957.

5   BROWN, JR., F. A. – Response of a living organism, under "constant conditions" including pressure, to a barometric-pressure-correlated, cyclic, external variable – *Biol. Bull.* 112–1957–288.

6   BROWN JR., F. A. – *Studies of the Timing Mechanisms of Daily, Tidal and Lunar Periodicities in Organisms* – Ref. 1958a, p. 269.

7   BROWN JR., F. A. – The Rhythmic Nature of Animals and Plants – *Northwest. Univ. Tri-Quarterly,* 1958.

8   BROWN JR., F. A. – An exogenous reference-clock for persistent, temperature-independent, labile, biological rhythms – *Biol. Bull.* 115–1958–81.

9   BROWN JR., F. A. – Living Clocks – *Science* 130/3388–1959–1535.

10   BROWN JR., F. A. – *Response to Pervasive Geophysical Factors and the Biological Clock Problem* – Ref. 1960c, p. 57.

11   BROWN JR., F. A. – *Extrinsic Rhythmicality and the Timing of the Circadian Rhythms* – Ref. 1961a, p. 28.

12   BROWN JR., F. A. – *Extrinsic Rhythmicality; A Reference Frame for Biological Rhythms under so-called Constant Conditions* – Ref. 1961c, p. 775.

13   BROWN JR., F. A. – *Biological Clocks* – Am. Inst. Biol. Sci, Biol. Sci. Curr. Study no 2, Oct. 1962, Heath Co. Boston, 1962.

14   BROWN JR., F. A., – An orientational response to weak γ-radiation – *Biol. Bull.* 125/2–1963–206.

15   BROWN, Jr. F.A. – How animals respond to magnetism – *Cycles* 15/8–1964–182 (reprinted from *Discovery,* Nov. 1964).

100   BROWN JR., F. A., M. F. BENNETT and C. L. RALPH – Apparent reversible influence of cosmic-ray induced showers upon a biological system – *Proc. Soc. Exp. Biol. (N.Y.)* 89–1955–332.

101   BROWN JR., F. A., M. F. BENNETT and H. M. WEBB – Persistent daily and tidal rhythms of O_2-consumption in fiddler crabs – *J. Cell. Comp. Physiol.* 44–1954–477.

102   BROWN JR., F. A., M. F. BENNETT and H. M. WEBB – An magnetic compass response of an organism – *Biol. Bull.* 119–1960–65.

103   BROWN JR., F. A., M. F. BENNETT, H. M. WEBB and C. L. RALPH – Persistent daily, monthly and 27 day cycles of activity in the oyster and quahog – *J. Exp. Zool.* 131–1956–235.

104   BROWN JR., F. A., W. J. BRETT, M. F. BENNETT, and F. H. BARNWELL – Magnetic response of an organism and its solar relationships – *Biol. Bull.* 118–1960–367.

105   BROWN JR., F. A., W. J. BRETT and H. M. WEBB – The rhythmic nature

of metabolism in Ilyanassa in constant conditions – *Biol. Bull.* 115–1958–345.

106 BROWN JR., F. A., M. FINGERMAN and M. N. HINES – A study of the mechanism involved in shifting of the phases of the endogenous daily rhythm by light stimuli – *Biol. Bull.* 106–1954–308.

107 BROWN JR., F. A., M. FINGERMAN, M. I. SANDEEN and M. H. WEBB – Persistent diurnal and tidal rhythms of color change in the fiddler crab *Uca pugnax* – *J. Exp. Zool.* 123–1953–29.

108 BROWN JR., F. A., R. O. FREELAND and C. L. RALPH – Persistent rhythms of O_2-consumption in potatoes, carrots and the seaweed *Fucus – Plant Physiol.* 30–1955–280.

109 BROWN JR., F. A., J. SHRINER and C. L. RALPH – Solar and lunar rhythmicity in the rat in "constant conditions" and the mechanism of physiological time measurement – *Am. J. Physiol.* 184–1956–491.

110 BROWN JR., F. A. and E. D. TERRACINI – Exogenous timing of rat spontaneous activity periods – *Proc. Soc. Exp. Biol. Med.* 101–1959–457.

111 BROWN JR., F. A. and H. M. WEBB – Temperature relations of endogenous daily rhythmicity in the fiddler crab *Uca* – *Physiol. Zool.* 21–1948–371.

112 BROWN JR., F. A. and H. M. WEBB – Studies of the daily rhythmicity of the fiddler crab *Uca:* Modifications by light – *Physiol. Zool.*, 22–1949–136.

113 BROWN JR., F. A., H. M. WEBB and M. F. BENNETT – Proof for an endogenous component in persistent solar and lunar rhythmicity in organisms – *Proc. Natl. Acad. Sci. (Wash.)* 41–1955–93.

114 BROWN JR., F. A., H. M. WEBB and M. F. BENNETT – Comparisons of soms fluctuations in cosmic radiation and organismic activity during 1954, 1955 and 1956 – *Am. J. Physiol.* 195–1958–237.

115 BROWN JR., F. A., H. M. WEBB, M. F. BENNETT, and M. I. SANDEEN – Temperature-independence of the frequency of the endogenous

tidal rhythm of *Uca* – *Physiol. Zool.* 27–1954–345.

116 BROWN JR., F. A., H. M. WEBB, M. F. BENNETT, and M. I. SANDEEN – Evidence for an exogenous contribution to persistent diurnal and lunar rhythmicity under so-called constant conditions – *Biol. Bull.* 109–1955–238.

117 BROWN JR., F. A., H. M. WEBB and W. J. BRETT – Exogenous timing of solar and lunar periodisms in metabolism of the mud snail – *Gunma J. Med. Sci.* 8–1959–233.

118 BROWN JR., F. A., H. M. WEBB and W. J. BRETT – Magnetic response of an organism and its lunar relationships – *Biol. Bull.* 118–1960–382.

119 BROWN JR., F. A., H. M. WEBB and E. J. MACEY – Lag-lead correlations of barometric pressure and biological activity – *Biol. Bull.* 113–1957–112.

120 BROWN JR., F. A. and A. HUTTRER – A relationship between photic and magnetic responses in snails – *Biol. Bull.* 119–1960–306.

121 BROWN JR., F. A., J. SHRINER and H. M. WEBB – Similarities between daily fluctuations in background radiation and O_2-consumption in the living organism – *Biol. Bull.* 113–1957–103.

122 BROWN JR., F. A. and G. C. STEPHENS – Studies of the daily rhythmicity of the fiddler crab, *Uca.* Modifications by photoperiod – *Biol. Bull. Woods Hole* 101–1951–71.

200 BROWN, H. E. – *Periodicity of Leucocytes in Normal and Adrenalectomized Mice* – Ref. 1961c, p. 995.

300 BROWN, H. E. and T. F. DOUGHERTY – The diurnal variation of blood leucocytes in normal and adrenalectomized mice – *Endocrinology* 58–1956–365.

1   BROWNE, R. C. – *The Day and Night Performance in Industry* – Ref. 1955 a, p. 61.

1   BRUCE, V. G. – *Environmental Entrainment of Circadian Rhythms* – Ref. 1960c, p. 29.

100 BRUCE, V. G. and C. S. PITTENDRIGH – *Endogenous Rhythms in Insects and Microorganisms* – Ref. 1956b, p. 179.

101 BRUCE, V. G. and C. S. PITTENDRIGH – Temperature independence in a unicellular "clock" – *Proc. Nat. Acad. Sci. (Wash.)* 42–1956–676.

102 BRUCE, V. G. and C. S. PITTENDRIGH – Resetting the Euglena clock with a single light stimulus – *Am. Nat.* 92–1958–295.

103 BRUCE, V. G., F. WEIGHT and C. S. PITTENDRIGH – Resetting the sporulation rhythm in Pilobolus with short light flashes of high intensity – *Science* 131–1960–728.

104 BRUCE, V. G. and C. S. PITTENDRIGH – An effect of heavy water on the phase and period of the circadian rhythm in *Euglena* – *J. Cell. Comp. Physiol.* 56–1960–25.

1 BRÜGGEMAN, W. – Tagesschwankungen im EKG bei Myokarditis – *Die Medizinische* 8–1954–256.

100 BRÜSCHKE, G. and G. VOLKHEIMER – Untersuchungen zur Frage tagesrhythmischer Schwankungen des Serumbilirubinspiegels – *Z. Ges. Inn. Med. Grenzgebiete* 11–1956–804.

100 BRUGER, M. and J. SOMACH – The diurnal variations of the cholesterol content of the blood – *J. Biol. Chem.* 97–1932–23.

1 BRUGSCH, T. – Die Periodik der Lebenserscheinungen beim Menschen – *Arch. Mikr. Anat.* 94–1920–500.

1 BRUN, R. – *Die Raumorientierung der Ameisen* – Fischer. Jena, 1914.

1 BRUNS, H. – Beobachtungen zum Verhalten (insbesondere Tagesrhythmus) der roten Waldameise *(Formica rufa)* während des Nährungserwerbes – *Z. Tierpsychol.* 11–1954–151.

1 BRUNT, D. – A periodogram analysis of the Greenwich temperature record – *A.J. Roy. Meteorol. Soc.* 45–1919–323.

2 BRUNT, D. – An investigation of periodicities in rainfall, pressure and temperature at certain European stations – *Q.J. Roy. Meteorol. Soc.* 53/221–1927–1.

300 BRUNT, E. E. VAN, W. F. GANONG and M. D. SHEPHERD – *Penetration of Light into the Brain of Mammals* – Ref. 1963b.

1 BRUSH, E. – Observations on the temporal judgement during sleep – *Am. J. Psychol.* 42–1930–408.

100 BRUSS, R. T., E. JACOBSON, F. HALBERG, R. A. ZANDER and J. J. BITTNER – Effects of lighting regimen and blinding upon gross motor activity of mice – *Fed. Proc.* 17–1958–21.

1 BRUUN, K. – Seasonal variations in the phosphate content of the blood during the first two years of life – *Acta Ped.* 7/suppl. 2–1928–226.

100 BRYSON, R.A. and J.A. DUTTON – *Some aspects of the variance spectra of tree rings and varves* – Ref. 1961e, p. 580.

1 BUCK, A. – Tagesschwankungen der Kalium-Calcium-Quotienten – *Arztl. Forsch.* 3–1949–64, 195.

200 BUCK, J. B. – Studies on the firefly – *Physiol. Zool.* 10–1937–45.

201 BUCK, J. B. – Synchronous rhythmic flashing of fireflies – *Quart. Rev. Biol.* 13–1938–301.

100 BUCKEL, M. and F. ELLIOTT – Diurnal fluctuation of plasmafibrinolytic activity in normal males – *Lancet* –1959I–660.

100 BÜHLER, C. and H. HETZER – *Inventar der Verhaltensweisen des ersten Lebensjahres* – Fisher. Jena, 1927.

200 BÜHLER, W. – *Über Mondwirksamkeiten in der Nativität* – Diss. Univ. Freiburg, 1940.

1 BÜHNEMANN, F. – *Die rhythmische Sporenbildung von Oedogonium cardiacum* – Diss. Univ. Giessen, 1954.

2 BÜHNEMANN, F. – Die rhythmische Sporenbildung von *Oedogonium cardiacum* – *Biol. Zbl.* 74–1955–1.

3 BÜHNEMANN, F. – Das endodiurnale System der Oedogonium-Zelle. II. Der Einfluss von Stoffwechselgiften und anderen Wirkstoffen – *Biol. Zbl.* 74–1955–691.

4 BÜHNEMANN, F. – Das endodiurnale System der Oedogonium-Zelle, III. Über den Temperatureinfluss – *Z. Naturforsch.* 10b,–1955c–305.

5 BÜHNEMANN, F. – Das endodiurnale System der Oedogonium-Zelle. IV. Die Wirkung verschiedener Spektralbereiche auf die Sporulations- und Mitoserhythmik – *Planta* 46–1955–227.

1   BÜNNING, E. – Untersuchungen über
    die autonomen tagesperiodischen
    Bewegungen der Primärblätter von
    Phaseolus multiflorus – *Jb. Wiss.
    Bot.* 75–1931–439.

2   BÜNNING, E. – Über die Erblichkeit
    der Tagesperiodizität bei den *Pha-
    seolus*-Blättern – *Jb. Wiss. Bot.* 77–
    1932–283.

3   BÜNNING, E. – Zur Kenntnis der
    erblichen Tagesperiodizität bei den
    Primärblättern von *Phaseolus multi-
    floris* – *Jb. Wiss. Bot.* 81–1935–411.

4   BÜNNING, E. – Zur Kenntnis der
    endogenen Tagesrhythmik bei In-
    sekten und bei Pflanzen – *Ber. D.
    Bot. Ges.* 53–1935–594.

5   BÜNNING, E. – Die endonome Tages-
    rhythmik als Grundlage der photo-
    periodischen Reaktion – *Ber. D.
    Bot. Ges.* 54–1936–590.

6   BÜNNING, E. – Phototropismus und
    Carotinoide I – *Planta* 36–1937–719.

7   BÜNNING, E. – *Die Physiologie des
    Wachstums und der Bewegungen* –
    Berlin, 1939.

8   BÜNNING, E. – Untersuchungen über
    der physiologischen Mechanismus
    der endogenen Tagesrhythmik bei
    Pflanzen – *Z. Bot.* 37–1942–433.

9   BÜNNING, E. – Die Anpassung der
    Pflanzen an den jahres- und tages-
    periodischen Wechsel der Aussen-
    bedingungen – *Naturwiss.* 31–1943–
    493.

10 BÜNNING, E. – Die allgemeinen
    Grundlagen der photoperiodischen
    Empfindlichkeit – *Flora* 38–1944–
    93.

11 BÜNNING, E. – Endonome Tages-
    rhythmik und Photoperiodismus bie
    Kurztagpflanzen – *Biol. Zbl.* 61–
    1944–161.

12 BÜNNING, E. – Weitere Versuche
    über die Beziehung zwischen en-
    dogener Tagesrhythmik und Pho-
    toperiodismus – *Z. Naturforsch.* 3b–
    1948–457.

13 BÜNNING, E. – Jahres- und tagespe-
    riodische Vorgänge in der Pflanze –
    Stud. Gen. 2–1949–73.

14 BÜNNING, E. – Über die photophile
    und skotophile Phase der endogenen
    Tagesrhythmik – *Planta* 38–1950–
    521.

15 BÜNNING, E. – Über Langtagpflan-
    zen mit doppelter photophiler Pha-

se – *Ber. D. bot. Ges.* 64/(2–3)–1951–
    85.

16 BÜNNING, E. – Über den Tagesrhyth-
    mus der Mitosehäufigkeit in Pflan-
    zen – *Z. Bot.* 40–1952–193.

17 BÜNNING, E. – *Neuere Untersuchun-
    gen über jahres-und tagesperiodische
    Erscheinungen bei Pflanzen* – Ref.
    1953a, p. 68.

18 BÜNNING, E. – Die Beziehung einiger
    photoperiodischer Phänomene bei
    Soja und *Xanthium* zur endogenen
    Tagesrhythmik – *Ber. D. Bot. Ges.*
    67–1954–421.

19 BÜNNING, E. – Der Verlauf der endo-
    genenen Tagesrhythmik bei photo-
    periodischen   Störlicht-Versuchen
    mit *Soja*–*Physiol. Plant.* 7–1954–538.

20 BÜNNING, E. – *Endogenous Diurnal
    Cycles of Activity in Plants* – Ref.
    1956a, p. 111.

21 BÜNNING, E. – Endogenous rhythms
    in plants – *Ann. Rev. Plant Physiol.*
    7–1956–71.

22 BÜNNING, E. – Versuche zur Beein-
    flussung der endogenen Tages-
    rhythmik durch chemische Fak-
    toren – *Z. Bot.* 44–1956–515.

23 BÜNNING, E. – Endogene Aktivitäts-
    rhythmen – *Hb. Pflanzenphysiol.* 2–
    1956–878.

24 BÜNNING, E. – *Physiological Mecha-
    nism and Biological Importance of
    the Endogenous Diurnal Periodicity
    in Plants and Animals* – Ref. 1957f.
    p. 507.

25 BÜNNING, E. – *Additional Remarks
    on the Role of the Endogenous Diur-
    nal Periodicity in Photoperiodism* –
    Ref. 1957f, p. 531.

26 BÜNNING, E. – *Diurnal Changes in
    Pigment Content and in the Photo-
    periodic Efficiency of Red and Far
    Red.* – Ref. 1957f, p. 537.

27 BÜNNING, E. – Über die Urethan-
    Vergiftung der endogenen Tages-
    rhythmik – *Planta* 48–1957–453.

28 BÜNNING, E. – *Mécanisme Physio-
    logique et Importance Biologique de
    la Périodicité Diurne Endogène* –
    Ref. 1958b, p. 7.

29 BÜNNING, E. – *Die physiologische
    Uhr* – Springer. Berlin 1958, 1963;
    English ed., Academic Press, New
    York, 1964.

30 BÜNNING, E. – Das Weiterlaufen der
    physiologischen Uhr im Säuger-

darm ohne zentrale Steuerung –
Naturwiss. 45–1958–68.

31   BÜNNING, E. – Über den Temperatureinfluss auf die endogene Tagesrhythmik, besonders bei *Periplaneta
americana* – *Biol. Zbl.* 77–1958–141.

32   BÜNNING, E. – Cellular clocks-*Nature* 181–1958–1169.

33   BÜNNING, E – Zur Analyse des Zeit-
sinns bei *Periplaneta americana* –
Z. Naturforsch. 14b–1959–1.

34   BÜNNING, E. – *Biological Clocks* –
Ref. 1960c, p. 1.

35   BÜNNING, E. – *Circadian Rhythms
and the Time Measurement in Photoperiodism* – Ref. 1960c, p. 249.

36   BÜNNING, E. – *Mechanism in circadian rhythms. Functional and Pathological Changes Resulting from Beats
and from Rhythm Abnormalities* –
Ref. 1961c, p. 901.

100   BÜNNING, E. and G. JOERRENS –
Tagesperiodische antagonistische
Schwankungen der Blauviolett- und
Gelbrot-Empfindlichkeit als Grund-
lage der photoperiodischen Diapau-
se-Induktion bei *Pieris brassicae* –
Z. Naturforsch. 15b–1960–205.

101   BÜNNING, E. and W. KÖNITZ –
Diurnale antagonistische Schwankungen von Hell- und Dunkelrot-
empfindlichkeit einer Kurztagspflanze–*Naturwiss.* 44/21–1957–568.

102   BÜNNING, E., and F. J. LEINWEBER
– Die Korrektion des Temperatur-
fehlers der endogenen Tagesrhythmik – *Naturwiss.* 43–1956–42.

103   BÜNNING, E. and M. RUDDAT –
Weitere Untersuchungen zur Deutung der physiologischen Uhr als
Kippschwingungssystem – *Naturwiss.* 47–1960–286.

104   BÜNNING, E. and G. SCHÖNE-
SCHNEIDERHÖHN – Die Bedeutung
der Zellkerne im Mechanismus der
endogenen Tagesrhythmik – *Planta*
48–1957–459.

105   BÜNNING, E. and K. STERN – Über
die tagesperiodischen Berwegungen
der Primärblätter von *Phaseolus
multiflorus.* II – *Ber. D. Bot. Ges.*
48–1930–227.

106   BÜNNING, E., K. STERN and R.
STOPPEL – Versuche über den Einfluss von Luftionen auf die Schlafbewegungen von *Phaseolus* – *Planta*
11–1930–67.

107   BÜNNING, E. and M. TAZAWA – Über
den Temperatureinfluss auf die endogene Tagesrhythmik bei *Phaseolus* – *Planta* 50–1957–107.

108   BÜNNING, E. and H. ETZGOLD –
Über die Wirkung von polarisier-
tem Licht auf keimende Sporen von
Pilzen, Moosen und Farnen – *Ber.
D. Bot. Ges.* 71–1958–304.

109   BÜNNING, E. and D. MÜLLER – Wie
messen Organismen lunare Zyklen?
Z. Naturforsch. 16B–1961–391.

1   BÜNSOW, R. C. – Endogene Tagesrhythmik und Photoperiodismus
bei *Kalanchoë blossfeldiana* – *Planta* 42–1953–220.

2   BÜNSOW, R. C. – Über tages- und
jahresrhythmische Änderungen der
photoperiodischen Lichtempfind-
lichkeit bei *Kalanchoë blossfeldiana*
und ihre Beziehungen zur endogenen
Tagesrhythmik – *Z. Bot.* 41–1953–
257.

3   BÜNSOW, R. C. – Über den Einfluss
der Lichtmenge auf die endogene
Tagesrhythmik bei *Kalanchoë blossfeldiana* – *Biol. Zbl.* 72–1953–465.

4   BÜNSOW, R. C. – *The Circadian
Rhythm of Photoperiodic Responsiveness in Kalanchoë* – Ref. 1960c,
p. 257.

1   BÜTTNER, I. – *Über den Verlauf der
nichterhöhten Rektaltemperatur bei
Gesunden und Kranken* – J.-D. Hamburg 1956.

1   BUGARD, P. – Los ritmos biologicos
en la vida y en la enfermedad del
hombre – *Prensa Med. Mex.* 28/(3–
4)–1963–127.

1   BULLOUGH, W. S. – A study of the
reproductive cycle of the Minnow
in relation to the environment –
Proc. Zool. Soc. (London) 109A–
1939–79.

2   BULLOUGH, W. S. – The effect of the
reduction of light in spring on the
breeding season of the Minnow –
Proc. Zool. Soc. (London) 110A–
1940–149.

3   BULLOUGH, W. S. – Mitotic activity
in the adult male mouse – *Proc.
Roy. Soc.* 135B–1948–212.

4   BULLOUGH, W. S. – The effect of
experimentally induced rest and
exercise on the epidermal mitotic
activity of the adult male mouse –
Proc. Roy. Soc. 135B–1948–233.

5 BULLOUGH, W. S. – *Vertebrate Sexual Cycles*. – Methuen. London, 1951.

6 BOULLOUGH, W. S. – The energy relation of mitotic activity – *Biol. Rev.* 27–1952–133.

7 BULLOUGH, W. S. *Vertebrate Photo-stimulation* – Ref. 1957f, p. 641.

8 BULLOUGH, W. S. – Stress and epidermal mitotic activity I – *J. Endocrinol.* 8–1952–265.

100 BURCH, N.R., W.J. NETTLETON Jr., J. SWEENEY and R.J. EDWARDS – Period analysis of the electroencephalogram on a general-purpose digital computer – *Ann. N.Y. Acad. Sci.* 115/2–1964–827.

1 BURCHARD, E. – *Re-setting a Biological Clock* – Thesis. Princeton University, 1958.

300 BURCKHARD, E., L. DONTCHEFF and C. KAYSER – Le rythme nycthéméral chez le pigeon – *Ann. Physiol.* 9–1933–303.

100 BURDICK, D. J. and E. H. KARDOS – The age structure of fall, winter, and spring populations of *Culex tarsalis* in Kern County, California – *Ann. Entomol. Soc. Am.* 56/4–1963–527.

1 BURGER, J. W. – Some experiments on the relation of the external environment to the spermatogenetic cycle of *Fundulus heteroclitus* – *Biol. Bull.* 77–1939–96.

2 BURGER, J. W. – Some further experiments on the relation of the external environment to the spermatogenetic cycle of *Fundulus heteroclitus* – *Anat. Rec.* 75/suppl.– 1939–138.

3 BURGER, J. W. – Some aspects of the roles of light intensity and the daily length of exposure to light in the sexual activation of the male starling – *J.Exp.Zool.* 81–1939–333.

4 BURGER, J. W. – On the relation of day length to the phases of testicular involution and inactivity of the starling – *J. Exp. Zool.* 105–1947–259.

5 BURGER, J. W. – A review of experimental investigations on seasonal reproduction in birds – *Wilson Bull.* 61–1949–211.

6 BURGER, J. W. – The effect of photic and psychic stimuli on the reproductive cycle of the male starling – *J. Exp. Zool.* 124–1953–227.

100 BURGER, J. W., T. H. BISSONETTE and H. D. DOOLITTLE – Some effects of flashing light on testicular activation in the male starling – *J. Exp. Zool.* 90–1942–73.

1 BURNS, N. B. – Seasonal variations of the symptomatology of pulmonary tuberculosis – *Bost. Med. Surg. J.* 168–1913–421.

1 BURR, H. S. – Diurnal potentials in the Maple tree – *Yale J. Biol. Med.* 17–1945–727.

1 BURRAGE, R. H. – Seasonal feeding of larvae of *Ctenicera destructor* and *Hypolithus bicolor* on potatoes placed in the field at weekly intervals – *Ann. Entomol. Soc. Am.* 56/3–1963–306.

1 BURROWS, W. – Periodic spawning of "Palolo" worms in Pacific waters – *Nature* 155–1945–47.

2 BURROWS, W. – Palolo; Notes on the periodic appearance of the annelid worm *Eunice viridis* in the Southwest Pacific Islands – *J. Polynes. Soc.* 64/1–1955–137.

1 BURSTRÖM, H. – *Influence on Root Growth of Light, Iron and Gibberellic Acid* – Ref. 1960b, p. 401.

1 BUSCH, G. – Über die photoperiodische Formänderung der Chloroplasten von *Selaginella serpens* – *Biol. Zbl.* 72–1953–598.

100 BUTENKO, R. G., A. A. NICHIPOROVICH and N. N. PROTASOVA – *Biological Activity of the Photosynthetic Products of Plants Illuminated in Light of Various Spectral Composition* – Ref. 1960b, p. 174.

100 BUTTERY, B.R. and S.G. BOATMAN – Turgor pressures in phloem – *Science* 145/3629–1964–285.

1 BYKOW, K. M. – *Studien über periodische Veränderungen physiologischer Funktionen des Organismus* – Akademie-Verlag. Berlin, 1954.

2 BYKOW, K. M. and A. D. SLONIM, – *Kortikale Mechanismen der Physiologie der Zeit im Organismus der Tiere und des Menschen* In: Bykow, Ref. 1, p. 1.

1 CALHOUN, J. B. – Twenty-four hour periodicities in the animal kingdom I. – *J. Tenn. Acad. Sci.* 19–1944– 179, 252; 20–1945–228, 291, 337; 21–1946–208, 281.

2 CALHOUN, J. B. – Diel activity rhythms of the rodents *Microtus*

ochrogaster and *Sigmodon hispidus* – *Ecology* 26–1945–250.

3   CALHOUN, J.B. – Population cycles and year frequency fluctuations in foxes of the genus *Vulpes* in Canada – *Can. J. Res.* 28D/2 –1950–47.

100 CALLAWAY III, E. and C. L. YEAGER – *Relation between Human Reaction Time and EEG α-Phase* – Ref. 1960a, p. 18.

100 CAMPBELL, I. A. and I. A. WEBSTER – Day and night urine during complete rest, laboratory routine, light muscular work and oxygen administration – *Biochem. J.* 15–1921–660.

101 CAMPBELL, J. A. and T. A. WEBSTER – Note on urinary tides and excretory rhythms – *Biochem. J.* 16–1922–507.

100 CANIGGIA, A. and T. DI PERRI – *Il Ritmo dell'Eliminazione Urinaria dell'Aldosterone nei Soggetti Normali e nei Cardiopatici* – Ref. 1028–1960a, p. 22.

101 CANIGGIA, A. and B. LETIZIA – La biorhythmo-pharmacologie de l'appareil cardiovasculaire – *Acta Med. Scand.* 135–1949–339.

1   CANNON, W. B. – Organization for physiological homeostasis – *Physiol. Rev.* 9–1929–399.

2   CANNON, W. B. – *The Wisdom of the Body* (2nd ed.) – Norton. New York, 1939.

1   CAPEL-BOUTE, C. – *Effects diurnes dans les Tests physiochimiques de Piccardi et dans la Précipitation du Carbonate de Calcium en Solutions diluées* – *Ref.* 1963c.

1   CARLETON, A. – A rhythmical periodicity in the mitotic division of animal cells – *J. Anat.* 68–1934–251.

1   CARPENTER, J. R. – Diurnal fluctuations in communities adjoining the forest edge near Urbana, Ill. – *Proc. Okla. Acad. Sci.* 14–1932–29.

1   CARPENTIER, J. – *Navigation par Inertie* – 1962.

1   CARR, A. – Orientation problems in the high seas travel and terrestrial movements of marine turtles – *Am. Sci.* 1962–359.

100 CARR, A. and L. OGREN – The ecology and migrations of sea turtles IV. – *Bull. Am. Mus. Nat. Hist.* 121–1960–48.

200 CARR, D. J. – The photoperiodic behaviour of short-day plants – *Physiol. Plants* 5–1952–70.

201 CARR, D. J. – A critical experiment on Bünning's theory of photoperiodism – *Z. Naturforsch.* 7b–1952–530.

1   CARROZZINI, B. – *On the Urinary Excretion of Combined Neutral* 17-*Ketosteroids and* 11-*Oxycorticosteroids in Short Term Collection Periods during* 24 *Hours* – Ref. 1960a, p. 24.

1   CARSON, R. L. – *The Sea Around Us* – Oxford Univ. Press, 1951.

1   CARTHY, J. – Do animals see polarized light – *New Scientist* 10/239–1961–660.

1   CARTWRIGHT, D. E. – The delusion of "sea-level" – *New Sci.* 20/359–1963–33.

1   CASPERS, H. – Mondumlauf und Fortpflanzungsrhythmik bei Tieren – *Forsch.-Fortschr.* 24/(7–8)–1948–89.

2   CASPERS, H. – *Beobachtungen über eine lunare Periodizität bei marinen Mücken* – Ref. 1949a, p. 36.

3   CASPERS, H. – Periodizitätserscheinungen bei Tieren und ihre kausale Deutung – *Stud. Gen.* 2/2–1949–78.

4   CASPERS, H. – Rhythmische Erscheinungen in der Fortpflanzung von Clunio marinus und das Problem der lunaren Periodizität bei Organismen – *Arch. Hydrobiol.* 18/suppl.–1951–415.

5   CASPERS, H. – *Neue Beobachtungen über den Palolowurm auf Samoa* – Ref. 1960a, p. 27.

6   CASPERS, H. – Beobachtungen über Lebensraum und Schwärmperiodizität des Palolowurmes – *Int. Rev. Ges. Hydrobiol.* 46/2–1961–175.

100 CASPERSSON, T. and H. HOLMGREN – Variationen der Kerngrösse während der verschiedenen Phasen der Leberarbeit – *Anat. Anz.* 79/(1–4)–1934–1.

1   CATHEY, H. M. – *Effects of Gibberellin on the Growth and Flowering of Chrysanthemum morifolium on Short Photoperiodics* – Ref. 1957f, p. 365.

100 CENKOVICH, F. S. and J. W. GERSTEN – Fourier analysis of the normal human electromyogram – *Am. J. Phys. Med.* 42/5–1963–192.

100 CERLETTI, A. and E. ROTHLIN – *Beitrag zur Frage rhythmischer*

Kreislaufphänomene – Ref. 1953a, p.
p. 48.

100 CHANCE, B., D. GARFINKEL, J. J. HIG-
GINS and B. HESS – Metabolic control mechanisms – *J. Biol. Chem.*
235/8–1960–2426.

101 CHANCE, B., J. J. HIGGINS and D.
GARFINKEL – Analogue and digital
computer representations of biochemical processes – *Fed. Proc.* 21/1–
1962–75.

102 CHANCE, B., A. GHOSH, J.J. HIGGINS,
and P.K. MAITRA – Cyclic and oscillatory responses of metabolic pathways involving chemical feedback
and their computer representations–
Ann. N.Y. Acad. Sci. 115/2–1964–
1010.

1 CHARLES, E. – The hour of birth, a
study of the distribution of times
of onset of labour and of delivery
throughout the 24-hour period –
Brit. J. Prev. Soc. Med., 7–1953–43.

100 CHASSAGNE, P. and F. BRICOUT – Epi-
démiologie générale des maladies
à virus entérigues et respiratoires:
études cliniques – *Arch. Ges. Virusforsch.* 13/(1–3)–1963–3.

100 CHAUDRY, A. P., F. HALBERG and
J. J. BITTNER – Epinephrine and
mitotic activity in pinnal epidermis
of the mouse – *J. Appl. Physiol.*
6/2–1956–265.

101 CHAUDRY, A. P., F. HALBERG,
C. E. KEENAN, R. N. HARNER and
J. J. BITTNER – Daily rhythms in
rectal temperature and in epithelial
mitoses of hamster pinna and pouch
– *J. Appl. Physiol.* 12/2–1958–221.

102 CHAUDRY, A. P. and F. HALBERG –
*Rhythms in Blood Eosinophils and
Mitoses of Hamster Pinna and
Pouch; Phase Alterations by Carci-
nogen* – Proc. 38th Annual Meeting
Internat. Assoc. Dental Res. 1960.

103 CHAUDRY, A. P. and F. HALBERG –
*Adrenalectomy Effects Upon Tempe-
rature and Pinnal Mitotic Rhythms
in Hamsters* – Proc. Int. Assoc.
Dent. Res. 1961.

104 CHAUDRY, A. P., F. HALBERG and
J. H. BITTNER – Mitoses in pinna
and interscapular epidermis of mice
in relation to physiologic 24 hour
periodicity – *Fed. Proc.* 15–1956–34.

1 CHOUARD, P. – Remarques sur l'ac-
coutumance des feuilles aux condi-

tions photopériodiques et sur les
effects du sens de variation de la
durée de la photopériode – *Bull.
Soc. Bot. Fr.* 104(9–10)–1957–608.

100 CHOUARD, P. and R. JACQUES –
*Rhythme Endogène dans la Mise à
Fleur du Chenopodium polyspermum
L.* – Ref. 1958b, p. 21.

1 CHRISTIAN, J. J. – The adrenopi-
tuitary system and population
cycles in mammals – *J. Mammal.*
31–1950–247.

1 CLAES, H. – *Die Beteiligung des dissi-
milatorischen Stoffwechsels an der
photoperiodischen Reaktion von Hyoscyamus niger* – Diss. Univ. Tübingen, 1945.

100 CLAES, H. and A. LANG – Die Blütenbildung von *Hyoscyamus niger*
in 48 stündigen Licht-Dunkel-Zy-
klen und in Zyklen mit aufgeteilten
Lichtphasen – *Z. Naturforsch.* 2b–
1947–56.

100 CLARK, L. B., S. L. LEONARD and
G. BUMP – Light and the sexual
cycle of game birds – *Science* 85–
1937–339.

200 CLARK, A. H. – Nocturnal animals –
J. Wash. Acad. Sci. 4–1914–139.

500 CLARK, R. H. and B. L. BAKER –
Circadian periodicity in the concentration of prolactin in the rat
hypophysis – *Science* 143/3604–1964
–375.

1 CLARKE, G. – Diurnal migration of
plankton in the Gulf of Maine and
its correlation with changes in submarine irradiation – *Biol. Bull.* 65–
1933–402.

100 CLARKE, G. and D. ZINN – Seasonal
production of zooplankton of
Woods Hole with special reference
to *Calamus fimnarchius* – *Biol. Bull.*
73–1937–464.

1 CLASING, D. – *Elektronische Blut-
druckmessungen im Nüchternzustand
zur Tages-rhythmik beim Sportler* –
Diss. Münster 1961.

1 CLAUSER, G. – *Die Kopfuhr* – Enke.
Stuttgart, 1954.

1 CLAUSS, H. – Der Blattfarbstoffge-
halt in verschiedenen Licht-Dun-
kel-Rhythmen gezogener Keimpflanzen – *Z. Bot.* 42–1954–215.

100 CLAUSS, H. und W. RAU – Über die
Blütenbildung von Hyoscyamus
niger und Arabidopsis in 72-Stun-

den-Zyklen – *Z. Bot.* 44–1956–437.

101 CLAUSS, H. and B. SCHWEMMLE – Substanzproduktion und Chlorophyllbildung von Keimpflanzen in 72-Stunden-Zyklen mit aufgeteilter Lichtphase – *Z. Bot.* 47–1959–226.

100 CLEGG, R. E. and P. E. SANDFORD – The influence of intermittent periods of light and dark on the rate of growth of chicks – *Poultry Sci.* 30–1951–760.

1 CLEMMOW, P. C. – MHD-waves in the earths environment – *New Sci.* 351–1963–297.

1 CLOUDSLEY-THOMPSON, J. L. – The water relation and cuticle of *Paradesmus gracilis* – *Quart. J. Micr. Sci.* 91–1950–453.

2 CLOUDSLEY-THOMPSON, J. L. – On the responses to environmental stimuli and the sensory physiology of millipedes – *Proc. Zool. Soc. (London)* 121–1951–253.

3 CLOUDSLEY-THOMPSON, J. L. – Studies in diurnal rhythms, I and II – *J. Exp. Biol.* 28–1951–165; 29–1952–295.

4 CLOUDSLEY-THOMPSON, J. L. – Studies in diurnal rhythms, III – *Ann. Mag. Nat. Hist. Ser.* 12–1953–705.

5 CLOUDSLEY-THOMPSON, J. L. – Studies in diurnal rhythms IV – *Proc. Roy. Entom. Soc. (London)* 28A–1953–117.

6 CLOUDSLEY-THOMPSON, J. L. – Studies in diurnal rhythms V – *J. Linn. Soc. Zool.* 43–1957–134.

7 CLOUDSLEY-THOMPSON, J. L. – Studies in diurnal rhythms, VI – *Ann. Mag. Nat. Hist.* 9/Ser. 12–1956–305.

8 CLOUDSLEY-THOMPSON, J. L. – Studies in diurnal rhythms VII – *J. Exp. Biol.* 33–1956–576.

9 CLOUDSLEY-THOMPSON, J. L. – The effect of wind upon the nocturnal emergence of woodlice and other terrestrial arthropods I–III – *Entomol. Mthly Mag.* 94–1958–106, 184, 283.

10 CLOUDSLEY-THOMPSON, J. L. – Studies in diurnal rhythms VIII – *J. Ins. Physiol.* 2–1958–275.

11 CLOUDSLEY-THOMPSON, J. L. – Studies in diurnal rhythms IX–X – *Ent. Exptl. Appl.* 2–1959–249; 3–1960–121.

12 CLOUDSLEY-THOMPSON, J. L. – Diurnal rhythm in animals – *Sci. News* 28–1953–76.

13 CLOUDSLEY-THOMPSON, J. L. – Diurnal rhythm of locomotory activity in isolated migratory locusts – *Entomol. Mthly Mag.* 89–1953–233.

14 CLOUDSLEY-THOMPSON, J. L. – The ecological significance of diurnal rhythms in terrestrial arthropods – *Sci. Progr.* 42–1954–46.

15 CLOUDSLEY-THOMPSON, J. L. – *Diurnal Rhythms in the Terrestrial Arthropoda* – Ref. 1955a, p. 66.

16 CLOUDSLEY-THOMPSON, J. L. – The design of entomological aktograph apparatus – *Entomologist* 88/1106–1955–153.

17 CLOUDSLEY-THOMPSON, J. L. – Diurnal rhythms of activity in terrestrial arthropods – *Nature* 178–1956–215.

18 CLOUDSLEY-THOMPSON, J. L. – The effect of rock cover on the diurnal range of microclimatic conditions – *Entomologist* 89–1956–213.

19 CLOUDSLEY-THOMPSON, J. L. – The ecological significance of diurnal rhythms in terrestrial arthropods – *Proc. 14th Intern. Congr. Zool. (Copenhagen)* 1956–415.

20 CLOUDSLEY-THOMPSON, J. L. – *The Evolution of Twenty-four-hour Periodicities in Terrestrial Arthropoda* – Rep. 15th Internat. Congr. Zool. Sect. 10, paper 21.

21 CLOUDSLEY-THOMPSON, J. L. – *Microclimates and Diurnal Rhythms in Terrestrial Arthropoda* – Ref. 1957e.

22 CLOUDSLEY-THOMPSON, J. L. – Some comments on the natural control of animal populations with especial reference to insects – *Entomologist* 90/1131–1957–195.

23 CLOUDSLEY-THOMPSON, J. L. – Water relations and diurnal rhythms in woodlice – *Ann. Appl. Biol.* 46/1–1958–117.

24 CLOUDSLEY-THOMPSON, J. L. – Microclimate, diurnal rhythms and the conquest of the land by Arthropods – *Int. J. Biometeorol.* 3/(sect. IIIB)–1959.

25 CLOUDSLEY-THOMPSON, J. L. – Animal clocks – *Nature* 184–1959–763.

26 CLOUDSLEY-THOMPSON, J. L. – *Adap-*

tive Functions of Circadian Rhythms Ref. 1960c, p. 345.

27 CLOUDSLEY-THOMPSON, J. L. – Diurnal rhythm of activity in insects and their ecological significance – *Entomologist* 1961–40, 70, 89.

28 CLOUDSLEY-THOMPSON, J. L. – *Rhythmic Activity in Animal Physiology and Behaviour* – Academic Press. New York, 1961.

29 CLOUDSLEY-THOMPSON, J. L. – Diurnal rhythms – *Trans. IX. Int. Congr. Entomol.*, (Amsterdam) 1951, 1–1952 –305.

100 CLOUDSLEY-THOMPSON, J. L. and M. GUPTA – The effect of wind upon the nocturnal emergence of woodlice and other terrestrial arthropods IV–*Entomol. Mthly, Mag.* 95–1960– 167.

101 CLOUDSLEY-THOMPSON, J. L. and SANKEY, J. H. P. – Some aspects of the fauna of the district around the Etang de Berre, Bouches-Du Rhone, France – *Ann. Mag. Nat. Hist.* 10/ser. 12–1957–417.

1 CLYNES, M. – *The Non-Linear Biological Dynamics of Unidirectional Rate Sensivity Illustrated by Analogical Computer Analysis, Pupillary Reflex to Light and Sound and Heart Rate behaviour* – Ref. 1961c, p. 806.

2 CLYNES, M. – Unidirectional rate sensitivity; a biocybernetic law of reflex and humoral systems as physiological channels of control and communication – *Ann. N.Y. Acad. Sci.* 92/3–1961–946.

100 COERMANN, R. R., E. B. MAGID and K. O. LANGE – Human performance under vibrational stress – *Human factors.* Oct. 1962–315.

100 COHEN, J. and E. C. DODDS – Twenty-four hour observation on the metabolism of normal and starving subjects – *J. Physiol.* 59–(1924– 1925)–259.

100 COHN, C., D. JOSEPH, L. BELL and A. OLER – Feeding frequency and protein metabolism – *Am. J. Physiol.* 205/1–1963–71.

1 COLE, K. S. – *Repetitive Nerve Action* – Ref. 1957c.

200 COLE, L. C. – Population cycles and random oscillations – *J. Wildlife Man.* 15–1951–233.

201 COLE, L. C. – *Some Features of*

Random Population Cycles – Ref. 1954b, p. 2.

202 COLE, L. C. – Biological clock in the Unicorn. – *Science* 125–1957–874.

500 COLE, C.L., and P.L. ADKISSON – Daily rhythm in the susceptibility of an insect to a toxic agent – *Science* 144/3622–1964–1148.

100 COLLATZ, L. and WETTERLING – *Methoden der mathematischen Statistik zur Untersuchung von Zeitreihen* – Ref. 1963a.

100 CONN, J. W., L. H. LOUIS, S. S. FAJANS, D. H. P. STREETEN and R. D. JOHNSON – Dependence of attacks of periodic paralysis upon retention of sodium – *Trans. Assoc. Am. Physiol.* 70–1957–167.

100 COOK, S. F. and J. D. CONNERS – The short-term side effects of the insecticidal treatment of Clear Lake, Lake County, California in 1962 – *Ann. Entomol. Soc. Am.* 56/6–1963– 819.

100 COOMBS, C. J. F. and A. J. MARSHALL – The effects of hypophysectomy on the internal testis rhythm in birds and mammals–*J.Endocrinol.* 13–1956–107.

1 COOPER, Z. K. – Mitotic rhythm in human epidermis – *J. Invest. Dermatol.* 2–1939–289.

100 COOPER, Z. K. and C. FRANKLIN – Mitotic rhythm in the epidermis of the mouse – *Anat. Rec.* 78–1940–1.

101 COOPER, Z. K. and A. SCHIFF – Mitotic rhythm in human epidermis – *Proc. Soc. Exp. Med.* 39–1938– 323.

1 CORBET, P. S. – *Patterns of Circadian Rhythms in Insects* – Ref. 1960c, p. 357.

2 CORBET, P. S. – The ovipositioncycles of certain sylvan culicine mosquitoes in Uganda – *Ann. Trop. Med. Parasitol.* 57/3–1963–371.

1 CORRSIN, S. – Turbulent flow – *Am. Sci.* 49/3–1961–300.

1 COSSA, P. – *La Cybernétique* – Masson. Paris. 1955.

1 COSSEL, L. – Zur Morphologie der Gallensekretion im Säuglings- und Kindesalter – *Acta Hepatol.* 4/(9–10) –1956–1.

1 COURSEY, DE P. J. – *Daily Activity Rhythms in the Flying Squirrel, Gvolans* – Diss. Univ. Wisc 1959.

2 COURSEY, P. J. DE – *Phase Control of Activity in a Rodent* – Ref. 1960c, p. 49.

3 COURSEY, P. J. DE – Daily light sensitivity rhythm in a rodent – *Science* 131–1960–33.

4 COURSEY, P. J. DE – Effect of light on the circadian activity rhythm of the flying squirrel, *Glaucomys volans* – *Z. Vgl. Physiol.* 1961–331.

1 COURTOT, Y. – Recherches sur la nutation de la première feuille du *Bulbine annua* – *C.R. Acad. Sci.* 242 –1955–274.

100 COURTOT, Y. and L. BAILLAUD – Sur la périodicité des différenciations libériennes chez le Tilleul – *Ann. Sci. Univ. (Besançon)* 8 Ser. 2–1956–73.

101 COURTOT, Y. and L. BAILLAUD – *Quelques Modalités du Rythme de la Différenciation dans le Liber des Cupressacées* – Ref. 1958b, p. 53.

100 COURTOT, Y. and L. BAILLAUD – Sur quelques modalités du rythme de la différenciation du liber chez les Cupressacées – *Bull. Soc. Franc. Physiol. Veget.* 4/3–1958–90.

103 COURTRIGHT, L. J. and A. B. – Inhalent sensitization and shock in guinea pigs under controlled atmospheric condition III – *J. Allerg.* 16/3–1945–146.

100 COUVREUR, J., C. M. COOK, C. CHANY and J. GERBEAUX – Une épédémie d'exanthème à virus ECHO de type 16 en milieu hospitalier avec bilan d'une enquête longitudinale – *Arch. Ges. Virusforsch.* 13/(1–3)–1963–215.

1 CRAIG-BENNETT, A. – The reproductive cycle of the three-spined stickleback – *Phil. Trans. Roy. Soc. (London)* 219B–1931–197.

1 CRAMÉR, H. – *Mathematical Methods of Statistics* – Princeton Univ. Press. Princeton, 1946.

200 CRAMER, M. – Über die Tagesschwankungen der Säuglingssterblichkeit – *Münch. Med. Wschr.* 1920 II–1341.

400 CRAMER, J. L. – *Periodicities underlying Mental Illnesses* – Ref. 1960a, p. 35.

1 CREUTZBERG, F. – *The Role of Tidal Streams in the Navigation of Migrating Elvers* – Ref. 1962d, p. 118.

1 CROWCROFT, P. – The daily cycle of activity in British shrews – *Proc. Zool. Soc. (London)* 123–1954–715.

1 CROZIER, W. J. – Some points concerning adaptation, (IV) – Persisting rhythms of light production in balanoglossids – *Anat. Rec.* 20–1920 –186.

100 CULLEN, G. E. and J. EARLE – The variation of acid-base condition in the individual throughout the day – *Am. J. Physiol.* 90–1929–322.

1 CULVER, J. – *Dynamic Linearization* – Systems Res. Center, Case Inst. Technol., Cleveland, Ohio, U.S.A., Jan. 1962.

1 CUNNINGHAM, W. J. – Noise – *Am. Sci.* 43/3–1955–479.

2 CUNNINGHAM, W. J. – The concept of stability – *Am. Sci.* 51/4–1963–425.

100 CURRY, G. M. and H. E. GRUEN – *Dose-Response Relationships at Different Wave-Lengths in Phototropism of Avena* – Ref. 1960b, p. 155.

101 CURRY, G. M. and K. V. THIMANN – *Phototropism: the Nature of the Photoreceptor in Higher and Lower Plants* – Ref. 1960b, p. 127.

1 CUSHING, P. H. – The vertical migration of planktonic *Crustacea* – *Biol. Rev.* 26–1951–158.

1 DAKIN, E. F. – Cycles in history – *Cycles* 12/10(repr. 7)–1961.

1 DAMSTE, P. H. – Experimental modification of the sexual cycle of the greenfinch – *J. Exp. Biol.* 24–1947–20.

1 DANIEL, R.S. – Electroencephalographic correlogram ratios and their stability – *Science* 145/3633–1964–721.

1 DANILYEVSKY, A.S. – Photoperiodism and the seasonal development of insects [in Russian] – *Leningrad State Univ. Publ.* 1961.

100 DANILYEVSKY, A. S. and K. F. GEISPITS – The influence on the daily periodicity of illumination on the seasonal rhythm of insects (Russian) – *Dokl. Acad. Nauk. SSSR* 59–1948–337.

101 DANILYEVSKY, A. S. and Y. J. GLINYANAYA – On the influence of the rhythm of illumination and temperature on the origin of diapause in insects (Russian) – *Dokl. Akad. Nauk. SSSR* 71–1950–963.

1 DAQUET, G. L. – Surveillance conti-

nue de l'endémie grippale par la réaction de fixation du complement – *Arch. Ges. Virusforsch.* 13/(1–3)– 1963–224.

100 DARTNALL, H. J. A., M. R. LANDER and F. W. MUNZ – *Periodic Changes in the Visual Pigment of a Fish* – Ref. 1960b, p. 203.

100 DARWIN, CH. and F. – *The Power of Movement in Plants* – 1880.

300 DARWIN, F. and D. F. M. PERTZ – On the artifical production of rhythm in plants I-II – *Ann. Bot.* 6–1892–245; 17–1903–93.

1 DAUDET, L. – *Les Rythmes de l'Homme* – Grasset. Paris, 1930.

100 DAVIDSON, H. and C. L. HAMNER – Photoperiodic response of selected woody ornamental shrubs – *Mich. Agr. Expt. Sta. Quart. Bull.* 40–1957 –327.

1 DAVIS, D. E. – A cycle in Northern Shrike emigrations – *Auk* 54–1937– 43.

200 DAVIS, D. H. S. – Rhythmic activity in the short tailed vole – *J. Anim. Ecol.* 2–1933–232.

400 DAVIS JR., E. A. – Seasonal changes in the energy balance of the English sparrow – *Auk* 72–1955–385.

600 DAVIS, H. – Homeostasis of cerebral excitability – *Electroenceph. Clin. Neurophysiol.* 2–1950–243.

800 DAVIS, R. E. – Daily rhythm in the reaction of fish to light – *Science* 137/3528–1962–430.

1100 DAVIS, L. D., K. PAPPAJOHN and I. M. PLAVNIEKS – Bibliography of the biological effects of magnetic fields – *Fed. Proc.* 21/5 (part II, Suppl. 12)–1962–1.

1 DEAN, P. – Atomic vibrations in alloys – *New Scientist* 15/298–1962– 258.

1 DEANE, H. W. – A cytological study of the diurnal cycle of the liver of the mouse in relation to storage and secretion – *Anat. Rec.* 88–1944–39.

1 DE CANDOLLE, A. P. – *Physiologie Végétale* – Paris, 1832.

1 DEEVEY, E. S. – The hare and the haruspex, a cautionary tale – *Am. Scient.* 48/3–1960–415.

1 DEHNEL, P. A. – Effect of photoperiod on the oxygen consumption of two species of intertidal crabs – *Nature* 181–1958–1415.

100 DELEANU, M. C. and T. FRITS – *Nonspecific Biological Action of Aero-Ionization* – Ref. 1963c.

1 DELL'ACQUA, G. – *Biochemische und klinische Bemerkungen über 24-Stunden-Rhythmen* – Ref. 1960a, p. 36.

2 DELL'ACQUA, G. – Biopatoritmi – *Minerva Med.* 41–1950–269.

3 DELL'ACQUA, G. – *The Serum P.B.T. Variability during 24 hours* – Ref. 1963a.

100 DELL'ACQUA, G. and G. GAMBASSI – *Le Variazioni Giornaliere della Sintesi del Colesterolo* – Ref. 1960a, p. 42.

1 DEMENT, W. – Dream recall and eye movements during sleep in schizophrenics and normals – *J. Nerv. Ment. Dis.* 122–1955–263.

100 DEMENT, W. and KLEITMAN, N. – Incidence of eye motility during sleep in relation to varying EEG pattern – *Fed. Proc.* 14–1955–37.

101 DEMENT, W. and N. KLEITMAN – The relation of eye movements during sleep to dream activity – *J. Exp. Psychol.* 53–1957–339.

102 DEMENT, W. and N. KLEITMAN – Cyclic variations in EEG during sleep and their relation to eye movements, body motility and dreaming– *Electroenceph. Clin. Neurophysiol.* 9–1957–673.

1 DENIER, A. – The microvibrations of the body as an expression of physiologic tonus – *EEG Clin. Neurophysiol.* 9–1957–362.

1 DENNIS, J.B. – The use of computers in speech research– *Ann. N.Y. Acad. Sci.* 115/2–1964–867.

1 DEPORTE, J. V. – The prevalent hour of still-birth – *Am. J. Obst. Gyn.* 23/ 1–1932.

1 DÉRER, L. – Concealed macroperiodicity in the reactions of the human organism – *Rev. Czechoslovak. Med.* 2–1956–4.

1 DEREVJAGIN, M.J. – Diurnal fluctuations of blood sugar levels in albino rats [in Russian] – *Fiziol. Zhurn. SSSR* 21–1936–124.

1 DETWILER, S. R. – The eye and its structural adaptations – *Am. Sci.* 44/1–1956–45.

100 DEUEL, H. J., J. S. BUTTS, L. F. HALLMANN, S. MURRAY and H.

BLUNDEN – Studies on ketosis. XIII. Diurnal changes in liver glycogen – *J. Biol. Chem.* 123–1938–257.

1 DEWAN, E. M. – Nonlinear oscillation and neuroelectric phenomena – Air Force Cambridge Research Lab., L.G. Hanscom Field, Mass., USA; Rep. AFCRL–63–149, June 1963.

1 DEWEY, E. R. – Cycle timing varies with latitude – *Cycles* 9/11–1958–228.

2 DEWEY, E. R. – The moon as a cause of cycles – *Cycles* 10/9–1959–197.

3 DEWEY, E. R. – *The Importance of Biological Rhythm in the Study of Periodicities in General* – Ref. 1960a, p. 44.

4 DEWEY, E. R. – The case for exogenous rhythms – *J. Cycle Res.* 9/4–1960–131.

1 DICKE, R. H. – Gravitation - an enigma – *Am. Sci.* 47/1–1959–25.

100 DICKSON, M. H. and S. E. CHUA – Effect of flashing light on plant-growth rate – *Nature* 198–1963–305.

1 DIECKMANN, D. – Mechanische Modelle für den vertikal schwingenden menschlichen Körper – *Intern. Z. Physiol. Arbeitsphysiol.* 17–1958–67.

1 DIGBY, P. B. – Flight activity in the blowfly, *Calliphora erythrocephalo,* in relation to light and radiant heat, with special reference to adaptation – *J. Exp. Biol.* 35/1–1958–1.

2 DIGBY, P. B. – Flight activity in the blowfly, *Calliphora erythrocephala* in relation to wind speed, with special reference to adaptation – *J. Exp. Biol.* 35/4–1958–776.

1 DIJKGRAAF, S. – Über das Problem der Fernorientierung bei Vögeln – *Österr. Zool. Z.* 1–1947–314.

1 DISSMAN, E. – Klinische Studien über den 24-Stunden-Rhythmus und seine Störungen bei Lungentuberkulösen – *Acta Tub. Scand.* 21– – 204.

2 DISSMAN, E. – Lungenblutung und 24-Stunden-Rhythmus – *Acta Tub. scand.* 24– –3.

3 DISSMAN, E. – Zur Frage von Eigenrhythmus und Grundrhythmus in den Tagesschwankungen der Vitalkapazität – *Acta Med. Scand.* 137–1950–441.

1 DJAVID, I. – Über die Tagesschwankungen der Eosinophilenzahl im Blut und die Beeinflussung der Eosinophilen durch Adrenalin – *Klin. Wschr.* 14–1935–930.

100 DOAN, C. J. and L. G. ZERFAS – The rhythmic range of the white blood cells in human pathological leucopenia and leucocytic states – *J. Exp. Med.* 46–1927–511.

100 DOBREFF, M. and T. SAPRJANOFF – Physiologische Tagesschwankungen im Liquor cerebrospinalis – *Z. Exp. Med.* 85–1932–299.

1 DOBROKHOTOV, V. N. – Regulation of rhythmic changes in mitotic activity in various tissues of the organism – *Pathol.-Biol.* 9/(5–6)–1961–507.

100 DOBROKHOTOV, V. N. and A. G. KURDYUMOVA – 24-hour periodicity of mitotic activity of the epithelium in the oesophagus of albino rats – *Bull. Exp. Biol. Med. USSR* /8–1962–81.

101 DOBROKHOTOV, V. N. and L. D. LIOSNER – Second conference on regeneration and cell proliferation – *Fol. Biol. (Prague)* 7/4–1961–294.

102 DOBROKHOTOV, V.N. and R. I. NIKANOROVA – 24-hour daily periodicity of cellular mitosis in adrenal glands of albino rats – *Bull. Exp. Biol. Med. USSR* – /9–1962–91.

1 DODD, E. L. – The problem of assigning a length to the cycle to be found in a simple moving average and in a double moving average of chance data – *Econometria* 9–1941–25.

100 DOE, R. P., J. A. VENNES and E. B. FLINK – Diurnal variation of 17-hydroxycorticosteroids, sodium, potassium, magnesium and creatinine in normal subjects and in cases of treated adrenal insufficiency and Cushing's syndrome – *J. Clin. Endocrinol.* 20–1960–253.

1 DÖMÖK, J. – Virological aspects of Coxsackie virus infections – *Arch. Ges. Virusforsch.* 13/(1–3)–1963–128.

1 DÖRING, G. K. – Über rhythmische Schwankungen von Atmung und Körpertemperatur im Menstruationszyklus – *Pflüger's Arch.* 250–1948–694.

2 DÖRING, G. K. – Über rhythmische

Veränderungen der Erythrocyten-konzentration und der Retikulo-cytenzahl im mensuellen Zyklus der Frau – *Pflüger's Arch.* 252–1950–292.

3 DÖRING, G. K. – Der Temperaturzy-klus der Frau – *Ärztl. Forsch.* 1–1952–13.

4 DÖRING, G. K. – *Rhythmische Ver-änderungen der Atmung im Zyklus der Frau* – Ref. 1953a, p. 154.

5 DÖRING, G. K. – Über Veränderun-gen der Atmung während des Cy-clus – *Arch. Gyn.* 182–1953–746.

6 DÖRING, G. K. – Über Veränderun-gen des Brustvolumens im Cyclus – *Arch. Gyn.* 184–1953–51.

7 DÖRING, G. K. – Zur Frage einer Ver-minderung geistiger Leistungsfähig-keit während der Menstruation – *Medizinische* 13–1954–425.

8 DÖRING, G. K. – Die Reaktion auf Sinnesreize im Verlauf des Men-struationszyklus – *D. Med. Wschr.* 79–1954–885.

9 DÖRING, G. K. – *Psychische Verän-derungen im Rhythmus des Men-struationszyklus* – Ref 1955a, p. 73.

100 DÖRING, G. K. and E. FEUSTEL – Über Veränderungen der Puls-frequenz im Rhythmus des Men-struationscyclus – *Klin. Wschr.* 31–1953–1000.

101 DÖRING, G. K. and E. FEUSTEL – Menstruationszyklus and Wasser-haushalt – *Die Medizinische* 51–1954–1713.

102 DÖRING, G. K. and H. RIECKE – Über tagesperiodische Schwankun-gen der Capillarresistenz – *Klin. Wschr.* 30/(45–46)–1952–1098.

103 DÖRING, G. K. and E. SCHAEFERS – Über die Tagesrhythmik der Pupil-lenweite beim Menschen – *Pflüger's Arch.* 252–1950–537.

104 DÖRING, G. K. and E. SCHAEFERS – Über Veränderungen der Pupillen-weite im Rhythmus des Menstrua-tionscyclus – *Arch. Gyn.* 179–1951–585.

105 DÖRING, G. K., E. SCHAEFERS and G. WEBER – Über die 24-Stunden Rhythmik im Eiweissgehalt des Blutserums beim Menschen – *Pflü-ger's Arch.* 253–1951–165.

106 DÖRING, G. K. and G. WEBER – Über Schwankungen des Eiweissgehaltes

des Blutserums im Rhythmus des Menstruationscyclus mit Hilfe der Bestimmung des spezifischen Ge-wichtes des Serums – *Arch. Gyn.* 179–1951–442.

107 DÖRING, G. K. and E. FEUSTEL – Über Veränderungen des Differen-tialblutbildes im Cyclus – *Arch. Gyn.* 184–1954–522.

1 DÖRKEN, H. – *Monat und Jahreszeit bei internen Krankheitsbildern* – Ref. 1963a.

1 DONLE, W. – *Jahreszeit und Witte-rung im Seuchengeschehen* – Enke. Stuttgart, 1956.

100 DONNOWAN, B. T. and G. W. HARRIS – The effect of pituitary stalk sec-tion on light induced oestrus in the ferret – *J. Physiol.* 131–1956–102.

100 DONTCHEFF, L, CH. KAYSER and P. REISS – Le rythme nycthémérale de la production de chaleur chez le pigeon – *Ann. Physiol. Physicochim Biol.* 11–1935–1185.

100 DOORENBOS, J. and S. J. WELLEN-SIEK – Photoperiodic control of flo-ral induction – *Ann. Rev. Plant Phys.* 10–1959–147.

1 DOUGLASS, A. E. – Tree rings and their relation to solar variations and chronology – *Ann. Rep. Smithson. Inst.* 1931–304.

2 DOUGLASS, A. E. – Climatic cycles and tree growth – *Carn. Inst. Wash. Publ.* 289–1936–171.

1 DOWNS, R. J. – *Photocontrol of Vege-tative Growth* – Ref. 1957f, p. 129.

100 DOWNS, R. J. and H. A. BORTHWICK – Effects of photoperiod on growth of trees – *Bot. Gaz.* 117–1956–310.

101 DOWNS, R. J. and A. A. PIRINGER – Effects of photoperiod and kind of supplemental light on vegetative growth of pines – *For. Sci.* 4–1958–185.

1 DRESLER, A. – Die subjective Photo-metrie farbiger Lichte – *Naturwiss.* 1941–225.

1 DRESSLER, O. – Properdin-Tages-rhythmus – *Klin. Wschr.* 36–1958–779.

100 DREYER, G., H. C. BAZETT and H. F. PIERCE – Diurnal variation in the hemoglobin contents of the blood – *Lancet* 1920 I–588.

1 DRISCHEL, H. – Die vegetative Re-gulation als theoretisches Problem

einer selbsttätigen Regelung – *Acta Neuroveg.* 6/(3–4)–1953–317.

2 DRISCHEL, H. – *Die Dynamik des Pupillen-Mechanismus, eines biologischen "Lichtstärke-Reglers"* – Ref. 1955a, p. 69.

3 DRISCHEL, H. – Untersuchungen über die Dynamik des Lichtreflexes der menschlichen Pupille I and II – *Pflüger's Arch.* 264–1957–145, 169.

1 DROESE, W. – Die Tagesschwankungen des Kalium-Calcium-Quotienten – *Ärztl. Forsch.* 3–1949–193.

1 DRZEWINA, A. – Les variations périodiques du signe du phototropisme chez les Pagures misanthropes – *C.R. Acad. Sci.* 145–1907–1208.

100 DUBLIN, W. B., R. O. GREGG and A. C. BRODERS – Mitosis in specimens removed during day and night from carcinomas of large intestine – *Arch. Pathol.* 30–1940–893.

1 DÜLL, B. – *Wetter und Gesundheit* – Leipzig, 1941.

100 DÜLL, B. and T. – Über die Abhängigkeit des Gesundheitszustandes von plötzlichen Eruptionen auf der Sonne und die Existenz einer 27-tägigen periode in den Sterbefällen – *Virch. Arch.* 293–1934–272.

101 DÜLL, B, and T. – Neue Untersuchungen über die Beziehungen zwischen der Zahl der täglichen Todesfälle und dem magnetischen Störungscharakter – *Bioklim. Beibl.* 2–1935–24.

102 DÜLL, B. and T. – Erd- und sonnenphysikalische Vorgänge in ihrer Bedeutung für Krankheits- und Todauslösung – *Nosokomeion* 9/2–1938–103.

103 DÜLL, B. and T. – Zur Frage solaraktiver Einflüsse auf die Psyche – *Z. Neur. Psychiatr.* 162–1938–495.

104 DÜLL, B., and T. – Kosmisch-physikalische Störungen der Ionosphäre, Trophosphäre und Biosphäre – *Bioklim. Beibl.* 1939–65, 121.

105 DÜLL, B. and T. – Neuer Beitrag zur Erforschung des Bioklimas – *Umschau* 93/31–1939–715.

1 DUHAMEL DU MONCEAU – *La physique des arbres* 2–1758–158.

1 DUKE, B. O. L. – Studies of the biting habits of *Chrysops* VI – *Ann. Trop. Med. Parasit.* 53–1959–203.

1 DUNCAN, G. G. – *Diseases of Metabolism* – Saunders. Philadelphia, 1953.

1 DUNNE, J. W. – *An Experiment with Time* – Faber and Faber. London, 1958.

1 DUNNING, R. A. – A diurnal rhythm in the emergence of *Pegomyia batae* Curtis from the puparium – *Bull. Ent. Res.* 47–1956–645.

100 DUREMAN, I., I. SCHOLANDER and H. SALDE – An apparatus for pupillography with intermittent infrared light – *J. Psychosom. Res.* 5–1961–224.

1 DUTROCHET, H. – *Mémoires pour Servir à l'Histoire des Végétaux et des Animaux* – Bruxelles, 1837.

1 DUYSENS, L. N. M. – *Cytochrome Oxidation by a Second Photochemical System in the Red Algae* – Ref. 1960b, p. 135.

1 DYSON-HUDSON, V. R. D. – The daily activity rhythm of *Drosophila subobscura* and *D. obscura* – *Ecology* 37–1956–562.

1 EADIE, G. S. – The variations of the blood sugar of the rabbit throughout the day and the effect of the subcutaneous injections of glucose – *Am. J. Physiol.* 63–(1922–1923)–513.

1 EASTROP, V. F. – Diurnal variation in the aerial density of *Aphididae* – *Proc. Roy. Entomol. Soc. (London)* 26A/(10–12)–1951.

1 EASTWOOD, E. – Radar's contribution to studies of birds – *New Scientist* 14/282–1962–23.

1 EBBECKE, U. – Über Gefässreaktionen der Niere und den Antagonismus von Glomerulus- und Tubulusdurchblutung – *Pflüger's Arch.* 226–1931–761.

1 EBBESEN, I. – *Seasonal variation in the ultraviolet and infrared radiation from sun and sky at Copenhagen* – Ref. 1960b, p. 102.

100 ECHAVE LLANOS, J. M. and R. S. PIEZZI – Twenty-four hour rhythm in the mitotic activity of normal mammary epithelium on normal and inverted lighting regimens – *J. Physiol.* 165/3–1963–437.

101 ECHAVE LLANOS, J. M. and E. G. BADE – Variation in the water and dry matter content of the liver during the second day of posthepatec-

tomy regeneration – *Naturwiss.* 80/ 3–1963–97.

102 ECHAVE LLANOS, J. M. and A. F. BADRAN – Ritmo de 24 horas en la actividad mitotica de un carcinoma mamario injertado de C₃H/mza hembra – *Rev. Soc. Argent. Biol.* 37–1961–226.

103 ECHAVE LLANOS, J. M. and A. F. BADRAN – Twenty-four hour rhythm in mitotic activity of mammary mice carcinoma – *Acta Physol. Lat.-am.*, 13/1–1963–78.

104 ECHAVE LLANOS, J. M. and C. BORDIN – The growth effect of regenerating liver homogenate as a function of the responsiveness of the receptor – *Naturwiss.* 50/14–1963–501.

105 ECHAVE-LLANOS, J.M. and A.F. BADRAN – 24-Hour rhythm in the mitotic activity of a grafted mammary carcinome in female C3H/M₃₀ -mice on normal and inverted lighting regimens – *J. Roy. Microscop. Soc.* 82/2–1963–75.

1 EDDINGTON, A. S. – *The Nature of the Physical World* – Macmillan. New-York, 1928.

100 EDLUND, Y. and H. HOLMGREN – Experimentelle Studien des Verhaltens der Narkose zu verschiedenen Zeiten der 24-Stundenperiode – *Z. Ges. Exp. Med.* 107/1–1939–26.

101 EDLUND, Y., and H. HOLMGREN – Zur Kenntnis der Lokalisation des Leberglykogens unter Adrenalinbeziehungsweise Insulin-Wirkung – *Z. Mikr-Anat.Forsch.* 47–1940–467.

102 EDLUND, Y. and H. HOLMGREN – The rhythmical variations of the liver glycogen and the pyruvic acid in the blood in experimental obstructive jaundice – *Acta Med Scand.* 120/(1–2)–1945–107.

1 EDMUNDS, L.N. – Replication of DNA and cell division in synchronously dividing cultures of *Euglena gracilis–Science* 145/3629–1964–266.

1 EECKHOUDT, J. P. v. D. – Recherches sur l'influence de la lumière sur le cycle sexual de l'Epinoche – *Ann. Soc. Zool. Belg.* 77–1946–83.

1 EGYED, L. – *Temperature and magnetic field* – Ref. 1961e, p. 72.

100 EHNI, L., G. HILDEBRANDTS-EVERS and H. BERGER – Grundlagen für

die oscillographische Diagnostik im Wachstumsalter – *Z. Kinderhlk.* 85–1961–100.

1 EHRENBERG, M. – Beziehungen zwischen Fermenttätigkeit und Blattbewegung bei *Phaseolus muṭiflorum* unter verschiedenen photoperiodischen Bedingungen – *Planta* 38/3–1950–244.

1 EHRENWALD, H. – Versuche zur Zeitauffassung des Unbewussten – *Arch. Ges. Psychol.* 45–1923–144.

2 EHRENWALD, H. – Störung der Zeiterfassung, der räumlichen Orientierung, des Zeichnens und des Rechnens bei einem Hirnverletzten – *Z. Ges. Neur. Psych.* 132–1931–518.

1 EHRET, C. F. – An analysis of the role of electromagnetic radiations in the mating reaction of *Paramecium bursaria* – *Physiol. Zool.* 26/3–1953–274.

2 EHRET, C. F. – The photoreactivability of sexual activity and rhythmicity in *Paramecium bursaria* – *Rad. Res.* 3–1955–34.

3 EHRET, C. F. – The effects of pre-and post-illumination on the scotophilic recovery phase of the *Paramecium bursaria* mating raction – *Anat. Rec.* 122–1955–456.

4 EHRET, C. F. – *Induction of Phase Shift in Cellular Rhythmicity by Far Ultraviolet and its Restoration by Visible Radiant Energy* – Ref. 1957f, p. 541.

5 EHRET, C. F. – Photobiology and biochemistry of circadian rhythms in non-photosynthesizing cells – *Fed. Proc.* 18/4–1959–1232.

6 EHRET, C. F. – *Effects of Light on Circadian Rhythm in Cells* – Ref. 1960a, p. 51.

7 EHRET, C. F. – *Action Spectra and Nucleic Acid Metabolism in Circadian Rhythms at the Cellular Level* – Ref. 1960c, p. 149.

100 EHRET, C. F. and J. S. BARLOW – *Toward a Realistic Model of a Biological Period-Measuring Mechanism* – Ref. 1960c, p. 217.

101 EHRET, C. F. and R. MATHER – Circadian rhythmicity in the incorporation of nucleic acid precursors into *Paramecium bursaria* – *J. Protozool.* 6/suppl. 1–1959–18.

1 EIDMANN, H. – *Über die Steuerung*

rhythmischer Vorgänge bei Insekten – Ref. 1955a, p. 76.

2 EIDMANN, H. – Über rhythmische Erscheinungen bei der Stabheuschrecke *Carausius morosus* – *Z. Vergl. Physiol.* 28–1956–370.

1 EIFF, A. W. VON – *Das Verhalten mehreren Körperfunktionen während eines 7-tägigen Rhythmus-Versuches und die Bedeutung des Zeitbewusstseins* – Ref. 1953a, p. 140.

100 EIFF, A. W. v., E. M. BÖCKH, H. GÖPFERT, F. PFLEIDERER and T. STEFFEN – Die Bedeutung des Zeitbewusstseins für die 24 Stunden-Rhythmen des erwachsenen Menschen – *Z. Ges. Exp. Med.* 120–1953 –295.

1 EISENTRAUT, M. – *Der Winterschlaf mit seinen ökologischen und physiologischen Begleiterscheinungen* – Fisher. Jena, 1956.

100 EKMAN, C. A. and H. HOLMGREN – An investigation of the rhythmic metabolism of the liver with the help of radio-active phosphorus – *Acta. Med. Scand.* suppl. 196–1947– 63.

101 EKMAN C. A. and H. HOLMGREN – The effect of alimentary factors on liver glycogen rhythm and the distribution of glycogen in the liver lobule – *Anat. Rec.* 104/2–1949–189.

100 ELFVIN, L. G., T. PETRÉN and A. SOLLBERGER – Influence of some endogenous and exogenous factors on diurnal glycogen rhythm in chicken – *Acta Anat.* 25–1955–286.

100 ELMADJIAN, F. and G. PINCUS – A study of the diurnal variations in circulating lymphocytes in normal and psychotic subjects – *J. Clin. Endocrinol.* 6–1946–287.

1 EMEIS, D. – Untersuchungen zur Lichtkompassorientierung des Wasserläufers *Velia currens F.* – *Z. Tierpsychol.* 16/2–1959–129.

1 EMERSON, H. – Seasonal variation in growth of school children – *JAMA* 89–1927–1326.

1 EMLEN, J. T. – Morning awakening time of a mocking bird – *Bird-band.* 8–1937–21.

300 EMLEN, S. T., and W. KEM – Activity rhythm in *Peromyscus*. Its influence on rates of recovery from Nembutal – *Science* 142/3600–1963–1682.

1 EMME, A. – *Time in the Living Nature* (in Russian) – Moscow, 1962.

1 ENDERLE, W. – Tagesperiodische Wachstums- und Turgorschwankungen in Gewebekulturen – *Planta* 39–1951–530.

100 ENGEL, H. and I. FRIEDERICHSEN – Das Licht als Ursache periodischer Guttationsschwankungen etiolierter Haferkeimlinge – *Planta* 39–1951– 309.

101 ENGEL, H. and I. FRIEDERICHSEN – Weitere Untersuchungen über periodische Guttation etiolierter Haferkeimlinge – *Planta* 40–1952–529.

200 ENGEL, R. – *Circadian Aspects of the Abnormal Human Electroencephalogram* – Ref. 1961a, p. 50.

201 ENGEL, R. – *Electroencephalographic Responses to Photic Stimulation, and their Correlation to Maturation* – Ref. 1963b.

300 ENGEL, R., F. HALBERG, W. L. P. DASSANAYAKE and J. DE SILVA – 24-hr. rhythms in blood eosinophils and *Wucheria bancrofti* microfilariae before and after 9α-Fluorocortisol – *Nature* 181–1958–1135.

301 ENGEL, R., F. HALBERG, W. L. P. DASSANAYAKE and J. DE SILVA – Adrenal effects on time relations between rhythms of microfilariae and eosinophils in the blood – *Am. J. Trop. Med. Hyg.* 11/5–1962–653.

302 ENGEL, R., F. HALBERG, Y. TICHY and R. DOW – Electrocerebral activity and epileptic attacks at various blood sugar levels – *Acta Neuroveg.* 9/(1–4)–1954–147.

303 ENGEL, R., F. HALBERG and R. J. GULLY – The diurnal rhythm in EEG discharge and in circulating eosinophils in certain types of epilepsy – *Electroenceph. Clin. Neurophysiol.* 4–1952–115.

100 ENGELBERTZ, P. and G. HILDEBRANDT-Tagesrhythmische Schwankungen im Elektrokardiogram – *Arch. Phys. Ther.* 5/6–1953–361.

1 ENGELS, W. L. – *The Influence of Different Daylengths on the Testes of a Transequatorial Migrant, the Bobolink* – Ref. 1957f, p. 759.

100 ENGSTRÖM, H., H. HOLMGREN and G. WOHLFART – Untersuchungen über 24-Stundenrhythmische Veränderungen in der Blutkörperchen-

menge der Leber, der Nebennieren und der Schilddrüse – *Anat. Anz.* 86/(8–10)–1938–129.

1 ENRIGHT, J.T. – The tidal rhythm of activity of a sand-beach amphipod, – *Z. Vergl. Physiol.* 46–1963–276.

1 ERÄNKÖ, O. – *25-Hours Day: One Solution to the Shiftwork Problem* – Intern. Kongr. Arb. Med. 3, Helsinki, 1957, p. 134.

100 ERB, K. E., F. N. ANDREWS and I. H. HILTON – Seasonal variation in the semen quality of the dairy bull – *J. Dairy Sci.* 25–1942–815.

1 ERICSON, L. A. – Twenty-four hourly variation of the aqueous flow – *Acta Ophthalm.* suppl. 50–1958–1.

2 ERICSON, L. A. – Twenty-four hourly variations in the inflow of the aqueous humour – *Acta Ophthalm.* 1958–381.

3 ERICSON, L. A. – Ögontryckets dygnsvariationer – *Nord. Med.* 61–1959–1001.

1 ERIKSEN, S. – Studying the composition of human breath – *New Scientist* 21/381–1964–608.

1 ERRINGTON, P. L. – *On the Hazards of Overemphasizing Numerical Fluctuations in Studies of "Cyclic" Phenomena in Muskrat Populations* – Ref. 1954b, p. 66.

2 ERRINGTON, P. L. – *Of Population Cycles and Unknowns* – Ref. 1957d, p. 287.

3 ERRINGTON, P.L. – Muskrat populations – *Iowa State Univ .Press,* Iowa 1963.

100 ERTEL, R. J., F. UNGAR and F. HALBERG – Circadian rhythm in susceptibility of mice to toxic doses of Su-4885 – *Fed. Proc.* 1963.

100 ESSLER W. O. and G. E. FOLK, JR – Determination of physiological rhythms of unrestrained animals by radio telemetry – *Nature* 190/4770–1961–90.

101 ESSLER, W.O. and G.E. FOLK, Jr. – Multichannel radio telemetry system used to obtain heart rates – *Bull.WildlifeTelemetry* 2/(4-5)–1963.

102 ESSLER, W.O., G.E. Folk, Jr. and G.E. ADAMSON – 24-Hour cardiac activity of unrestrained cats – *Fed. Proc.* 20–1961–129.

1 ESTEL, V. – Neue Versuche über den Zeitsinn–*Philosoph.Stud.* 2–1885–37.

1 ETZOLD, H. – Die Wirkungen der linear polarisierten Lichtes auf Pilze und ihre Beziehungen zu den tropistischen Wirkungen des einseitigen Lichtes – *Exp. Cell. Res.* 25–1961–229.

1 EUGSTER, J. – *Weltraumstrahlung* – Bern, 1955.

100 EULER, U. S. v. und A. G. HOLMQUIST – Tagesrhythmik der Adrenalinsekretion und des Kohlenhydratstoffwechsels beim Kaninchen und Igel – *Pflüger's Arch.* 234–1934–210.

1 EVANS, H. M. – On some seasonal changes in the pituitary gland of the eel – *Brit. Med. J.* 4–1940–565.

100 EVERETT, J. W. and C. H. SAWYER – A 24-hour periodicity in the "LH-release apparatus" of female rats, disclosed by barbiturate sedation – *Endocrinology* 47–1950–198.

1 EVERSON, R. A. – Daily rhythmic variation of blood coagulation times in four species of rodents – *Physiol. Zool.* 33/4–1960–281.

1 EYSTER, B. – Quantitative measurement of the influence of photoperiod, temperature and season on the activity of captive songbirds – *Ecol. Monogr.* 24–1954–1.

1 FAIRBRIDGE, R.W. – *Convergence of evidence on climatic change and ice ages* – Ref. 1961e, p. 542.

1 FARNER, D. S. – The annual stimulus for migration – *Condor* 52–1950–104.

2 FARNER, D. S. – *Photoperiodic Cycles of Annual Gonadal Cycles in Birds* – Ref. 1957f, p. 717.

3 FARNER, D. S. – *The Testicular Response of White-Crowned Sparrows to Stimulatory Photoperiods in Ahemeral Cycles* – Ref. 1960b, p. 438.

4 FARNER, D. S. – Comparative physiology: Photoperiodicity – *Ann. Rev. Physiol.* 23–1961–71.

5 FARNER, D.S. – The photoperiodic control of reproductive cycles in birds – *Am. Sci.* 51/1–1964–137.

100 FARNER, D. S. and L. R. MEWALDT – The relative roles of diurnal periods of activity and diurnal photoperiods in gonadal activation in male *Zonotrichia leucophrys gambeli* (Nutall) – *Experientia (Basel)* 9–1953–221.

101 FARNER, D. S., L. R. MEWALDT and

S. D. IRVING – The roles of darkness and light in the photoperiodic response of the testes of white-crowned sparrows – *Biol. Bull.* 105–1953–431.

102 FARNER, D. S., L. R. MEWALDT and J. R. KING – The diurnal activity patterns of caged migratory white-crowned sparrows in late winter and spring – *J. Comp. Physiol. Psych.* 47–1954–148.

100 FARRAR, J.T., L. ELFENBEIN, C.A. STEINBERG and A. BLOOM – Wave form analysis of gastro-intestinal pressure dynamics – *Ann. N.Y. Acad. Sci.* 115/2–1964–680.

1 FARRIS, E. J. – A formula for selecting the optimum time for conception – *Am. J. Obst. Gyn.* 63–1952–1143.

2 FARRIS, E. J. – *Human Ovulation and Fertility* – Lippincott Co. Philadelphia, 1956.

1 FAURÉ-FREMIET, E. – Le rythme de marée du *Strombidium oculatum* – *Bull. Biol.* 82–1948–3.

2 FAURÉ-FREMIET, E. – Rythme de marée d'une *Chromulina psammophile* – *Bull. Biol.* 84–1950–207.

1 FECHNER, G. T. – Über die Frage des Weberschen Gesetzes und Periodizitätsgesetzes – *Abh. Math.-Phys. Kl. Königl. Sächs. Ges. Wiss.* 13/1–1884–1.

1 FELLOWS, E. W. – Cyclical variation in scientific activity – *J. Cycle Res.* 8/4–1959–108.

1 FÉRÉ, M. C. – De la fréquence des accés d'épilepsie suivant les heures – *C.R. Soc. Biol.* 40–1888–740.

1 FERGUSON, D. E. – *Orientation in Three Species of Anuran Amphibians* – Ref. 1962d, p. 128.

300 FERGUSON, D. J., M. B. VISSCHER, F. HALBERG and L. M. LEVY – Effects of hypophysectomy on daily temperature variation in C$_3$H mice – *Am. J. Physiol.* 190–1957–502.

1 FILATOWA, L. G. – 24-*Stunden-Rhythmus bei Nagetieren und Insektenfressern und Versuch seiner experimentellen Erforschung* – In: Bykow, Ref. 1, p. 114.

1 FINGERMAN, M. – Factors influencing the rate of oxygen consumption of the dwarf crawfish, *Cambarellus*

shufeldtii – *Tulane Stud. Zool.* 3/6–1955–103.

2 FINGERMAN, M. – Persistent daily and tidal rhythms of color change in *Callinectes sapidus* – *Biol. Bull.* 109/2–1955–255.

3 FINGERMAN, M. – *Lunar Rhythmicity in Marine Organisms* – Ref. 1956b, p. 167.

4 FINGERMAN, M. – Phase difference in the tidal rhythms of color change of two species of fiddler crab – *Biol. Bull.* 110/3–1956–274.

5 FINGERMAN, M. – Relation between position of burrows and tidal rhythm of *Uca* – *Biol. Bull.* 112/1–1957–7.

6 FINGERMAN, M. – *Tidal Rhythmicity in Marine Organisms* – Ref. 1960c, p. 481.

100 FINGERMAN, M. and A. D. Lago – Endogenous twenty-four hour rhythms of locomotor activity and oxygen consumption in the crawfish, *Oronectes clypeatus* – *Am. Midl. Nat.* 58/2–1957–383.

101 FINGERMAN, M., A. D. LAGO and M. E. LOWE – Rhythms of locomotor activity and O$_2$-consumption of the grashopper, *Romalea microptera* – *Am. Midl. Nat.* 59/1–1958–67.

102 FINGERMAN, M. and M. E. LOWE – Twenty-four hour rhythm of distal retinal pigment migration in the dwarf crawfish – *J. Cell. Comp. Physiol.* 50/3–1957–371.

103 FINGERMAN, M., M. E. LOWE and W. C. MOBBERLY JR – Environmental factors involved in setting the phases of tidal rhythm of colour changes in the fiddler crabs, *Uca pugilator* and *Uca minae* – *Limnol. Oceanograph.* 3/3–1958–271.

1 FINN, J. C. – *An Investigation of Long- and Short-Day Plants for an Endodiurnal Rhythmicity in the Flowering Response* – Thesis Univ. Calif., 1958.

1 FINSEN, N. R. – Om periodiske aarlige swingninger i blodets haemoglobinmängde – *Hospitalstidende (Norway)* 2/(49–50)–1894–1209.

1 FISCHER, K. – Experimentelle Beeinflussung der inneren Uhr bei der Sonnenkompassorientierung und der Laufaktivität von *Lacerta viridis*

(Laur) – *Naturwiss.* 47/12–1960–287.

100 FISCHER, K. and G. BIRUKOW – Dressur von Smaragdeidechsen auf Kompassrichtung – *Naturwiss.* 47/4–1960–93.

200 FISHER, R. A. – Tests of significance in harmonic analysis – *Proc. Roy. Soc.* 125A–1929–54.

201 FISHER, R. A. – *Statistical Methods for Research Workers* – 12th Ed. Oliver and Boyd. London, 1954.

300 FISHER, R. A. and F. YATES – *Statistical Tables for Biological, Agricultural and Medical Research* – 4th Ed. Oliver and Boyd. London, 1953.

400 FISHER, W. – Die Verteilung der Todesfälle auf die einzelnen Stunden des Tages – *Münch. Med. Wschr.* – 1932 II–1449.

700 FISHER, L. R. and E. H. GOLDIE – *Pigments of Compound Eyes* – Ref. 1960b, p. 153.

900 FISCHER, R. and S. ENGLAND – *Power spectra of rhythms in the mating song of the North American Katydid and in selected readings from English literature* – Ref. 1963a.

901 FISCHER, R., F. GRIFFIN and L. LISS – Biological aspects of time in relation to (model) psychoses – *Ann. N.Y. Acad. Sci.* 96/1–1962–44.

100 FISKE, V. M. and S. E. LEEMAN – *Observations on Adrenal Rhythmicity in the Rat and Associated Phenomena* – Ref. 1963b.

1 FLACH, E. – Grundbegriffe und Grundtatsachen der Bioklimatologie – *Linkes Meteorol. Taschenb.* 3–1957–178.

100 FLEESON, W., B. C. GLUECK, JR. and F. HALBERG – Persistence of daily rhythms in eosinophil count and rectal temperature during regression induced by intensive electroshock therapy – *Physiologist* 1–1957 –28.

100 FLEISCH, A. and R. BECKMANN – Die raschen Schwankungen der Pulsfrequenz registriert mit dem Pulszeitschreiber – *Z. Ges. Exp. Med.* 80–1932–487.

1 FLIESS, W. – *Der Ablauf des Lebens* – Deiticke. Leipzig, 1906.

2 FLIESS, W. – *Zur Periodenlehre* – Diederichs. Jena, 1924.

100 FLINK, E. B. and R. P. DOE – Effect of sudden time displacement by air travel on synchronization of adrenal function – *Proc. Soc. Exp. Biol. Med.* 100–1959–498.

101 FLINK, E. B. and F. HALBERG – Clinical studies on eosinophil rhythm – *J. Clin. Endocrinol.* 12–1952–922.

1 FLÜGEL, A. – Die Gesetzmässigkeiten der endogenen Tagesrhythmik – *Planta* 37–1949–337.

1 FOGG, G. E. – Diurnal fluctuation in a physical property of leaf cuticle – *Nature* 154–1944–515.

1 FOLK, G. E. JR. – *Modification by Light and Feeding of the 24-Hour Rhythm of Activity in Rodents* – Ref. 1955a, p. 80.

2 FOLK G. E. JR. – *Twenty-four Hour Rhythms of Mammals in a Cold Environment* – Ref. 1956b, p. 153.

3 FOLK, G. E. JR. – Modification by light of 24-hour activity of white rats – *Proc. Iowa Acad. Sci.* 66–1959 –399.

4 FOLK, G. E. JR. – *Day-Night Rhythms and Hibernation* – Proc. 1st Internat. Symp. Mammal. Hibernation. C. Lyman, Editor. Cosmos Press, 1960.

5 FOLK, G. E. JR. – *Circadian Aspects of the Circulation* – Ref. 1961a, p. 86.

6 FOLK, G. E., JR. – *Observations on the Daily Rhythms of Body Temperature-labile Mammals* – Ref. 1961c, p. 954.

7 FOLK, Jr. G.E. – The effects of continuous light upon 24-hour activity of arctic mammals – *Bull. Ecol. Soc. Am.* 42–1961–161.

8 FOLK, Jr. G.E. – Day-night physiological rhythms of mammals exposed to extreme changes in arctic daylight–*Symp. Fed. Proc.* 23–1964.

100 FOLK, G. E. JR. and J. R. CARTER – The effects of three winters and hibernation upon thirteen lined ground squirrels – *Anat. Rec.* 128/3– 1957–551.

101 FOLK, G. E. JR. and D. E. GRINDELAND – Estrous cycles of cold-exposed hamsters – *J. Animal Techn. Assoc.* 10/2–1959.

102 FOLK, G. E. JR. and F. SARGENT – *Environmental Extremes and Mammalian Survival* – Univ. Iowa, 1960.

103 FOLK, G. E., JR., M. R. MELTZER and R. E. GRINDELAND – A mammalian activity rhythm independent of

temperature – *Nature* 181–1958–1598.

104 FOLK, G. E., JR. and R. R. SCHELLINGER – The diurnal rhythm of body temperature in the hamster – *Anat. Rec.* 120–1954–787.

105 FOLK, Jr. G.E., R.B. SCHELLINGER and D. SNYDER – Day–night changes after exercise in body temperatures and heart rates of hamsters – *Proc. Iowa Acad. Sci.* 68–1961–594.

106 FOLK, Jr. G.E., G.L. SHOOK, R.S. HEDGE, M.C. BREWER, and M.A. FOLK – Daily (circadian) physiological rhythms of arctic carnivores in continuous light – *Am. Zool.* 3/4–1963.

1 FONTAINE, M. – Des facteurs physiologique déterminant les migrations reproductrices des Cyclostomes et poissons potamotoques – *Bull. Inst. Océan. (Monaco)* 848–1943–1.

2 FONTAINE, M. – Vues actuelles sur les migrations des poissons – *Experientia* 2–1946–233.

3 FONTAINE, M. – Du rôle joué par les facteurs internes dans certaines migrations des poissons – *J. Conseil* 15–1948–284.

4 FONTAINE, M. – De l'hibernation naturelle à "l'hibernation expérimentale" – *Rev. Pathol. Gén. Comp.* 644–1953–53.

5 FONTAINE, M. – Du determinisme physiologique des migrations – *Biol. Rev.* 29–1954–390.

100 FONTAINE, M. and O. CALLAMAND – Sur certaines facteurs des migrations de l'Anguille – *Bull. Soc. Zool. Franç.* 66–1941–68.

101 FONTAINE, M. and O. CALLAMAND – Les aspects physiologiques d'une vie cyclique de l'Anguille d'Europe – *Bull. Mus. Hist. Nat.* 15–1943–373.

102 FONTAINE, M. and J. LELOUP – L'iodémie du saumon au cours de sa migration reproductrice – *C.R. Acad. Sci. (Paris)* 230–1950–1216.

103 FONTAINE, M. and M. OLIVEREAU – L'hypophyse du saumon à diverses étapes de sa migration – *C.R. Acad. Sci . (Paris)* 228–1949–772.

1 FOREL, A. – *Das Sinnesleben der Insekten* – Reinhardt. München, 1910.

1 FORSGREN, E. – Zur Kenntnis der Histologie der Leberzellen und der Gallensekretion – *Anat. Anz.* 51–1918–309.

2 FORSGREN, E. – *Mikroskopiska och Experimentella Leverundersökningar* – Diss. Stockholm, 1927.

3 FORSGREN, E. – On the relationship between the formation of bile and glycogen in the liver of rabbits – *Skand. Arch. Physiol.* 53–1928–137.

4 FORSGREN, E. – Mikroskopische Untersuchungen über die Gallenbildung in den Leberzellen – *Z.Zellforsch. Mikr. Anat.* 6–1928–647.

5 FORSGREN, E. – Über die rhythmische Funktion der Leber und ihre Bedeutung für den Kohlenhydratstoffwechsel bei Diabetes und für die Insulinbehandlung – *Klin. Wschr.* 8–1929–110.

6 FORSGREN, E. – Über Glykogen und Gallenbildung in der Leber – *Skand. Arch. Physiol.* 55–1929–144.

7 FORSGREN, E. – Om leverns rytmiska funktion och insulinets inverkan på leverns glykogenhalt – *Hygiea (Swed.)* 91–1929–369.

8 FORSGREN, E. – The anatomical qualities of the liver during the various stages of its functional activities – *J. Morph. Physiol.* 47–1929–519.

9 FORSGREN, E. – *Om Dygnsvariationer i Blodets Restkvävehalt* – Rep. Swed. Int. Med. Soc. 1930.

10 FORSGREN, E. – The connection between the functional activities of the liver and the susceptibility of the organism to insulin – *Acta Med. Scand.* 73–1930–60.

11 FORSGREN, E. – 24-Stunden-Variationen des Reststickstoffgehaltes im Blute – *Acta. Med. Scand.* 73–1930–213.

12 FORSGREN, E. – 24-Stunden Variationen der Gallensekretion – *Skand, Arch. Physiol.* 59–1930–217.

13 FORSGREN, E. – Über die Beziehungen zwischen Schlaf und Leberfunktion – *Skand. Arch. Physiol.* 60–1930–299.

14 FORSGREN, E. – Om leverfunktion och insulinkänslighet – *Svenska Läkaresällsk. Förhandl.* –1930–231.

15 FORSGREN, E. – Über Leberfunktion, Harnausscheidung und Wasserbelastungsproben – *Acta Med. Scand.* 76/3–1931–285.

16 FORSGREN, E. – Om urobilinuriens dygnsvariationer – *Hygiea (Swed.)* 93–1931–337.

17 FORSGREN, E. – Till frågan om blodsockrets dygnsvariationer – *Hygiea (Swed.)* 93/11–1931–431.

18 FORSGREN, E. – Über Leberfunktion und Insulinempfindlichkeit – *Klin. Wschr.* 11–1932–1429.

19 FORSGREN, E. – *Uber die Rhythmik der Leberfunktion, des Stoffwechsels und des Schlafes* – Stockholm, 1935.

20 FORSGREN, E. – Über die Insulintoleranz bei drei Fällen von Diabetes mellitus, die durch febrile Lungentuberkulose kompliziert waren – *Z. Klin. Med.* 129–1936–774.

21 FORSGREN, E. – Ämnesomsättningens rytmik och insulintoleransen vid fall av diabetes mellitus, komplicerade med ftis – *Nord. Med. Tidskr.* 11–1936–899.

22 FORSGREN, E. – Om leverns assimilationskapacitet – *Nord. Med. Tidskr.* 11–1936–937.

23 FORSGREN, E. – Om människoorganismens dygnsrytm och dess betydelse för medicinen – *Nord. Med. Tidskr.* 12–1936–1143.

24 FORSGREN, E. – *Die Rhythmik der Leberfunktion und des Stoffwechsels* – Ref. 1937a, p. 743.

25 FORSGREN, E. – Något om människans kroppstemperatur – *Med. Fören. Tidskr.* (Stockholm) 1937–92.

26 FORSGREN, E. – Om oväderssjukan – *Hygiea (Swed.)* 100/2–1938–33.

27 FORSGREN, E. – Om behandlingen av sockersjuka vi⟨ lungtuberkulos med någon hänsyn även till leverrytmen – *Hygiea (Swed.)* 100/9–1938–338.

28 FORSGREN, E. – Om middagsvilans betydelse ur ryt misk och ortostatisk synpunkt – *Hygiea (Swed.)* 100/16–1938–642.

29 FORSGREN, E. – Om rytmforskningens metoder, resultat och mål – *Nord. Med. Tidskr.* 15–1938–330.

30 FORSGREN, E. – Några ämnesomsättningsfaktorers storleksordning med särskild hänsyn till leverrytmen och diabetesterapien – *Nord. Med.* 2–1939–1507.

31 FORSGREN, E. – *Om Tidsinställning av Några Funktioner, spec. Leverns och Ventrikelns hos Människan* – Ref. 1941a, p. 18.

32 FORSGREN, E. – Ventrikelfunktionen hos tuberkulösa med särskild hänsyn till dygnsvariationerna och deras betydelse för diagnos, hygien och terapi – *Nord. Med.* 17–1943–339.

33 FORSGREN, E. – *24-Hour Variations of Gastric Function and their Significance for Diagnosis, Prophylaxis and Treatment of Dyspepsia, especially in Tuberculosis* – Lund, 1946.

34 FORSGREN, E. – *Gewichtsvariationen und Assimilationskapazität der Leber* – Ref. 1949a, p. 51.

35 FORSGREN, E. – *24-Stunden-Variationen der Ventrikelacidität und einige Grundbegriffe über ihre Rhythmik* – Ref. 1949a, p. 89.

36 FORSGREN, E. – Leverrythm och behandling av sockersjuka och akyli vid lungtuberkulos – *Svensk. Läkartidn.* 57/45–1960–3186.

100 FORSGREN, E. and R. SCHNELL – On the rhythm of metabolism – *Acta Med. Scand.* 82–1934–155.

101 FORSGREN, E., O. WILANDER, G. Ågren and H. HOLMGREN – Über die Einwirkung des Insulins auf die Leber – *Acta Med. Scand.* 70–1929–139.

1 Fox, H. M. – Lunar periodicity in living organisms – *Sci. Progr.* 17–1922–273.

2. Fox, H. M. – Lunar periodicity in reproduction – *Proc. Roy. Soc.* 95B–1923–523.

3 Fox, H. M. – The effect of light on the vertical movement of aquatic organisms – *Proc. Camb. Phil. Soc. Biol.* 1–1925–219.

4 Fox, H. M. – Lunar periodicity in reproduction – *Nature* 130–1932–23.

1 FRAISSE, P. – *La Structure Temporelle des Mouvements Volontaires Rythmés* – C.R. 11. Congr. Intern. Psychol. 1937.

2 FRAISSE, P. – Contribution et l'étude du rythme en tant que forme temporelle – *J. Psychol. Norm. Pathol.* 39/3–1946–283.

3 FRAISSE, P. – Movements rythmiques et arythmiques – *L'Ann. Psychol.* (47–48)–(1946–1947)–11.

4 FRAISSE, P. – Rythmes auditifs et rythmes visuels – *L'Ann. Psychol.* 49–1948–21.

5   FRAISSE, P. – *Théorie Psychologique du Rythme* – C.R. 12. Congr. Intern. Psychol. 1948, p. 62.

6   FRAISSE, P. – *The Psychology of Time* – Harper and Row. New York, 1963.

100   FRAISSE, P. and S. EHRLICH – Note sur la possibilité de syncoper en fonction du tempo d'une cadence – *l'Ann. Psychol.* 55/1–1955–61.

101   FRAISSE, P. and M. JAMPOLSKY – Premières recherches sur l'induction rythmique des réactions psychogalvaniques et l'estimation de la durée – *l'Ann. Psychol.* 52/2–1952–363.

102   FRAISSE, P. and G. OLÉRON – La structuration intensive des rythmes – *l'Ann. Psychol.* 54/1–1954–35.

103   FRAISSE, P., G. OLÉRON, and J. PAILLARD – Les effets dynamogéniques de la musique – *l'Ann. Psychol.* 53/1–1953.

104.   FRAISSE, P., P. PICHOT and G. CLAIROUIN – Les aptitudes rythmiques; Etudes comparée des oligophrènes et des enfants normaux – *J. Psychol. Norm. Pathol.* 1949–309.

1   FRAJOLA, W. J. – *Circadian Aspects of Enzyme Activity* – Ref. 1961a, p. 74.

100   FRANCAVIGLIA, A., V. CORSI, M. GAGLIO and G. MODICA – *Il Bioritmo Nictemerale delle Sieroproteine* – Ref. 1960a, p. 51.

1   FRANCK, U. F. – Elektrochemische Modelle zur saltatorischen Nervenleitung – *Z. Elektrochem.* 55/6–1951–535.

2   FRANCK, U. F. – Elektrochemische Modelle zur saltatorischen Nervenleitung – *Z. Naturforsch.* 7b/4–1952–220.

3   FRANCK, U. F. – Models for biological excitation process – *Progr. Biophys. Res.* 6–1956–171.

100   FRANCK, U. F. and L. MEUNIER – Gekoppelte periodische Elektrodenvorgänge – *Z. Naturforsch.* 8b/8–1953–396.

1   FRANCK, G. – *Circadian Aspects of the Normal Human Electroencephalogram* – Ref. 1961a, p. 48.

100   FRANK, G., R. HARNER, J. MATTEWS, E. JOHNSON and F. HALBERG – Circadian periodicity and the human electroencephalogram – Proc.

15th Annual Mtg. *Am. Electroenc. Soc.* –1961–24.

200   FRANK, H. – Abhängigkeit des Längenwachstums der Säuglinge von den Jahreszeiten – *Arch. Kinderhlk.* 75–1924–1.

1   FRANKE, H. – Elektrokardiographische Studien über den 24-Stunden-Rhythmus bei Gesunden und Kranken – *Z. Inn. Med. (Wien).* 28–1947–103.

2   FRANKE, H. – Über den 24-Stunden-Rhythmus des Kreislaufs bei Gesunden und Herzkranken – *Ber. Phys. – Med. Ges. (Würzburg)* 65 NF–1951–48.

200   FRANKE, K. – *Natürliche Heilweisen und Körperrhythmik* – Ref. 1953a, p. 185.

201   FRANKE, K. – *Wiederherstellung der durch Berufsüberlastung und Krankheit veränderten Tagesrhythmik* – Ref. 1955a, p. 81.

1   FRANZ, J. – Über Ernährung und Tagesrhythmus einiger Vögel im arktischen Winter – *J. Ornithol.* 91–1943–154.

2   FRANZ, J. – Jahres- und Tagesrhythmik einiger Vögel in Nordfinnland – *Z. Tierpsychol.* 6–1949–309.

1   FRAPS, R. M. – The relation between body temperatures, times of ovulation and time of feeding in hens under continuous lighting – *Anat. Rec.* 96–1946–524.

2   FRAPS, R. M. – Neural basis of diurnal periodicity in release of ovulation inducing hormone in fowl – *Proc. Nat. Acad. Sci. (Wash.)* 40–1954–348.

3   FRAPS, R. M. – *Photoperiodism in the Female Domestic Fowl* – Ref. 1957f, p. 767.

100   FRAPS, R. M., B. H. NEHER and I. ROTSCHILD – The imposition of diurnal ovulatory and temperature rhythms by periodic feeding of hens maintained under continuous light – *Endocrinology* 40–1947–241.

1   FRAUCHIGER, E. – *Rhythmus und Takt in der Lehre vom Leben bei Klages* – Ref. 1953a, p. 32.

1   FREDENHAGEN, C. – Über die Passivität des Eisens und über an Eisenelektroden beobachtete periodische Erscheinungen – *Z. Physikal. Chem.* 43–1903–1.

1 FREEMAN, W. J. – Distribution in time and space of prepyriform electrical activity – *J. Neurophysiol.* 22–1959–644.

2 FREEMAN, W. J. – Correlation of electrical activity of prepyriform cortex and behaviour in cat – *J. Neurophysiol.* 23–1960–111.

3 FREEMAN, W. J. – Repetitive electrical stimulation of prepyriform cortex in cat – *J. Neurophysiol.* 23–1960–383.

4 FREEMAN, W. J. – Q-meter for measuring frequency of cortical reactivity to electrical stimulation – *J. Appl. Physiol.* 16/4–1961–750.

5 FREEMAN, W. J. – Harmonic oscillation as model for cortical excitability changes with attention in cats – *Science* 133/3470–1961–2058.

300 FREEMAN, G. L. and C. I. HOOLAND – Diurnal variations in performance and related physiological processes – *Psychol. Bull.* 31–1934–777.

1 FRENCH, C. S. – *Action Spectra and Optical Properties of Cellular Pigments* – Ref. 1957f, p. 15.

1 FREY, S. – Der Tod des Menschen in seinen Beziehungen zu den Tages- und Jahreszeiten – *D. Z. Chir.* 218–1929–366.

200 FREY, W. – *Atmosphäre und vegetatives Nervensystem* – Ref. 1953a, p. 53.

1 FRIEDERICH, H. C. – Haarwachstumsgeschwindigkeit am Tage grösser als in der Nacht – *Ther. Woche* 10–(1959–1960)–119.

100 FRIEDRICH, L., T. GARAI and E. A. FALUCHI – Quantitative Untersuchung der Tagesschwankungen der Urobilinogenausscheidung – *Z. Ges. Inn. Med.* 13–1958–900.

1 FRIESNER, R. C. – Daily rhythm of elongation and cell division in certain roots – *Am. J. Bot.* 7–1920–380.

1 FRISCH, K. v. – Psychologie der Bienen – *Z. Tierpsychol.* 1–1937–9.

2 FRISCH, K. v. – Die Tänze und das Zeitgedächtnis der Bienen im Widerspruch – *Naturwiss.* 28/5–1940–65.

3 FRISCH, K. v. – Die Polarisation des Himmelslichtes als orientierender Faktor bei den Tänzen der Bienen – *Experientia* 5–1949–142.

4 FRISCH, K. v. – Die Sonne als Kompass im Leben der Bienen – *Experientia* 6–1950–210.

5 FRISCH, K. v. – Orientierungsvermögen und Sprache der Bienen – *Naturwiss.* 38–1951–105.

6 FRISCH, K. v. – *The Dancing Bees. An Account of the Life and Senses of the Honey-Bee* – Methuen. London, 1954.

100 FRISCH, K. v. and M. LINDAUER – Himmel und Erde in Konkurrenz bei der Orientierung der Bienen – *Naturwiss.* 41–1954–245.

1 FROBENIUS, K. – Über die zeitliche Orientierung im Schlaf und einige Aufwachphänomene – *Z. Psychol.* 103–1927–100.

1 FRÖBA, M. – Über die Diurese im Säuglings- und Kleinkindesalter unter Berücksichtigung der Rhythms und ihrer Beeinflussung durch Salzgaben – *Jb. Kinderhlk.* 151–1938–26.

1 FUCHS, J. – *Physical Alterations which occur in the Blind and are illustrated on Ancient Egyptian Works of Art* – Ref. 1963b.

100 FUDEMA J. J., Y. I. OESTER, P. J. TALSO and M. F. GLYNN – Electromyography and electrodiagnosis in familial periodic paralysis – *Bull. Am. Assoc. Electromyography Electrodiathermy* 9–1962–7.

100 FUHRMAN, G. J., E.D. MC. KIN and M.L. TURNER – The effect of time of day on the metabolic rate of albino mice – *Am. J. Physiol* 147–1946–284.

1 FUJIKURA, T. – Placental calcification and seasonal difference – *Am. J. Obst. Gyn.* 87/1–1963–46.

1 FUNCK, H. – *Die renale Ausscheidung von Natrium bei Neugeborenen und Säuglingen* – Diss. Ludwig–Maximilians–Univ. München, 1960.

1 FUZEAU-BRAESCH, S. – Ajustement du cycle de vie avec les saisons chez un insecte univoltine – *C.R. Acad. Sci.* 256/3–1963–792.

100 GABINUS, O. and G. HÖGBERG – Periodisk sjukdom – *Nord. Med.* 60–1958–1726.

100 GADERMANN, E., G. HILDEBRANDT and H. JUNGMANN – Über harmonische Beziehungen zwischen Pulsrhythmus und arterieller Grundschwingung – *Z. Kreislaufforsch.* 50 –1961–805.

100 GALAMBOS, J. T. and R. G. CORNELL

– The diurnal variation of urinary coproporphyrin excretion in health and disease – *Am. J. Med. Sci.* 235–1958–532.

1 GALANT, J. – Über Saison-stottern und über sonstige klimatisch-meteorologische Einflüsse auf die Sprachstörung der Stotterer – *Wien. Med. Wschr.* 86–1936–539.

100 GALBRAITH, J. J. and S. SIMPSON – Conditions influencing the diurnal wave in the temperature of the monkey – *Proc. Physiol. Soc. Lond.* 30–1903–20.

101 GALBRAITH, J. J. and S. SIMPSON – Temperature variation in nocturnal and other birds – *J. Physiol.* 30–1904–19.

1 GALICHICH, J. H. – *Circadian Systems after Brain Ablation* – Ref. 1961a, p. 44.

2 GALICICH, J. H. – *The Role of Central Nervous System Structures in Circadian Synchronization as Revealed by Ablation Experiments*–Ref. 1963b.

100 GALICICH, J. H., F. HALBERG and L. A. FRENCH – Circadian adrenal cycle in C mice kept without food and water for one and one-half days – *Nature* 197–1963–811.

1 GALLEMAERTS, V. – De la zonation dans les cultures des champignons en boîtes de Petri – *Rec. Inst. Bot. Leo Errera* 8–1911–211.

1 GALLENKAMP, F. – Zur Frage der dispositionellen Bedingtheit des "Wintergipfels der Diphterie" – *Z. Kinderhlk.* 58–1937–645.

1 GALLO, V. – *Statistica Ematologica* – Bibl. Haematol.11–Pavia 1950.

1 GALSTON, A. W. – *Studies on Indoleacetic Acid Oxidase Inhibitor and its Relation to Photomorphogenesis* – Ref. 1957f, p. 137.

1 GAMSTORP, J. – Adynamia episodica hereditaria – *Acta Ped.* 108/suppl.–1956–1.

100 GAMSTORP, J. M. HAUGE, H. F. HELWIG-LARSEN, M. MJONES and V. SAGILD–Adynamia episodica hereditaria–*Am. J. Med.* 23–1957–385.

100 GANNT, W. H. and W. MUNCIE – Rhythmic variations of muscular activity in normal and neurotic dogs correlated with secretion and with conditioned reflexes – *Am. J. Physiol.* 133–1941–287.

1 GANS, M. – Sleep and third circulation – *J. Nerv. Ment. Dis.* 103/5–1946–473.

2 GANS, M. – Der Schlaf und die dritte Zirkulation – *Schweiz. Arch. Neur. Psychiatr.* 64–1949–88.

3 GANS, M. – *Rhythmus diei Inversus* – Ref. 1955a, p. 85.

1 GARDNER, M. – Curious properties of a cycloid curve – *Sci. Am.* 211/1–1964–110.

100 GARDNER, W.R. and R.H. NIEMAN – Lower limit of water availability to plants–*Science* 143/3613–1964–1460.

100 GARFINKEL, D., R.H. MACARTHUR and R. SACK – Computer simulation and analysis of simple ecological systems – *Ann. N.Y. Acad. Sci.* 115/2–1964–943.

1 GARNER, W. W. – Photoperiodism – In B. M. Duggar: *"Biological effects of radiation"*. London. 2–1936–677.

100 GARNER, W. W. and H. A. ALLARD – Flowering and fruiting of plants as controlled by the length of day – *Yearb. U.S. Dept. Agricult.* 1920–377.

101 GARNER, W. W. and H. A. ALLARD – Effect of the relative length of day and night and other factors of the environment on growth and reproduction in plants – *J. Agr. Res.* 18–1920–553.

1 GARREY, W. E. – The nature of fibrillary contractions of the heart– *Am. J. Physiol.* 33–1914–397.

100 GASTAUT, H. and E. BECK – Brain rhythms and learning – *New Scientist* 13/276–1962–496.

1 GATES, A. I. – Diurnal variations in memory and association – *Univ. Calif. Publ. Psychol.* 1–1916–323.

2 GATES, A. I. – Variations in efficiency during the day – *Univ. Calif. Publ. Psychol.* 2–1916–1.

200 GATES, D.M. – The energy environment in which we live – *Am. Sci.* 51/3–1963–327.

1 GAUL, A. T. – The awakening and diurnal flight activities of Vesperine wasps – *Proc. R. Ent. Soc. (London)* 27A–1952–33.

1 GEHLKEN, K. – *Tageszeitliche Schwankungen des Atemrhythmus bei endogenen Psychosen* – Ref. 1963a.

100 GEHLKEN, K., G. HILDEBRANDT and M. FRANKE – Psychophysische Kor-

relationen im Kurverlauf – *Arch. Physikal. Ther.* 13/2–1961–171.

1 GEISPITS, K.F. – On the mechanism of perception of light stimuli during the photoperiodic reactions of lepidopterous larvae [in Russian] –*Zool. Zhur.* 36–1957–548.

1 GENERALES, C. D. J. – Space medicine and the physician – *N.Y. State J. Med.* 60/11–1960–1741.

1 GEORGI, F. – Psychophysische Korrelationen – *Schweiz. Med. Wschr.* 74–1944–539; 77–1947–1276.

2 GEORGI, F. – *Rhythmusstörungen im psychophysischen Geschehen* – Ref. 1949a, p. 120.

3 GEORGI, F. – L'état actuel des recherches sur le rythme et les relations entre le rythme et le système neurovégétatif – *Med. Hyg.* 12/(274–275)–1954–344, 359.

100 GERENCSER, W. F., M. F. BARNOTHY, and J. M. – *The Effect of a Magnetic Field on Bacteria during their Growth Cycle* – 1st Intern. Biophysics Congr. Stockholm 1961.

100 GERGEN, J. A. and P. D. MACLEAN – *The Limbic System* – Ref. 1963b.

100 GERLICH, N. and H. WIELE – Über den Einfluss des Tagesrhythmus auf den Glykogen ansatz in Leber, Herz und Körpermuskulatur nach Invert- und Traubenzuckergaben – *Arch. Exp. Path. Pharmak.* 210–1950–98.

1 GERRITZEN, F. – *Der 24-Stundenrhythmus in der Diurese* – Ref. 1937a, p. 746.

2 GERRITZEN, F. – Der 24-Stunden-Rhythmus der Chlorausscheidung – *Pflüger's Arch.* 238–1937–483.

7 GERRITZEN, F. – *The Rhythmic Function of the Human Liver* – Ref. 1939a, p. 121.

4 GERRITZEN, F. – *La Diurèse comme Epreuve d'Oedème* – Congr. Diurèse. Vittel 1939.

5 GERRITZEN, F. – *Der Stoffwechselstrom* – Ref. 1953a p. 150.

6 GERRITZEN, F. – Liver–diuresis as the result of the rhythmic function of the liver – *Acta Med. Scand.* 89–1936–101.

7 GERRITZEN, F. – The 24-hour rhythm in diabetes, *Acta Med. Scand.* – 111/2–1942–212.

8 GERRITZEN, F. – *The Diurnal Rhythm in Water, Chloride, Sodium and Potassium Excretion during a Rapid Displacement from East to West and vice versa* Ref. 1963a.

9 GERRITZEN, F. – Spontane Diurese – *Acta Med. Scand.* 85/(1-2)–1935–154.

1 GESELL, A. – *Infant and Child in the Culture of Today* – Yale Univ. Press. Yale, 1943.

1 GESSLER, H. – Die täglichen Schwankungen der Körpertemperatur – *Pflüger's Arch.* 207–1925–390.

1 GESSNER, F. – *Hydrobotanik* – D. Verlag Wiss. Berlin, 1955.

1 GHATA, J. – *Nycthemeral Variations of Urinary Potassium Excretion in Normal Subjects and in Diabetic Patients* – Ref. 1955a p. 88.

100 GHATA, J. and A. REINBERG – Variations nycthémérale, saisonnière et géographique de l'élimination urinaire du potassium et de l'eau chez l'Homme adulte sain – *C.R. l'Acad. Sci.* 239–1954–1680.

1 GIAO, A. – *Relativistic Interpretation of the Annual Variation of the Piccardi Physio-Chemical D–Test and its Cosmological Meaning* – Ref. 1958 c, p. 139.

2 GIAO, A. – Astrofisica teorica – *Rend. Accad. Naz. Lincei,* 25 Ser. 8/(1–2)–1958–1.

1 GIBSON, R. B. – The effects of transposition of the daily routine on the rhythm of temperature variation – *Am. J. Med. Sci.* 129–1905–1048.

1 GIESE, A. C. – *Reproductive Cycles of some West Coast Invertebrates* – Ref. 1957f, p. 625.

2 GIESE, A.C. (Ed.) – *Photophysiology, I–II* – Academic Press, New York 1964.

100 GIESE, A. C., B. McGAW and R. CORNELL – Retartion of division of three ciliates by intermittent and continuous ultraviolet radiations at different temperatures – *J. Gen. Physiol.* 46/5–1963–1095.

100 GILBERT, T.F. and W.T. JAMES – The dependency of cyclical feeding behaviour on internal and external cues – *J. Comp. Physiol. Psychol.* 49–1956–342.

100 GILLIES, M. T. and I. J. WILKES – Observations on nulliparous and parous rates in a population of *Anopheles funestus* in East Africa –

Ann. Trop. Med. Parasitol. 57/2–1963–204.

1 GISS, G. – Ein Beitrag zum Rhythmus der Thrombocytenzahl – *Z. Klin. Med.* 148–1951–148.

1 GJESSING, R. – Beiträge zur Kenntnis der Pathophysiologie periodischer katatoner Zustände I–IV, – *Arch. Psychiatr.* 96–1932–319, 393; 104–1936–355; 109–1939–525.

2 GJESSING, R. – Beiträge zur Symptomatologie der periodischen Katatonie – *Arch. Psychiatr.* 191–1953–191.

3 GJESSING, R. – *Die periodische Katatonie, ein Beispiel von Periodik im Formenkreis der sogenannten schizophrenen Psychosen* – Ref. 1955a, p. 89.

1 GLASS, R. – Kritisches und Experimentelles über den Zeitsinn – *Phil. Stud.* 4–1888–423.

1 GLICK, D. – *Circadian Rhythms involving Adrenal Enzymes and Coenzymes* – Ref. 1961a, p. 67.

100 GLICK, D., R. B. FERGUSON, L. J. GREENBERG and F. HALBERG – Circadian studies on succinic dehydrogenase pantothenate and biotin of rodent adrenal – *Am. J. Physiol.* 200/4–1961–811.

101 GLICK, J.L. and W.D. COHEN – Nocturnal changes in oxidative activities of rat liver mitochondria – *Science* 143/3611–1964–1184.

100 GLOCK, W. S. and S. AGERTER – Anomalous patterns in tree rings – *Endeavour* 22/85–1963–9.

100 GLYNN, M. F., P. J. TALSO, Y. T. OESTER and J. FUDEMA – Studies in familial periodic paralysis – *Clin. Res.* 10–1962–226.

1 GODLEWSKI, G. – Über die tägliche Periodizität des Längenwachstums – *Bull. Int. l'Acad. Sci. (Krakau)* 55–1889.

100 GÖBEL, P. and H. FISHER – Untersuchungen von 24-Stunden-Schwankungen verschiedener Körperfunktionen – *D. Arch. Klin. Med.* 198–1951–600.

100 GÖNCZY, I., J. Kiss and Z. ENYEDY – Über den Venendruck und dessen Tagesschwankungen – *Z. Exp. Med.* 70–1930–236.

1 GOFFERJÉ, F. – Die Tagesschwankungen der Körpertemperatur beim gesunden und beim kranken Säugling – *Jb. Kinderhlk.* 68–1908–131.

1 GOLDACRE, R. J. – The regulation of movement and polar organization in *Amoeba* by intracellular feedback – Proc. 1st Internat. Congr. Cybernetics, Namur 1956, p. 715.

2 GOLDACRE, R. J. – Biological rhythms and self-regulating mechanisms – *Penguin Sci. Survey* 1963B–161.

1 GOLDECK, H. – *24-Stunden-rhythmische Blutmauserung bei der Ratte* – Ref. 1949a, p. 83.

2 GOLDECK, H. – Der 24-Stunden-Rhythmus der Erythropoese – *Ärztl. Forsch.* 2–1948–22.

100 GOLDECK, H. and W. D. HEINRICH – Die Tagesperiodischen Spontanschwankungen der Blutmauserung bei der Laboratoriumsratte – *Acta Haem.* 2–1949–167.

101 GOLDECK, H., G. HERRNRING and U. RICHTER – Die 24-Stunden-Periodik der Thrombozyten – *D. Med. Wschr.* 75–1950–702.

102 GOLDECK, H. and P. SIEGEL – Die 24-Stunden-Periodik der Blutreticulozyten unter vegetativen Pharmaka – *Ärztl. Forsch.* 2–1948–245.

1 GOLDMAN, D. E. – Effects of vibration on man – In: *Handbook of Noise Control.* C. M. Harris Editor. McGraw-Hill. New York, 1957.

100 GOLDSMITH, J. R. and N. M. PERKINS – *Seasonal Variations in Mortality* – Ref. 1963c.

100 GOLENHOFEN, K. and G. HILDEBRANDT – Über spontan-rhythmische Schwankungen der Muskeldurchblutung der Menschen – *Z. Kreislaufforsch.* 46–1957–257.

100 GOLLWITZER-MEIER, K. and C. KROETZ – Über den Blutchemismus im Schlaf – *Biochem Z.* 154–1924–. 82.

1 GOLOLOBOVA, M. T. – Changes in mitotic activity of rats depending on the time of the day – *Bull. Exp. Biol. Med. USSR* 1958–118.

2 GOLOLOBOVA, M. T. – Mitotic activity in the mice cornea in infliction of burns at different times of the day – *Bull. Exp. Biol. Med. USSR* 3–1959–94.

3 GOLOLOBOVA, M. T. – The 24-hour rhythm of cellular multiplication in the epidermis of rats during healing

of skin wounds – *Bull. Exp. Biol. Med. USSR* 10–1960–118.

1 GOODDY, W. – Time and the nervous system. The brain as a clock – *Lancet* 1958 I–1139, 1959 II–1155.

100 GOODENOUGH, D. R., A. SHAPIRO, M. HOLDEN and L. STEINSCHRIBER – A comparison of dreamers and nondreamers – *J. Abnorm. Soc. Psychol.* 59/3–1959–295.

1 GOODMAN, L. – *On the Dynamics of Pulmonary Ventilation in Quiescent Man* – Thesis. Case Inst. Techn. Ohio, 1962.

100 GORNALL, A. G., B. EGLITIS, A. MILLER, A. B. STOKES and J. G. DEWAN – Longterm clinical and metabolic observations in periodic katatonia – *Am. J. Psychiatr.* 109–1953–584.

1 GOTS, J. S. – Purine metabolism in bacteria V, Feedback inhibition – *J. Biol. Chem.* 228–1957–57.

1 GOTTLIEB, I. M. – *Basic Oscillators* – Rider. New York, 1963.

1 GOULD, E. – Orientation in boxturtles – *Biol. Bull.* 112–1957–336.

1 GRABENSBERGER, W. – Untersuchungen über das Zeitgedächtnis der Ameisen und Termiten – *Z. Vergl. Physiol.* 20–1933–1.

2 GRABENSBERGER, W. – Experimentelle Untersuchungen über das Zeitgedächtnis von Bienen und Wespen nach Verfütterung von Euchinin und Jodthyreoglobulin – *Z. Vergl. Psychol.* 20–1934–338.

3 GRABENSBERGER, W. – Der Einfluss von Salicylsäure, gelbem Phosphor und weissem Arsenik auf das Zeitgedächtnis der Ameisen – *Z. Vergl. Physiol.* 20–1934–501.

100 GRABFIELD, G. P., E. G. MARTIN, G. H. BIGELOW and G. B. WILBUR – Variations in the sensory threshold for faradic stimulation in normal human subjects I–II – *Am. J. Physiol.* 31–1913–300, 33–1914–415.

1 GRADMANN, H. – Das Winden und Ranken der Pflanzen – *Erg. Biol.* 5–1929–166.

100 GRAF, K. and W. and S. ROSELL – Spontan-rhythmische und unregelmässige Schwankungen der Leberdurchblutung des Menschen – *Acta Physiol.* 43–1958–233.

200 GRAF, O. – *Die biologische Tages-rhythmik des elektrischen Hautwiderstandes und die physiologische Leistungsbereitschaft* – Ref. 1955a, p. 95.

201 GRAF, O. – *Physiologische Leistungsbereitschaft und nervöse Belastung* – Jb. Max Planck-Ges. 1955.

202 GRAF, O. – Untersuchungen über die Wirkung zwangsläufiger zeitlicher Regelung von Arbeitsvorgängen II–IV. – *Arbeitsphysiol.* 7–1933–333 358, 381.

203 GRAF, O. – Zur Frage der Arbeits- und Pausengestaltung bei Fliessarbeit I–VI – *Arbeitsphysiol.* 11– (1940–1941)–185, 331, 503; 12– (1941–1942)–19, 332, 348.

204 GRAF, O. – *Erforschung der geistigen Ermüdung und nervösen Belastung* – Westdeutscher Verlag. Köln, 1955.

205 GRAF, O. – Welche Menschen eignen sich nicht zur Nachtarbeit? – *D. Med. Wschr.* 82–1957–2236.

400 GRAF, W. – Patterns of human liver temperature – *Acta Physiol. Scand.* 46/suppl. 16–1959–1.

500 GRAF, W. and K. – The rectum–liver gradient in man – *Acta Physiol, Scand.* 41–1957–139.

501 GRAF, W. and J. G. PORJÉ – *Diurnal Rhythm of Liver Temperature in Man* – Ref. 1955a, p. 96.

502 GRAF, E., J. G. PORJÉ and A. M. ALLGOTH – Observations on the temperature of human liver parenchyma – *Gastroenterologia* 83–1955–233.

100 GRANIT, R., L. LEKSELL and C. R. SKOGLUND – Fibre interaction in injured or compressed region of nerve – *Brain* 67–1944–125.

100 GRASSHEIM and LUKAS – Über den Phosporgehalt des Serums bei Nierenkrankheiten – *Z. Klin. Med.* 107 –1928–172.

100 GRAUE, L. C. and J. G. PRATT – Directional differences in pigeon homing in Sacramento, Calif. and Cedar Rapids, Iowa – *Ann. Behav.* 7–1959 –201.

1 GRAY, J. – Undulatory propulsion – *Quart. J. Microsc. Sci.* 94/3rd ser.– 1953–551.

2 GRAY, J. – The movement of sea urchin spermatozoa – *J. Exp. Biol.* 32/4–1955–755.

100 GRAY, J. and HANCOCK, G. J. – The propulsion of sea urchin spermato-

zoa–*J. Exp. Biol.* 32/4–1955– 802.

101 GRAY, J. and H.W. LISSMAN – The locomotion of nematodes– *J. Exp. Biol.* 41/1–1964–135.

1　GREBE, J. J. – *Time; its Breadth and Depth in Biological Rhythms* – Ref. 1961c, p. 1206.

100 GREELY, F. and R. K. MEYER – Seasonal variation in testis-stimulating activity of male pheasant pituitary glands – *Auk* 70–1953–350.

1　GREEN, E. I. – The story of Q – *Am. Sci.* 43/4–1955–584.

100 GREGORY, C.C.L. and A. KOHSEN – The O-structure. An introduction to psychophysical Cosmology – Inst. *Stud. Ment. Images,* Hampshire, England 1959 (also publishing a journal '*Cosmos*').

300 GREGORY, F. G., J. SPEAR and K. V. THIMANN – The interrelation between CO_2 metabolism and photoperiodism in *Kalanchoe* – *Plant. Physiol.* 29–1954–220.

100 GREULACH, V. A. and J. G. HOES-LOOP – *Influence of gibberellic acid on the flowering of Xanthium in relation to number of induction periods* – Ref. 1957f, p. 359.

100 GRIESER, K. C. and L. G. BROWMAN – Total gonadotrophic potency of mule deer pituitaries–*Endocrinology* 58/2–1956–206.

1　GRIFFIN, D. R. – Bird navigation – *Biol. Rev.* 27–1952–359.

2　GRIFFIN, D. R. – Sensory physiology and the orientation of animals – *Am. Sci.* 41–1953–209.

100 GRIFFIN, D. R. and J. H. WELSH – Activity rhythms in bars under constant external conditions – *J. Mammal.* 18–1937–337.

300 GRIFFIN, J. E. and I. H. KORNBLUCH – Ionization of the air – *Int. J. Biometeor.(*Ref. J. e.) 6/1 – 1962–29.

100 GRIFFITHS, G. M. and J. T. FOX – Rhythm in epilepsy – *Lancet* 235–1938–409.

1　GRIPENBERG, R. – Viktökningens beroende av årstiderna – *Finska Läk. Sällsk. Handlr.* 59–1917–640.

100 GROB. D., R. J. JOHNS and A. LILJE-STRAND – Potassium movement in patients with periodic paralysis – *Am. J. Med.* 23–1957–356.

100 GROSS, MESSERICH and PARENT – Ursache und Bedeutung der Tages-schwankungen des EKG – *Ärztl. Wschr.* 9–1954–226.

200 GROSS, A. – Zeitsinn und Traum – *Int. Z. Psycho-anal.* 19–1934–613.

1　GROSSENBACHER, K. A. – Diurnal fluctuation in root pressure – *Plant. Physiol.* 13–1938–669.

2　GROSSENBACHER, K. A. – Autonomic cycle of rate of exsudation of plants – *Am. J. Bot.* 26–1939–107.

100 GROSSMAN, L. S. and B. M. BRICK-MAN – Comparison of diurnal and nocturnal pH values of saliva – *J. Dent. Res.* 16–1937–179.

1　GROSZKOWSKI, J. – *Frequency of Self-oscillation*–Pergamon, London 1964.

1　GROTE, L. R. – Der kranke Mensch und die Zeit – *Münch. Med. Wschr.* 101–1959–841.

1　GRÜNBAUM, A. – Time and entropy – *Am. Sci.* 43/4–1955–550.

1　GÜNTHER, W. – Bestehen Zusammenhänge zwischen Geburtstermin, Geschlecht des Kindes und Mondstellung – *Zbl. Gynäk* 1938–1196.

1　GUGGENHEIM, R. – Über den Wintergipfel der Säuglingssterblichkeit – *Klin. Wschr.* 2 – 1923–2290.

100 GUMBEL, E. J., J. A. GREENWOOD and D. DURAND – The circular normal distribution, Theory and tables – *J. Am. Stat. Ass.* 48/261–1953–131.

1　GUNN, A. L. – Mond und Menstruation–*Zbl. Geburtshlk.* 62–1938–1527.

300 GUNN, D., L. JENKIN and A. L. GUNN – Menstrual periodicity – *J. Obst. Gynaecol.* 44–1937–839.

400 GUNN, D. L. – The daily rhythm of activity of the cockroach, *Blatta orientalis* L. – *J. Exp. Biol.* 17/3– 1940–267.

500 GUNN, D. L. and H. S. HOPF – The biology and behaviour of *Ptinu-stectus boie,* a pest of stored products – *J. Exp. Biol.* 18/3–1942–278.

100 GUSTAFSON, F. L., and F. G. BENE-DICT – The seasonal variation in basal metabolism – *Am. J. Physiol.* 86–1928–43.

100 GUTHMANN, H. and BIENHÜLS – Wehenbeginn, Geburtsstunde und Tageszeit – *Mschr. Geburtshilf. Gyn.* 103–1936–337.

1　GUYSELMAN, J. B. – Solar and lunar rhythm of locomotor activity in the crayfish–*Physiol. Zool.* 30–1957–70.

1 GYLLENSWÄRD, Å. – The rhythm of body temperature in children, studied with continuous registration – *Acta Ped.* 40/suppl. 83–1951–177.

100 HABER, A. H. and N. E. TOLBERT – *Effects of Giberellic Acid, Kinetin, and Light on the Germination of Lettuce Seed* – Ref. 1957f, p. 197.

1 HADDOW, A. J. – Further observation on the biting-habits of *Tabanidae* in Uganda – *Bull. Entomol. Res.* 42-1952-659.

2 HADDOW, A. J. – Studies of the biting-habits of African mosquitoes – – *Bull. Entomol. Res.* 45–1954–199.

3 HADDOW, A. J. – Rhythmic biting activity of certain East African mosquitoes – *Nature* 177–1956–531.

1 HAEBERLIN, C. – *Lebensrhythmen und menschliche Rhythmusstörungen* – Berlin, 1933.

1 HAFITZ, A. – Cultural studies on *Aschochyta rabiei* with special reference to zonation – *Trans. Brit. Mycol. Soc.* 34–1951–259.

1 HAGBERG, S. – Variations in volume of the canine liver and the effect thereon of dibenamine and of hypothermia in standardized hemorrhagic shock – *Acta Chir. Scand.* suppl. 203–1955–1.

1 HAGEN, W. – Periodische, konstitutionelle und pathologische Schwankungen im Verhalten der Blutcapillaren – *D. Med. Wschr.* 1922 II–1507.

1 HAGENTORN, A. – Was wissen wir über den Zusammenhang von Wetter und Krankheit – *Münch. Med. Wschr.* 79–1932–1181.

1 HAGIWARA, S. – On the fluctuation of the interval of the rhythmic excitation I–II – *Sci. Rep. Physiograph. Inst. (Tokyo)* 3–1949–19; 4–1950–28.

1 HAGUE, E. B. – Uveitis, dysacousia, alopecia, poliosis and vitiligo – *Arch. Ophtalm.* 31–1944–520.

1 HAINE, E. – Häutung, Abflug und Landung der Blattläuse in Wechselwirkung auf die Blattlauszahlen in der Luft – *Mitteil. Biol. Bundesanstalt (Berlin-Dahlem)* 85–1956–23.

2 HAINE, E. – Periodicity in aphid moulting and reproduction in constant temperature and light – *Z. Angew. Entomol.* 40/1–1957–99.

3 HAINE, E. – Nehmen Luftelektrische Faktoren Einfluss auf die Aktivitätswechsel kleiner Insekten, insbesondere auf die Häutungs- und Reproduktionszahlen von Blattläusen – *Forsch. ber. 974 des Landes Nordrhein–Westphalen* 1961.

4 HAINE, E. – Beeinflussen luftelektrische Faktoren, insbesondere Sonnenkonzentrationswechsel der Luft, Periodizitätserscheinungen im Häuten der Blattläuse? – *Z. Angew. Entomol.* 50/2–1962–222.

1 HALBERG, F. – *Experimentelles zur Physiologie des Nebennierenzyklus* – Ref. 1953a, p. 117.

2 HALBERG, F. – Some physiological and clinical aspects of 24-hour periodicity – *Lancet* 73–1953–20.

3 HALBERG, F. – Beobachtungen über 24–Stundenperiodik in standardisierter Versuchsanordnung vor und nach Epinephrektomie und bilateraler optischer Enukleation – *Ber. Ges. Physiol.* 162–1954–354.

4 HALBERG, F. – *Methodological Aspects of Studies on Physiologic Rhythms with Special Reference to the Adrenal Cycle* – Ref. 1955a, p. 98.

5 HALBERG, F. – Temperature maintenance and survival of adrenalectomised mice in relation to steroidal structure – *J. Cell Comp. Physiol.* 46/2–1955–358.

6 HALBERG, F. – Physiologic 24-hour periodicity; General and procedural considerations with reference to the adrenal cycle – *Z. Vit.Horm. Fermentforsch,* 10–1959–225.

7 HALBERG, F. – *Circadian Temporal Organization and Experimental Pathology* – Ref. 1960a, p. 52.

8 HALBERG, F. – *Temporal Coordination of Physiologic Function* – Ref. 1960c, p. 289.

9 HALBERG, F. – Symposium on some current research methods and results with special reference to the central nervous system – *Am. J. Ment. Def.* 65/2–1960–156.

10 HALBERG, F. – The 24-hour scale; A time dimension of adaptive functional organization – *Persp. Biol. Med.* 3–1960–491.

11 HALBERG, F. – *Lighting Regimen and Experimental Method* – 12. Ann.

Conf. Electr. Techn. Med. Biol. Winner. New York, 1960.

12 HALBERG, F. – *Application of General Harmonic Analysis to Circadian Systems* – Ref. 1961a, p. 23.

13 HALBERG, F. – *Circadian Aspects of Mitosis and Metabolism* – Ref. 1961 a, p. 41.

14 HALBERG, F. – *The Adrenal Cycle* – Ref. 1961a, p. 57.

15 HALBERG, F. – *Circadian Rhythms; a Determinant of Response to Environmental Agents* – Proc. 1st Internat. Symp. Submarine Space Med. New London, Conn., USA, 1958.

16 HALBERG, F. – *The Time Structure of Organisms with Special Reference to the Role played by the Eye* – Ref. 1963b.

17 HALBERG, F. – *Discussion of Glycogen Metabolism* – 40th Ross Conf. Ped. Res., p. 31.

18 HALBERG, F. – Circadian rhythms, a basis of human engineering for aero-space – In: B. Flaherty: *"Psychophysiological Aspects of Space Flight"* Columbia University Press, 1961, p. 166.

19 HALBERG, F. – Circadian (about 24-hour) rhythms in experimental medicine – *Univ. of Minn. Med. Bull.* 34–1962–158.

20 HALBERG, F. – *Physiologic 24-Hour Rhythms: A Determination of Response to Environment Agents* – In Schaefer, Ref. 2, p. 48.

21 HALBERG, F. – Circadian (about 24-hour) rhythms in experimental medicine – *Proc. Royal Soc. Med.* 56–1963–253.

22 HALBERG, F. – *Circadian Rhythms in Experimental Medicine* – Ref. 1962c, p. 253.

23 HALBERG, F. – *Significance of the Study of Biological Rhythms for Zoological Biometeorology* – Ref. 1963c.

100 HALBERG, F., P. G. ALBRECHT and C. P. BARNUM, JR – Phase shifting of liver glycogen rhythm in intact mice – *Am. J. Physiol.* 199/3–1960–400.

101 HALBERG, F., P. G. ALBRECHT and H. A. ZANDER – Persistence of eosinophil rhythm after splenectomy in rats – *Proc. Soc. Exp. Biol. Med.* 86–1954–404.

102 HALBERG, F. and C. P. BARNUM – Continuous light or darkness and circadian periodic mitosis and metabolism in C and D_8 mice – *Am. J. Physiol.* 201/2–1961–227.

103 HALBERG, F., C. P. BARNUM, R. H. SILBER and J. J. BITTNER – 24-hour rhythms at several levels of integration in mice on different lighting regimen – *Proc. Soc. Exp. Biol. Med.* 97–1958–897.

104 HALBERG, F., J. J. BITTNER and H. L. COLE – Activity rhythm and breast cancer in pituitary-isograft C and D_8 mice; effect on hypothalamus – *Proc. Soc. Exp. Biol. Med.* 102–1959–650.

105 HALBERG, F., J. J. BITTNER, H. L. COLE, E. HAUS and J. H. KAISER – Adrenal corticosterone in C mice following ovariectomy – *Endocrinology* 69/1–1961–184.

106 HALBERG, F., J. J. BITTNER, R. J. GULLY, P. G. ALBRECHT and E. L. BRACKNEY – 24-hour periodicity and audiogenic convulsions in I mice of various ages – *Proc. Soc. Exp. Biol. Med.* 88–1955–169.

107 HALBERG, F., J. J. BITTNER and D. SMITH – Belichtungswechsel und 24-Stundenperiodik von Mitosen im Hautepithel der Maus – *Z. Vit.-Horm.-Ferm. Forsch.* 9/(1–2)–1957–69.

108 HALBERG, F., J. J. BITTNER and D. SMITH – Mitotic rhythm in mice, mammary tumor milk agent, and breast cancer – *Proc. Am. Ass. Cancer Res.* 2–1958–305.

109 HALBERG, F., J. J. BITTNER and M. B. VISSCHER – Diurnal rhythm in tail blood eosinophil levels – *Cancer Res.* 2–1951–253.

110 HALBERG. F. and R. L. CONNER – Circadian organization and microbiology; variance spectra and a periodogram on behaviour of *Escherichia coli* growing in fluid culture – *Minn. Acad. Sci. Proc.* 29–1961–227.

111 HALBERG, F. and R. ENGEL – The application of the 24-hour eosinophil rhythm to the study of seizure mechanisms – *Epilepsia*, 1, ser. 3–1952.

112 HALBERG, F., E. B. FLINK and M. B. VISSCHER – Alteration in diurnal

rhythm in circulating eosinophil level in adrenal insufficiency – *Am. J. Physiol.* 167–1951–791.

113 HALBERG, F., G. FRANK, R. H. HARNER, J. MATTHEWS, H. AAKER, H. GRAVEM and J. MELBY – The adrenal cycle in men on different schedules of motor and mental activity – *Experientia* 17–1961–282.

114 HALBERG, F., M. J. FRANTZ and J. J. BITTNER – Phase difference between 24-hour rhythm in cortical adrenal mitosis and blood eosinophils in the mouse – *Anat. Rec.* 129/3–1957–349.

115 HALBERG, F., L. A. FRENCH and R. J. GULLY – 24-hour rhythms in rectal temperature and blood eosinophils after hemidecortication in human subjects – *J. Appl. Physiol.* 12/3–1958–381.

116 HALBERG, F. and E., C. P. BARNUM, and J. J. BITTNER – *Physiologic 24-hour Periodicity in Human Beings and Mice; The Lighting Regimen and Daily Routine* – Ref. 1957f, p. 803.

117 HALBERG, F. and E. and J. J. BITTNER – *Daily Periodicity of Convulsions in Man and in Mice* – Ref. 1955a, p. 97.

118 HALBERG, F. and E., D. C. WARGO and M. B. Visscher – Eosinophil levels in dogs with surgically established arteriovenous anastomoses – *Am. J. Physiol.* 174/2–1953–313.

119 HALBERG, F., O. HAMERSTON and J. J. BITTNER – Sex difference in eosinophil counts in tail blood of mature B₁ mice – *Science* 125/3237–1957–73.

120 HALBERG, F., E. HAUS and A. N. STEPHENS – Susceptibility to ouabain and physiologic 24-hour periodicity – *Fed. Proc.* 18/1–1959.

121 HALBERG, F. and R. B. HOWARD – 24-hour periodicity and experimental medicine; examples and interpretations – *Postgrad. Med.* 24–1958 –349.

122 HALBERG, F., E. JACOBSSEN, G. WADSWORTH and J. J. BITTNER – Audiogenic abnormality spectra, twenty-four hour periodicity and lighting – *Science* 128/3325–1958–657.

123 HALBERG, F., E. A. JOHNSON, B. W. BROWN and J. J. BITTNER – Sus-

ceptibility rhythm to *E. coli* endotoxin and bioassay – *Proc. Soc. Exp. Biol. Med.* 103–1960–142.

124 HALBERG, F. and I. H. KAISER – Lack of physiologic eosinophil rhythm during advanced pregnancy of a patient with Addisons disease – *Acta Endocrinol.* 16–1954–227.

125 HALBERG, F. and H. PANOFSKY – Human thermo-variance spectra I–II – *Exp. Med. Surg.* 19/4–1961–284, 323.

126 HALBERG, F. and P. C. ROYCE – Evaluation of "maximal eosinopenia" following the subcutaneous implantation of cortisone acetate in intact mice of several stocks – *Arch. Int. Pharmacodyn.* 95/(3–4)–1953–315.

127 HALBERG, F., W. W. SPINK, P. G. ALBRECHT and R. J. GULLY – Resistance of mice to *Brucella* somatic antigen, 24-hour periodicity and the adrenals – *J. Clin. Endocrinol. Metab.* 15–1955–887.

128 HALBERG, F., W. W. SPINK and J. J. BITTNER – Protection by aldosterone and 11,17-oxycorticoids against effects of *Brucella* somatic antigen in adrenalectomized mice – *Endocrinology* 59/3–1956–380.

129 HALBERG, F. and A. N. STEPHENS – Twenty-four-hour periodicity in mortality of C mice from *E. coli* lipopolysaccharide – *Fed. Proc.* 17/1 –1958.

130 HALBERG, F. and A. N. STEPHENS – Susceptibility to Ouabain and physiologic circadian periodicity – *Proc. Minn. Acad. Sci.* 27–1959–139.

131 HALBERG, F., H. VERMUND, E. HALBERG and C. P. BARNUM – Adrenal hormones and phospholipid metabolism in liver cytoplasm of adrenalectomized mice – *Endocrinoly* 59/3–1956–364.

132 HALBERG, F. and M. B. VISSCHER – Regular diurnal physiological variation in eosinophil levels in five stocks of mice – *Proc. Soc. Exp. Biol. Med.* 75–1950–846.

133 HALBERG, F. and M. B. VISSCHER – *The Dependence of an Adrenal Cycle in the Mouse upon Lighting* – 19th Internat. Physiol. Congr., Ther. Frères, Montreal 1953, p. 428.

134 HALBERG, F. and M. B. VISSCHER –

Some Physiologic Effects of Lighting – Ref. 1954a, p. 396.

135 HALBERG, F., M. B. VISSCHER and J. J. BITTNER – Eosinophil rhythm in mice; range of occurrence, effects of illumination, feeding and adrenalectomy – *Am. J. Physiol.* 174/1–1953–109.

136 HALBERG, F., M. B. VISSCHER and J. J. BITTNER – Relation of visual factors to eosinophil rhythm in mice – *Am. J. Physiol.* 179–1954–229.

137 HALBERG, F., M. B. VISSCHER, E. B. FLINK, K. BERGE and F. BOCK – Diurnal rhythmic changes in blood eosinophil levels in health and in certain diseases – *Lancet* 71/8–1951–312.

138 HALBERG, F., H. A. ZANDER, M. W. HOUGLUM and H. R. MÜHLEMANN – Daily variations in tissue mitosis, blood eosinophils and rectal temperatures of rats – *Am. J. Physiol.* 177/3–1954–361.

139 HALBERG, F., R. E. PETERSON and R. H. SILBER – Phase relations of 24-hour periodicities in blood corticosterons, mitoses in cortical adrenal parenchyma and total body activity – *Endocrinology* 64 –1959–222.

140 HALBERG, F., G. ADKINS and E. MARTE – Reserpine effect upon the variance spectrum of human rectal temperature – *Fed. Proc.* 21–1962–347.

141 HALBERG, F., P. G. ALBRECHT and J. J. BITTNER – Corticosterone rhythm of mouse adrenal in relation to serum corticosterone and sampling – *Am. J. Physiol.* 197–1959–1083.

142 HALBERG, F., J. J. BITTNER and R. J. GULLY – Twenty-four-hour periodic susceptibility to audiogenic convulsions in several stocks of mice – *Fed. Proc.* 14–1955–67.

143 HALBERG, F. and F. BOCK – Eosinopenia during the last third of pregnancy and after delivery in several stocks of mice – *Proc. Soc. Expt. Biol. Med.* 83–1953–338.

144 HALBERG, F., R. ENGEL, E. HALBERG and R. J. GULLY – Diurnal variations in amount of electroencephalographic paroxysmal discharge and diurnal eosinophil rhythm of epileptics on days with clinical seizures – *Fed. Proc.* 11–1952–63.

145 HALBERG, F. and E., and R. J. GULLY – Effects of modifications of the daily routine in healthy subjects and in patients with convulsive disorder – *Epilepsia* 2–1953–150.

146 HALBERG, F. and E. HAUS – Frequency structure of human metabolism resolved by variance spectra – In: *Proc. 22nd Internat. Physiol. Congr.* 2/456–1962, Leiden.

147 HALBERG, F., L. LEVY and M. B. VISSCHER – Relation of 24-hour rhythm in body temperature to lighting conditions and to the adrenal – *Fed. Proc.* 12–1953–59.

148 HALBERG, F., R. LOEWENSON, R. WINTER, J. BEARMAN and G. H. ADKINS – Differences in period of circadian rhythms or in their component frequencies – *Proc. Minn. Acad. Sci.* 28–1960–53.

149 HALBERG, F., R. E. PETERSON and R. H. SILBER – Phase relations of 24-hour periodicities in blood corticosterone, mitoses in cortical adrenal parenchyma and total body activity – *Endocrinology* 64–1959–222.

150 HALBERG, F. and W. W. SPINK – The influence of *Brucella* somatic antigen (endotoxin) upon the temperature rhythm of intact mice – *Investigation* 5–1956–283.

151 HALBERG, F., F. UNGAR and E. HAUS – Adrenal corticosterone production and responsiveness to ACTH, *in vitro* in mice with ectopic pituitary isografts – *Proc. Am. Assoc. Cancer Res.* 4–1963–25.

152 HALBERG, F., H. VERMUND and J. J. BITTNER – Daily eosinophil rhythm in mice bearing a transplanted mammary carcinoma – *J. Nat. Cancer Inst.* 17–1956–139.

153 HALBERG, F. and M. B. VISSCHER – A difference between the effects of dietary caloric restriction on the estrous cycle and on the 24-hour adrenal cortical cycle in rodents – *Endocrinology* 51–1952–329.

154 HALBERG, F. and M. B. VISSCHER – Effect of light and of availability of food upon the 24-hour rhythm in number of circulating eosinophils in mice–*Am. J. Physiolg.* 171–1952–732.

155 HALBERG, F. and M. B. VISSCHER –
Temperature rhythms in blind mice
– *Fed. Proc.* 13–1954–65.

156 HALBERG, F., C. S. DELEA, P.
SCHOECK, J. J. RYAN and F. C.
BARTTER – A simulated car crash –
Minn. Med. 1963–535.

157 HALBERG, F., M. DIFFLEY, M. STEIN,
H. PANOFSKY and S. ADKINS –
Computer techniques in the study of
biological rhythms – *Ann. N.Y.
Acad. Sci.* 115/2–1964–695.

158 HALBERG, F., and C. HAMBURGER –
17-Ketosteroid and volume of human
urine – *Minnesota Med.* 47–1964–
916.

1 HALE, J. K. – *Oscillations in Nonlinear Systems* – McGraw-Hill, 1963.

1 HALL, M. P. – An analysis of the
factors controlling the growth form
of certain fungi with special reference to *Sclerotinia (Monilia) fruc-
tigena* – *Ann. Bot.* 47–1933–543.

200 HALL, W. – The time sense – *J. Ment.
Sci.* 73–1927–421.

1 HALLDAL, P. – *Action Spectra of
Phototaxis in Unicellular Algae* –
Ref. 1960b, p. 121.

100 HALLIDAY, A.M. and J.W.T. RED-
FEARN – An analysis of finger tremor
in healthy subjects – *J. Physiol* 134–
1956–600.

1 HAMAR, N. – Über Tagesschwankungen des Glucoseresorptionsvermö-
gens des Dünndarms – *Pflüger's
Arch.* 244–(1940–1941)–164.

1 HAMBURGER, F. – Jahreszeitliche
Schwankungen der Tuberkulinem-
pfindlichkeit – *Münch. Med. Wschr.*
1920–398.

100 HAMERSTON, O., L. ELVEBACK, F.
HALBERG and R. J. GULLY – Correlation of absolute basophil and
eosinophil counts in blood from in-
stitutionalized human subjects –
J. Appl. Physiol. 9/2–1956–205.

100 HAMILTON, L. D., C. J. GUBLER, G.
E. CARTWRIGHT and M. M. WIN-
TROBE – Diurnal variation in the
plasma iron level of man – *Proc. Soc.
Exp. Biol. Med.* 75–1950–65.

200 HAMILTON, W. J., JR. – The biology
of microtine cycles – *J. Agr. Res.*
54–1937–779.

400 HAMILTON III, W. J. – Celestial
orientation in juvenal waterfowl –
Condor 64–1962–19.

500 HAMILTON III, W. J. and M. C.
HAMMOND – Oriented overland
spring migration of pinioned Canada
geese – *Wilson Bull.* 72/4–1960–385.

1 HAMMEN, TH. VAN – *Upper cretace-
ous and tertiary climatic periodicities
and their causes* – Ref. 1961e, p. 440.

1 HAMMOND, J. – Control of reproductive and pelt changes in ferrets;
Some experiments with animals
kept entirely upon artificial light
– *J. Agr. Sci.* 42–1952–293.

2 HAMMOND, J. – Photoperiodicity in
animals; The role of darkness –
Science 117 – 1953–389.

1 HAMNER, K. C. – Interrelation of
light and darkness in photoperiodic
induction – *Bot. Gaz.* 101–1940–
658.

2 HAMNER, K. C. – Hormones and
photoperiodism – *C.S.H. Symp.
Quant. Biol.* 10–1942–49.

3 HAMNER, K. C. – *Photoperiodism and
Circadian Rhythms* – Ref. 1960c, p.
269.

100 HAMNER, K. C. and J. BONNER –
Photoperiodism in relation to hormones as factors in floral initiation
and development – *Bot. Gaz.* 100–
1938–388.

1 HAMPP, H. – Die Tagesrhythmischen
Schwankungen der Stimmung und
des Antriebes beim gesunden
Mensch – *Arch. Psychiat. Nervenkr.*
201–1961–355.

1 HANN, H. W. – The relation of
castration to migration in birds –
Bird-Banding 10–1939–122.

1 HANNAN, E. J. – *Time Series Analysis* – Methuen Co. London, 1960.

100 HARDER, R. and O. BODE – Über die
Wirkung von Zwischenbelichtungen
während der Dunkelperiode auf das
Blühen, die Verlaubung und die
Blattsukkulenz bei der Kurztag-
pflanze *Kalanchoe blossfeldiana* –
Planta 33–1943–469.

300 HARDER, W. and G. HEMPEL – Studien zur Tagesperiodik der Aktivität von Fischen I. – *Mitt. Inst.
Fisch. Hamb.* 15–1954–22.

1 HARDERECK, H. – *Einige tagesrhythmische Erscheunngen bei Nierenkranken unter besonderer Berücksichtigung der CO_2-Abatmung und ihrer
Auswirkung auf die Urin-pH-Werte*
– Diss. Hamburg, 1949.

100 HARICHAUX, P., and J. MOUVENOT – Action of catecholamines on the periodicity of pyloric evacuation in the rat and mouse–*C.R. Soc. Biol.* 156–1962–1141.

1 HARKER, J. E. – The diurnal rhythm of activity of mayfly nymphs – *J. Exp. Biol.* 30–1953–525.

2 HARKER, J. E. – Diurnal rhythms in *Periplaneta americana* L. – *Nature* 173–1954–689.

3 HARKER, J. E. – Control of diurnal rhythms of activity in *Periplaneta americana* L. – *Nature* 175–1955–773.

4 HARKER, J. E. – Factors controlling the diurnal rhythm of activity of *Periplaneta americana* L. – *J. Exp. Biol.* 33–1956–224.

5 HARKER, J. E. – Diurnal rhythms in the animal kingdom – *Biol. Rev.* 33/1–1958–1.

6 HARKER, J. E. – Experimental production of midgut tumours in *Periplaneta americana* L. – *Exp. Biol.* 35–1958–251.

7 HARKER, J. E. – The effect of perturbations in the environmental cycle on the diurnal rhythm of activity of *Periplaneta americana* L. – *J. Exp. Biol.* 37–1960–154.

8 HARKER, J. E. – Internal factors controlling the suboesophageal ganglion neurosecretory cycle in *Periplaneta americana* – *J. Exp. Biol.* 37–1960–164.

9 HARKER, J. E. – *Endocrine and Nervous Factors in Insect Circadian Rhythms* – Ref. 1960c, p. 279.

100 HARMOEN, A.M. and VAN GRONINGEN–On the physiology of tremor – *EEG Clin. Neurophysiol.* 10–1958–4.

1 HARMS, E. – *Problems of Sleep and Dream in Children*–Macmillan, New York 1964.

1 HARNER, R. N. – *Quantification of Convulsive Periodicity* – Ref. 1961a, p. 45.

100 HARNER, R. N. and F. HALBERG – Electrocorticographic differences in D_8 mice at times of daily high and low susceptibility of audiogenic convulsions–*Physiologist* 1/4–1958–34.

1 HARRINGTON, R. W. – Pre-seasonal breeding by the bridled shiner, induced under light-temperature control – *Copeia* 4–1950–304.

2 HARRINGTON, R. W. – *Photoperiodism in Fishes in Relation to the Annual Sexual Cycle* – Ref. 1957f, p. 651.

1 HARRISON, J. L. – Breeding rhythms of Selangor rodents – *Bull. Raffles Mus.* 24–1952–109.

2 HARRISON, J. L. – The moonlight effect on rat breeding – *Bull. Raffles Mus.* 25–1954–166.

1 HART, J. S. – Photoperiodicity in Suffolk Sheep – *J. Agr. Sci.* 40–1950–143.

2 HART, J. S. – Photoperiodicity in the female ferret – *J. Exp. Biol.* 28 1951–1.

3 HART, J.S. – Interrelations of daily metabolic cycle activity and environmental temperature of mice – *Canad. J. Res.* 28D/6–1950–293.

4 HART, J.S. – Seasonal changes in insulation of the fur–*Canad. J. Zool.* 34–1956–53.

1 HARTLAND-ROWE, R. – Lunar rhythm of emergence of an epheromeropteran – *Nature* 176–1955–657.

2 HARTLAND-ROWE, R. – The biology of a tropical mayfly – *Rev. Zool. Bot. Afr.* 58/(3–4)–1958–185.

1 HARTMAN, C. G. – *Science and The Safe Period* – Williams and Wilkins. Baltimore, 1962.

1 HASLER, A. D. – Odour perception and orientation in fishes – *J. Fish. Res. Bd. Canada* 11–1954–107.

2 HASLER, A. D. – Influence of environmental reference points on learned orientation in fish – *Z. Vergl. Physiol.* 38–1956–303.

3 HASLER, A. D. – *Perception of Pathways by Fishes in Migration* – Ref. 1958a, p. 451.

100 HASLER, A. D., R. M. HORRALL, W. J. WISBY and W. BRAEMER – Sun orientation and homing in fishes – *Limnol. Oceanogr.* 3–1958–353.

101 HASLER, A. D. and H. O. SCHWASSMANN – *Sun Orientation of Fish at Different Latitudes* – Ref. 1960c, p. 429.

102 HASLER, A. D. and J. WILLEMONTE – Observations of the daily movements of fishes – *Science* 118–1953–321.

1 HASTINGS, J. W. – Unicellular clocks – *Ann. Rev. Microbiol.* 13–1959–297.

2   HASTINGS, J. W. – *Biochemical As-*
    pects of Rhythms; Phase Shifting by
    Chemicals – Ref. 1960c, p. 131.
3   HASTINGS, J. W. – *Enzymes-substrate*
    Interactions along the Twenty-four-
    hour Scale – Ref. 1961a, p. 76.
100 HASTINGS, J. W. and L. ASTRACHAN
    – A diurnal rhythm of photosynthe-
    sis – *Fed. Proc.* 18–1959–65.
101 HASTINGS, J. W. and V. C. BODE –
    Biochemistry of Rhythmic Systems –
    Ref. 1961c, p. 876.
102 HASTINGS, J. W. and B. M. SWEENEY
    – *The Gonyaulax Clock* – Ref. 1957f,
    p. 567.
103 HASTINGS, J. W. and B. M. SWEENEY,
    – On the mechanism of temperature
    independence in a biological clock –
    Proc. Nat. Acad. Sci. (Wash.) 43–
    1957–804.
104 HASTINGS, J. W. and B. M. SWEENEY
    – A persistent diurnal rhythm of
    luminescence in *Gonyaulax polyedra*
    – *Biol. Bull.* 115–1958–440.
105 HASTINGS, J. W. and B. M. SWEENY
    – The action spectrum for shifting
    the phase of the rhythms of lumi-
    nescence in *Gonyaulax polyedra* – J.
    Gen. Physiol. 43–1960–697.
106 HASTINGS, J. W., M. WIESNER, J.
    OWENS and M. B. SWEENEY – The
    rhythm of luminescence in a marine
    dinoflagellate – *Anat. Rec.* 125–1956
    611.
1   HAUENSCHILD, C. – Photoperiodizi-
    tät als Ursache des von der Mond-
    phase abhängigen Metamorphose-
    Rhythmus beim Polychaeten *Pla-*
    tynereis Dumerilii – *Z. Naturforsch.*
    10b–1955–658.
2   HAUENSCHILD, C. – Neue experimen-
    telle Untersuchungen zum Problem
    der Lunarperiodizität – *Naturwiss.*
    43–1956–361.
3   HAUENSCHILD, C. – Zyklische Ver-
    änderungen an den inkretorischen
    Drüsenzellen im Prostomium des
    Polychaeten *Platynereis dumerilii*
    als Grundlage der Schwärmeperio-
    dizität – *Z. Naturforsch.* 14b–1959–
    81.
4   HAUENSCHILD, C. – *Lunar Periodici-*
    ty – Ref. 1960c, 491.
1   HAUFF, J. – *Über den 24-Stunden-*
    Rhythmus menschlicher Körperfunk-
    tion, der Urinausscheidung und des
    Blutwassergehaltes – Tübingen, 1941.

1   HAURWITZ, B. – Atmospheric tides –
    Science 144/3625–1964–1415.
1   HAUS, E. – *Biologisch-klinische Fak-*
    toren in der Wahl von Methoden zur
    Frequenzanalyse – Ref. 1963a.
1   HAWKING, F. – *Circadian Rhythms*
    in Filariasis – Ref. 1962c, p. 260.
1   HAUKER, V. – Über jahreszeitliche
    Veränderungen und klimatisch be-
    dingte Verschiedenheiten der Vo-
    gelschilddrüse – *Schweiz. Med.*
    Wschr. 1926 I–337.
1   HAUS, E. – Endokrines System und
    Blut – *Hb. Ges. Hämatol.* 2/1–1959–
    181.
2   HAUS, E. – *Circadian Aspects of*
    Adrenal Reaction to Unspecific Sti-
    mulation and ACTH – Ref. 1961a,
    p. 64.
3   HAUS, E. – *The Adrenal Cycle* – Ref.
    1961c.
4   HAUS, E. – *Periodicity in Susceptibi-*
    lity to Agents Affecting the Central
    Nervous System – Ref. 1963b.
100 HAUS, E. and F. HALBERG – 24-
    hour rhythm in susceptibility of
    C-Mice to toxic dosis of ethanol –
    J. Appl. Physiol. 14–1959–878.
101 HAUS, E., E. M. HANTON and F.
    HALBERG – 24-hour susceptibility
    rhythm to ethanol in fully-fed
    starved and thirsted mice and the
    lighting regimen – *Physiologist* 2/3–
    1959–54.
102 HAUS, E. and F. HALBERG – *Stage of*
    Adrenal Cycle Determining Different
    Corticosterone Responses of C Mice
    to Unspecific Stimulation and ACTH
    – Com. 1st. Intern. Congr. Endo-
    crinol. 1960–219.
103 HAUS, E. and F. HALBERG – Der
    circadiane Adrenalzyklus und seine
    Bedeutung für die Reaktionsbereit-
    schaft der Nebennierenrinde – *Wien.*
    Z. Inn. Med. 43–1962–261.
1   HAUTY, G. T. – *Modifiability of Day-*
    NightCycling within an Impoverished
    Sensory Environment – Ref. 1960 a,
    p. 70.
2   HAUTY, G. T. – *Circadian System*
    Analysis in Aerospace Medicine –
    Ref. 1961a, p. 88.
3   HAUTY, G. T. – *Periodic Desynchro-*
    nization in Humans under Outer
    Space Conditions – Ref. 1961c, p.
    1116.
100 HAUTY, G. T., G. R. STEINKAMP,

W. R. HAWKINS and F. HALBERG – Circadian performance rhythms in men adapting to an 8-hour day – *Fed. Proc.* 19–1960–54.

100 HAVILL, B. G., J. E. PEARSON and S. A. SELF – Programming circular autocorrelation for cycle research – *J. Cycle. Res.* 9/3–1960–117.

1 HAWKING, F. – Periodicity of microfilariae of Loa Loa III-IV-VII – *Trans. Roy. Soc. Trop. Med. Hyg.* 47/1–1953–82;50/4–1956–397; 49/2–1955–132.

2 HAWKING, F. – *Microfilaria Infestation as an Instance of Periodic Phenomena seen in Host–Parasite Relationship* – Ref. 1961c, p. 940.

100 HAWKING, F., and J. P. THURSTON – The periodicity of microfilariae I-II- *Trans. Roy. Soc. Trop. Med. Hyg.* 45/3–1951–307, 329.

1 HAWKINS, T. H. – Effects of light-intensity and day-length on reproduction in the English sparrow – *Nature* 163–1949–966.

1 HAYDU, G. G. – *Manic–depressive Rhythm; its Pharmacological Modification and the Nature of the Self Structure* – Ref. 1961, p. 1126.

1 HAYS, F. A. – Artificial light for activating males and females to higher fertility – *Poultry Sci.* 33–1954–325.

1 HECKERT, H. – *Die Bedeutung der statistischen Darstellungsweise und die Sicherung des Ergebnisses bei der Untersuchung synodisch–lunarer Rhythmen* – Ref. 1955a, p. 99.

2 HECKERT, H. – *Mond-periodische Schwankungen in einer Sterberate einer Grosstadtbevölkerung und Bemerkungen zu Problemen bei der Untersuchung synodisch–lunarer Einflüsse* – Diss. Med. Fak. Hamburg, 1956.

3 HECKERT, H. – *Entwicklung, Grundlagen und Aussagewert der Lehre einer endogenen sogenannten "Biorhythmik"* – Ref. 1960a, p. 70.

4 HECKERT, H. – Lunationsrhythmen des menschlichen Organismus – *Probl. Bioklim.* 7, *Akad. Verlagsges.* Leipzig, 1961.

5 HECKERT, H. – *Theoretische und praktische Aspekte der Bartelschen Zufallsmethoden und der Bestimmung signifikanter Kriterien bei statistischen Rhythmen* – Ref. 1963a.

1 HEDGECOCK, G. G. – Zonation in artificial cultures of *Cephalothecium* and other fungi – *Ann. Rep. Mo. Bot. Gard.* 17–1906–115.

100 HEDGES, E. S. and J. E. MYERS – The periodic dissolution of metals in certain reagents – *J. Chem. Soc.* 125–1924–604.

101 HEDGES, E. S. and J. E. MYERS – *The Problem of Physico–Chemical Periodicity* – Longmans. New York, 1926.

1 HEGGLIN, H. – Über die nächtliche Säureausscheidung bei Magengesunden und Magenkranken – *Schweiz. Med. Wschr.* 28–1952–720.

200 HEGGLIN, R. – The differential diagnosis of dyspnoea – *Triangle* 5/3–1961–130.

1 HEIDE, A. VON DER – *Beobachtungen über das Auftreten kurzer Wellen im Tagesablauf der Körpertemperatur bei Kranken und bei Rekonvaleszenten* – Diss. Hamburg, 1960.

1 HEIMANN, M. – Einfluss periodischer Beleuchtung auf die Guttationsrhythmus – *Planta* 38–1950–157.

1 HEINTZ, E. – Le comportement d'Apis mellifica sous l'influence de broyats d'Apis mellifica; Variations saisonnières et journalières – *Ann. Biol.* 34(1–2)–1958–53.

1 HELLBRÜGGE, T. – *The Development of Circadian Rhythms in Infants* – Ref. 1960c, p. 311.

2 HELLBRÜGGE, T. – *Die Entwicklung biologischer Rhythmen beim Menschenkind* – Ref. 1963a.

100 HELLBRÜGGE, T., J. F. LANGE and J. RUTENFRANZ – Über die Entwicklung von Tagesperiodischen Veränderungen der Pulsfrequenz im Kinderalter – *Z. Kinderhlk.* 78–1956–703.

101 HELLBRÜGGE, T., J. F. LANGE and J. RUTENFRANZ – Schlafen und Wachen in der kindlichen Entwicklung – *Arch. Kinderhlk.* suppl. 39–1959.

102 HELLBRÜGGE, T., J. LANGE, J. RUTENFRANZ and H. STEHR – Über das Entstehen einer 24-Stunden-Periodik physiologischer Funktionen im Säuglingsalter – *Fortschr. Med.* 81–1963–19.

100 HELLEBRANDT, F. A., R. H. TEPPER, H. GRANT and R. CATHERWOOD – Nocturnal and diurnal variations in the acidity of the spontaneous

secretion of gastric juice – *Am. J. Dig. Dis.* 3–1936–477.

1 HELLPACH, W. – *Das Wellengesetz unseres Lebens* – Hamburg, 1941.

100 HELMS, C. W. and W. H. DRURY JR. – Winter and migratory weight and fat – *Bird–banding* 31/1–1960–1.

100 HEMMINGSEN, A. M. and N. B. KRARUP – Rhythmic diurnal variations in the oestrous phenomena of the rat and their susceptibility to light and dark – *Kgl. Dansk Vidensk. Selskab. Biol. Medd.* 13–1937–1.

100 HEMPEL, G. and J. – Über die tägliche Verteilung der Laufaktivität bei Käfern des hohen Nordens – *Naturwiss.* 42–1955–77.

1 HENDRICKS, S. B. – Control of growth and reproduction by light and darkness – *Am. Sci.* 44/3–1956–229.

2 HENDRICKS, S. B. – *Control of Periodicity in Plant Growth* – Ref. 1957c.

3 HENDRICKS, S. B. – *The Photoreaction and Associated Changes of Plant Photomorphogenesis* – Ref. 1957f, p. 423.

4 HENDRICKS, S. B. – *Rates of Change of Phytochrome as an Essential Factor Determining Photosynthesis in Plants* – Ref. 1960c, p. 245.

5 HENDRICKS, S. B. – Metabolic control of timing – *Science* 141/3575–1963–21.

1 HENROTTE, J. G. – *Interaction between Housing Comfort and Seasonal Influence on Ketosteroid Excretion in South-Indian Men* – Ref. 1963c.

1 HERDAN, G. – *Statistics of Therapeutic Trials* – Elsevier. Amsterdam, 1955.

100 HERON, W. and H. ANCHEL – Synchronous sensory bombardment of young rats–*Science* 145/3635–1964–946.

1 HERRICK, E. M. – Seasonal and diurnal variation in the somatic values and suction tension values in the aerial portions of *Ambrosia trifida* – *Am. J. Bot.* 20–1933–18.

100 HERRING, V.V. and S. BRODY – Diurnal metabolic and activity rhythms–*Univ. Missouri Agr. Coll. Res. Bul.* no. 274–1938.

1 HERSEY, R. B. – Emotional cycles in man – *J. Ment Sci.* 77–1931–151.

1 HERTZ, M. – To psykiatriske tilfaelde af "periodisk disease" – *Nord. Med.* 64–1960–1420.

100 HERTZBERG, N. C. E. and C. SCHIÖTZ – Aarstiders og feriers indflydelse paa legemsutvicklingen hos skolelever – *Med. Revue* 39–1922–49.

1 HERZ, F. – Selbstbeobachtung über freiwillige Schlafentziehung – *Pflüger's Arch.* 200–1923–429.

100 HESS, A. F. and M.A. LUNDAGEN – A seasonal tide of blood phosphate in children – *JAMA* 79–1922–2210.

200 HESS, C. – Untersuchung über die Rhythmik der Schichtenbildung beim Stärkekorn – *Z. Bot.* 43–1955–181.

400 HESS, W. R. – Der Schlaf – *Klin. Wschr.* 1933 I–129.

1 HEUSNER, A. – Mise en évidence d'une variation nycthémérale de la calorification indépendante du cycle de l'activité chez le rat – *C.R. Soc. Biol.* 150/6–1956–1246.

100 HEUSNER, A. and J. P. ZAHNEL – Etude de la consommation d'oxygène de l'embryon de Poulet au cours du nycthémère – *C. R. Soc. Biol.* 157/7–1963–1498.

100 HIATT, R. W. and H. I. FISHER – The reproductive cycle of the ring-necked pheasants in Montana – *Auk* 64–1947–528.

1 HICKEY, J. J. – *Mean Intervals in Indices of Wildlife Populations* – Ref. 1954b, p. 90.

1 HICKLING, C. F. – Seasonal changes in the ovary of the immature hake – *J. Mar. Biol. Ass. U.K.* 20–1935–443.

100 HIEBEL, G. and C. KAYSER – Le rythme nycthéméral de l'activité et de la calorification chez l'embryon de poulet et le jeune poulet – *C.R. Soc. Biol.* 143–1949–864.

100 HIGGINS, G. M., J. BERKSON and E. FLOCK – The diurnal cycle in the liver I–II – *Am. J. Physiol.* 102–1932–673; 105–1933–177.

1 HIGHKIN, H. R. – *The Effect of Constant Temperature Environments and of Continuous Light on the Growth and Development of Pea Plants*–Ref. 1960c p. 231.

100 HIGHKIN, H. R. and L.B. HANSON – Possible interaction between light-dark cycles and endogenous daily rhythms on the growth of tomato

plants – *Plant. Physiol.* 29–1954–301.

1　HILDEBRANDT, G. – Sobre los periodos diarios de la termoregulation física – *Fol.Clin.Internat.* 12–1952–3.

2　HILDEBRANDT, G. – *Über tagesrhythmische Schwankungen des Thermoindifferenzpunktes* – Ber. Internat. Kongr. I.S.M.H. Germany, 1952, p. 158.

3　HILDEBRANDT, G. – *Untersuchungen über die rhythmische Funktionsordnung von Puls und Atem* – Ref. 1953a, p. 175.

4　HILDEBRANDT, G. – Rhythmusforschung und Balneologi – *Arch. Physik. Ther.* 5/4–1953–241.

5　HILDEBRANDT, G. – Über die Balneotherapeutische Beeinflussung der rhythmischen Funktionsordnung von Puls und Atem – *Arch. Physikal. Ther.* 5/6–1953–353.

6　HILDEBRANDT, G. – Über den Tagesgang der Atemfrequenz – *Z. Klin. Med.* 1953–433.

7　HILDEBRANDT, G. – Über die rhythmische Funktionsordnung von Puls und Atem – *Z. Klin. Med.* 150–1953–445.

8　HILDEBRANDT, G. – Die Bedeutung der rhythmischen Funktionsordnung von Puls und Atem für den Badearzt – *Z. Angew. Bäder–Klimahlk.* 1/1–1954–1.

9　HILDEBRANDT, G. – Bäderkuren und biologische Rhythmen – *D. Med. Wschr.* 79/38–1954–1404.

10　HILDEBRANDT, G. – *Zur Frage der Beziehung von Rhythmus und Regulation* – Ref. 1955a, p. 105.

11　HILDEBRANDT, G. – Prinzipen der Regulation und ihre balneotherapeutische Bedeutung – *Arch. Physik. Ther.* 7/5–1955–415.

12　HILDEBRANDT, G. – Über die Bedeutung biologischer Rhythmen für die Balneotherapie – *Hippokrates* 26/16–1955–485.

13　HILDEBRANDT, G. – Grundlagen einer angewandten medizinischen Rhythmusforschung – *Heilkunst* 1958–1.

14　HILDEBRANDT, G. – Umstellungen des Atemrhythmus im Kurverlauf –*Arch.Physikal.Ther.* 11/1–1959–23.

15　HILDEBRANDT, G. – Über die Variabilität des Pulsrhythmus (Pulsperiodenstreuung) und ihre Beeinflussung durch die CO_2-Badekur – *Arch.Physikal.Ther.* 11/2–1959–132.

16　HILDEBRANDT, G. – Balneologie und vegetative Regulation – *Die Therapiewoche* 9/10–1959–4€5.

17　HILDEBRANDT, G. – *Reaktive Perioden and Spontanrhythmik* – Ref. 1960a, p. 75.

18　HILDEBRANDT, G. – Spontane Schwankungen der Thermoregulation und physikalische Therapie – *Berl. Med.* 11–1960–37.

19　HILDEBRANDT, G. – Hat die Atemstossmessung praktische Bedeutung – *Berl. Med.* 11–1960–108.

20　HILDEBRANDT, G. – Balneologie und Rhythmusforschung – *Allg. Therap.* (6–7)–1961.

21　HILDEBRANDT, G. – Rhythmus und Regulation – *Med. Welt* 2–1961–73.

22　HILDEBRANDT, G. – Über Tagesrhythmische Steuerung der Reagibilität–*Arch.Phys.Ther.* 9–1957–293.

23　HILDEBRANDT, G. – *Die rhythmische Funktionsordnung von Puls und Atmung* – Schattauer Verlag. Stuttgart, 1960.

100　HILDEBRANDT, G., H. BERGÉR, W. STALLING and L. STEINKE – Balneotherapie und vegetative Regulation – *Ärztl. Praxis* 11/48–1959–1809.

101　HILDEBRANDT, G. and P. ENGELBERTZ – Über tagesrhythmische Veränderungen der Asymetrie der Hauttemperaturen – *Arch. Physikal. Ther.* 4/6–1952–385.

102　HILDEBRANDT, G. and P. ENGELBERTZ – Bedeutung der Tagesrhythmik für die physikalische Therapie – *Arch. Physikal. Ther.* 5/2–1953–160.

103　HILDEBRANDT, G., P. ENGELBERTZ and G. HILDEBRANDT EVERS – Physiologische Grundlagen für eine tageszeitliche Ordnung der Schwitzprozeduren – *Z. Klin. Med.* 152–1954–446.

104　HILDEBRANDT, G. and K. GEHLKEN – Aktuelle Probleme der Balneologie – *Ärztl. Forsch.* 15/2–1961–76.

105　HILDEBRANDT, G. and K. GOLENHOFEN – Zur Physiologie der Muskelruhedurchblutung des Menschen – *Arch. Physikal. Ther.* 10/4–1958–217.

106 HILDEBRANDT, G. and O. HANKE –
Über spontane Schwankungen des
Oszillometrischen Quotienten – Z.
Kreisslaufforsch. 1954–89.

107 HILDEBRANDT, G. and O. HANKE –
Über die Sicherheit des oszillo-
graphischen Befundes bei periphe-
ren Durchblutungsstörungen – Arch.
Physikal. Ther. 7/2–1955–150.

108 HILDEBRANDT, G., O. HANKE and P.
ENGELBERTZ – Tagesschwankungen
im EKG – Die Medizinische 8/42–
1954–1414.

109 HILDEBRANDT, G., H. JUNGMAN and
L. STEINKE – Über die Beeinflussung koordinativer Leistungen
durch Bäder- und Klimakuren –
Z. Angew. Bäder–Klimahlk. 6/2–
1959–126.

100 HILDÉN, A. and K. S. STENBÄCK –
Zur Kenntnis der Tagesschwankungen der Körpertemperatur bei den
Vögeln – Skand. Arch. Physiol. 34–
1916–382.

1 HILL, A. V. – Wave transmission as
the basis of nerve activity – Cold
Spring Harbor Symp. Quant. Biol.
1–1933–146.

300 HILL, M. and A. S. PARKES – Studies
on the hypophysectomized ferret
(V); Effect of hypophysectomy on
the response of the female ferret to
additional illumination during an
oestrus – Proc. Roy. Soc. (London)
113B–1933–537.

301 HILL, M. and A. S. PARKES – Effect
of absence of light on the breeding
season of the ferret – Proc. Roy. Soc.
(London) 115B – 1934–14.

1 HILLMAN, W. S. – Injury of tomato
plants by continuous light and un-
favorable photoperiodic cycles –
Am. J. Bot. 43–1956–89.

2 HILLMAN, W. S. – Interaction of
Growth Substances and Photoperiod-
ically Active Radiations on the
Growth of Pea Internode Sections –
Ref. 1957f, p. 181.

100 HIMMEL, G. K., T. M. MARTHALER,
K. H. RATEITSCHAK and H. R.
MÜHLEMANN – Experimental changes of diurnal periodicity in the
physical properties of periodontal
structures – Helv. Odont. Acta 1/1–
1957–10.

1 HINMAN, E. H. – Attempted reversal
of filarial periodicity in Dirofilaria

immitis – Proc. Soc. Exp. Biol. 33–
1936–524.

100 HINTZSCHE E. and A. VON MURALT –
Die Lage des Augapfels als Indikator der vegetativen Stimmung des
Menschen – Schweiz. Med. Wschr.
76/(40–41)–1946–190.

1 HIRNAIK, J. – Zur Frage der periodischen Reaktionen – Z. Physikal.
Chemie 75–1910–675.

100 HIROKAWA, A., K. YANAGIHARA and
K. TATAI – Seasonal variation of
uropepsin excretion – Bull. Inst.
Publ. Health Jap. 7/1–1958–37.

1 HIRSCH, G. C. – Arbeitsrhythmus der
Verdauungsdrüsen – Biol. Zbl. 38–
1918.

2 HIRSCH, G. C. – Daten zum Arbeitsrhythmus der Drüsenzelle und der
Drüse – Tabul. Biol. 1939.

3 HIRSCH, G. C. – Die Ursachen des
Rhythmus der Drüsen – Ref. 1949a,
p. 137.

100 HIRSCH, G. C. and W. JACOBS – Arbeitsrhythmus der Mitteldarmdrüse
von Astacus I–II – Z. Vergl. Physiol. 8–1928; 12–1930.

101 HIRSCH, G. C. and R. F. J. v. PELT –
Der Rhythmus des Glykogengehal-
tes der Leber der weissen Maus,
dargestellt durch die Stufenzahl-
methode – Proc. Kon. Akad. Wetensch. 40–1937–11.

200 HIRSCH, H. M. – Interrelationship of
the Genetic, the Biochemical and the
Circadian Components – Ref. 1961a
p. 71.

1 HISAW, F. L. – Endocrine Cycles in
Vertebrates – Ref. 1957c.

1 HITCHCOCK, H. B. – Airplane observation of homing pigeons – Proc.
Am. Phil. Soc. 96–1952–270.

100 HJORT, P. F., C. F. BORCHGREVINK,
O. H. IVERSEN and H. STORMOR-
KEN – The effect of heparin on the
bleeding time – Thromb. Diath. Hem.
4–1959–389.

1 HOAGLAND, H. – Pacemakers in Relation to Aspects of Behaviour – Macmillan. New York, 1935.

2 HOAGLAND, H. – Some pacemaker
aspects of rhythmic activity in the
nervous system – Cold Spring Harb.
Symp. Quant. Biol. 4–1936–267.

100 HOAGLAND, H. v, CAMERON and RUBIN
– The electroencephalogram of schizophrenics during insulin hypo-

glycemia and recovery – *Am. J. Psychol.* 120–1937–559.

1 HOAR, W. S. – Diurnal variations in feeding activity of young salmon and trout – *J. Fish. Res. Bd. Canad.* 6–1942–90.

2 HOAR, W. S. – Control and timing of fish migration–*Biol. Rev.* 28–1953–1.

3 HOAR, W. S. – Photoperiodism and thermal resistance of gold fish – *Nature* 178–1956–364.

100 HOAR, W. S. and G. M. BELL – The thyroid gland in relation to the seaward migration of Pacific salmon – *Can. J. Res. D.* 28–950–126.

1 HOESCH, K. – Tagesantidiurese und Nykturie bei Lues Cerebrospinalis – *Z. Klin. Med.* 118–1931–49.

1 HOFFMANN, K. – Die Einrechnung der Sonnenwanderung bei der Richtungsweisung der sonnenlos aufgezogenen Stares – *Naturwiss.* 40–1953–148.

2 HOFFMANN, K. – Experimentelle Änderung des Richtungsfindens beim Star durch Beeinflussung der inneren Uhr – *Naturwiss.* 40–1953–608.

3 HOFFMANN, K. – Versuche zu der im Richtungsfinden der Vögel enthaltenen Zeitschätzung – *Z. Tierpsychol.* 11–1954–453.

4 HOFFMANN, K. – Aktivitätsregistrierungen bei frisch geschlüpften Eidechsen – *Z. Vergl. Physiol.* 37–1955–253.

5 HOFFMANN, K. – Über den Einfluss der Temperatur auf die Tagesperiodik bei einem Poikilothermen – *Naturwiss.* 44–1957–358.

6 HOFFMANN, K. – Angeborene Tagesperiodik bei Eidechsen – *Naturwiss.* 44–1957–359.

7 HOFFMANN, K. – Die Richtungsorientierung von Staren unter der Mitternachtssonne – *Z. Vergl. Physiol.* 41–1959–471.

8 HOFFMANN, K. – *Experimental Manipulation of the Orientational Clock in Birds* – Ref. 1960c, p. 379.

9 HOFFMANN, K. – Versuche zur Analyse der Tagesperiodik I – *Z. Vergl. Physiol.* 43–1960–544.

10 HOFFMANN, K. – Repetition of an experiment on bird orientation – *Nature* 181–1958–1435.

200 HOFFMANN, R. W. – Periodischen Tageswechsel und andere biologi-

sche Rhythmen bei den poikilothermen Tieren – *Hb. Norm. Path. Physiol.* 17–1926–644.

400 HOFFMAN, R. A. – Speciation and incidence of *Tabanidae* in the Missisippi delta – *Ann. Entomol. Soc. Am.* 56/5–1963–624.

1 HOFMEISTER, W. – *Die Lehre von der Pflanzenzelle* – Leipzig, 1867.

1 HOHAUS, H. – *Die renale Ausscheidung von Kalium bei Neugeborenen und Säuglingen* – Diss. Ludwig-Maximilians-Univ. München, 1960.

1 HOLLWICH, F. – *Auge und Zwischenhirn* – Enke. Stuttgart, 1955.

2 HOLLWICH, F. – Augenlicht und vegetative Funktionen – *Med. Monatsspiegel (Merck)* 5/1–1956–1.

3 HOLLWICH, F. – *The Influence of Light via the Eyes on Animals and Man* – Ref. 1963b.

100 HOLLWICH, F. and S. TILGNER – Der Einfluss der Lichteinwirkung über das Auge auf Schilddrüse und Hoden – *D. Med. Wschr.* 87/52–1962–2674.

101 HOLLWICH, F. and S. TILGNER – Das Verhalten der Eosinophilen-Zahl als Indikator der okularen Lichtreizwirkung – *Klin. Mbl. Augenhlk.* 142/3 – 1963–531.

100 HOLMES, R. M. and I. J. BASSETT – Effect of meteorological events on ragweed pollen count – *Int. J. Biometeorol.* 7/1–1963–27.

1 HOLMGREN, H. – Beitrag zur Kenntnis von der Leberfunktion – *Z. Mikr. Anat. Forsch.* 24/4–1931–632.

2 HOLMGREN, H. – Till frågan om den rytmiska leverfunktionen – *Svenska Läkartidn.* 10–1933.

3 HOLMGREN, H. – Något om den rytmiska leverfunktionen – *Med. Fören. Tidskr. (Sthlm)* 11–1934–276.

4 HOLMGREN, H. – Studien über 24–Stundenrhythmische Variationen des Darm-Lungen-und Leberfetts – Diss., *Acta. Med. Scand.* suppl. 124–1936–1.

5 HOLMGREN, H. – *Leberrhythmus und Fettresorption* – Ref. 1937a, p. 744.

6 HOLMGREN, H. – *Försök till Bestämning av Blodsockrets Dagsvariationer vid olika Psykoser* – Sv. Psyk. Fören. Förh. (Sweden), 1937.

7 HOLMGREN, H. – 24-Stunden-Varia-

tionen des Gewichts der Leber, Lunge und Milz der grossen weissen Ratte – *Morph. Jb.* 81–1938–653.

8 HOLMGREN, H. – *Der Leberrhythmus bei Tieren welche in dauerndem Dunkel gezüchtet sind* – Ref. 1939a, p. 102.

9 HOLMGREN, H. – *Die Beziehungen zwischen der rhythmischen Leberfunktion und der Empfindlichkeit für Insulin und Adrenalin* – Verh. 14. Tag. Ges. Verdauungs–Stoffwechselkrankh. Thieme. Leipzig, 1939.

10 HOLMGREN, H. – Några reflexioner kring den andra internationella konferensen för biologisk rytmforskning – *Med. Fören. Tidskr. (Sthlm)* 12–1939–304.

11 HOLMGREN, H. – *Till fragan om de faktorer vilka utlösa och utforma rytmen* – Ref. 1941a, p. 43.

12 HOLMGREN, H. – Beitrag zur Kenntnis des Leberrhythmus bei im Dunkel geborenen und aufgezogenen Tieren – *Z. Ges. Exp. Med.* 109–1941–315.

13 HOLMGREN, H. – Die Variationen des Blutzuckers bei wiederholter Zuführung von Adrenalin sowie Insulin – *Z. Ges. Exp. Med.* 110–(4–5)–1941–494.

14 HOLMGREN, H. – Något om leverrytmen och dess betydelse för kliniken – *Nord. Med.* 10–1941–1545.

100 HOLMGREN, H. and C. A. EKMAN – *Leberrhythmus bei Mäusen und Ratten* – Ref. 1949a, p. 46.

101 HOLMGREN, H. and Å. SWENSSON – *Der Einfluss des Lichtes auf den 24-Stunden-Rhythmus der Aktivität, des Leberglykogens und der Körpertemperatur* – Ref. 1949a, p. 71.

102 HOLMGREN, H., O. WILANDER and G. ÅGREN – The connection between the functional activities of the liver and the susceptibility of the organism to insulin – *Acta Med. Scand.* 73–1930–60.

103 HOLMGREN, H. and S. WOHLFAHRT – Blutzuckerstudien mit einer neuen Methode bei Geisteskranken und psychisch Abnormen – *Acta Psych. Neurol.* suppl. 25–1944.

104 HOLMGREN, H. and B. NAUMANN – The oxygen consumption of the liver, kidneys and pancreas at different times during the 24 hours – *Acta Med. Scand.* 128–1947–326.

1 HOLMQUIST, A. G. – Beiträge zur Kenntnis der 24-stündigen Rhythmik der Leber – *Z. Mikr. Anat. Forsch.* 25–1931–30.

2 HOLMQUIST, A. G. – Der Zusammenhang zwischen dem Schlaf und dem Adrenalingehalt der Nebennieren – *Skand. Arch. Physiol.* 65–1933–18.

3 HOLMQUIST, A. G. – Tägliche cyclische Schwankungen im Calciumgehalt des Blutes bei Menschen und Kaninchen – *Z. Exp. Med.* 93–1934–370.

1 HOLST, E. v. – Bausteine zur einer vergleichenden Physiologie der lokomotorischen Reflexe bei Fischen II – *Z. Vergl. Physiol.* 24/4–1937–532.

2 HOLST, E. v. – Vom Wesen der Ordnung im Zentralnervensystem – *Naturwiss.* 25–1937–625, 641.

3 HOLST, E. v. – Die relative Koordination – *Erg. Physiol.* 42–1939–228.

4 HOLST, E. v. – *Periodisch–rhythmische Vorgänge in der Motorik* – Ref. 1955a, p. 7.

5 HOLST, E. v. – Die relative Koordination als Phänomen und als Methode zentralnervöser Funktionsanalyse – *Ergebn. Physiol.* 42–1939–228.

1 HOLT-HANSEN, K. – *The Rhythmic Space and Space–Time Relation* – Ref. 1960a, p. 82.

2 HOLT-HANSEN, K. – Oscillation experienced in the perception of figures – *Hist. Filos. Medd. Dan. Vid. Selsk.* 39/7–1962–1.

3 HOLT-HANSEN, K. – Herings illusion – *Brit. J. Phychol.* 52–1961–317.

100 HOOGENHUYZE, C. J. C. and J. NIEUWENHUYSE – Der Einfluss der Jahreszeit auf den respiratorischen Gaswechsel in Ruhe und bei Muskelarbeit – *Jber. Tier–Chem.* 42–499.

100 HOOVER, R. E. and H. E. HUBBARD – Modification of the sexual cycle of trout by control of light – *Copeia* 4–1937–206.

1 HOPMAN, R. – Die jahreszeitlichen Schwankungen der Krankheiten – *Münch. Med. Wschr.* 1928–2043.

2 HOPMAN, R. – *Insulinbehandlung unter Berücksichtigung des 24-Stunden-Rhythmus des Diabetes mellitus* – Ref. 1939a, p. 143.

1 HOPPING, A. – Seasonal changes in

the gases und sugar of the blood and the nitrogen distribution in the blood and urine of the alligator – *Am. J. Physiol.* 66/1–1923–145.

1 HORN, J. – Zu welcher Tageszeit fängt die Geburt an und wann schliesst sie ab – *Norsk Mag. Lägervet.* 1910.

1 HOSEMANN, H. – Umwelteinflüsse und Wehenbeginn – *Naturwiss.* 33–1946–182.

2 HOSEMANN, H. – *Extraterrestrische Einflüsse auf Nativität und die Menstruationszyklus* – Ref. 1949a, p. 129.

3 HOSEMANN, H. – Unterliegen der Menstruationszyklus der Frau und die tägliche Geburtenzahl solaren und lunaren Einflüssen? – *D. Med. Wschr.* 75–1950–815.

100 HOSHIZAKI, T. and K.C. HAMNER – Circadian leaf movements: Persistence in bean plants grown in continuous high-intensity light–*Science* 144/3623–1964–1240.

1 HOSSEUS, C. C. – *Über die Beeinflüssung der autonomen Variationsbewegungen durch einige äussere Faktoren* – Diss. Leipzig, 1903.

1 HOWE, R. W. – A method for obtaining a controlled daily temperature cycle – *Ann. Appl. Biol.* 44–1956–188.

1 HOWELL, W. H. – A contribution to the physiology of sleep, based upon plethysmographic experiments – *J. Exp. Med.* 2–1897–313.

1 HUBER, B. – Physiologische Rhythmen in Baum – *Meteorol. Rdsch.* 1 (5–6)–1947–144.

100 HUBERT, A. A. and H. J. BAKER – The persistence of foci of *Leptotrombidium akamushi* along a transect in Malaya – *Am. J. Hyg.* 78/2–1963–143.

100 HÜBENER, H. J., H. KREUZIGER, R. HEINTZ and M. KOCH – Flammenphotometrische Bestimmungen der tagesrhythmischen Ausscheidung von Natrium und Kalium beim Menschen – *Z. Ges. Exp. Med.* 119–1952–523.

1 HUESTIS, R.R. – Seasonal pelage differences in *Peromyscus–J. Mammol.* 12–1931–372.

1 HUFELAND, C. W. – *The Art of Prolonging Life* – Bell, London, 1797.

1 HUFSCHMIDT, H. J. – *Der Willkürtremor als Regelvorgang* – Ref. 1955a, p. 112.

1 HUGGER, H. – Zur objektiven Auswertung des Elektrencephalogramms unter besonderer Berücksichtigung der gleitenden Koordination – *Pflüger's Arch.* 244–(1940–41) –181.

1 HUGON, E. – *Variation Périodique de l'Influence des Barrières de Glycholate de Sodium et d'Acide-9-anthroique sur les Corrélations entre les Cotylédons et leurs Bourgeons Axillaires* – Ref. 1958b, p. 33.

100 HUNGERLAND, H. and M. WALTER – Über die Bedeutung des Wilder'schen Ausgangswertgesetzes – *Klin. Wschr.* 35/3–1957–105.

1 HUNTEN, D.M. – Metallic emissions from the upper atmosphere–*Science* 145/3627–1964–26.

1 HUNTINGTON, E. – Season of birth, its relation to human abilities (excerpts) – *Cycles* /repr. 31–1958–160.

2 HUNTINGTON, E. – *Mainspring of Civilization* – Mentor Books MT 248. New York, 1959.

1 HURWICZ, L. – *Basic Mathematical and Statistical Considerations in the Study of Rhythms and Near–Rhythms* – Ref. 1961c, p. 851.

300 HURWITZ, H.M.B., and J.B. APPEL – Light-onset reinforcement as a function of the light–dark maintenance schedule for the hooded rat – *J. Comp. Physiol. Psychol.* 52–1959–710.

1 HUSSEY, G. – Experiments with two long-day plants designed to test Bünning's theory of photoperiodism – *Physiol. Plant.,* 7–1954–253.

1 HUTCHINSON, G. E.–*Theoretical Notes on Oscillatory Populations* – Ref. 1954b, p. 107.

1 HUTTER, K.–Jahreszeitliche Schwankungen bei Magen- und Zwölffingerdarmgeschwür – *Arch. Klin. Chir.* 151–1928–651.

2 HUTTER, K. – Frühjahrsgipfel beim Pylorospasmus bei Säuglingen – *Grenzgeb. Inn. Med. Chir.* 41/1– 1929.

100 IBERALL, A. S. and S. Z. CARDON – *Control in Biological Systems–A Physical Review* – Ref. 1963b.

1 IKEMOTO, A. – Effect of daylength and temperature on the elongation

of main axis in first year seedlings *J. Jap. For. Soc.*, 42–1960–172.

100 IMANOW, W. and J. BASILEWITSCH – Über periodische Schwankungen in der Senkungsgeschwindigkeit des Erythrocyten – *Klin. Wschr.* 1927 I–497.

1 INCE, E. L. – *Integration of Ordinary Differential Equations* – Univ. Math. Texts. Oliver and Boyd. London, 1949.

100 INGOLD, C. T. and V. J. COX – Periodicity of spore discharge in *Daldinia* – *Ann. Bot.* 19–1955–201.

1 ISAACS, J.D. – Night-caught and day-caught larvae of the California Sardine – *Science* 144/3622–1964–1132.

1 ISACHSEN, L. – Om periodiske variationer i blodets sammansättning – – *Arch. Math. Naturwidensk.* 32/10–1911.

1 JACOB, F. – Zur Kenntnis der Lichtwirkung auf die Entwicklung der Sporangienträger der Sammelart *Pilobolus kleinii* van Tieghem – *Arch. Mikrobiol.* 33–1959–83.

1 JACOBI, M. – *The Question of Rest in Women* – New York, 1876.

1 JACOBJ, W. – Über das rhythmische Wachstum der Zellen durch Verdoppelung ihres Volumens – *Arch. Entw. Mechan.* 106–1925–124.

100 JACOBS, W. P., R. V. DAVIS JR and B. BULLWINKEL – *Some Interrelations of Compensatory Growth, Flowering, Auxin and Day Length* – Ref. 1957f, p. 393.

1 JÄRVI, O. – Über die Restitution des Sekreststoffes in der grossen Unterzungendrüse der Katze, geprüft durch die Stufenuntersuchungsmethode I–II – *Z. Zellforsch. Mikr. Anat.* 30–1939–98, 156.

1 JAFFE, J. J. – Diurnal mitotic periodicity in regenerating rat liver – *Anat. Rec.* 120/4–1954–935.

200 JAFFE, L. – The effect of polarized light an the growth of a transparent cell – *J. Gen. Physiol.* 43–1960–897.

300 JAFFE, L. and H. ETZOLD Orientation and locus of tropic photoreceptor molecules in spores – *J. Cell. Biol.* 13/1–1962–13.

1 JAHN, T. – Optische Gleichgewichtsregelung und zentrale Kompensa-

tion bei Amphibien, insbesondere bei der Erdkröte – *Z. Vergl. Physiol.* 43–1960–119.

100 JAMNBACK, H. and T. MATTHEWS – Studies of populations of adult and immature *Culicoides sanguisuga* – *Ann. Entomol. Soc. Am.* 56/6–1963–728.

1 JANDA, V. – Contribution à l'étude des changements périodiques de la coloration chez *Dixippus morosus* – *Vestu. Kral. Cos. Spol. Nauk. (Praha)* 44–1934.

1 JANDER, R. – Die optische Richtungsorientierung der roten Waldameise – *Z. Vergl. Physiol.* 40–1957–162.

100 JANDER, R. and T. H. WATERMAN – Sensory discrimination between polarized light and light intensity patterns by arthropods – *J. Cell. Comp. Physiol.* 56–1960–155.

1 JANKOWIAK, J. – *Measurements of the Intensity of Solar Radiation in the Health-Resort Kolobrzeg as Basic Data for Use in Heliotherapy* – Ref. 1963c.

1 JANTZ, H. – Stoffwechseluntersuchungen bei paroxysmaler Lähmung – *Nervenarzt* 18–1947–360.

200 JARDETZKY, W.S. – *Investigations of of Milankovitch and the quaternary curve of effective solar radiation* – Ref. 1961e, p. 418.

100 JARDETZKY, C. D., C. ECKERT, F. HALBERG, C. P. BARNUM and J. J. BITTNER – Periodicity of eosinophil count in partially hepatectomized mice – *Exp. Med. Surg.* 15/1–1957–11.

101 JARDETZKY, C. D., C. P. BARNUM and F. HALBERG – Physiologic 24-hour periodicity in nucleic acid metabolism and mitosis of immature growing liver – *Am. J. Physiol.* 187–1956–608.

1 JENKINSON, I. S. – Transcient bioelectric potentials produced by electrically stimulated bean roots – *Austr. J. Biol. Sci.* 11/4–1958–485.

100 JENKINSON, I. S. and B. I. H. SCOTT – Bioelectric oscillations of bean roots; further evidence for a feedback oscillator – *Austr. J. Biol. Sci.* 14/2–1961–231.

100 JENNER, C. E. and W. I. ENGELS – The significance of dark period in

the photoperiodic response of male juncos and white-throated sparrows – *Biol. Bull.* 103–1952–345.

1 JENNY, E. – Tagesperiodische Einflüsse auf Geburt und Tod – *Schweiz. Med. Wschr.* 63/1–1933–15.

2 JENNY, E. – Umwelteinflüsse auf Geburtenzahl und Knabenüberschuss – *Schweiz. Med. Wschr.* 1944–630.

1 JENS, G. – Über den lunaren Rhythmus der Blankaalwanderung – *Arch. Fischereiwiss.* 4–(1952–1953)–94.

2 JENS, G. – Über den Rhythmus der Blankaalwanderung – *Ber. Limnol. Flusstation Freudenthal IV* 1953.

3 JENS, G. – Untersuchungen über rhythmische Erscheinungen beim Heringsfang in der Nordsee – *Arch. Fischereiwiss.* 5/(3–4)–1954–113.

1 JEREBZOFF, S. – Action de la durée de la lumipériode sur la croissance des conidiophores fertiles et l'apparation des zonation chez *Monilia fructicola* – *C.R. Acad. Sci.* 242–1956–1059.

2 JEREBZOFF, S. – *Répercussion du Rythme Endogène sur la Croissance des Conidiophores Fertiles de Monilia fructicola au cours de l'Apparition des Zonations et Modifications Provoquées de ce Rythme* – Ref. 1958b, p. 23.

3 JEREBZOFF, S. – Rythme interne et apparition des zonations chez *Monilia fructicola* – *C.R. Acad. Sci.* 246–1958–976.

4 JEREBZOFF, S. – L'extrait de levure contient un facteur qui permet la formation de zonations chez *Monilia fructicola* développé a l'obscurité et sous éclairement continu – *C.R. Acad. Sci.* 247–1958–1348.

5 JEREBZOFF, S. – Activité de differentes radiations lumineuses sur la croissance des conidiophores fertiles et le déclenchement du rythme interne de zonations chez *Monilia fructicola*–*C.R. Acad. Sci.* 250–1960–1549.

6 JEREBZOFF, S. – *Etude de Phénomènes Périodiques Provoqués par des Facteurs Physiques et Chimiques chez quelques Champignons* – Diss. 495. Univ. Toulouse, 1961.

7 JEREBZOFF, S. – En relation avec la composition du milieu de culture *Alternaria tenuis* montre soit un rythme exogène de zonations, soit un rythme endogène de 50 h. – *C.R. Acad. Sci.* 252–1961–163.

8 JEREBZOFF, S. – Dépendence de la période du rythme endogène de zonations d'*Alternaria tenuis auct.* vis-à-vis de la température ou de la composition du milieu nutritif – *C.R. Acad. Sci.* 252–1961–782.

9 JEREBZOFF, S. – Action de la fraction "non ionique" de l'extrait de malt et de quelques sucres sur le rythme endogène de zonations d'*Alternaria tenuis auct.* – *C.R. Acad. Sci.* 252–1961–4034.

10 JEREBZOFF, S. – *Chemical Factors Evoking Endogenous Rhythms of Zonations or Influencing the Length of their Period in some Fungi* – Ref. 1963a.

1 JÖCHLE, W. – Über das Vorkommen eines Pigmenthormons in der Plazenta von Haussäugetieren – *Endokrinologie* 33/(1–2)–1955–63.

2 JÖCHLE, W. – Über den Einfluss des Lichtes auf Sexualentwicklung und Sexualperiodik bei Säugern – *Endokrinologie* 33/(3–4)–1956–129.

3 JÖCHLE, W. – Über die Wirkungen eines in Bildung und Auschüttung lichtabhängigen Hormons bei Säugern – *Endokrinologie* 33/(3–4)–1956 –190.

4 JÖCHLE, W. – Exogene und endogene Einflüsse auf Tragzeitdauer und Geschlechtsverteilung der Nachkommen beim Pferd – *Zuchthyg. Fortpflanzungsstör. Besamung Haustiere* 1–1957–238.

5 JÖCHLE, W. – *Über die Wirkung von Dauerbelichtung auf Cyclus, Zuchterfolg und spontane Mammatumorwachstum bei Mäusen* – Ref. 1960a, p. 87.

6 JÖCHLE, W. – *Trends in Photophysiologic Concepts* – Ref. 1963b.

100 JÖCHLE, W. and H. MATHIES – Physiologische Hormonwirkungen I–VI – *Med. Heute* 6/6–1957–283; 6/7– 1957–332; 6/8–1957–390; 6/10–1957 –494; 6/12–1957–592; 7/1–1958–17.

101 JÖCHLE, W. and H. UNGEHEUER – Psychisches Verhalten von Ratten unter extremen Haltungsbedingungen in Abhängigkeit von Wettereinflüssen – *Z.Naturforsch.* 12b/1– 1957–48.

1 JOHANSEN, K. – Response to heat and cold in lower mammals – *Int. J. Biometeor. (Ref. J.e.)* 6/1–1962–3.

100 JOHANSEN, K. and J. KROG – Diurnal body temperature variations and hibernation in the birchmouse – *Am. J. Physiol.* 196–1959–1200.

1 JOHANSSON, J. E. – Über die Tagesschwankungen des Stoffwechsels und der Körpertemperatur in nüchternem Zustand und vollständiger Muskelruhe – *Skand. Arch. Physiol.* 8–1898–85.

1 JOHNSON, C. G. – Aphid migration – *New Scientist* 15/305–1962–622.

100 JOHNSON, C. G., E. HAINE, A. J. COCKBAIN and L. R. TAYLOR – Moulting rhythm in the aliencolae of *Aphis fabae scop.* in the field – *Ann. Appl. Biol.* 45/4–1957–702.

101 JOHNSON, C. G. and L. R. TAYLOR – Periodism and energy summation with special reference to flight rhythms in aphids – *J. Exp. Biol.* 34/2–1957–209.

102 JOHNSON, C. G., L. R. TAYLOR and E. HAINE – The analysis and reconstruction of diurnal flight curves in alienicolae of *Aphis fabae scop.* – *Ann. Appl. Biol.* 45/4–1957–682.

200 JOHNSON, M. S. – Effect of continuous light on periodic spontaneous activity of white-footed mice – *J. Exp. Zool.* 82–1939–315.

1 JORDAN, H. – Variationen der Pulszeitstreuung beim Karotisdruckversuch am Menschen in Fällen von vegetativ–endokrinen Regulationsstörungen – *Arch. Kreislaufforsch.* 18–1952–344.

2 JORDAN, H. – Rhythmologische Beobachtungen am menschlichen Herzen bei totalem AV-block – *Z. Klin. Med.* 151–1953–65.

3 JORDAN, H. – Die zeitlichen Schwankungen der Herzschlagintervalle bei absoluter Arrhytmie – *Arch. Kreislaufforsch.* 21–1954–40.

4 JORDAN, H. – Sinussynchrone Schwankungen der Überleitungszeit – *Z. Ges. Inn. Med. Grenzgeb.* 9/4–1954–199.

5 JORDAN, H. – Herzschlagrhythmik und Lebensalter – *Z. Altersforsch.* 9/(1–2)–1955–141.

6 JORDAN, H. – Rhythmische Schwankungen der Kammerschlagfolge bei perpetueller Flimmerarrhythmie – *Z. Kreislaufforsch.* 48–1959–1021.

7 JORDAN, H. – *Nachweis periodischer Langwellenschwankungen bei der absoluten Arrhythmie des Herzen* – Ref. 1960a, p. 91.

8 JORDAN, H. – Die kurzzeitlichen Schwankungen der Herzperiodendauer des Menschen – *Z. Ges. Inn. Med. Grenzgeb.* (ser. Cardiol. X)/17–1963–136.

1 JORES, A. – Die Urineinschränkung in der Nacht – *D. Arch. Klin. Med.* 175–1933–244.

2 JORES, A. – Über Nykturie – *D. Arch. Klin. Med.* 175–1933–484.

3 JORES, A. – Tag- und Nachtwechsel in seiner Wirkung auf den Menschen – *Klin. Wschr.* 1933 II–1538.

4 JORES, A. – Nykturie als Symptom zentral–nervöser Störungen – *Klin. Wschr.* 1934 I–130.

5 JORES, A. – Die 24-Stundenperioden des Menschen – *Med. Klin.* 30/14–1934 I–468.

6 JORES, A. – Über den Einfluss des Lichtes auf die 24-Stundenperioden des Menschen – *D. Arch. Klin. Med.* 176–1934–544.

7 JORES, A. – Das Problem der Tagesperiodik in der Biologie – *Med. Klin.* 1935.

8 JORES, A. – Die Nykturie als zentral bedingte Funktionsstörung des vegetativen Systems – *D.Z. Nervenhlk.* 138–1935–1.

9 JORES, A. – Physiologie und Pathologie der 24-Stunden-Rhythmik des Menschen – *Erg. Inn. Med. Kinderhlk.* 48–1935–574.

10 JORES, A. – *Die Ursache der Rhythmik vom Gesichtspunkt des Menschen* – Ref. 1937a, p. 995.

11 JORES, A. – *Endokrines und vegetatives System in ihrer Bedeutung für die Tagesperiodik* – Ref. 1937a, p. 989.

12 JORES, A. – Die 24-Stunden Periodik in der Biologie – *Tabul. Biol.* 14–1937–77.

13 JORES, A. – *Rhythmusstudien am hypophysektomierten Tier* – Ref. 1939a, p. 114.

14 JORES, A. – Periodizität beim Menschen – *Stud. Gen.* 2–1949–82.

15 JORES, A. – Neuere Ergebnisse der Rhythmusforschung – *Ärztl. Mh.*, 5 –(1949–1950)–355.

100 JORES, A. and H. BECK, – Nykturie und Ulcuskrankheit – *Klin. Wschr.* 14–1935 I–526.

101 JORES, A. and J. FREES – Die Tagesschwankungen der Schmerzempfindung – *D. Med. Wschr.* 63–1937–962.

100 JOSEPHSON, B. and H. LARSSON – Über die Periodizität der Gallensekretion bei einem Patienten mit Gallenfistel – *Skand. Arch. Physiol.* 69–1934–227.

1 JOST, L. – Besprechungen über die Arbeiten Klebs 1911 und 1912 – *Z. Bot.* 4–1912–643.

1 JÓZEFACIUK, W. – Observations on the influence of meteorological conditions on the height increment of forest trees – *Int. J. Biometeorol. (Ref. J. e.)* 6/1–1962–55.

1 JUNDELL, I. – Über die nykthemeralen Temperaturschwankungen im ersten Lebensjahre des Menschen – *Jb. Kinderhlk.* 59–1904–521.

1 JUNG, R. – *Neurophysiologie der rhythmischen Vorgänge im Nervensystem* – Ref. 1955a, p. 16.

1 JUNGMANN, H. – Über den Einfluss von Tageszeit, Nahrungsaufnahme und Nüchternzustand auf den Kreislauf – *Z.Kreislaufforsch.*43–1954–120.

1 JUSATZ, H. J. – *Saisonkrankheiten und bioklimatologische Klassification* Ref. 1963c.

100 JUSATZ, H. J., and E. ECKHARDT – Die häufigste Todesstunde – *Münch. Med. Wschr.* 1924 I–709.

1 JUSTICE, K. E. – *Nocturnalism in Three Species of Desert Rodents* – Diss. Abstr. 21/3–1960.

100 JUVENELLE, A., J. LIND and C. WEGELIUS – Quelques possibilités offertes par l'hypothermie générale profonde provoquée – *Presse Med.* 60–1952–973.

100 KABLE, G. W., F. Fox and A. LUNN – Electric light for increasing egg production – *Bull. Oregon Agricult, Exp. St.* 1928–231.

1 KÄHLER, K. – Biologische Wirkungen der Luftelektrizität und der künstlichen Ionisierung – *Naturwiss.* 25–1937–92, 110.

1 KAGEYAMA, M. – Two cases of glaucoma with daily variations of isopters [in Japanese] – *J. Clin. Ophthal.* (Tokyo) 16–1962–135.

100 KAINE, H. D., H. S. SELTZER and J. W. CONN – Mechanisms of diurnal eosinophil rhythm in man – *J. Lab. Clin. Med.* 45–1955–247.

1 KAISER, I. H. – *Circadian Aspect of Human Birth* – Ref. 1961a, p. 33.

100 KAISER, I. H. and F. HALBERG – *Circadian Periodic Aspects of Birth* – Ref. 1961c, p. 1056.

300 KAISER, F. and J. MAURATH – Kreislaufdynamische 24-Stunden-Rhythmik beim Menschen – *Klin. Wschr.* 27–1949–659.

1 KALLIO, P. – The effect of continued illumination on the desmids – *Arch. Soc. Zool. Bot. Fenn.,* 8–1953–58.

1 KALMUS, H. – Über die Natur des Zeitgedächtnisses der Bienen – *Z. Vergl. Physiol.* 20–1934–405.

2 KALMUS, H. – Periodizität und Autochronie als zeitregelnde Eigenschaften der Organismen – *Biol. Gen.* 11–1935–93.

3 KALMUS, H. – Vorversuche über die Orientierung der Biene im Stock – *Z. Vergl. Physiol.* 24/2–1936–166.

4 KALMUS, H. – Periodizität und autochronie als zeitregelnde Eigenschaften bei Tier und Mensch – *Tab. Biol.* 16–1938–60.

5 KALMUS, H. – Über das Problem der sogenannten exogenen und endogenen, sowie der erblichen Rhythmik, und organische Periodizität überhaupt – *Riv. Biol.* 24–1938–191.

6 KALMUS, H. – Tagesperiodisch verlaufende Vorgänge an der Stabheuschrecke und ihre experimentelle Beeinflüssung – *Z. Vergl. Physiol.* 25–1938–494.

7 KALMUS, H. – *New Research in the Diurnal Periodicity of Animals* – Ref. 1939a, p. 227.

8 KALMUS, H. – Diurnal rhythms in the Axolotl larva and in *Drosophila* – *Nature* 145/3663–1940–72.

9 KALMUS, H. – *Repetition, Autonomy and Synchronization in the Living World* – Ref. 1949a, p. 19.

10 KALMUS, H. – *Genetical Responses to Season and Day* – Ref. 1953a, p. 59.

11 KALMUS, H. – Sun navigation by animals – *Nature* 173–1954–657.

12 KALMUS, H. – *Concepts of Information and Biological Rhythms* – Ref. 1955a p. 113.

13 KALMUS, H. – Sun navigation of

Apis mellifica L. in the southern hemisphere – *J. Exp. Biol.* 33–1956–554.

14 KALMUS, H. – Biological rhythms – *Nature* 180–1957–1100.

15 KALMUS, H. – *Periodic Phenomena in Genetic Systems* – Ref. 1961c, p. 1083.

100 KALMUS H. and L. A. WIGGLESWORTH – Shock Excited Systems as Models for Biological Rhythms – Ref. 1960 c, p. 211.

1 KAMIYA, N. – Die Rhythmik des metabolischen Formwechsels der Euglenen – *Ber. D. Bot. Ges.* 57/6–1939–231.

2 KAMIYA, N. – The motive force responsible for protoplasmic streaming in the myxomycete plasmodium – *Ann. Rep. Sci. Works, Sci. Fac. Univ. (Osaka)* 1–1953–53.

3 KAMIYA, N. – Protoplasmic streaming – *Ann. Rep. Sci. Works, Sci. Fac. Univ. (Osaka)* 8–1960–13.

4 KAMIYA, N. – Physics and chemistry of protoplasmic streaming – *Ann. Rev. Plant Physiol.* 11–1960–323.

100 KAMIYA, N. and H. NAKAJIMA – Some aspects of rhythmicity of the protoplasmic streaming in the myxomycete plasmodium – *Jap. J. Bot.* 15/1–1955–49.

101 KAMIYA, N., H. NAKAJIMA and S. ABE – Physiology of the motive force of protoplasmic streaming – *Protoplasma* 48–1957–94.

1 KANFOR, I. S. – *Einfluss des Phenamins auf den 24-Stunden-Rhythmus der Veränderungen des Blutzuckerspiegels bei Affen* – Bykow, Ref. 1., p. 84.

1 KARLSSON, S. – *A Contribution to the Methods of Recording the Motility of the Human Uterus* – Stockholm 1944.

1 KARLSTROM, T.N.V. – *The glacial history of Alaska*–Ref. 1961e, p. 290.

1 KARNELL, J. – Coarctatio aortae – *Opusc. Med. (Stockh.)* suppl. 1–1959.

1 KARNOP, F. – 24-Stunden Rhythmus im EKG des Kindes–*Ärztl. Wschr.* 14–1959–866.

1 KÁRPÁTI, J. – *Research Work on the Annual Periodical Rhythm of Plant Communities and its Methods in Hungary* – Ref. 1963c.

1 KARSTEN, G. – Über embryonales Wachstum und seine Tagesperiode – *Z. Bot.* 7–1915–1.

2 KARSTEN, G. – Über Tagesperiode der Kern- und Zellteilungen – *Z. Bot.* 10–1918–1.

1 KASSIMOV, R. Y. – Diurnal rhythm of motor activity in some species of sturgeons and their hybrids – *J. Zool. Acad. USSR* 40/1–1961–63.

1 KATHAN, K. – *Über Veränderungen der Kreatin–Kreatinin und Phosphatausscheidung im Verlauf der kindlichen Entwicklung* – Diss. Ludwig-Maximilians–Univ. München, 1960.

100 KATSCH. G. and H. PANSDORF – Die Schlafbewegungen des Blutdruckes – *Münch. Med. Wschr.* 1922 II–1715.

1 KATZ, G. – Artidsvariationen av prematurfrekvensen – *Nord. Med. (Sthlm)* 50/48–1953.

1 KAYSER, C. – Echanges respiratoires des hibernants – *Ann. Physiol.*, 15–1939–1087.

2 KAYSER, C. – Le sommeil hibernal – *Biol. Rev.* 25–1950–255.

3 KAYSER, C. – Hibernation et hypothermie des mammifères – *Acta Neuroveg.* 11–1955–38.

4 KAYSER, C. – Le sommeil hibernal. Problème de thermorégulation – *Rev. Canad. Biol.* 16–1957–303.

5 KAYSER, C. – Le sommeil hibernal et les glandes surrénales – *C.R. Soc. Biol.* 151–1957–985.

100 KAYSER, C. and M. ARON – Cycle d'activité saisonnière des glandes endocrines chez un hibernant, le hamster – *C.R. Soc. Biol.* 129–1938–225.

101 KAYSER, C. and M. ARON – Le cycle saisonnier des glandes endocrines chez les hibernants – *Arch. Anat. Histol. Embryol.* 33–1950–21.

102 KAYSER, C. and C. MARX – *Le Rythme Nycthéméral de l'Activité et la Mémoire du Temps chez le Lézard (Lacerta agilis et Lacerta muralis)* – Rep. XX Congr. Int. Phil. Sci. Paris 6 Biol. – 1949–96.

1 KEHLER, E. – Zum vegetativen Mechanismus des Asthma-Anfalls – *Med. Monschr.* 14/11–1960–711.

1 KEITH, L.B. – *Wildlifes ten-year cycle* – Univ. Wisconsin Press 1962.

1 KELLER, C. – Vergleichende Zellen- und Kernmessungen bei grossen und kleinen Hühnerrassen zur Prüfung

der genetisch bedingten Wuchsunterschiede – *Z. Zellforsch.* 19/1–1933 –511.

200 KELLER, S. – Über die Wirkung chemischer Faktoren auf die tagesperiodischen Blattbewegungen von *Phaseolus multiflorus* – *Z. Bot.* 48–1960–32.

1 KELLERMAN, K. F. – A review of the discovery of photoperiodism: the influence of the length of daily light periods upon the growth of plants – *Quart. Rev. Biol.* 1–1926–87.

1 KELLERSMANN, A. – *Elektrokardiografische Untersuchungen im Nüchterzustand zur Tagesrhythmik beim Sportler* – Diss. Münster, 1961.

1 KELLICOTT, W. – The daily periodicity of cell division and of elongation in the root of *Allium* – *Bull. Torrey. Bot. Club* 31–1904–529.

1 KENDALL, M. G. – *Contribution to the Theory of Oscillatory Time Series* – Cambridge Univ. Press. New York, 1946.

2 KENDALL, M. G. – Oscillatory timeseries – *Nature* 161–1948–187.

1 KENDEIGH, S. C. – Length of day and energy requirements for gonad development and egg-laying in birds – *Ecology* 22–1941–237.

2 KENDEIGH, S. C. – Effects of temperature and season on energy resources of the english sparrow – *Auk* 66–1949–113.

100 KENEDI, I. and G. BIGE – Über die diurnalen Veränderungen des pathologischen Elektrokardiogramms – *Cardiologia* 32/5–1958–278.

1 KENNEDY, C. H. – Evolutionary level in relation to geographic, seasonal and diurnal distribution of insects – *Ecology* 9–1928–367.

100 KENNETH, P. and E. MILLMAN – *A Linear Model for Circadian Rhythms* – Ref. 1960a, p. 92.

1 KENNEY, J. F. – *Mathematics of Statistics* – Nostrand Co. New York, 1950.

100 KÉRDÖ, I. and I. ÖRMÉNYI – *Variations of the pH Level of Urine influenced by Meteorological and Cosmic Factors* – Ref. 1963c.

100 KERKUT, G. A. and B. J. R. TAYLOR – Effect of temperature on the spontaneous activity from the isolated ganglia of the slug, cockroach and crayfish – *Nature* 178–1956–426.

1 KERLING, L. C. P. – Developmental processes of the rice plant in relation to photoperiodism – *Proc. Kon. Med. Akad. Wet.* 53–1950–3.

1 KIKUCHI, K. – Diurnal migrations of plankton *Crustacea* – *Quart. Rev. Biol.* 5–1930–189.

200 KIKUCHI, M. – *A Seasonal Rhythm in the Occurrence of Infection* – Ref. 1962c.

1 KILBINGER, A. – *Assimilation und Dissimilation* – Ref. 1953a, p. 99.

1 KIRCHHOFF, H. – Umweltfaktoren und Genitalfunktion – *Geburtshlk. Frauenkr.* 10– –377.

2 KIRCHHOFF, H. – Unterliegt der Wehenbeginn kosmischen Einflüssen? – *Z. Gyn.* 59–1935–134.

100 KIRCHOFF, H. and HARFST – Besteht ein Einfluss der Gezeiten auf die Geburt? – *Zbl. Gynäk.* 59–1935–1216.

1 KIRKPATRICK, C. M. – *Interrupted Dark Period; Test for Refractoriness in Bobwhite Quail Hens* – Ref. 1957f, p. 751.

100 KIRKPATRICK, C. M. and A. C. LEOPOLD – The role of darkness in sexual activity of quail – *Science* 116–1952–280.

1 KIRSCH, O. – Der Wintergipfel der Atmungskrankheiten – *Z. Kinderhlk.* 48–1929–298.

1 KLAGES, L. – *Vom Wesen des Rhythmus* – Gropengiesser. Zurich, 1944.

1 KLAUS, E. J. – Untersuchungen zur Tagesrhythmus und Pulswellengeschwindigkeit beim Sportler– *Sportärztl. Praxis* 23–1961.

100 KLAUS, E. J. and D. CLASING – Untersuchungen zur Tagesrhythmik der Pulswellengeschwindigkeit beim Sportler– *Intern. Z. Angew. Physiol. Arbeitsphysiol.* 18–1960–319.

1 KLEBER, E. – Hat das Zeitgedächtnis der Bienen biologische Bedeutung? – *Z. Vergl. Physiol.* 22–1935–221.

1 KLEBS, G. – Über die Rhythmik in der Entwicklung der Pflanzen – *Sitz. Ber Mat.* – *Nat. Kl. (Heidelberg) Akad. Wiss.* 1911.

2 KLEBS, G. – Über periodisch wachsende tropische Baumarten – *Sitz. ber. (Heidelberg), Akad. Wiss. Math.* – *Nat. Kl.,* 2–1926.

1 KLEIN, W. H. – *Interaction of Growth Factors with Photoprocess in Seedling Growth* – Ref. 1957f, p. 207.

200 KLEIN, H. – Die periodischen Schwankungen der Blut-, Milz-, Darm- und Leberleukocyten – *Virchows Arch. Pathol. Anat. Physiol. Klin. Med.* 316–1949–97.

1 KLEINBAUM, H. – Über die Amino-Stickstoff-Ausscheidung im Urin bei Säuglingen mit akuten Ernährungsstörungen – *Z. Kinderhlk.* 79–1957–465.

1 KLEINHOLZ, L. H. – Studies in the pigmentary system of *Crustacea* I; Color changes and diurnal rhythm in *Ligia baudiniana* – *Biol. Bull.* 72–1937–24.

100 KLEINHOLZ, L. H. and J. H. WELSH – Colour changes in Hippolyte varians – *Nature* 140–1937–851.

1 KLEINHOONTE, A. – *De door het Licht geregelde autonome bewegingen der Canavalia-bladeren.* – Diss. Univ. Utrecht. Delft, 1928.

2 KLEINHOONTE, A. – Über die durch das Licht regulierten autonomen Bewegungen der Canavalia-Blätter – *Arch. Néerl. Sci. Exp. Nat.* 5 III b –1929–1.

3 KLEINHOONTE, A. – Untersuchungen über die autonomen Bewegungen der Primärblätter von *Canavalia ensiformis* – *Jb. Wiss. Bot.* 75–1932 –679.

4 KLEINHOONTE, A. – *Die Tagesperiodik in der Pflanzenwelt* – Ref. 1937a, p. 738.

1 KLEITMAN, N. – Studies on the physiology of sleep I – *Am. J. Physiol.* – 66/1–1923–67.

2 KLEITMAN, N. – Studies on the physiology of sleep II – *Am. J. Physiol.* 74/2–1925–225.

3 KLEITMAN, N. – Studies on the physiology of sleep V – *Am. J. Physiol.* 84–1928–386.

4 KLEITMAN, N. – Sleep – *Physiol. Rev.* 9–1929–624.

5 KLEITMAN, N. – Studies on the physiology of sleep VIII – *Am. J. Physiol.* 104–1933–449.

6 KLEITMAN, N. – *Sleep and Wakefulness* – Univ. Chicago Press. Chicago, 1939 and 1964.

7 KLEITMAN, N. – The modifiability of the diurnal pigmentary rhythm in isopods – *Biol. Bull.* 78–1940–403.

8 KLEITMAN, N. – Basal temperature graphs and ovulation – *JAMA* 125– 1944–82.

9 KLEITMAN, N. – Biological rhythms and cycles – *Physiol. Rev.* 29–1949– 1.

10 KLEITMAN, N. – *A Brief Activity Cycle in Man* – Ref. 1955a, p. 115.

11 KLEITMAN, N. – Sleep, wakefulness and consciousness – *Psychol. Bull.* 54–1957–354.

12 KLEITMAN, N. – *Development of Circadian Rhythm in the Infant* – Ref. 1961a, p. 35.

13 KLEITMAN, N. – A scientific solution of the multiple shift problem – *Proc. Industr. Hyg. Found. Amer.* 7–1942 –19.

14 KLEITMAN, N. – The sleep–wakefulness cycle of submarine personnel – *Publ. Nat. Res. Council* 1949, p. 329.

100 KLEITMAN N. and E. – Effects of non-twenty-four hour routines of living on oral temperature and heart rate – *J. Appl. Physiol.* 6–1953–283.

101 KLEITMAN, N. and A. DOKTORSKY – Studies on the physiology of sleep VII – *Am. J. Physiol.* 104–1933– 340.

102 KLEITMAN, N. and T. G. ENGELMAN – *The Development of the Diurnal (24-hour) Sleep–Wakefulness Rhythm in the Infant* – Ref. 1953a, p. 106.

103 KLEITMAN, N. and T. G. ENGELMANN – Sleep characteristics of infants – *J. Appl. Physiol.* 6–1953–269.

104 KLEITMAN, N. and D. P. JACKSON – Body temperature and performance under different routines – *J. Appl. Physiol.* 3–1950–309.

105 KLEITMAN, N. and A. RAMSAROOP – Periodicity in body temperature and heart rate – *Endocrinology* 43/1–1948 –1.

106 KLEITMAN, N., S. TITELBAUM and H. HOFFMANN – The establishment of the diurnal temperature cycle – *Am. J. Physiol.*, 119–1937–48.

1 KLOMP, H. – On the theories of host parasite interactions – *Arch. Neerl. Zool.* 13/1–1958–134.

1 KLOTTER, K. – *General Properties of Oscillating Systems* – Ref. 1960c, p. 185.

2 KLOTTER, K. – *Theoretical Analysis of some Biological Models* – Ref.

1960c, p. 189.

1 KLUG, H. – Neurosekretion und Aktivitätsperiodik bei Carabiden – *Naturwiss.* 45–1958–141.

1 KLUYVER, H. N. – Notes on body-weight and time of breeding in the great Tit – *Ardea* 40–1952–123.

1 KNAUS, H. – *Periodic Fertility and Sterility in Women* – Maudrich. Vienna, 1934.

1 KNIEP, H. – Über rhythmische Lebensvorgänge bei den Pflanzen – *Verh. Physik–Med. Ges. (Würzburg)* 44 N.F.–1915–107.

2 KNIEP, H. – Über den rhythmischen Verlauf pflanzlicher Lebensvorgänge – *Naturwiss.* 3–1915–462, 472.

100 KNUDSEN, E. A., J. V. CHRISTIANSEN and H. BRODTHAGEN – *Seasonal Variations in Light-Sensitivity* – Ref. 1960b, p. 521.

1 KOBAYASHI, H. – Failure of reduction of the daily light-period to induce molting in the canary during the period between the end of September and the middle of May – *Annotat. Zool. Jap.* 27–1954–63.

1 KOCH, A. – *Untersuchungen über den Kaurhythmus* – Ref. 1955a, p. 116.

200 KOCH, H. J. – Cause physiologique possible des migrations des animaux aquatique – *Ann. Soc. Roy. Zool. Belg.* 73–1942–57.

300 KOCH, H. J. and M. J. HEUTS – Regulation osmotique, cycle sexual et migration de reproduction chez les Epinoches – *Arch. Int. Physiol.* 53–1943–253.

301 KOCH, H. J. and M. J. HEUTS – La cycle de la régulation cosmotique et minérale du crabe chinois – *Ann. Soc. Roy. Zool. Belg.* 75–1944–87.

100 KOEHLER, F., F. K. OKANO, L. R. ELVEBACK, F. HALBERG and J. J. BITTNER – Periodograms for study of daily physiologic periodicity in mice and man – *Exp. Med. Surg.* 14/1–1956–5.

200 KOEHLER, O. – *Drei Beispiele für angeborenes bzw. erlerntes rhythmisches Verhalten bei Tieren* – Ref. 1953a, p. 38.

400 KÖHLER, U. – Ein 24-Stunden-Rhythmus des Herz- und Milzglykogens der weissen Laboratoriumsratte – *Experientia* 11/11–1955–448.

1 KÖLLNER – Über die regelmässigen täglichen Schwankungen des Augendruckes und ihre Ursache – *Arch. Augenhlk.* 81–1916–120.

100 KÖNIG, H. L. and E. HAINE – Registrierung besonders niderfrequenter elektrischer Signale während der Sonnenfinsternis am 15. Februar 1961 – *Z. Angew. Physik* 13/10–1961 –478.

101 KÖNIG, H. L., E. HAINE and C. ANTONIADIS – Messung von "atmospherics" geringster Frequenzen in Bonn – *Z. Angew. Physik,* 13/8– 1961–364.

1 KÖNITZ, W. – Blühhemmung bei einer Kurztagpflanze durch Hell- und Dunkelrotlicht während der photo- und skotophilen Phase – *Planta* 51– 1958–1.

1 KOEPCHEN, H. P. – *Über das Zusammenwirken endogener Rhythmik und reflektorischer Tonisierung bei der nervösen Steuerung der Herzfrequenz* – Ref. 1960a, p. 94.

2 KOEPCHEN, H. P. – *Die Blutdruckrhythmik* – Steinkopff. Darmstadt, 1962.

3 KOEPCHEN, H. P. – Concepts of servo-control and rhythmicity in the theory of cardiovascular regulation – Proc. 22. Congr. Internat. Union Physiol. Sci, Leiden 1962; *Excerpta Med. Internat. Congr.* Ser. No. 47, p. 44.

4 KOEPCHEN, H. P. – Homeostase und Rhythmus in der Kreislaufregulation – Bad Oeynhausener Gespräche (V) über Probleme der zentralnervösen Regulation. Springer. Berlin, 1962, p. 29.

100 KOEPCHEN, H. P., P.-H. WAGNER and H. P. LUX – Über die Zusammenhänge zwischen zentraler Erregbarkeit, reflektorischem Tonus und Atemrhythmus bei der nervösen Steuerung der Herzfrequenz – *Pflüger's Arch.* 273–1961–443.

101 KOEPCHEN, H. P., J. POLSTER and P. LANGHORST – *Rhythmic Contractions of Resistance Vessels, induced by Efferent Nerve Stimulation* – Ref. 1963a.

1 KÖRNER, I. – Zeitgedächtnis und Alarmierung bei den Bienen – *Z. Vergl. Physiol.* 27–1940–445.

1 KÖSTER, M. – Zuordnung von Wet-

ter- und Gleitvorgängen auf bestimmte Tagesstunden – *Ann. Meteorol.* (1–2)–(1955–1956)–102.

1 KONDIGS, L. – Diurnal rhythm in the adrenal of albino mice – *Acta Biol. Acad. Sci. Hung.* 13–1962–265.

100 KORÖSY, G. and I. KENEDI – Az artériás értónus napi változása kórhazli betegeken és egészséges kontrollcsoportban – *Magy. Belorv. Arch.* 1960–179.

1 KORRINGA, P. – Relations between the moon and periodicity in the breeding of marine animals – *Ecol. Monogr.*, 17–1947–347.

2 KORRINGA, P. – Lunar periodicity. In J. W. Hedgpeth: *"Treatise on Marine Ecology and Paleoecology"* – *Mem. Geol. Soc. Amer.* 1–1957–917.

100 KOSHTOYANTS, H. S. and J. SALANKI – On the physiological principles underlying the periodical activity of *anodonta* – *Acta Biol. Acad. Sci. Hung.* 8/4–1958–361.

1 KOSKIMIES, J. – *Ultimate Causes of Cyclical Fluctuations in Numbers in Animal Populations* – Pap. on Game – Res., (Helsingfors). 1955, no. 15.

1 KOTSOVSKY, D. – *Uber den Rhythmus des Alterns* – Ref. 1953a, p. 167.

1 KOUMANS, A. K. J. – Die Entstehung von Vorhofflimmern und Blockzuständen auf Grund neuer Anschauungen über die Reizbildung im Herzmuskel – *Arch. Kreislaufforsch.* 2/(9–12)–1938–327.

2 KOUMANS, A. K. J. – *Der Herzrhythmus als Relaxationsschwingung* – Verh. D. Ges. Kreislaufforsch. 1939.

1 KOVACS, J. – Diurnal changes in the interstitial cells of the testicles of albino mice – *Acta Biol. Acad. Sci. Hung.* 10/1–1959–69.

1 KRAEPELIN, E. – *Klinische Psychiatrie* – Barth. Leipzig, 1913.

1 KRAMER, G. – Orientierte Zugaktivität gekäfigter Singvögel – *Naturwiss.* 37–1950–188.

2 KRAMER, G. – Weitere Analyse der Faktoren welche die Zugaktivität des gekäfigten Vogels orientieren, *Naturwiss.* 37–1950–377.

3 KRAMER, G. – Eine neue Methode zur Erforschung der Zugorientierung und die bisher damit erzielten

Ergebnisse – *Proc.* 10*th. Internat. Onithol. Congr. (Uppsala)* 1951–271.

4 KRAMER, G. – Die Sonnenorientierung der Vögel – *Verh. D. Zool. Ges. (Freiburg),* 94–1952–72.

5 KRAMER G. – Experiments on bird orientation – *Ibis* 94–1952–265.

6 KRAMER, G. – Wird die Sonnenhöhe bei der Heimfindeorientierung verwertet – *J. Ornithol.* 94–1953–201.

7 KRAMER, G. – Experiments on bird orientation and their interpretation – *Ibis* 99–1957–196.

8 KRAMER, G. – Recent experiments on bird orientation – *Ibis* 101–1959–399.

100 KRAMER, G. and U. v. ST. PAUL – Stare lassen sich auf Himmelsrichtungen dressieren – *Naturwiss.* 37–1950–526.

101 KRAMER, G., J. G. PRATT and U. v. ST. PAUL – Two direction experiments with homing pigeons and their bearing on the problem of goal orientation – *Am. Nat.* 91/856–1957–37.

102 KRAMER, G., J. G. PRATT and U. v. ST. PAUL – Neue Untersuchungen über den "Richtungseffekt" – *J. Ornithol.* 99/2–1958–178.

103 KRAMER, G. and E. RIESE – Die Dressur von Brieftauben auf Kompassrichtung im Wahlkäfig – *Z. Tierpsychol.* 9–1952–245.

1 KRANZFELD, B. – Zur Frage über die physiologischen Tagesschwankungen der Thrombocytenzahle – *Pflüger's Arch.* 210–1925–583.

1 KRASNJANSKY, L. M. – Die Tagesschwankungen des Blutzuckergehaltes beim Menschen – *Biochem. Z.* 205–1929–180.

1 KREBS, C. J. – Lemming cycle at Baker Lake, Canada, during 1959–1962 – *Science* 140/3567–1963–674.

100 KREITNER, H., M. PANLITSCHO and G. GLÖKLER – 24-Stunden Kurven der Magensäuresekretion – *Wien. Z. Inn. Med.* 31–1950–26.

1 KRETSCHMER, W. – El problema de los ritmos en psiquiatria – *Fol. Clin. Internat.* 13/1–1963–3.

2 KRETSCHMER, W. – El problema del ritmo en psiquiatria – *Prensa Med. Mex.* – 28/(3–4)–1963–134.

1 KRIBBEN, F. J. – Zu den Theorien des Photoperiodismus – *Beitr. Biol.*

Pfl. 31–1955–297.

1 KRIJGSMAN, B. J. – Arbeitsrhythmus der Verdauungsdrüsen bei *Helix Pomatia* I–II – *Z. Vergl. Physiol.* 2–1925; 8–1928.

1 KRIS, C. – *Time Series Analysis of Diurnal Fluctuations in Physiological and Performance Measures; Demonstration of the Cyclical Technique for the Descriptive and Predictive Study of the Individual Case* – Diss. Univ. Chicago, 1951.

2 KRIS, C. – Diurnal variation in periorbitally measured eye potential level – *Electroenceph. Clin. Neurophysiol.* 9–1957–382.

3 KRIS, C. – Corneo-fundal potential variations during light and dark adaption – *Nature* 182–1958–1027.

1 KROETZ, C. – *Der 24-Stunden-Rhythmus der Kreislaufregulation* – Ref. 1939a, p. 234.

2 KROETZ, C. – Ein biologischer 24-Stunden-Rhythmus des Blutkreislaufs bei Gesundheit und bei Herzschwäche – *Münch. Med. Wschr.* 87–1940–284, 314.

100 KRUEGER, A. P., S. KOTAKA and P. C. ANDRIESE – Some observations on the physiological effects of gaseous ions – *Int. J. Biometeorol. (Ref. J. e.)* 6/1–1962–33.

1 KU, Y. H. – *Transient Circuit Analysis* – Nostrand. New York, 1961.

1 KUCHLER, W. – Jahrescyclische Veränderungen im histologischen Bau der Vogelschilddrüse – *J. Ornithol.* 85–1935–415.

100 KÜCHMEISTER, H., J. MEINICKE, and H. W. MEYER – Der 24–Stunden–Rhythmus des Muskelinnendruckes und seine Beziehungen zum Wasserhaushalt – *Z. Ges. Exp. Med.* 118–1952–296.

1 KÜHNAU, J. – Der Einfluss des Wetterwechsels auf den normalen menschlichen Organismus – *D. Med. Wschr.* 63–1937–617.

1 KUIPER, N. H. – Tests concerning random points on a circle – *Proc. Konink. Ned. Akad. Wetenschap.* 63 (Ser. A) – 1960–38.

1 KUKSOVA, M.J. – Season and diurnal fluctuations of red cells in monkeys, in: *Theoretical and practical problems of medicine and biology in the experiment on monkeys* (J.A. UTKIN, Ed.),

[in Russian]–Medgiz, Moscow 1956, p. 98.

2 KUKSOVA, M.J. – The effect of fenamine and barbiturate derivatives on diurnal changes of the morphology of blood in monkeys, in: *Problems of physiology and pathology in monkeys* (N.J. LAGUTINA, Ed.), [in Russian] – Sukhumi 1961.

1 KÜNKEL, H. – *Autokorrelationsfunktion und harmonische Analyse beim Studium paroxysmaler Phänomene im Elektroencephalogramm* – Ref. 1963a.

1 KÜSTNER, H. – Haben Lichtstrahlen einen Einfluss auf die Hormone? – *Z. Geburtsh.* 103–1932–305.

1 KUNZE, G. – Balneologische Aufgaben bei der Erforschung des rhythmischen Ablaufes biologischer Vorgänge – *Baleneologe* 1935–450.

300 KUNZE, K., D.W. LÜBBERS and B. RYBAK – Mesure de la tension d'origine de la surface interne du coeur battant en place d'un Mammifère–*C. R. Acad. Sci.* 253–1961–904.

1 KURASHIMA, A. – *Rhythms of Weather* – Ref. 1962c.

1 KURCZ, M. – Vergleichende Untersuchung der spontanen Aktivität von Albino- und Wanderratten – *Acta Physiol. Acad. Sci. Hung* 16/suppl–1959–41.

2 KURCZ, M. – Diurnal variation in the volume and composition of the urine of albino rat – *Acta Biol. Acad. Sci. Hung.* suppl. 3–1959–43.

3 KURCZ, M. – A comparative study of the spontaneous activity of the white rat and the brown or wharf rat – *Acta Biol. Acad. Sci. Hung.* 11/3–1960–271.

1 LACHIVER, F. – Cycle annual de l'iode thyroidien d'un hibernant – *J. Physiol.,* 44–1952–279.

1 LACK, D. – *Cyclic Mortality* – Ref. 1954b, p. 25.

2 LACK, D. – Migration across the North Sea studied by radar – *Ibis* 102–1960–26.

3 LACK, D. – *The Natural Regulation of Animal Numbers* – Clarendon Press. Oxford, 1954.

100 LADERMAN, A. D. and H. N. GUTTMANN – Induction of sexuality by alteration of photoperiod in the rotifer *Brachionus rubens* – *J. Exp.*

Zool. 152/1–1963–5.

100 LAIBACH, F., and F. J. KRIBBEN – Die Blütenbildung als photoperiodische Reaktion – *Z. Naturforsch.*, 5b/3–1950–160.

100 LAIDLAW, J. C., D. JENKINS, W. J. REDDY and T. JAKOBSON – The diurnal variation in adreno-cortical secretion – *J. Clin. Invest.* 33–1954–950.

1 LAKATUA, D. – *Analysis of Estrous Smears by Periodograms and Variance Spectra* – Ref. 1963b.

100 LAMOND, D. R. and A. W. H. BRADEN – Diurnal variation in response to gonadotropin in the mouse – *Endocrinology* 64/6–1959–921.

1 LAMPERT, H. – *Rhythmische Reizbarkeitsänderungen des Organismus und ihre Bedeutung für die Krankenbehandlung* – Ref. 1949a, p. 141.

1 LAMPORT, H. – Periodic changes in blood estrogen – *Endocrinology* 27/4–1940–673.

100 LANDAU, J. and S. FELDMAN – Diminished endogenous morning esinopenia in blind subjects – *Acta Endocrinol.*, 15–1954–53.

1 LANDIS, C. – Electrical phenomena of the body during sleep – *Am. J. Physiol.* 81–1927–6.

1 LANG, A. – *The Influence of Gibberellin and Auxin on Photoperiodic Induction* – Ref. 1949a, p. 329.

100 LANG, A. and G. MELCHERS – Die photoperiodische Reaktion von *Hyoscyamus niger* – *Planta* 33–1943 –653.

200 LANG, K. – *Der intermediäre Stoffwechsel* – Springer. Berlin, 1952.

400 LANG, R. – Über Tagesschwankungen in dem Schwefel und Tryptophangehalt der menschlichen Serumeiweisskörper – *Arch. Exp. Path.* 154–1930–342.

100 LANGDON-DOWN, M. and W. R. BRAIN – Time of day in relation of convulsions in epilepsy – *Lancet* 1–1929–1029.

100 LANGE, H. and J. SCHLOSS – Das Verhalten des Blutzuckers in der Nacht und in den Morgenstunden – *Arch. Exp. Pathol.* 139–1929–274.

200 LANGE, J. F. – *Über die Entwicklung einer Tagesperiodik verschiedener Körperfunktionen unter besonderer Berücksichtigung der Pulsfrequenz,* der Schlaf–Wachverteilung und der Körpertemperatur – Diss. München, 1957.

400 LANGE, N. – Beiträge zur Theorie der sinnlichen Aufmerksamheit und der aktiven Apperception – *Phil. Stud.* 4–1888–390.

600 LANGE, A. H. – The effect of temperature and photoperiod on the growth of *Carica papaya* – *Ecology* 42–1961–481.

900 LANGE, K. O. and R. R. COERMANN – Visual acuity under vibration – *Human Factors,* Oct. 1962–291.

100 LANGENDORFF, L. and W. PAPPERITZ – Über die Wirkung einer einzeitig verabreichten Röntgendosis auf das Knochenmark der weissen Maus – *Strahlenther.* 65–1939–624.

1 LARKS, S. D. – Viscosity and specific gravity of urine; Menstrual-cycle variations – *Obst. Gyn.* 5/3–1955–352.

2 LARKS S. D. – *Electrohysterography* – Thomas. 1960.

3 LARKS, S. D. – *Fetal Electrocardiography* – Thomas. 1961.

4 LARKS, S.D. – Resemblance of the fetal ECG complex to the standard lead II QRS of the newborn – *Obst. Gynecol.* 24/1–1964–1.

100 LARKS, S. D., N. S. ASSALI, D. G. MORTON and W. A. SELLE – Electric activity of the uterus in labor – *J. Appl. Physiol.* 10/3–1957–479.

101 LARKS, S. D., K. DASGUPTA, N. S. ASSALI, D. G. MORTON and A. W. BELLAMY – The human electrohysterogram; electrical evidence for the existence of pacemaker function in the parturient uterus – *J. Obst. Gyn.* 66/2–1959–229.

1 LAROCHE, G. – Los ritmos biologicos – *Prensa Med. Mex.* 28/(3–4)–1963–148.

1 LARSSON K. – Age differences in the diurnal periodicity of male sexual behaviour – *Gerontologia* 2/2–1958–64.

100 LASCH, C. H. and H. U. BILLICH – Die täglichen Schwankungen der Erythrocytenzahlen – *Z. Exp. Med.* 48–1926–651.

1 LAURELL, H. – Människan och kosmos – *Nord. Med.* 2–1939–1329.

2 LAURELL, H. – Neurologiska och rytmbiologiska synpunkter på ul-

cusproblemet – *Nord. Med.* 23–1944 –1473.

3 LAURELL, H. – *Kosmobiologiska Perspektiv* – Astr. Sällsk. Tycho Brahe Årsbok, 1945.

4 LAURELL, H. – *Cosmic Influences upon the Human Nervous System* – Ref. 1955a, p. 118.

100 LAWRENCE, D.H. and W.A. MASON – Food intake in the rat as a function of deprivation intervals and feeding rhythms – *J. Comp. Physiol. Psychol.* 48–1955–267.

1 LAY, W. A. – Über das Morgen- und Abendlernen – *Z. Erforsch. Behandl. Jugendl. Schwachsinns* 5–1912–285.

100 LEAKE, C. D., M. KOHL and G. STEBBINS – Diurnal variations in the blood specific gravity and erythrocyte count in healthy human adults – *Am. J. Physiol.* 81–1927–493.

1 LEATHES, J. B. – On diurnal and nocturnal variations in the excretions of uric acid – *J. Physiol.* 35–(1906–1907)–125.

1 LECOMTE DU NOÜY – *Le Temps et la Vie* – Gallimard. Paris, 1936.

1 LEDERER, R. – Der Wintergipfel der Atmungserkrankungen I–II – *Z. Kinderhlk.* 46–1928–723, 736.

1 LEE, Y. W. – Application of statistical methods to communication problems – *Electron. Res. Lab. M.I.T. Techn. Rep.* 181, 1950.

1 LEES, A. D. – Environmental factors controlling the evocation and termination of diapause in the fruit tree red spider mite – *Ann. Appl. Biol.* 40–1953–449.

2 LEES, A. D. – The significance of the light and dark phases in the photoperiodic control of diapause in *Metatetranychus ulmi* Koch – *Ann. Appl. Biol.* 40–1953–487.

3 LEES, A. D. – The physiology of diapause in arthropods – *Cambr. Monogr. Exp. Biol.* 4–1955.

4 LEES, A. D. – *Photoperiodism in Insects and Mites* – Ref. 1957f, p. 567.

5 LEES, A. D. – The role of photoperiod and temperature in the determination of parthenogenetic and sexual forms in the aphid *Megoura viciae* Buckton I–II – *J. Ins. Physiol.* 3–1959–92; 4–1960–154.

6 LEES, A. D. – *Some Aspects of Animal*

Photoperiodism – Ref. 1960c, p. 261.

7 LEES, A. D. – Aphid clocks – *New Scientist* 11/244–1961–148.

8 LEES, A.D. – The location of the photoperiodic receptors in the aphid – *J. Exp. Biol.* 41/1–1964–119.

1 LINDQUIST, T. – Finger tremor and alpha waves of the electroencephalogram – *Acta Med. Scand.* 108–1941–580.

100 LEES, A. D. and A. MILNE – The seasonal and diurnal activities of individual sheep ticks *(Ixodes ricinus L.)* – *Parasitology* 41–1951–189.

100 LE GROS-CLARK, W. E., T. McKEOWN and S. ZUCKERMAN – Visual pathways concerned in gonadal stimulation in ferrets – *Proc. Roy. Soc. (London)* 126B–1938–449.

1 LEHMANN, G. – *Tagesrhythmik und Leistungsbereitschaft* – Ref. 1949a, p. 108.

2 LEHMANN, G. – *Praktische Arbeitsphysiologie* – Thieme. Stuttgart, 1953.

3 LEHMANN, G. – *Biologische Rhythmen und Arbeitsablauf* – Ref. 1955a p. 35.

1 LEHTONEN, L. – Über den Anfangs- und Endzeitpunkt der Tagesaktivität beim grauen Fliegenschnäpper – *Orn. Fenn.* 26–1949–35.

1 LEINWEBER, F. J. – Über die Temperaturabhängigkeit der Periodenlänge bei der endogenen Tagesrhythmik von *Phaseolus* – *Z. Bot.* 44–1956–337.

1 LEONG, Y. S. – The use of an iterated moving average in measuring seasonal variations – *J. Am. Stat. Assoc.* 297–1962–149.

1 LEOPOLD, A. C. – Photoperiodism in plants – *Quart. Rev. Biol.* 26–1951–247.

1 LEPESCHKIN, W. W. – Light and the permeability of protoplasm – *Am. J. Bot.* 17–1930–953.

1 LESSE, S. – Experimental studies on the relationship between anxiety, dreams and dream-like states – *Am. J. Psychother.* 13/2–1959–440.

100 LEVI, R and J.-F. CUENDET – Psychophysische Korrelationen II – *Schweiz. Med. Wschr.* 77–1947–1203.

100 LEVIN, E., J. B. KIRSNER, W. L. PALMER and C. BUTLER – The variability and periodicity of the noctur-

nal gastric secretion in normal individuals–*Gastroenterol.* 10–1948–939.

1 LEVINS, R., – Theory of fitness in a heterogenous environment I–II – *Am. Nat.* 96/891–1962–361 (II, Am. Nat, in the press).

1 LEWINSKA, K. – Rhythmic changes in food intake and blood sugar level in the rabbit as a function of food deprivation intervals – *Acta Biol. Exptl. Polish Acad. Sci.* 23/3–1963–193.

100 LEWIS, P. R. and M. C. LOBBAN – Patterns of electrolyte excretion in human subjects during a prolonged period of life on a 22 h day – *J. Physiol.* 133–1956–670.

101 LEWIS P. R. and M. C. LOBBAN – Dissociation of diurnal rhythms in human subjects living on abnormal time routines – *Quart. J. Exp. Physiol.* 42–1957–371.

102 LEWIS, P. R. and M. C. LOBBAN – The effect of prolonged periods of life on abnormal time routines upon excretory rhythms in human subjects – *Quart. J. Exp. Physiol.* 42–1957–356.

103 LEWIS, P. R. and M. C. LOBBAN – The effects of exercise on diurnal excretory rhythms in man – *J. Physiol.* 143–1958–8.

104 LEWIS, P. R., M. C. LOBBAN and T. I. SHAW – Patterns of urine flow in human subjects during a prolonged period of life on a 22 h day – *J. Physiol.* 133–1956–659.

105 LEWIS, P. R. and M. C. LOBBAN – Persistance of a 24-hour pattern of diuresis in human subjects living on a 22-hour day – *J. Physiol.* 125–1954–348.

300 LEWIS, C. B. and J. D. BLETCHLY – The emergence rhythm of the Dung-fly – *J. Anim. Ecol.* 12–1943–11.

500 LEWIS, H. and F. W. WENT – Plant growth under controlled conditions IV – *Am. J. Bot.* 32–1945–1.

700 LEWIS, H. E. and J. P. MASTERTON – Sleep and wakefulness in the Arctic – *Lancet* 1957 I–1262.

800 LEWIS, I. – *Diurnal Flight Periodicity* – Ref. 1963c.

1 LEYDEN, C. E. D. F. v. – Some observations on periodic nuclear division in the cat – *Proc. Sci. Sect. Kon. Akad. Wetenschap. (Amsterdam)* 19–

1917–38.

2 LEYDEN, C. E. D. F. v. – Day and night period in nuclear divisions – *Proc. Sci. Sect. Kon. Akad. Wetenschap. (Amsterdam)* 29–1926–979.

1 LIEBER, A. – Der Jahreszyklus der Schilddrüse von *Misgurnis fossilis* und seine experimentelle Beeinflussbarkeit – *Z. Wiss. Zool.* 148–1936–364.

1 LIESE, W. – Die Jahreszeitliche Anpassung des Menschen – *D. Med. Wschr.* 68–1942–896.

1 LILLIE, R. S. – The conditions of recovery of transmissivity of newly repassivated iron vires in nitric acid – *J. Gen. Physiol.* 14/3–1931–349.

100 LIMAN, S. and J. JANKOWIAK – *Tuberculous Pulmonary Bleedings in their Relation to Weather and to Seasonal Climatic Variations* – Ref. 1963c.

1 LINCOLN, F. C. – *Migration of Birds* – Doubleday. New York, 1952.

1 LINDAUER, M. – Bienentänze in der Schwarmtraube I–II – *Naturwiss.* 38–1951–509; 40–1953–379.

2 LINDAUER, M. – Dauertänze im Bienenstock und ihre Beziehungen zur Sonnenbahn – *Naturwiss.* 41–1954–507.

3 LINDAUER, M. – Über die Verständigung der Indischen Bienen – *Z. Vergl. Physiol.* 38–1956–521.

4 LINDAUER, M. – Sonnenorientierung der Bienen unter der Äquatorsonne und zur Nachtzeit – *Naturwiss.* 44–1957–1.

5 LINDAUER, M. – Angeborene und erlernte Komponenten in der Sonnenorientierung der Bienen – *Z. Vergl. Physiol.* 42–1959–43.

6 LINDAUER, M. – *Time-Compensated Sun Orientation in Bees* – Ref. 1960c p. 371.

7 LINDAUER, M. – *Kompassorientierung* Ref. 1962d, p. 158.

1 LINDHARD, J. – The seasonal periodicity in respiration – *Skand. Arch. Physiol.* 26–1912–221.

100 LINDHOLM, H. and Å. RYDÉN – Periodisk feber – *Nord. Med.* 60–1958–1730.

100 LINDSLEY, D. B., R. H. WENDT, D. F. LINDSLEY, J. HOWELL and W. R. ADEY – *EEG and Behavioral*

Responses in Visually Deprived Monkeys – Ref. 1963b.

1 LINKE, F. – *Kosmische und terrestrische Rhythmen* – Ref. 1939a, p. 26.

100 LINKE, F. and B. DE RUDDER – *Medizinisch–meteorologische Statistik* – Berlin, 1937.

1 LINNAEUS, C. – *Philosophia Botanica* – Stockholm, 1751.

2 LINNAEUS, C. – *Växternas Sömn* – in a translation of some selected papers by Carl v. Linné by the Swedish Linnaean Society, Uppsala, 1921.

1 LINNEWEH, W. – Die spezifisch-dynamische Wirkung des Eiweisses im 24-Stunden-Rhythmus – *Z. Ges. Exp. Med.* 105–1939–345.

100 LIOSNER, L. D., N. S. ARTEMIEVA, A. G. BABAEVA, L. K. ROMANOVA, Z. A. RYABININA, V. F. SIDOROVA and G. V. KHARLOVA – On the mitotic activity level and daily rhythm in hypophysectomized rats – *Bull. Exp. Biol. Med. USSR* 8–1962–77.

100 LIPP, J. A., J. R. KNOTT and G. E. FOLK, JR – EEG and heart rates of hypothermic cats – *Fed. Proc.* 19–1960–179.

1 LIPPERT, S. (Ed.) – *Human vibration research* – Pergamon, New York 1963.

1 LIPPI, M. – Modificazioni della colinesterasi serica nelle 24 ore in sogetti normali – *Minerva Med.* 41–1950–301.

100 LIPPI, M. and L. AGRICOLAS – La colesterina nelle 24 ore in sogetti normali – *Minerva Med.* 41–1950–307.

100 LIPPOLD, O.C.J., J.W.T. REDFEARN and J. VUCO – The rhythmic activity of groups of motor units in the voluntary contraction of muscle – *J. Physiol.* 137–1957–473.

100 LISSMANN, H. W. and K. E. MACHIN – Electric receptors in a non-electric fish *(Clarias)*–*Nature* 199/4888–1963–88.

1 LITHANDER, B. – Periodisk hypersomnia – *Opuscula Med. (Stockholm)* 4/2–1959–53.

1 LIVERMAN, J. L. – *Control of Leaf Growth by an Interaction of Chemicals and Light* – Ref. 1957f, p. 161.

1 LOAN, C. C. – The bionomics of *Sitona scissifrons* and its parasite – *Ann. Entomol. Soc. Am.* 56/5–1963–600.

100 LOBASHOV, M. E. and V. B. SABBATEEV – *Physiology of the Daily Rhythm of Living Beings* – (In Russian). Moscow, 1959.

1 LOBBAN, M. C. – Excretory rhythms in indigenous arctic peoples – *J. Physiol.* 143–1958–69.

2 LOBBAN, M. C. – *The Entrainment of Circadian Rhythms in Man* – Ref. 1960c, p. 325.

3 LOBBAN, M.C. – Human renal diurnal rhythms in an artic mining community–*J. Physiol.* 165/2–1963–758

1 LOBEL, H. – *Resonance of Pulsations in Elastic Tubes* – Biophys. Meeting M.I.T., Feb. 7th, 1958.

2 LOBEL, H. – *The Application of Electromagnetic Wave Theory to an Anatomical Discovery in the Arterial System* – Fluid Dynamics Meeting. John Hopkins Univ. Baltimore November 1960.

1 LOCKARD, R.B. – Self-regulated exposure to light by albino rats as a function of rearing luminance and test luminance – *J. Comp. Physiol. Psychol.* 56/3 –1963–558.

1 LOCKHART, J. A. – *Control of Stem Growth by Light and Gibberellic Acid* – Ref. 1957f, p. 217.

2 LOCKHART, J. A. – The influence of red and far-red radiation on the response of *Phaseolus vulgaris* to gibberellic acid – *Physiol. Plant.* 11–1958–487.

3 LOCKHART, J. A. – *On the Hormonal Mechanism of Photoinhibition of Plant Stem Growth* – Ref. 1960b, p. 401.

1 LOEB, J. – Der Einfluss des Lichtes auf die Oxydationsvorgänge in tierischen Organismen – *Arch. Ges. Physiol.* 42–1888–393.

1 LÖRCHER, L. – Die Wirkung verschiedener Lichtqualitäten auf die endogene Tagesrhythmik von *Phaseolus* – *Z. Bot.* 46–1958–209.

100 LOFTS, B. and A. J. MARSHALL – The experimental regulation of Zugunruhe and the sexual cycle in the brambling – *Ibis* 102–1960–209.

1 LONA, F. – *Some Aspects of Photothermal and Chemical Control of Growth*

and Flowering – Ref. 1957f, p. 351.

100 LOOMIS, A. L., E. N. HARVEY and C. MACRAE – The intrinsic rhythm of the turtle heart studied with a new type of chronograph, together with the effects of some drugs and hormones – *J. Gen. Physiol.* 14–1930–105.

1 LOOSLI, C. G. (EDITOR) – Conference on newer respiratory disease viruses – *Ann. Rev. Resp. Dis.* 88/3 (part 2)–1963–1.

1 LORENZEN, H. – Synchrone Zellteilungen von *Chlorella* bei verschiedenen Licht-Dunkel-Wechseln – *Flora* 144–1957–473.

2 LORENZEN, H. – Periodizität von Nuklealreaktion und Kernteilung in *Chlorella* – *Ber. D. Bot. Ges.* 71/2–1958–89.

1 LOTKA, A. J. – Contribution to the theory of periodic reactions – *J. Phys. Chem.* 14–1910–271.

2 LOTKA, A. J. – Undamped oscillations derived from the law of mass action – *J. Am. Chem. Soc.* 42–1920–1595.

3 LOTKA, A. J. – *Elements of Mathematical Biology* – Dover. New York, 1956.

4 LOTKA, A. J. – Analytical note on certain rhythms in organic systems – *Proc. Nat. Acad. Sci. Wash.* 6–1920–410.

100 LOUCH, C., R. K. MEYER and J. T. EMILEN – Effect of stress on diurnal fluctuations in eosinophils of the laboratory mouse – *Proc. Soc. Exp. Biol. Med.* 82–1953–668.

100 LOWENSTEIN, O and I. E. LOEWENFELD – Pupillography – *A.M.A. Arch. Opht.* 59–1958–352.

101 LOWENSTEIN, O. and I. E. LOEWENFELD – *The Sleep–Waking Cycle and Pupillary Activity* – Ref. 1963b.

1 LUBELL, D. – *The Spontaneous Diurnal Variation of Urinary Phosphate Excretion and its Relation to the Parathyroid Hormone Test* – Diss. Univ. Zürich, 1957.

1 LÜDERITZ, B. – *Über Beziehungen zwischen der Harnausscheidung und der Rhythmik der Temperatur* – Ref. 1949a, p. 99.

2 LÜDERITZ, B. – *Über Störungen im Schlaf–Wachrhythmus* – Ref. 1953a, p. 191.

3 LÜDERITZ, B. – Untersuchungen über die Rhythmik, der Körpertemperatur – *D. Arch. Klin. Med.* 196–1949–123, 318, 383, 400.

100 LUETSCHER, J. A. and R. H. CURTIS – Tag–Nacht–Schwankungen der 17-Hydroxycorticoide im Urin – *Ann. Intern. Med.* 43–1955–658.

1 LUMSDEN, W. H. R. – Periodicity of biting behaviour of some African mosquitoes – *Proc. 10th Internat. Congr. Entomol. (Montreal)* 3–1958–785.

1 LUNDBERG, U. – *Studies in Blood Sugar during different Stresses in Air Force Personnel* – Diss. Lund, 1955.

100 LUTHERER, L.O., G.E. Folk, Jr. and W.O. ESSLER–Daily activity pattern of reindeer in arctic continuous light – *Am. Zool.* 2/4–1962.

1 LUTZ, F. E. – Experiments with *Orthoptera* concerning diurnal rhythm – *Amer. Mus. Novitates* 550 –1932.

1 LYMAN, C. P. – Hibernation in mammals and birds – *Am. Sci.* 51/2–1963–127.

1 MCARDLE, B. – Familial periodic paralysis – *Brit. Med. Bull.* 12–1956–229.

100 MCAULAY, A. L. and B. I. H. SCOTT – A new approach to the study of electric fields produced by growing roots – *Nature* 174–1954–924.

1 MCCLELLAND, T. B. – The photoperiodism of *Tephrosia candida* – *J. Agr. Res.* 28–1924–445.

200 MCCLELLAND, G. A. H. – Observations on the mosquito, Aedes Aegypti in East Africa I–II – *Bull. Entomol. Res.* 50/2,4 – (1959–60)–227, 687.

1 MCCLUSKEY, E. S. – Daily rhythms in male harvester and argentine ants – *Science* 128/3323–1958–536.

1 MCCOY – Population ecology of the common species of *Drosophila* in Indiana – *J. Econ. Entomol.* 55/6–1962–978.

1 MCDONALD, J. C.–The importance of respiratory viral diseases in Western Europe – *Am. Rev. Resp. Dis.* 88/3 (part 2)–1963–35.

100 MCFADZEAN, J. A. and F. HAWKING – The periodicity of *Microfilariae*, V. – *Trans Roy. Soc. Trop. Med. Hyg.* 50–1956–543.

1   McHugh, R. B. – *Validity and Efficiency in the Design of Transverse Physiologic Periodicity Experiments* – Ref. 1963a.

100 McHugh, R. B. and F. J. Wall – Estimating the precision of time period effects in longitudinal models with serially correlated and heterogenous errors – *Biometrics* 18/4–1962–520.

1   McIntosh, R. P. – Ecosystems, evolution and relational patterns of living organisms – *Am. Sci.* 52/2–1963–246.

1   McKay, C. G. R. – The rising of the Palolo. A reliable astronomical formula for predicting the rising of the Palolo – *South Pacific. Comm. Quart. Bull.* 3/3–1953–35.

200 McKay, R. S. – Negative resistance – *Am. J. Physics* 26/2–1958–60.

1   McKeever, S. – Seasonal changes in body weight, reproductive organs, pituitary, adrenal glands, thyroid gland, and spleen of the Belding ground squirrel – *Am. J. Anat.* 113/1–1963–153.

1   MacLean, K. S. – *High Magnetic Fields in Terminal Cancer and Other Illnesses* – Ref. 1963c.

100 McLeod, D. G. R., and S. D. Beck – Photoperiodic termination of diapause in an insect – *Biol. Bull.* 124/1–1963–84.

1   Machin, K. E. – Wave propagation along flagellae – *J. Exp. Biol.* 35/4–1958–796.

100 Machin, K. E. and J. W. S. Pringle, The physiology of insect fibrillar muscle II – *Proc. Roy. Soc.* 151B–1959–204.

100 Maddock, R. W., L. O. Rutz and D. E. Havens – Bio-atmosphere table – Douglas Rep. SM–44576, Aug. 1963 (Douglas Aircraft Co, 3000 Ocean Park Blvd, Santa Monica, Calif. U.S.A.).

100 Magaro, M., A. V. Greco, S. Sensi and V. Maggi – *Le Rythme de l'Activité de certaines Enzymes Tesstarales et Sériques chez le Rat et chez l'Homme Adulte* – Ref. 1960a, p. 95.

1   Magee, M. C. – Excretion of creatine and creatinine; hourly excretion in normal children and in children with progressive muscular atrophy – *Am. J. Dis. Child.* 43/2–1932–322.

1   Magnus, I. A. – *Action Spectra in Human Skin* – Ref. 1960b, p. 144.

200 Magnus, P. v. – Influenza: diagnosis, epidemiology, prophylaxis – *Arch. Ges. Virusforsch.* 13/(1-3)–1963–232.

Mahieu, P. and R. Pasleau – Contrôle hormonal du metabolisme du fer XVIII – *Ann. d'Endocrinol.* 24/4–1963–713.

1   Mainland, D. – *Elementary Medical Statistics* – Saunders. Philadelphia, 1952.

1   Mairan De – Observation botanique – *Hist. Acad. Roy. Sci. Paris,* 1729, p. 35.

1   Maiselis, M.R. – Time and circumstances of physical performance as factors determining diurnal rhythmicity [in Russian]–*Biul. Eksp. Biol. Med.* 45–1958–10.

100 Maiselis, M. R. and S. O. Ruttenburg – *Stunden–Rhythmus der Aktivität und der Körpertemperatur bei Ratten* – Bykow, Ref. 1, p. 129.

1   Makai, E. – Über Anaphylaxieerscheinungen nach Serieninjektionen artfremden Serums – *D. Med. Wschr.* 1922–257.

1   Malek, J. – The manifestation of biological rhythms in delivery – *Gynaecologia* 133–1952–365.

2   Malek, J. – Der Einfluss des Lichtes und der Dunkelheit auf den klinischen Geburtsbeginn – *Gynaecologia* 138/3–1954–402.

3   Malek, J. – *The Daily Rhythm of the Onset of Labour, of Excretion of Pregnandiol, of White Blood Cell Count, of Blood Pressure, Pulse Rate and Temperature in Pregnancy and the Daily Rhythm of the Beginning of Menstruation* – Ref. 1960 a, p. 97.

4   Malek, J. – Bily kvreni obraz za porodu – *Roz Ceskoslov. Akad. Ved.* Prague, 1961.

5   Malek, J. – *The Daily Rhythm of the Human Lactation* – Ref. 1963a.

6   Malek, J. – Experiments with pregnant guineapigs in low-pressure chamber – *Nuclear Hematol.* 3/3–1964–4.

100 Malek, J., J. Budinsky and M. Budinska – Analyse du rythme journalière du debut clinique de l'accouchement – *Rev. Franc. Gyn. d'Obst.* 45–1950–222.

101 MALEK, J., J. GLEICH and V. MALY –
Characteristics of the Daily Rhythm
of Menstruation and Labor – Ref.
1961c, p. 1042.

102 MALEK, J., J. HORAK and J. STASTNY
– Über die Leukozyten- und Lym-
phozytenverschiebung unter der
Geburt mit Berücksichtigung des
Tagesrhythmus – Gynaecologia 141–
1956–31.

103 MALEK, J., V. MALY, E. MOJZISKOVA
and P. BLAZKOVA – Denni rytmus
leukocytu a lymfocytu u tehotnych
– Sbornik Lekar. Fak. 60/1–1958–24.

104 MALEK, J., K. SUK, M. BRESTAK and
V. MALY – Daily Rhythm in Leucocytes, Blood Pressure, Pulse Rate
and Temperature during Pregnancy
– Ref. 1961c, p. 1018.

1 MALL, G. – Beitrag zur Gjessing'-
schen Thyroxinbehandlung der periodischen Katatonien – Arch. Psychiat. 187–1952–381.

2 MALL, G. – Probleme der Vitalität und
Mortalität bei Genialen unter dem As-
pekt endogener biologischer Rhythmen – Ref. 1960a, p. 103.

1 MALM, M. – Oscillations in the Osmotic Regulation of the Yeast Cell –
Ref. 1955a, p. 123.

1 MANN, L. K. – Effect of some environmental factors on floral initiation in Xanthium – Bot. Gaz. 102–
1940–339.

200 MANN, K. H. – Seasonal variation
in the respiratory acclimatization of
the leech – J. Exp. Biol. 35/2–1958–
314.

500 MANN, P. M. and R. H. STINSON –
Activity of the short-tailed shrew –
Can. J. Zool. 35–1957–171.

1 MANSON, P. – On the periodicity of
filarial migration to and from the
circulation – Quckett Micr. Club J.
6–(1879–1881)–239.

1 MARCK, E. v. – Über die Kern-
Plasma–Relation differenzierter Ge-
webezellen – Z.Zellforsch. 32–1943–
557.

1 MARCOVITCH, S. – The migration of
Aphididae and the appearance of
sexual forms as affected by the
relative length of the daily light
exposure – J. Agr. Res. 27–1924–
513.

1 MARG, E. – The Accessory Optic System – Ref. 1963b.

100 MARGOLINA, O. J. and E. J. BRANDT
– 24–Stunden–Rhythmus physiologischer Funktionen beim Menschen –
Bykow, Ref. 1, p. 62.

1 MARKELOVA, I. V. – The 24-hour
rhythm of the mitotic activity of
exocrine epithelium of rat pancreas–
Bull. Exp. Biol. Med. USSR. 6–
1962–74.

100 MARSDEN, H.M. and F.H. BRONSON
– Estrus synchrony in mice–Science
144/3625–1964–1469.

1 MARSH, H. D. – The diurnal course of
efficiency – Col. Univ. Contrib. Philos. Psychol. 14–1906–1.

1 MARSHALL, A. J. – Weather factors
and spermatogenesis in birds – Proc.
Zool. Soc. (London) 119A–1949–711.

2 MARSHALL, A. J. – The refractory
period of testis rhythm in birds and
its possible bearing on breeding and
migration – Wilson Bull. 63–1951–
238.

3 MARSHALL, A. J. – The interstitial
cycle in relation to autumn and
winter sexual behaviour in birds –
Proc. Zool. Soc. (London) 121–1952–
727.

4 MARSHALL, A. J. – The rôle of the
internal rhythm of reproduction in
the timing of avian breeding seasons,
including migration – XIIth Internat. Ornithol. Congr. Helsinki, 1958.

5 MARSHALL, A. J. – Internal and environmental control of breeding –
Ibis 101–1959–456.

6 MARSHALL, A. J. – Annual Periodicity in the Migration and Reproduction in Birds – Ref. 1960c, p. 499.

100 MARSHALL, A. J. and C. J. F.
COOMBS – The interaction of environmental, internal and behavioural
factors in the rook – Proc. Zool. Soc.
(London) 128–1957–545.

101 MARSHALL, A. J. and H. J. DE S.
DISNEY – Photostimulation of an
equatorial bird – Nature 177–1956–
143.

102 MARSHALL, A. J. and H. J. DE S.
DISNEY–Experimental induction of
the breeding season in a xerophi-
lous bird – Nature 180–1957–647.

103 MARSHALL, A. J. and D. L. SERVEN-
TY – Experimental demonstration
of an internal rhythm of reproduction in a trans–equatorial migrant –
Nature 184–1959–1704.

200 MARSHALL, F. H. A. – Sexual periodicity and the causes which determine it – *Philos. Trans. Roy. Soc.*
226B–1936–423.
201 MARSHALL, F. H. A. – On the change-
over in the oestrus cycle in animals
after transference across the equator – *Proc. Roy. Soc. (London)* 122B
–1937–413.
202 MARSHALL, F. H. A. – Exteroceptive
factors in sexual periodicity – *Biol.
Rev.* 17–1942–68.
300 MARSHALL, F. H. A. and F. P. Bow-
DEN – The effect of irradiation with
different wave-length on the oestrus
cycle of the ferret – *J. Exp. Biol.* 11
–1934–409.
500 MARSHALL, J. and E.G. WALSH –
Physiological tremor–*J. Neurosurg.
Psychiat.* 19–1956–260.
1 MARTE, E. – *Circadian Susceptibility
in Relation to Administration of
Pharmacological Agents* – Ref. 1961
a, p. 52.
100 MARTE, E. and F. HALBERG – Circadian susceptibility rhythm to Librium – *Fed. Proc.*, 20–1961–305.
100 MARTIN, E. M. and A. O. HAUGEN –
Seasonal changes in wood duck
roosting flight habits – *Wilson Bull.*
72–1960–238.
1 MARTINI, E. – Über Provokations-
epidemien – *Zbl. Bakt.* 110–1929–
245.
300 MARTINI, L., A. PECILE and G.
GIULIANI – The feedback regulation of ACTH-secretion – *Mem. Soc.
Endocrinol.* 19–1960–34.
1 MARUYAMA, M. – The second cybernetics – *Am. Sci.* 51/2–1963–164.
1 MASLENIKOW, A. – Über Tagesschwankungen des intraocularen
Druckes – *Z. Augenhlk.* 11–1904–
564.
1 MASONI, A. – *24-Hour Rhythms of
Cardiovascular Functions in Normal and Hypertensive Subjects* –
Ref. 1960a, p.110.
2 MASONI, A. – L'elettrocardiogramma
nelle 24 ore – *Minerva Med.* 41–
1950–283.
1 MASTER, A. M. – The rôle of effort
and occupation in coronary occlu-
sion – *JAMA* 174–1960–942.
1 MATTHES, K. – *Kreislaufuntersuchun-
gen an Menschen mit fortlaufend
registrierenden Methoden* – Thieme.

Stuttgart, 1951.
1 MATTHEWS, G. V. T. – The experimental investigation of navigation
in homing pigeons – *J. Exp. Biol.*
28–1951–508.
2 MATTHEWS, G. V. T. – Sun navigation in homing pigeons – *J. Exp.
Biol.* 30–1953–243.
3 MATTHEWS, G. V. T. – Orientation of
untrained pigeons – *J. Exp. Biol.*
30–1953–268.
4 MATTHEWS, G. V. T. – An investigation of the "chronometer" factor in
bird navigation – *J. Exp. Biol.* 32/1
–1955–39.
5 MATTHEWS, G. V. T. – *Bird Navigation* – Cambridge Univ. Press. England, 1955.
200 MATTHEWS, S. A. – The effect of light
and temperature on the male sexual
cycle in *Fundulus* – *Biol. Bull.* 77–
1939–92.
1 MATTINGLY, P. F. – Studies on West-
African Forest mosquitos I – *Bull.
Entom. Res.* 40–1949–149.
2 MATTINGLY, P. F. – Recent work on
cyclical behaviour in the *Nemato-
cera* – *Trans. IXth Int. Congr. Entomol. Amsterdam* 1951, 1–1952–375.
100 MAYER, A and G. NICHITA – Sur les
variations du métabolisme du
lapin après exposition au froid –
Ann. Physiol. Physicochim. Biol.
5–1929–621.
100 MAYERSBACH, H. V., G. HORVATH,
and R. LESKE – *Biorhythmik und
Histochemie* – Ref. 1963a.
100 MAYERSON, H., S. GUNTHER and H.
LAURENS – The physiological action of darkness, daylight and of
carbon arc radiation I–III – *Am.
J. Physiol.* 75–1925/26–399, 421, 443.
1 MAYNARD, D. M. – Activity in a
crustacean ganglion I–II – *Biol.,
Bull.* 104–1953–156; 109–1955–420.
2 MAYNARD, D. M. – Correlations between heart rate and size in the lobster – *Anat. Rec.* 132/3–1958–475.
3 MAYNARD, D. M. – Heart rate and
body size in the spiny lobster –
Physiol. Zool. 33/4–1960–241.
1 MEDICAL NEWS (New York) – Prenatal and natal experience leave
imprint on teeth – 7/12–1961–15.
1 MÉDIONI, J. – L'orientation "astro-
nomique" des arthropodes et des
oiseaux – *Ann. Biol.* 32–1956–37.

1   MEHNER, M. – Zur Lehre vom Zeit-
    sinn – *Philosoph. Studien* 2–1885–
    546.
1   MEIDINGER, F. – *Fréquences Cardia-
    ques et Respiratoires Statistiques* –
    Ref. 1960a, p. 111.
1   MEIJER, G. – *Photomorphogenesis in
    Different Spectral Regions* – Ref.
    1957f, p. 101.
100 MEIJER, G. and R. VAN DER VEEN –
    *Dual Effect of Red Light on the
    Photoperiodic Response of Salvia
    Occidentalis* – Ref. 1960b, p. 387.
1   MELCHERS, G. – Die Beteiligung der
    endonomen Tagesrhythmik am Zu-
    standekommen der photoperiodi-
    schen Reaktion der Kurztagpflanze
    Kalanchoë blossfeldiana – *Z. Natur-
    forsch.* 11b–1956–544.
1   MELLANBY, K. – *Rhythmic Activity
    in Domestic Insects* – Ref. 1939a,
    p. 89.
2   MELLANBY, K. – The daily rhythm
    of activity in the cockroach II – *J.
    Exp. Biol.* 17–1940–278.
1   MEMMESHEIMER, A. M. – Der Früh-
    jahrsgipfel des Ekzems und seine
    Erklärungsmöglichkeiten – *Derm.
    Z.* 57–1929–27.
1   MENAKER, M. – Endogenous rhythms
    of body temperature in hibernating
    bats – *Nature* 184–1959–1251.
2   MENAKER, M. – The freerunning pe-
    riod of the bat clock; seasonal varia-
    tions at low body temperatures –
    J. Cell. Comp. Physiol. 57–1961–81.
3   MENAKER, M. – X-rays; are there
    cyclic variations in radiosensitivity
    – *Science* 143/3606 – 1964–597.
200 MENAKER, W. and A. – Lunar perio-
    dicity in human reproduction; a
    likely unit of biological time – *Am.
    J. Obst. Gyn.* 77/4–1959–905.
1   MENGER, W. – Der Einfluss atmos-
    phärischer Störungen auf die Tuber-
    kulos im Kindesalter – *Z. Kinder-
    hlk.* 74–1954–568.
2   MENGER, W. – Wettereinflüsse auf
    Krankheiten des Kinderalters -
    Mon. schr. Kinderhlk. 104/3–1956–
    119.
1   MENKE, H. – Periodische Bewegun-
    gen und ihr Zusammenhang mit
    Licht und Stoffwechsel – *Arch. Ges.
    Physiol.* 46–1911–37.
1   MENNINGER-LERCHENTHAL, E. –
    Phasen der menschlichen Produkti-

    vität – *Wien. Arch. Psychiat. Neu-
    rol.* 3–1953–1.
2   MENNINGER-LERCHENTHAL, E. –
    Physiologie und Pathologie der
    Tagesschablone – *Wien. Z. Nerven-
    hlk.* 15–1958–201.
3   MENNINGER-LERCHENTHAL, E. – *Pe-
    riodizität in der Psychopathologie* –
    Maudrich. Wien, 1960.
1   MENZEL, W. – *Über einen 24-Stunden-
    Rhythmus in Blutkreislauf des Men-
    schen* – Ref. 1939a, p. 166.
2   MENZEL, W. – Der 24-Stunden-
    Rhythmus des menschlichen Blut-
    kreislaufes – *Erg. Inn. Med. Kinder-
    hlk.* 61–1941–1.
3   MENZEL, W. – Zum Wesen der Ta-
    gesrhythmik – *Ärztl. Wschr.* 1947–
    705.
4   MENZEL, W. – *Wellenlänge, Phasen-
    lage und Amplitude in der Nieren-
    rhythmik des Menschen* – Ref. 1949a,
    p. 95.
5   MENZEL, W. – Wellenlänge und Pha-
    senlage der menschlichen Nieren-
    Rhythmik mit Analysen nach dem
    Blumeschen Verfahren, I – *Z. Ges.
    Exp. Med.* 116–1950–237.
6   MENZEL, W. – Zur Physiologie und
    Pathologie des Nacht- und Schicht-
    arbeiters – *Arbeitsphysiol.* 14–1950–
    304.
7   MENZEL, W. – Endogene Änderun-
    gen der Tagesrhythmik bei Gesun-
    den und Kranken – *Med. Meteorol.
    Hefte* 5–1951–28.
8   MENZEL, W. – Über den heutigen
    Stand der Rhythmenlehre in Bezug
    auf die Medizin – *Z. Altersforsch.*
    6/(1–2)–1952–26, 104.
9   MENZEL, W. – *Klinische Ziele der
    Rhythmusforschung* – Ref. 1953a, p.
    107.
10 MENZEL, W. – Der Einfluss atmos-
    phärischer Störungen auf die Tuber-
    kulose im Kindesalter – *Z. Kinder-
    hlk.* 74–1954–568.
11 MENZEL, W. – Therapie unter dem
    Gesichtspunkt biologischer Rhyth-
    men – *Erg. Physikal.–Diätet. Ther.*
    5–1955–1.
12 MENZEL, W. – Über die Dauer lang-
    welliger Perioden bei menschlichen
    Körperfunktionen – *Fortschr. Med.*
    73/2–1955–31.
13 MENZEL, W. – Spontane Leistungs-
    schwankungen im menschlichen Or-

ganismus – *Verh. D. Ges. Arbeits-schutz* 3–1955–232.

14 MENZEL, W. – Perioden menschlicher Körperfunktionen in Diagnose und Therapie – *Die Medizinische* 43–1956–1521.

15 MENZEL, W. – *Über latente Perioden* – Ref. 1960a, p. 112.

16 MENZEL, W. – *Periodicity in Urinary Excretion in Healthy and Nephropathic Persons* – Ref. 1961c, p. 1007.

17 MENZEL, W. – *Menschliche Tag-Nacht-Rhythmik und Schichtarbeit* – Schwabe. Basel, 1962.

18 MENZEL, W. – Zur Tagesrhythmik des Wasserhaushaltes bei Gesunden und Herzkranken – *Zbl. Inn. Med.* 59–1938–529.

19 MENZEL, W. – Weitere Untersuchungen zur Tagesrhythmik des Wasserhaushaltes – *Zbl. Inn. Med.* 60–1939–16.

20 MENZEL, W. – Ein Tagesrhythmus der Flüssigkeits- und Blutmengenveränderungen beim Menschen – *Klin. Wschr.* 19–1940–29.

21 MENZEL, W. – Tag–Nacht-Rhythmik menschlicher Körperfunktionen – *Forsch. Fortschr. D. Wiss.* 18–1942–140.

22 MENZEL, W. – Die klinische Bedeutung der Tagesrhythmik – *Z. Ärztl. Fortbild.* 4–1944–141.

23 MENZEL, W. – Der Tagesrhythmus in seiner Bedeutung für Pathologie und Klinik – *Neue D. Klinik* 8–1944–406.

24 MENZEL, W. – Bedeutung und Probleme der Tagesrhythmik – *Klin. Wschr.* (24–25)–1947–415.

25 MENZEL, W. – Die Rhythmik im Leben des Menschen – *Universitas* 3–1948–545.

26 MENZEL, W. – Zur Pathophysiologie des Nacht- und Schichtarbeiters – *Verh. D. Ges. Inn. Med.* 56–1950–169.

27 MENZEL, W. – Ist Nachtarbeit gesundheitsschädlich? – *Ärzt. Dienst D. Bundesbahn* 11–1950–87.

28 MENZEL, W. – Über die Periodik der Nierentätigkeit bei Gesunden und Nierenkranken – *Verh. D. Ges. Inn. Med.* 58–1952–292.

29 MENZEL, W. – Wellenlänge, Phasenlage und Amplitude der menschlichen Nierenrhythmik – *Ärztl.*

Forsch. 6–1952–455.

30 MENZEL, W. – Periodenforschung in der Medizin – *Fortschr. Med.* 70–1952–501.

31 MENZEL, W. – Langwellige Organperiodik im Rahmen von Regulationsvorgängen – *Verh. D. Ges. Inn. Med.* 59–1953–399.

32 MENZEL, W. – Leistungsschwankungen aus innerer Ursache – *Ärztl. Dienst D. Bundesbahn* 8–1955.

33 MENZEL, W. – Wesen und Auswirkungen der Nacht- und Schichtarbeit – *Therapiewoche* 9–1959–356.

34 MENZEL, W. – Neues aus der Periodenforschung in der Biologie und Medizin – *Mat. Med. Nordmark* 15/12–1963–449.

100 MENZEL, W., J. BLUME and E. LUA – Untersuchungen zur Nieren-Rhythmik III – *Z. Ges. Exp. Med.* 120–1953–396.

101 MENZEL, W., J. BLUME and F.-L. VON SCHROEDER – Klassifizierung klinischer Verläufe durch Periodenanalyse – *Z. Klin. Med.* 155–1958–249.

102 MENZEL, W., J. BLUME and R. SILBER – Weitere Untersuchungen zur Nieren-Rhythmik II – *Z. Ges. Exp. Med.* 119–1952–654.

103 MENZEL, W., R. TIMM and G. HERRNRING – Über den diagnostischen Wert der Tag–Nacht-Schwankung des erhöhten Blutdrucks – *Verh. D. Ges. Kreislaufforsch.* 15–1949–256.

104 MENZEL, W., I. JARCK and H. GÖTTSCH – Tageszeitliche Schwankungen der Blutverteilung als kreislaufregulierender Faktor – *Ärztl. Forsch.* 11–1948–448.

105 MENZEL, W. and I. OTHLINGHAUS – Inversion des Blutzuckerrhythmus durch Percorten – *D. Med. Wschr.* 73–1948–326.

106 MENZEL, W., I. BÜTTNER, S. KRAFT and A. v.D. HEIDE – Klassifizierung von klinischen Temperaturkurven durch die Periodenanalyse nach Blume – *Verh. 69. Kongr. D. Ges. Inn. Med.* 1963–772.

1 MERCER, D. M. A. – *Analytical Methods for the Study of Periodic Phenomena obscured by Random Fluctuations* – Ref. 1960c, p. 73.

2 MERCER, D. M. A. – *Objective Methods for Extracting Small Periodici-*

ties from Irregular Records – Ref. 1963a.

100 MERCIER, E. and G. W. SALESBURY – Fertility level in artificial breeding associated with seasons, hours of daylight and the age of cattle – *J. Dairy Sci.* 30–1947–74.

1 MERKEL, F. W. – Untersuchungen über tages- und jahresperiodische Aktivitätsänderungen bei gekäfigten Zugvögeln – *Z. Tierpsychol.* 13/2 –1956–278.

1 MERTEN, R. – *24-Stunden-Rhythmus der Urokathepsin- und Uropepsinausscheidung* – Ref. 1953a, p. 192.

1 MERTENS, H.-G. – Metabolismo mineral y sistema nervioso – *Fol. Clin. Internac.* 12/11–1962–496.

1 MEUNIER, K. – Experimentelles über den Schwärmtrieb und das periodische Auftreten verschiedener Aktivitätsformen beim Maikäfer *(Melolontha melolontha* L.) – *Z. Angew. Entomol.,* 14–1928–91.

100 MEYER, A. and N. T. DELEANO – Die periodischen Tag- und Nachtschwankungen der Atmungsgrösse in Dunkeln befindlicher Laubblätter I-II – *Z. Bot.* 3–1911–657; 5–1913–209.

1 MEYER-LOHMANN, J. – Über den Einflussäglicher Futtergaben auf die 24-Stunden-Periodik der lokomotorischen Aktivität weisser Mäuse – *Pflüger's Arch.* 260–1955–292.

1 MICHAL, K. – Oszillationen im Sauerstoffverbrauch der Mehlwurmlarven *(Tenebrio molitor)* – *Zool. Anz.* 95–1931–65.

1 MIEGE, J. – *Les Phénomènes de Nutation chez les Dioscorea* – Ref. 1958b, p. 63.

100 MIGEON, C. J., F. H. TYLER, J. P. MAHONEY, A. A. FLORENTIN, H. CASTLE, E. L. BLISS and L. T. SAMUELS – The diurnal variation of plasma levels and urinary excretion of 17-hydroxy-cortico-steroids in normal subjects, night workers and blind subjects – *J. Clin. Endocrinol. Metab.* 16–1956–622.

1 MILES, G. H. – *Telemetering Techniques for Periodicity Studies* – Ref. 1961c, p. 858.

1 MILLER, A. H. – Potentiality for testicular recrudescence during the annual period of the golden crowned sparrow – *Science* 109–1949–546.

2 MILLER, A. H. – Breeding cycles in a constant equatorial environment in Columbia – *Experientia (Basel)* – suppl. 3–1955–495.

3 MILLER, A. H. – Reproductive cycles in an equatorial sparrow – *Proc. Nat. Acad. Sci.* 45–1959–1095.

200 MILLER, R. S. – Activity rhythms in the wood mouse, *Apodemus sylvaticus* and the bank vole *Clethrionomys glareolus* – *Proc. Zool. Soc. (London)* 125–1955–505.

1 MILLS, G. – *Climate makes the Man* – New York, 1942.

200 MILLS, J. N. – Diurnal rhythms in urine flow – *J. Physiol.* 113–1951–528.

201 MILLS, J. N. – *The Part played by the Adrenals in Human Circadian Renal Rhythms* – Ref. 1962c, p. 259.

300 MILLS, J. N. and S. W. STANBURY – Persistent 24-h renal excretory rhythms on a 12-h cycle of activity – *J. Physiol.* 117–1952–22.

301 MILLS, J. N. and S. W. STANBURY – *Rhythmic Diurnal Variations in the Behaviour of the Human Renal Tubule* – Ref. 1953a, p. 95.

302 MILLS, J. N., S. THOMAS and P. A. YATES – Reappearance of renal excretory rhythm after forced disruption – *J. Physiol.* 125–1954–466.

1 MINES, G. R. – On dynamic equilibrium in the heart – *Am. J. Physiol.* 46–1913–349.

1 MISLIN, H. – *Die rhythmischen Spontanentladungen im Zentralnervensystem der Tintenfische* – Ref. 1953a, p. 58.

1 MITCHELL, R. K. – Computer art – *New Sci.* 19/357–1963–614; (20/359–1963–41).

300 MITCHELL, D. E. and C. EPLING – The diurnal periodicity of *Drosophila* in southern California – *Ecology* 31/4–1951–696.

100 MITRAKOS, K., E. BÜNNING and F. EBERHARDT – Endogen-tagesperiodische Schwankungen der Chloroplastenfarbstoffe – *Z. Naturforsch.* 12b–1957–813.

1 MITTELSTÄDT, H. – *Regelungsvorgänge in der Biologie* – Oldenburg. München, 1956.

2 MITTELSTÄDT, H. – *Regelungsvorgänge in lebenden Wesen* – Oldenburg.

München, 1961.

3 MITTELSTÄDT, H. – *Bikomponenten-Theorie der Orientierung* – Ref. 1962 d, p. 253.

4 MITTELSTÄDT, H. – Control systems, of orientation in insects – *Ann. Res. Entomol.* 7–1962–177.

100 MÖDLINGER, G., L. KONDICS, J. KOVACS, M. KURCZ and M. M. ODORFER – Diurnal rhythm in the endocrine organs of white mice – *Acta Biol. Acad. Sci. Hung.* suppl. 2–1958–38.

1 MOGABGAB, W. J. – Viruses associated with upper respiratory illnesses in adults – *Ann. Internat. Med.* 59/3–1963–306.

1 MÖLLERBERG, H. – Mitotic rhythm in the epidermis of the frog – *Acta Anat.* 4/3–1948–393.

1 MÖLLERSTRÖM, J. – Action de la plasma sanguin – *C.R. Soc. Biol.* 98–1928–1361.

2 MÖLLERSTRÖM, J. – Om dygnsvariationer i blod- och urinsockerkurvan hos diabetiker – *Hygiea (Swed.)* 91–1929–379.

3 MÖLLERSTRÖM, J. – Om kortperiodiska förändringar i blodets suspensionsstabilitet – *Hygiea (Swed.)* 91–1929–497.

4 MÖLLERSTRÖM, J. – En klinisk–experimentell studie över blod- resp. urinsockerhaltens dygnsvariationer vid näringstillförsel hos friska och diabetici (Diss.) – *Acta Soc. Med. Suec.* 56–1930–211.

5 MÖLLERSTRÖM, J. – Periodicity in the carbohydrate metabolism – *Acta Med. Scand.* 50–1932–250.

6 MÖLLERSTRÖM, J. – Periodicity of carbohydrate metabolism and rhythmic functioning of the liver – *Arch. Int. Med.* 52–1933–649.

7 MÖLLERSTRÖM, J. – The treatment of diabetes with reference to the endogenous periodicity of the carbohydrate metabolism – *Acta Med. Scand.* suppl. 69–1934–145.

8 MÖLLERSTRÖM, J. – Some new observations and principles concerning diabetes research and their practical application to diabetic therapy – *Acta Med. Upsaliensis (Swed.)* 41–1935–287.

9 MÖLLERSTRÖM, J. – *Die therapeutische Bedeutung der menschlichen Rhyth-*

mik – Ref. 1937a, p. 990.

10 MÖLLERSTRÖM, J. – Om diabetes och diabetesbehandling – *Nord. Med. Tidskr.* 14–1937–1693.

12 MÖLLERSTRÖM, J. – *Der Einfluss der Erkenntnisse des Leberrhythmus auf unsere Anschauungen über Diabetestherapie* – Ref. 1939a, p. 156.

13 MÖLLERSTRÖM, J. – *Om Pyridinderivatens Periodiska Utsöndring vid Diabetes* – Ref. 1941a, p. 29.

14 MÖLLERSTRÖM, J. – Das Diabetesproblem – *Acta Med. Scand.* suppl. 147, Sthlm., 1943.

15 MÖLLERSTRÖM, J. – Sockersjukans patofysiolgi – *Nord. Med.* 24–1944–1946.

16 MÖLLERSTRÖM, J. – Über Störungen des Zwischenstoffwechsels bei chronischer Alkoholvergiftung – *Ark. Kemi Mineralogi Geologi (Swed.)* 19A/10–1945.

17 MÖLLERSTRÖM, J. – Sockeromsättningen i den levande organismen – *Socker-Handl.(Swed.)* 2/8–1946–291.

18 MÖLLERSTRÖM, J. – Theoretical considerations and practical results in the management of diabetes – *Acta Med. Scand.* suppl. 196–1947–12.

19 MÖLLERSTRÖM, J. – Sockersjukan, dess orsaker och behandling – *SOU (Swed.)* 33–1948–113.

20 MÖLLERSTRÖM, J. – *Rhythmus, Diabetes und Behandlung* – Ref. 1949a, p. 110.

21 MÖLLERSTRÖM, J. – Diurnal rhythm in severe diabetes mellitus – *Diabetes (Am.)* 3/3–1954–188.

22 MÖLLERSTRÖM, J. – Diabetessjukdomens teori och klinik I–III – *Svensk Läkartidn.* 57/51–960–3589; 58/6–1961–325; 60/3–1963–145.

100 MÖLLERSTRÖM, J. and A. SOLLBERGER – The 24-hour rhythm of metabolic processes in diabetes; Citric acid in the urine – *Acta Med. Scand.* 160–1958–25.

101 MÖLLERSTRÖM, J. and A. SOLLBERGER – Diabetessjukdomens teori och klinik I–II – *Med. Fören. Tidskr. (Stockholm)* 2, 4–1959–47, 127.

102 MÖLLERSTRÖM, J. and A. SOLLBERGER – *Fundamental Concepts underlying the Metabolic Periodicity in Diabetes* – Ref. 1961c, p. 984.

103 MÖLLERSTRÖM, J. and Å. SWENSSON – *Stoffwechselrhythmus bei Diabetikern*

     – Ref. 1953a, p. 132.

104 MÖLLERSTRÖM, J. and R. ULLMARK – *Der Einfluss von Muskelarbeit auf den Blutzucker während verschiedener Phasen der rhythmischen Leberfunktion* – Ref. 1939a, p. 132.

105 MÖLLERSTRÖM, J. and S. FORSSMAN – Zur Frage der Normalen Variationen der Wasserdiurese und Wasserbelastungsprobe – *Acta Med. Scand.* 97/(5–6)–1938–508.

106 MÖLLERSTRÖM, J. and A. SOLLBERGER – *Biological Rhythms in the Metabolism, as exemplified in Diabetes* – Ref. 1963a.

1 MOHR, H. – *The Effects of Long Visible and Near Infra-red Radiation on Plants* – Ref. 1960b, p. 44.

1 MOMIYAMA, M. – *The Changing Rhythm of Seasonal Disease* – Ref. 1962e.

1 MONGELLI-SCIANNAMEO, N. – *Untersuchungen über Beziehungen zwischen Arbeit–Ruherhythmus und Nierenrhythmus* – Ref. 1960a, p. 117.

1 MONNIER, M. – Die Regulierung der Wach- und Schlafzustände als physiologisches Problem – *Schweiz. Med. Wschr.* 90–1960–1406.

100 MOORE, T. O. and D. K. MEYER – 24-hour rhythm in phosphorylase activity in mouse – *Fed. Proc.* 22/2 (part 1)–1963–636.

1 MORAN, P. A. P. – The oscillatory behaviour of moving averages – *Proc. Cambr. Philos. Soc.* 46/2–1950–272.

2 MORAN, P. A. P. – *The Logic of the Mathematial Theory of Animal Populations* – Ref. 1954b, p. 60.

100 MORENG, R. E., K. L. BRYANT and D. C. GOSSLEE – Physiological reaction of chicks to limited light – *Poultry Sci.* 35–1956–977.

1 MORHARDT, P. E. – Rythmes physiologiques et pathologiques – *Presse Méd.* 61–1953–706.

1 MORI, S. – Daily rhythmic activity of the sea-pen – I–VII, XIII–XIV, *Zool. Mag.* 55–1943–247, 285; 56–1944–81, 86, 91, 96, 101; 65–1956–359; 66–1957–284.

2 MORI, S. – Daily rhythmic activity of the sea-pen, VIII – *Kyodai Seiri Seitai* 1945–19.

3 MORI, S. – Daily rhythmic activity of the sea-pen IX–XII – *Physiol.*

Ecol. 1–1947–8; 2–1948–34; 3–1949–32; 4–1950–14.

4 MORI, S. – Individuality of daily rhythmic activity and working hours – *Kyodai Seiri Seitai* 1945–18.

5 MORI, S. – General considerations on the relation between the behaviour rhythms and the environmental periodicity – *Kyodai Seiri Seitai* 1945–39.

6 MORI, S. – A concept of the endogenous daily rhythmic activity – *Mem. Coll. Sci. Univ. Tokyo,* 19B–1947–213.

7 MORI, S. – Harmony between behaviour rhythm and environmental rhythm – *Mem. Coll. Sci. Kyoto Univ.* 19B–1948–71.

8 MORI, S. – *Influence of Environmental and Physiological Factors on the Daily Rhythmic Activity of a Sea-Pen* – Ref. 1960c, p. 333.

9 MORI, S. – Effects of the total solar eclipse on the rhythmic diurnal activities of some animals – *Ann. Zool. (Japan)* 18(2)–1939–115.

10 MORI, S.–Inheritance of daily rhythmic types in emerging behaviour in some *Drosophila*-mutants (In Japanese) – *Jap. J. Genet.* 24–1949–150.

11 MORI, S. – Daily rhythmic phenomena in the life history of *Drosophila* (In Japanese) – *Seibut. Gyos.* 4–1949–121.

12 MORI, S. – Population effect on the daily periodic emergence of *Drosophila* – *Mem. Coll. Sci. Kyoto* 21B–1954–49.

13 MORI, S. – *On the Origin of the Pattern of Daily Rhythmic Activity* – Ref. 1963a.

100 MORI, S. and K. MATUTANI – Studies on the daily rhythmic activity of the starfish – *Publ. Seto Marine Biol. Lab.* 2/2–1952–213.

101 MORI, S. and Y. ONDO – Daily rhythmic activity of the sea-pen XV – *Publ. Seto Marine Biol. Lab.* 6/1–1957–79.

1 MORO, E. – Über den Frühjahrsgipfel der Tetanie – *Münch. Med. Wschr.* 191–1281.

2 MORO, E. – Übererregbarkeit des vegetativen Nervensystems im Frühjahr und Ekzemtod – *Münch. Med. Wschr.* 1920–657.

3 MORO, E. – Über die Tetanie als Saisonkrankheit und vom biologischen Frühjahr–*Klin. Wschr.* 5–1926–925.

100 MORTON, G.W., W.E. TOLLES and L.M. HELLMAN–Methods of characterizing wave forms of fetal heart rate–*Ann. N.Y. Acad. Sci.* 115/2–1964–687.

1 MORUZZI, G. – The physiology of sleep – *Endeavour* 22/85–1963–31.

1 MOURS-LAROCHE, M.-E. – *Contributions à l'Etude des Variations Nycthémérales des Mouvements d'Eau de Chlore et de Magnésium chez l'Homme Normal* – Diss. Strasbourg, 1955.

100 MÜHLEMANN, H. R., T. M. MARTHALER and P. LOUSTALOT – Daily variation in mitotic activity of adrenal cortex, thyroid, and oral epithelium of the rat – *Proc. Soc. Exp. Biol. Med.* 90–1955–467.

101 MÜHLEMANN, H. R., H. A. ZANDER and F. HALBERG – Mitotic activity in the periodontal tissues of the rat molar – *J. Dent. Res.* 33–1954–459.

1 MÜHLMANN, M. – Über die Ursache der täglichen Schwankung der Körpertemperatur – *Pflüger's Arch.* 69–1898–613.

100 MUELLER S. C. and G. E. BROWN – Hourly rhythms in blood pressure in persons with normal and elevated pressures – *Ann. Intern. Med.* 3–1930–1190.

200 MÜLLER, K. – Diurnal rhythm in organic drift of *Gammarus pulex* – *Nature* 198–1963–806.

201 MÜLLER, K. – Temperatur und Tagesperiodik der "Organischen Drift" von *Gammarus pulex* – *Naturwiss.* 50/11–1963–410.

300 MÜLLER, K., A. KURECK and A. MÜLLER-HAECKEL – Zur Tagesperiodik von *Niphargus* – *Naturwiss.* 50/17–1963–579.

100 MÜLLER-LIMMROTH, W. and H. CASPERS – Theorien über den Entstehungsmechanismus der Spontanrhythmen im normalen Elektroencephalogramm – *Klin. Wschr.* 34/(13–14)–1956–337.

100 MULAY, I. L. and L. N. – Effect of a magnetic field on sarcoma 37 ascites tumour cells – *Nature* 190/4780–1961–1019.

100 MULLER, A. F., A. M. RIONDEL and

E. L. MANNING – L'excrétion de l'aldostérone au cours du nycthémère – *Helv. Med. Acta* 24–1957–463.

1 MUNCH-PETERSEN, S. – The variations in serum copper in the course of 24 hours – *Scand. J. Clin. Lab. Invest.* 2–1950–48.

1 MUNK, M. – Theoretische Betrachtung über die Ursachen der Periodizität – *Biol. Zbl.* 24–1914–621.

100 MURALT, A. v. and R. STÄMPLI – Die photochemische Wirkung von Ultraviolettlicht auf den erregten Ranvierschen Knoten der einzelnen Nervenfaser – *Helv. Physiol. Pharmacol. Acta* 11–1953–182.

1 NAHAS, G. G. (Ed.) – Regulation of respiration – *Ann. N.Y. Acad. Sci.* 109/2–1963–411.

1 NALBANDOV, A. V. – *The Role of the Endocrine System in the Control of Certain Biological Rhythms in Birds* – *Ref.* 1961c, p. 916.

100 NANDA, K. K. and K. C. HAMNER – Studies on the nature of the endogenous rhythm affecting photoperiodic response of *Biloxi* soybean. – *Bot. Gaz.* 120–1958–14.

1 NAYLOR, E. – Tidal and diurnal rhythms of locomotory activity in *Carcinus maenas* – *J. Exp. Biol.* 35/3–1958–602.

2 NAYLOR, E. – Locomotory rhythms in *Carcinus maenas* (L.) from non-tidal conditions – *J. Exp. Biol.* 37/3–1960–481.

3 NAYLOR, E. – Spontaneous locomotor rhythm in mediterranean *Carcinus* – *Publ. Staz. Zool. Napol.* 32–1961–58.

4 NAYLOR, E. – Temperature relationships of the locomotor rhythms of *Carcinus* – *J. Exp. Biol.* 40–1963–669.

1 NELSON, J. H. – Do the planets cause sunstorms? – *Cycles (Ref. J. c.)* 14/2–1963–32.

1 NEWMAN, J. A. – Electrical determination of transport of 3-indoleacetic acid in *Avena* – *Nature* 184/28–1959–1728.

1 New York Academy of Science – Cardiac pacemakers (H.E. WHIPPLE and W.W.L. GLENN, Eds.)–*Ann. N.Y. Acad. Sci.* 111/3–1964–813.

2 New York Academy of Science –

Computers in medicine and biology (H.E. WHIPPLE and W.E. FOLLES, Eds.)–*Ann. N.Y. Acad. Sci.* 115/2–1964–543.

1 NICHOLSON, A. J.–Population oscillations caused by competition for food – *Nature* 165–1950–476.

2 NICHOLSON, A. J. – *The Self-Adjustment of Populations to Change* – Ref. 1957d, p. 153.

1 NICOL, J. A. C. – Luminescence in animals – *Endeavour* 22/85–1963–37.

100 NICOLSON, M. M., D. R. HARTREE and D. G. PADFIELD – *Fundamental Techniques of Mathematics for Scientists* – Longmans. London, 1961.

1 NIEBROJ, T.–Über die Tagesrhythmik der aktivität der neurosekretorischen Zellen im Hypothalamus der weissen Maus – *Naturwiss.* 45–1958–67.

1 NIELAND, H. – *Zur Frage des Einflusses von Mondkulmination und Gezeiten auf die Geburten* – Diss. Leipzig, 1940.

1 NIGGESCHMIDT, W. – *Über die Tagesrhythmik des elektrischen Widerstandes der Haut bei Kindern* – Diss. München, 1958.

1 NILSSON, S. E. – Periodiskt uppträdande sjukdomssymtom – *Svenska Läkartidn.* 60/49–1963–3661.

1 NITSCH, J. P. – Growth response of woody plants to photoperiodic stimuli – *Proc. Am. Soc. Sci.* 70–1957–512.

2 NITSCH, J. P. – Photoperiodism in woody plants – *Proc. Am. Soc. Hort. Sci.* 70–1957–526.

100 NITSCH, J. P. and F. W. WENT – *The induction of flowering in Xanthium pensylvanicum under long days* – Ref. 1957f, p. 311.

101 NITSCH, J. P., and L. SOMOGYI – Le photopériodisme des plantes ligneuses – *Ann. Soc. Nat. d'Horticult. France* 16–1958–466.

1 NOGUCHI, K. – A new harmonic analyser – *Engineering* 118 II–1924–876.

1 NOHARA, F. S. – Die Ursache der Rhythmik vom Gesichtspunkt der Menschen – *D. Med. Wschr.* 64–1938–1196.

1 NORN, M. – Schwankungen der K-, Na-, Cl-Ausscheidung durch die Niere im Laufe des Tages – *Skand. Arch. Physiol.* 55–1922–184.

1 NOTHDURFT, H. – *Die Beeinflüssung der Mäuseaktivität durch Licht und Dunkelheit als Beispiel für die Anpassung eines endogenen Rhythmus an 24-Stunden-periodische Aussenreize* – Ref. 1949a, p. 77.

1 NOVICK, A. – Orientation in paleotropic bats I–II – *J. Exp. Zool.* 137/3–1958–443; 138/1–1958–81.

2 NOVICK, A. – Acoustic orientation in the cave swiftlet – *Biol. Bull.* 117/3–1959–497.

3 NOVICK, A. – *Pulse Duration in the Echolocation of Insects by the Bat Pterotonus* – Ref. 1962d, p. 21.

100 NOWOSIELSKI, J.W. and R.L. PATTON–Studies on circadian rhythm of the house cricket – *J. Insect. Physiol.* 9–1963–401.

101 NOWOSIELSKI, J.W. and R.L. PATTON–Daily fluctuation in the blood sugar concentration of the house cricket,–*Science* 144/3615–1964–180.

1 NUSSBAUM, M. – Vergleich der rhythmischen Fähigkeiten des Vorhofs mit denen der Kammer und die Abhängigkeit der mechanischen Latenz der Kammer von Frequenz und Stärke künstlicher rhythmischer Reize, untersucht an Amphibienherzen – *Pflüger's Arch. Physiol.* 239–1937–21.

1 NYLIN, G. – Periodical variations in growth, standard metabolism and oxygen capacity of the blood in children (Diss.) – *Acta Med. Scand.* suppl. 31–1929–1.

100 OATMAN, E. R., E. F. LEGNER and R. F. BROOKS – Bionomics of the eye-spotted bud moth – *J. Econ. Entomol.* 55/6–1962–930.

1 OBERHOFFER, G. – *Methodik der optischen Frequenzanalyse rhythmischer Vorgänge* – Ref. 1953a, p. 76.

2 OBERHOFFER, G. – Normographische Frequenzbestimmung aus dem Phasendiagramm der modifizierten Periodogrammanalyse kurzer Kurvenzüge – *Z. Kreislaufforsch.* 43–1954–418.

1 OECHSLER, O. – *Über einen 24-Stunden-Rhythmus der Vitalkapazität der Lunge* – Diss. Tübingen, 1940.

1 OGATA, K. – Body temperature regulation in a hot environment with

special reference to seasonal variations – *Int. J. Biometeorol.* 7/1–1963–78.

100 OGATA, K. and T. SASAK – *Diurnal Variations in Body Temperature with Special Reference to Observations made during a Sea Voyage* – Ref. 1962c.

1 OGINO, K. – Ovulationstermin und Konzeptionstermin – *Zbl. Gynäk.* 54 –1930–464.

100 O'HARA, G. J. and P. F. CUNNIFF – A numerical method for the transient response of nonlinear systems – U.S. Naval Research Lab. Rep. 5917, June 21, 1963.

100 OHLMEYER, P., H. BRILMAYER and H. HÜLLSTRUNG – Periodische Vorgänge im Schlaf – *Pflüger's Arch.* 248–1944–559.

100 OHLSSON, B. and G. BLIX – On cyclic changes in the lipid content of the liver in the rat – *Scand. Arch. Physiol.* 69–1934–182.

100 OKA, H. and H. HASHIMOTO – Lunare Periodizität in der Fortpflanzung einer pazifischen Art von *Clunio* – *Biol. Zbl.* 78–1959–545.

1 OLNJANSKAJA, R. P. and T. W. POPOWA – *24-Stunden-Periodik der Körpertemperatur bei alimentärer Dystrophie* – Bykow. Ref. 1, p. 93.

1 OLTMANNS, O. – Über den Einfluss der Temperatur auf die endogene Tagesrhythmik und die Blühinduktion bei der Kurztagspflanze *Kalanchoë blossfeldiana* – *Planta* 54–1960–233.

100 OMWAKE, K. T. and LORANZ M. – Study of ability to wake at a specified time – *J. Appl. Psychol.* 17–468.

100 ONO, M. and T. ABE – *Variations in the Amounts of Sunlight of Different Wavelengths in some Areas of Tokyo* – Ref. 1962c.

1 OORDT, G. J. v. – *Regulation of the Spermatogenetic Cycle of the Common Frog* – Diss. Univ. Utrecht, 1956.

100 OPPENHEIM, F. and L. RITTER – Über die Tageschwankungen der Sterblichkeit – *Münch. Med. Wschr.* 1920 II–1339.

1 OREL, H. – Über den Einfluss der Jahreszeit auf die Gewichtszunahme unterernährter tuberkulöser Kinder – *Z. Kinderhlk.* 41–1926–409.

1 ORSZAG, O. – Über den Einfluss der Jahreszeiten auf das Ergebnis der Sanatoriumsbehandlung – *Brauers Beitr. Klin. Tuberk.* 38–1918–145.

100 ORTAVANT, R., P. MAULEON and C. THIBAULT – *Photoperiodic Control of Gonadal and Hypophyseal Activity in Mammals* – Ref. 1963b.

1 OSBORN, C. M. – Spontaneous diurnal activity in a genetically hypopituitary animal, the dwarf rat – *Anat. Rec.* 78–1940–137.

1 OSBORNE, C. – Body temperature and periodicity – *J. Physiol.* 36–(1907–1908)–18.

1 OSTER, G. – *Reversible Photochemical Properties of Dyes* – Ref. 1957f, p. 3.

100 OSTERBERG, E. and C. G. L. WOLF – Day and night urines – *J. Biol. Chem.* 3–1907–165.

1 OSTWALD, W. – Periodisch veränderliche Reaktionsgeschwindigkeiten – *Physikal. Z.* 1–1899–87.

1 OSWALD – Mond und Menstruation – *Mschr. Geburtsh.* 103–1936–232.

200 OSWALD, I. – New light on dreaming – *New Scientist* 13/272–1962–251.

1 OTT, J. – *My Ivory Cellar* – 20th Century Press. Chicago, 1958.

1 OTTO, W. – *Biorhythmische Beobachtungen an verschiedenen Wuchsformen und an Geschwulstkranken* – Ref. 1955a, p. 126.

2 OTTO, W. – Jahreszeitliches Wachstum von Schulkindern – *Kinderärztl. Prax.* 27/2–1959–94.

3 OTTO, W. – Jahreszeit und Geburtenfrequenz – *Z. Ges. Hyg. Grenzgeb.* 5/2–1959–106.

4 OTTO, W. – Über das Jahreszeitenprofil der Erkrankungen und Unfälle im Bezirk Potsdam – *Ärztl. Wschr.* 14/6–1959–117.

5 OTTO, W. – *Jahreszeiteneinflüsse auf Totgeborenen.* Festschrift zum 80. Geburtstag von J.H. Schultz – Anthropol. Inst, Hamburg 1964.

100 OTTO, W. and G. REISSIG – Betrachtungen zum Jahresrhythmus der Geburtenfrequenz – *Forsch. u. Fortschr.* 33/4–1959–107.

101 OTTO, W. and G. REISSIG – Die monatliche Verteilung der Geburtenzahlen des Jahrganges 1959 der DDR – *Z. Ärztl. Fortbild.* 57/17–1963–977.

102 Otto, W. and G. Reissig – Zur Anthropologie der Neugeborenen IV –*Mber. D. Akad. Wiss. (Berlin)* 5/(8-9)–1963–549.

1 Overland, L. – Endogenous rhythm in opening and odor of flowers of *Cestrum nocturnum – Am. J. Bot.* 47–1960–378.

1 Paal, H. – Über periodische Vorgänge im Organismus – *Klin. Wschr.* 1932 I–649.

1 Palmén, E. – Periodic emergence in some chironomids – an adaptation to nocturnalism – *"Bertil Hanström, Zoological papers in honour of his sixty fifth birthday"* (K. G. Wingstrand, Editor). Lund, 1956.

2 Palmén, E. – Diel periodicity of pupal emergence in some North European chironomids – *Proc. Xth Intern. Congr. Entomol. Montreal* 2–1958–219.

1 Palmgren, P. – Studien über den zeitlichen Ablauf der Zugerregung bei gekäfigten Kleinvögeln – *Ornis Fenn.* 15–1938–1.

2 Palmgren, P. – Zur Tagesrhythmik der Finkenvögel – *Ornis Fenn.* 20–1943–99.

3 Palmgren, P. – Tagesrhythmik gekäfigter Kleinvögel bei konstanter Dauerbeleuchtung – *Ornis Fenn.* 21 –1944–25.

4 Palmgren, P. – Some remarks on the short-term fluctuations in the numbers of northern birds and mammals – *Oikos* 1–1949–1.

5 Palmgren, P. – Studien über die Tagesrhythmik gekäfigter Vögel – *Z. Tierpsychol.* 6–1949–44.

6 Palmgren, P. – On the diurnal rhythm of activity and rest in birds – *Ibis* 91–1949–561.

7 Palmgren, P. – *Tagesrhythmik von Instinkthandlungen, namentlich bei Vögeln* – Ref. 1955a, p. 127.

1 Panofsky, H. – *Power Spectrum Analysis* – Ref. 1961a, p. 24.

100 Panofsky, H. and F. Halberg – *The Concomitant Evaluation of circadian and Menstrual Components in the Variance Spectrum of Body Temperatures* – Ref. 1963b.

100 Pansini, R. and A. Casaula – Il bioritmio dell'alcoolemia nelle 24 ore – *Minerva Med.* 43–1952–11.

101 Pansini, R. and M. Lippi – Studio comparativo fra i ritmi della cloruremia e della colesterinemia nelle 24 ore nei sogetti sani – *Minerva Med.* 41–1950–280.

1 Papi, F. – Orientamento astronomico in alcuni *Carabidi – Atti Soc. Tosc. Sci. Nat.* 62–1955–83.

2 Papi, F. – Experiments on the sense of time in *Talitrus saltator – Experientia (Basel)* 11/5–1955–201.

3 Papi, F. – Astronomische Orientierung bei der Wolfspinne *Arctosa perita – Z. Vergl. Physiol.* 37–1955–230.

4 Papi, F. – Ricerche sull'orientamento astronomico die *Arctosa perita – Publ. Staz. Zool. Napol.* 27–1956–76.

5 Papi, F. – *Orientation by night; the moon* – Ref. 1960c, p. 475.

100 Papi, F. and L. Pardi – Ricerche sull'orientamento di *Talitrus saltator* II – *Z. Vergl. Physiol.* 35–1953–490.

101 Papi, F. and L. Serretti – Sull'esistenza di un senso del tempo in *Arctosa perita – Atti. Soc. Tosc. Sci. Nat.* 62B–1955–98.

102 Papi, F., L. Serretti and S. Parrini – Nuove richerche sull'orientamento e il senso del tempo di *Arctosa perita – Z. Vergl. Physiol.* 39–1957 –531.

103 Papi, F. and L. Pardi – On the lunar orientation of sandhoppers – *Biol. Bull.* 124/1–1963–97.

104 Papi, F. and P. Tongiorgi – *Innate and Learned Components in the Astronomical Orientation of Wolf Spiders* – Ref. 1962d, p. 259.

1 Pardi, L. – Esperienze sull'orientamento di *Talitrus saltator – Boll. Ist. Mus. Zool. (Torino)* 4/9–(1953–1954)–128.

2 Pardi, L. – Über die Orientierung von *Tylos latreillii – Z. Tierpsychol.* 11–1954–175.

3 Pardi, L. – Orientamento solare di un *Tenbrionide alofilo – Boll. Ist. Mus. Zool. (Torino)* 5–1955–1.

4 Pardi, L. – *Innate Components in the Solar Orientation of Littoral Amphipods* – Ref. 1960c, p. 395.

100 Pardi, L. and M. Grassi – Experimental modification of direction finding in *Talitrus saltator* and *Talorchestia deshayesi – Experientia (Basel)* 11–1955–202.

101 PARDI, L. and F. PAPI – Die Sonne als Kompass bei *Talitrus saltator* – *Naturwiss* 39–1952–262.

102 PARDI, L. and F. PAPI – Ricerche sull'orientamento di *Talitrus saltator* – *Z. Vergl. Physiol.* 35–1953–459.

100 PARIS, O. H. and C. E. JENNER – *Photoperiodic Control of Diapause in the Pitcherplant Midge* – Ref. 1957f, p. 601.

1 PARK, O. – Studies in nocturnal ecology III – *Ecology* 16–1935–152.

2 PARK, O. – Studies in nocturnal ecology. Further analysis of activity in the beetle, *Passalus cornutus*, and description of audiofrequency recording apparatus – *J. Animal Ecol.* 6–1937–239.

3 PARK, O. – Studies in nocturnal ecology VII – *Ecology* 19–1938–208.

4 PARK, O. – Nocturalism; the development of a problem – *Ecol. Monogr.* 10–1940–485.

5 PARK, O. – Quantitative determination of rhythmicity in organisms – *Ohio J. Sci.* 41–1941–39.

100 PARK, O., A. BARDEN and E. WILLIAMS – Studies in nocturnal ecology, IX – *Ecology* 21–1940–122.

101 PARK, O. and J. G. KELLER – Studies in nocturnal ecology II – *Ecology* 13–1932–335.

102 PARK, O., J. A. LOCKETT and D. J. MYERS – Studies in nocturnal ecology with special reference to climax forest – *Ecology* 12–1931–709.

103 PARK, O., T. W. ROBERTS and S. J. HARRIS – Preliminary analysis of activity of the cave crayfish, *Cambarus pellucidus* – *Amer. Nat.* 75–1941–154.

104 PARK, O. and O. SEJBA – Studies in nocturnal ecology, IV – *Ecology* 16–1935–164.

1 PARKER, J. – Seasonal changes in some chemical and physical properties of living cells of Pinus ponderosa and their relation to freezing resistance – *Southern Forest. Exp. St. Marianna (Flv.)* 1956.

300 PARKER, M. W., S. B. HENDRICKS and H. A. BORTHWICK – Action spectrum for photoperiodic control of floral initiation of the long-day plant *Hyoscyamus niger* – *Bot. Gaz.* 111–1950–242.

301 PARKER, M. W., S. B. HENDRICKS, H. A. BORTHWICK and N. J. SCULLY – Action spectrum for the photoperiodic control of floral initiation of short-day plants – *Bot. Gaz.* 108–1946–1.

1 PASCHER, A. – Von der merkwürdigen Bewegungsweise einiger Flagellaten – *Biol. Zbl.* 37/9–1917–421.

1 PASK, G. – *An Approach to Cybernetics* – Harper. New York, 1961.

1 PATRY, F. L. – The relation of time of day, sleep and other factors to the incidence of epileptic seizures – *Am. J. Psychiatr.* 10–1931–789.

1 PATTON, R.L. – *Introductory insect physiology*–Saunders, Philadelphia 1963.

1 PAUL, H. v. – Der jahreszeitliche Gang der Kreislaufgrössen – *Arch. Kreislaufforsch.* 9–1941–164.

200 PAUL, U. v. ST. – Nachweis der Sonnenorientierung bei nächtlich ziehenden Vögeln – *Behaviour* 6–1953–1.

201 PAUL, U. v. ST. – Compass directional training of western meadowlarks – *Auk* 73–1956–203.

100 PAULIAN, R. and A. SERFATY – Le rythm nycthéméral des larves d'Aseschnes – *Bull. Mus. Hist. Nat.* 16–1944–442.

100 PAVAN, D., T. DOBZHANSKY and H. BUPLA – Diurnal behaviour of some neotropical species of *Drosophila* – *Ecology* 31/1–1950–36.

100 PAYNE, R. W. and H. E. DE WARDENER – Reversal of urinary diurnal rhythm following head injury– *Lancet* i –/7030–1958 I–1098.

100 PEARSON, E. S. and H. O. HARTLEY, *Biometrica Tables for Statisticians I* – Univ. Press. Cambridge, 1954.

1 PEIPER, A. – Pendelinduktion zwischen Atemzentrum und Saugzentrum – *Mschr. Kinderhlk.* 75–1938–78.

100 PELLEGRINI, P. and B. CARROZZINI – *Sulle Variazioni Bioritmiche nelle 24 Ore degli Ergoni Adrenosimpatici Eliminati con le Urine* – Ref. 1960a, p. 123.

101 PELLEGRINI, L. and L. AGRICOLAS – La fosforemia nelle 24 ore – *Minerva Med.* 41–1950–315.

102 PELLEGRINI, P. and M. LIPPI, La curva polarographica del siero nelle 24 ore – *Minerva Med.* 41–1950–312.

1   PENNYCUICK, C. J. – The physical
    basis of astro–navigation in birds –
    J. Exp. Biol. 37–1960–572.
1   PERDECK, A. C. – Two types of
    orientation in migrating starlings
    and chaffinches – *Ardea* 46–1958–1.
1   PERGOLA, DE – *Blood Leucocyte Count
    during the Sexual Cycle in Women* –
    Ref. 1960a, p. 43.
100 PERGOLA, DE and F. LONERO –
    *Research on a Sexual and Adrenal
    Rhythm in Man* – Ref. 1960a, p. 43.
100 PERKEL, D.H., J.H. SCHULMAN, T.H.
    BULLOCK, G.P. MOORE and J.P. SE-
    GUNDO –Pacemaker neurons – *Scien-
    ce* 145/3627–1964–61.
100 PERKOFF, G. T., K. EIK-NES, C. A.
    NUGENT, H. L. FRED, R. A. NIMBER,
    L. RUSH, L. T. SAMUELS and F. H.
    TYLER – Studies of the diurnal
    variation of plasma 17-hydroxycor-
    ticosteroids in man – *J. Clin. Endo-
    crinol.* 19–1959–432.
1   PERPEET, W. – Was ist Zeit? – *Stud.
    Gen.* 8–1955–531.
100 PERRY, T. O. and W. C. WU – In-
    vestigation of the photoperiod res-
    ponse and racial variation in loblolly
    pine – *Res. Rep. Univ. Florida
    School Forestry* 4–1957–21.
1   PERTTUNEN, V. – Seasonal changes
    in the humidity reaction of the
    common earwig *Forficula auricula-
    ria* – *Nature* 170–1952–209.
2   PERTTUNEN, V. – *Effect of Dessica-
    tion on the Light Reactions of some
    Terrestrial Arthropods* – Ref. 1962d,
    p. 90.
100 PERTTUNEN, V. and K. LAGERSPETZ
    – Dissociation of the pulsation
    rhythm in the anterior and poste-
    rior parts of the heart at low and
    high temperatures in the larva of
    Corethra plumicornis (Dipt., *Culici-
    dae*) – *Ann. Ent. Fenn.* 23–1957–
    179.
100 PETERS, W. and S. H. CHRISTIAN –
    The bionomics, ecology and distri-
    bution of some mosquitoes in the
    territory of Papua and New Guinea
    – *Acta Tropica* 20/1–1963–35.
1   PETERSEN, G. A. – *Beitrag zur 24-
    Stunden-Rhythmik der Körpertempe-
    ratur beim Menschen* (Diss.) – Greifs-
    wald, 1935.
200 PETERSEN, W. F. – *The Patient and
    the Weather* – Edwards Brthrs Inc.

Ann Arbor., 1938.
201 PETERSEN, W. F. – *Man, Weather
    and Sun* – C.C. Thomas. Spring-
    field, Ill., 1947.
100 PETERSON, J. E., A. A. WILCOX,
    M. I. HALEY and R. A. KEITH –
    Hourly variation in total serum chol-
    esterol – *Circulation* 22/2–1960–247.
1   PETRÉN, T. – Die 24-Stundenrhyth-
    mik des Leberglykogens bei *Cavia
    cobaya* nebst Studien über die Ein-
    wir kung der "chronischen" Mus-
    kelarbeit auf diese Rhythmik –
    Morph. Jahrb. 83–1939–256.
2   PETRÉN, T. – *Weitere Untersuchun-
    gen über den Tagesrhythmus von
    Hühnerembryonen und Kücken* –
    Ref. 1953a, p. 42.
100 PETRÉN, T. and A. SOLLBERGER –
    *Die 24 Stunden Rhythmik des Leber-
    glykogens bei Hühnerembryonen und
    Küken verschiedenen Alters nebst
    Studien über die Unabhängigkeit der
    Rhythmik von äusseren Faktoren* –
    Ref. 1949a, p. 54.
1   PETROPOLOUS, S.F. – Automatic
    sampling device for study of syn-
    chronized cultures of microorganisms
    – *Science* 145/3629–1964–268.
2   PETROPULOS, S.F. – Ultraviolet in-
    activation of chloroplast formation in
    synchronously dividing *Eyglena gra-
    cilis* – *Science* 145/3630–1964–392.
100 PETROVIC, A. and C. KAYSER –
    Variations saisonnières du seuil
    réactionnel de la thyroide à la
    thyréostimuline chez le hamster –
    J. Physiol. 50–1958–446.
1   PEYRER – Jahreszeitliche Schwan-
    kungen der Tuberkulinempfindlich-
    keit und mancher Tuberkuloseer-
    krankungen – *Brauers Beitr. Klin.
    Tuberk.* 48–1921–137.
100 PFAFF, F. and W. BALCH – An ex-
    perimental investigation of some of
    the conditions influencing the secre-
    tion and composition of human
    bile – *J. Exp. Med.* 2–1897–49.
1   PFEFFER, W. – *Die periodischen Be-
    wegungen der Blattorgane* – Leipzig,
    1875.
2   PFEFFER, W. – Die Entstehung der
    Schlafbewegungen bei Pflanzen –
    Biol. Zbl. 28–1908–389.
3   PFEFFER, W. – Untersuchungen über
    die Entstehung der Schlafbewe-
    gungen der Blattorgane – *Abh. Kgl.*

Sächs. Ges. Wiss. Math.–Phys. Kl. 30–1909–257.

4 PFEFFER, W. – Beiträge zur Kenntnis der Entstehung der Schlafbewegungen – *Abh. Kgl. Sächs. Ges. Wiss. Math.–Phys. Kl.* 34–1915–1.

1 PHILIPSBORN, E. v. – *Rhythmische Erscheinungen bei den lebenden Blutleukocyten* – Ref. 1939a, p. 192.

2 PHILIPSBORN, E. V. – *Über den Atemrhythmus* – Ref. 1953a, p. 156.

3 PHILIPSBORN, E. v. – *Bedeutung der ökologischen Betrachtungsweise für die Rhythmusforschung* – Ref. 1955a, p. 128.

1 PHILPOTT, S. J. F. – Fluctuations in human output – *Brit. J. Psychol.* 6/monograph XVII–1932.

1 PICCARDI, G. – Sur la désincrustation physique des chaudières et sur l'influence de facteur ambiant sur certains phénomenes physico–chimiques – *Mem. Soc. Roy. Belge Ingénieurs et Industriels* 3–1953.

2 PICCARDI, G. – Physikalische, chemische und biologische Effekte als Ausdruck von Weltraumeinflüssen – *Wien. Med. Wschr.* 106–1956–975.

3 PICCARDI, G. – *Expose Introductif* – Ref. 1958c, p. 9.

4 PICCARDI, G. – *Les Tests Chimiques* – Ref. 1958c, p. 21.

5 PICCARDI, G. – *Une Hypothèse Solaire* – Ref. 1958c, p. 121.

6 PICCARDI, G. – Kosmische Phänomene und Bioklimatologie – *Wien. Med. Wschr.* 108/6–1958–126.

7 PICCARDI, G. – The problem of the relationship between spacial and terrestrial phenomena and chemical tests – *Atti Fond. G. Ronchi* 16/2–1961–109.

8 PICCARDI, G. – The numerical data from the chemical tests gathered in Florence in 1961 I–II – Internat. Committee Chem. Tests Internat. Soc. Biometeorol. Florence 1961 and 1962.

9 PICCARDI, G. – *The chemical basis of medical climatology* – Thomas, Springfield 1963.

1 PICON, J. M. O. – Über Zellteilungsfrequenz und Zellteilungsrhythmus in der Epidermis der Maus – *Z. Zellforsch. Mikr. Anat.* 19–1933–488.

100 PIENKOWSKI, R. L. and J. T. MEDLER – Effects of Alfalfa cuttings on the potato leafhopper – *J. Econ. Entomol.* 55/6–1962–973.

1 PIERACH, A. – *Nachtarbeit und Schichtwechsel beim gesunden und kranken Menschen* – Ref. 1953a, p. 159.

2 PIERACH, A. – Die vegetative Tagesrhythmik und ihre klinische Bedeutung – *Münch. Med. Wschr.* 96–1954–465.

3 PIERACH, A. – *Klinische Beobachtungen über vegetative Regulationsstörungen beim Einschlafen, Aufwachen und während des Schlafes* – Ref. 1955a, p. 130.

4 PIERACH, A. – Nachtarbeit und Schichtwechsel beim gesunden und kranken Menschen – *Int. J. Prophyl. Med. Soz.–Hyg.* 4/6–1960–1.

1 PIERON, H. – La réaction aux marées par anticipation réflexes chez *Actinia equina* – *C.R. Soc. Biol.* 61–1906–658.

2 PIERON, H. – La rythmicité chez *Actinia equina* L. – *C.R. Soc. Biol.* 65–190–726.

1 PILCZ, A. – *Die periodischen Geistesstörungen* – Fischer. Jena, 1901.

1 PILET, P. E. and L. BAILLAUD – Activité des auxines–oxydases et circumnutation des tiges du *Phaseolus multiflorus* – *C.R.Acad. Sci.* 224–1957–1530.

1 PILSUM, J. F. v. – *Circadian Rhythm in Mouse Kidney Transaminidase* – Ref. 1963b.

1 PINCUS, G. – On the temperature characteristics for frequency of breathing movements in inbred strains of mice and in their hybrid offspring I – *J. Gen. Physiol.* 14–1931–421.

2 PINCUS, G. – A diurnal rhythm in the excretion of urinary ketosteroids by young men – *J. Clin. Endocrinol.* 3–1943–195.

100 PINCUS, G., L. P. ROMANOFF and J. CARLO – Diurnal rhythm in excretion of neutral reducing lipids by man and its relation to 17-ketosteroid rhythm – *J. Clin. Endocrinol.* 80–1948–221.

100 PIRINGER, A. A. and H. A. BORTHWICK – Photoperiodic response of coffee – *Turrialba* 5–1955–72.

101 PIRINGER, A. A., R. J. DOWNS and

H. A. Borthwick – Effects of photoperiods on *Rauwolfia – Am. J. Bot.* 45–1958–323.

1   Pirquet, C. v. – Die Todeskrankheiten in ihrer jahreszeitlichen Verteilung – *Z. Kinderhlk.* 44–1927–414.

1   Pirson, A. – Stoffwechselperiodizität bei Grünalgen – *Ber. D. Bot. Ges.* 68–1955.

100   Pirson, A. und H. Döring – Induzierte Wachstumsperioden bei Grünalgen – *Flora* 139–1952–314.

101   Pirson, A. and H. Lorenzen – Ein endogener Zeitfaktor bei der Teilung von *Chlorella – Z. Bot.* 46/1–1958–53.

102   Pirson, A. and W. J. Schön – Versuche zur Analyse der Stoffwechselperiodik bei *Hydrodictyon – Flora* 144–1957–447.

103   Pirson, A., W. J. Schön and H. Döring – Wachstums- und Stoffwechselperiodik bei *Hydrodictyon – Z. Naturforsch.* 9b–1954–349.

1   Pirtkien, R. – *Über den Einfluss der Arbeit auf die Rhythmik des vegetativen Nervensystems* – Ref. 1955a, p. 131.

2   Pirtkien, R. – Über die 24-Stunden-Rhythmik des Menschen und das vegetative Nervensystem – *Int. Z. Angew. Physiol.* 16–1957–198.

1   Pitelka, F. A. – *Some Aspects of Population Structure in the Short-term Cycle of the Brown Lemming in Northern Alaska* – Ref. 1957d, p. 237.

100   Pitre, H. N. Jr. and E. J. Kantack – Biology of the banded cucumber-beetle – *J. Econ. Entomol.* 55/6–1962–904.

1   Pittendrigh, C. S. – On temperature independence in the clock-system controlling emergence time in *Drosophila – Proc. Nat. Acad. Sci.* 40–1954–1018.

2   Pittendrigh, C. S. – *Diurnal Rhythms as Clocks* – Ref. 1957c.

3   Pittendrigh, C. S. – *Perspectives in the Study of Biological Clocks* – Ref. 1958a, p. 239.

4   Pittendrigh, C. S. – Adaptation, natural selection and behaviour – A. Loe and G. G. Simpson, *Behaviour and Evolution.* Yale Univ. Press. Yale, 1958, p. 390.

5   Pittendrigh, C. S. – *The Major Features of Circadian Rhythms* – Ref. 1960a, p. 127.

6   Pittendrigh, C. S. – *Circadian Rhythms and the Circadian Organization of Living Systems* – Ref. 1960c, p. 159.

7   Pittendrigh, C.S. – The entrainment of circadian oscillations by skeleton photoperiod – *Science* 144/3618–1964–565.

100   Pittendrigh C. S. and V. G. Bruce – *An Oscillator Model for Biological Clocks* – Ref. 1956a, p. 75.

101   Pittendrigh, C. S. and V. G. Bruce – *Daily Rhythms as Coupled Oscillator Systems and their Relation to Thermoperiodism and Photoperiodism* – Ref. 1957f, p. 475.

102   Pittendrigh, C. S., V. G. Bruce and P. Kaus – On the significance of transients in daily rhythms – *Proc. Nat. Acad. Sci.* 44–1958–965.

103   Pittendrigh, C. S., V. G. Bruce, N. S. Rosensweig and M. L. Rubin – Growth patterns in *Neurospora – Nature* 184–1959–169.

1   Pitts, G. C. – A diurnal rhythm in blood sugar of the white rat –*Am. J. Physiol.* 139–1943–109.

100   Pizzarello, D.J., D. Isaak, K.E. Chua and A.L. Rhyne–Circadian rhythmicity in the sensitivity of two strains of mice to whole-body radiation – *Science* 145/3629–1964–286.

1   Pohl, R. – Tagesrhythmus im phototaktischen Verhalten der *Euglena gracilis – Z. Naturforsch.* 3b–1948–367.

1   Pohyakallio, O. – *Über die Wirkung der Tagesdauer auf das Überwintern von Klee* – Ref. 1960b, p. 390.

1   Pokrovsky, G. I. – On the relation of the sun's activity to some biological factors – *Science* 67–1928–1737.

1   Pol, B. v.d. – On relaxation oscillations – *Philos. Mag. and J. Sci.* 2–1926–978.

2   Pol, B. v.d. – Über Relaxationschwingungen – *Jb. Drahtl. Te- legr. Teleph.* 28–1926–178; 29–1927–114.

3   Pol, B. v.d. – The nonlinear theory of electric oscillations – *Proc. I.R.E.* 22–1934–1051.

4   Pol, B. v.d. – *Biological Rhythms considered as Relaxation Oscillations* – Ref. 1939a, p. 76.

100 POL, B. V.D. and J. V.D. MARK – The heart beat considered as a relaxation oscillation and an electrical model of the heart – *Philos. Mag.* 6/7th series 1928–763.

101 POL, B. V.D. and J. V.D. MARK – The heartbeat considered as a relaxation oscillation and an electrical model of the heart – *Arch. Neerl. Physiol* 14–1929–418.

102 POL, B. V.D., and J. V.D. MARK – Frequency demultiplication – *Nature* 120/3019–1927–363.

100 POLAK, F. and F. KNOBLOCH – Ist das Ausgangswertgesetz von Wilder ein Naturgesetz? – *Acta Neuroveg.* 15–1957–473.

300 POLAK, B., J.W. NOWOSIELSKI, and J.A. NAEGELE – Daily sensitivity rhythm of the two spotted spider mite to DDVP – *Science* 145/3630–1964–405.

1 POLDER, J. J. W. – Cyclical changes in testis and ovary related to maturity stages in the North-Sea herring – *Arch. Neerl. Zool.* 14/1 – 1961–45.

1 POMMERENKE, W. T. – Phenomena correlated with ovulation as guides to the appraisal of the so-called safe period – *J. Obst. Gyn.* 60–1953–519.

1 PONUGAJEWA, A. G. – *Herdenform and 24-Stunden-Periodik bei Fledermäusen* – Bykow, Ref. 1, p. 102.

1 POPOVIC, V. – Endocrines in hibernation – *Bull. Mus. Comp. Zool.* 124–1960–105.

1 PORTER, W. T. – The seasonal variation in the growth of Boston schoolchildren – *Am. J. Physiol.* 52–1920–121.

100 POSKANZER, D. C. and D. N. S. KERR – A third type of periodic paralysis – *Am. J. Med.* 31–1961–328.

101 POSKANZER, D. C. and D. N. S. KERR – Periodic paralysis with response to spirolactone – *Lancet* 2–1961–511.

1 POTTER, R. G. JR. – *Farris Formula for Predicting Fertile Days* – Ref. 1957d, p. 175.

1 POULET, G. – *Studies in Human Time* – Harper. New York, 1959.

1 PRATT, D. M. – Analysis of population development in *Daphnia* at different temperatures – *Biol. Bull.* 85–1943–116.

200 PRATT, J. G. – An investigation of homing ability in pigeons without previous homing ability – *J. Exp. Biol.* 32/1–1955–70.

300 PRATT, J. G. and R. H. THOULESS – Homing orientation in pigeons in relation to opportunity to observe the sun before release – *J. Exp. Biol.* 32/1–1955–140.

301 PRATT, J. G. and H. G. WALLRAFF – Zwei-Richtungs-Versuche mit Brieftauben – *Z. Tierpsychol.* 15/3–1958–332.

1 PRECHT, H. – Einige Versuche zum Heimfindevermögen von Vögeln – *J. Ornithol.* 97–1956–377.

1 PRESCOTT, D. M. – *Relations between Cell Growth and Cell Division* – Ref. 1956a, p. 59.

1 PRICE-JONES, C. – The diurnal variation in the sizes of red blood cells – *J. Pathol. Bact.* 23–1920–371.

1 PRINGLE, J. W. S. – *Myogenic Rhythms* – Rec. Adv. Invert. Physiol., Univ. Oregon Publ. Oregon, 1957, (p. 99).

2 PRINGLE, J. W. S. – *The Proprioceptive Background to Mechanisms of Orientation* – Ref. 1962d, p. 1.

100 PRUNTY, F. T. G., R. R. MC SWINEY, J. H. MILLS and M. SMITH – The effects of aldosterone in Addison's disease and adrenal pseudohermaphroditism – *Lancet* 1954 II–620.

100 PUNTRIANO, G. and J. MEITES – The effect of continuous light or darkness on thyroid function in mice – *Endocrinology* 48–1951–217.

1 PYE, J. D. – Echolocation by bats – *Endeavour* 20/78–1961–101.

2 PYE, J. D. – *Mechanisms of Echolocation* – Ref. 1962d, p. 12.

1 QUARRINGTON, B. – Cyclical variation in stuttering frequency and some related forms of variation – *Can. J. Psychol.* 10/3–1956–179.

1 QUILGHINI, D. – *Les Elements Cinématiques du Mouvement de la Terre referé aux Etoiles les plus proches du Soleil* – Ref. 1958c, p. 131.

1 QUINKE, H. – Über Tag- und Nachtharn – *Arch. Exp. Path.* 32–1893–211.

1 RABB, R. L. – Biology of *Conoderus vespertinus* in the Piedmont section of North Carolina – *Ann. Entomol. Soc. Am.* 56/5–1963–669.

1   RABINOVITSCH, I. M. – Variations in the percentage of hemoglobin in man during the day – *J. Lab. Clin. Med.* 9–1923–120.

1   RABINOWITCH, J. E. – *Photosynthesis and Related Processes* – Interscience. New York, 1956.

1   RADNOT, M. – Die Wirkung der Belichtung auf das Neuroendokrine System – *Acta Morph. Acad. Sci. Hung.* 5/(3–4)–1955–369.

2   RADNOT, M. – *Significance of the Retina in the Optico–Vegetative function* – Ref. 1960a, p. 127.

3   RADNOT, M. – L'importance de l'oeil dans le fonctionnement des organes à sécrétion interne – *Ann. d Oculistique* 193/4–1960–298.

4   RADNOT, M. – *Effects of Testicular Extirpation upon Intraocular Pressure* – Ref. 1963b.

100   RADNOT, M. and I. OLAH – Die Wirkung des Lichtes auf die Zahl der Eosinophilen Blutzellen – *Acta Med. Hung.* 11/3–1958–393.

101   RADNOT, M. and T. ORBAN – Die Wirkung der Belichtung auf die sekundären sexuellen Merkmale – *Acta Med. Acad. Sci. Hung* 7/(3–4) –1955–369.

102   RADNOT, M. and T. ORBAN – Die Wirkung des Lichtes auf die Funktion der Schildrüse – *Acta Morph. Acad. Sci. Hung.* 6/4–1956–375.

103   RADNOT, M. and E. TÖRÖK – Die Tagesschwankung der Eosinophilenzahl und des intraokularen Druckes – *Klin. Monatsbl. Augenhlk.* 130 /6–1957–763.

104   RADNOT, M., E. WALLNER and M. KÖNIG – Netzhautfunktion und optico–vegetatives System – *Acta Chir. Hung.* 2/4–1961–419.

105   RADNOT, M., E. WALLNER and E. TÖRÖK – Die Wirkung des Lichtes auf die Nebennierenrindenfunktion – *Acta Med. Hung.* 9/3–1956–231.

106   RADNOT, M. and E. WALLNER – *Periodicity in the Eosinophil Count in the Adrenal Cycle* – Ref. 1963b.

100   RAHN, H. and F. ROSENDALE – Diurnal rhythm of melanophore hormone secretion in the Anolis pituitary – *Proc. Soc. Exp. Biol. Med.* 48–1941–100.

1   RALPH, C. L. – Persistent rhythms of activity and O_2-consumption in the earthworm – *Physiol. Zool.* 30–1957–41.

2   RALPH, C. L. – Modification of activity rhythms of *Periplaneta americana* induced by carbon chloride and nitrogen – *Physiol. Zool.* 32–1959–57.

1   RAMANATHAN, O. – Light and sexual periodicity in Indian buffaloes – *Nature* 130–1932–169.

1   RANSON, S. W. – Somnolence caused by hypothalamic lesions in the monkey – *Arch. Neurol. Psychiat.* 41–1939–1.

1   RAO, K. P. – Tidal rhythmicity of rate of water propulsion in Mytilus and its modifiability by transplantation – *Biol. Bull.* 106–1954–353.

1   RAPPE, G. – *Yearly Rhythm of Grass Growth and Soil Conditions* – Ref. 1955a, p. 136.

1   RASHEVSKY, N. – Mathematical biophysics of the cell with reference to the contractility of tissues and amoeboid movements – *Bull. Math. Biophys.* 1/1–1939–47.

2   RASHEVSKY, N. – *Mathematical Biophysics* – Univ. Chicago Press. Chicago, 1948.

100   RATEITSCHAK, K. H. and H. R. MÜHLEMANN – The effect of cold stress at two different times of day on the oral epithelium 24-hour-mitosis-periodicity in albino rats – *Helv. Odont. Acta* 1/1–1957–19.

1   RAU, P. – Rhythmic periodicity and synchronous flashing in the fire fly – *Ecology* 13/1–1932–7.

100   RAU, P. and N. – The sex attraction and rhythmic periodicity in giant saturniid moths – *Trans. Acad. Sci. (St. Louis)* 26–1929–81.

200   RAU, W. – Über die Wirkung des zu verschiedenen Tageszeiten gebotenen Lichts auf Substanzproduktion und Stickstoffgehalt von Keimpflanzen – *Z. Bot.* 42–1954–305.

1   RAUTENBERG, W. – Vergleichende Untersuchungen über den Energiehaushalt des Bergfinken und des Haussperlings – *J. Ornithol.* 98/1–1957–36.

1   RAVITZ, L. J. – *History, Measurement and Applicability of Periodic Changes in the Electromagnetic Field in Health and Disease* – Ref. 1961c,

p. 1144.

1   RAWSON, K. S. – Sun compass orientation and endogenous activity rhythms of the starling – Z. Tierpsychol. 11–1954–446.

2   RAWSON, K. S. – Homing Behavior and Endogenous Activity Rhythms – Harvard Univ. Thesis, 1956.

3   RAWSON, K. S. – Experimental Modification of Mammalian Endogenous Activity Rhythms – Ref. 1957f, p. 791.

4   RAWSON, K. S. – Effects of Tissue Temperature on Mammalian Activity Rhythms – Ref. 1960c, p. 105.

100   RAY, H. and M. CHAKRAVERTY – Lunar periodicity in the conjugation of Conchophthirius lamellidens gosh – Nature 134–1934.

100   REDING, G.R., W.C. RUBRIGHT, A. RECHTSCHAFFEN and R.W. DANIELS – Sleep pattern of tooth-grinding – Science 145/3633-1964–725.

100   REED, C. I. and N. KLEITMAN – Studies on the physiology of sleep; The effect of sleep on the respiration – Am. J. Physiol. 75–1925–600.

1   REGELSBERGER, H. – Tagesrhythmik und Reaktionstypen des Polarisationswiderstandes der menschlichen Haut II – Z. Ges. Exp. Med. 70–1930–438.

2   REGELSBERGER, H. – Rhythmenverlust durch Lebererkrankung – Ref. 1953a, p. 170.

200   REGELSBERGER JR, H. S. – Führt eine Störung der vegetativen Rhythmik zu tropischen Gewebsdefekten? – Acta Neuroveg. 8/1–1953–119.

201   REGELSBERGER H. S. JR, – Temporäre Ausschaltung des Ggl. stellatum im Bilde des Elektrodermatogramms und Elektroencephalogramms – Acta Neurochir. 3/4–1953 329.

1   REICH, H. J. – Functional Circuits and Oscillations – Nostrand. New York, 1961.

1   REICHLE, F. – Untersuchungen über Frequenzrhythmen bei Ameisen – Z. Vergl. Physiol. 30–1943–227.

1   REID, J. H. – The prediction of solar activity– New Sci. 18/342–1963–540.

1   REIMANN, H. A. – Periodic disease – JAMA 136–1948–239.

2   REIMANN, H. A. – Periodic disease – JAMA 141–1949–175.

3   REIMANN, H. A, – Periodicity in disease – New Engl. J. Med. 256–1957–652.

4   REIMANN, H. A. – Hepatitis, a feature of periodic peritonitis – JAMA 178–1961–334.

5   REIMANN, H. A. – Periodic pancreatosis – J. Indian Med. Prof. 9/5–1962–4189.

6   REIMANN, H. A. – Biorhythms and disease – JAMA 183/10–1963–879.

7   REIMANN, H. A. – Neuro–Hypothalamic–Hypophyseal Influence in Periodic Diseases – Ref. 1963b.

8   Reimann, H. A. – Biological Rhythm as a Cause of Periodic Disease in Man – Ref. 1963a.

9   REIMANN, H. A. – Periodic Disease – F. A. Davis. Philadelphia, 1963.

100   REIMANN, H. A. and A. P. ANGELIDES – Periodic arthralgia in 23 members of five generations of family – JAMA 146–1951–713.

101   REIMANN, H. A. and C. T. DE BERARDINIS – Periodic neutropenia – Blood 4–1949–1109.

102   REIMANN, H. A. and J. N. LINDQUIST – Periodic sialorrhea – JAMA 149–1952–1465.

103   REIMANN, H. A., L. C. MILLS and J. H. NODINE – Periodic hypertension – Am. J. Med. Sci. 244/2–1962–145.

104   REIMANN, H. A., J. MOADIE, S. SEMERDIJAN and P. F. SAHYOUN –Periodic peritonitis – JAMA 154–1954–1254.

105   REIMANN, H. A. and H. ZELLWEGER – Periodische Krankheit – Ref. 1953a p. 196.

100   REINBERG, A. and J. GHATA – Rythmes et Cycles Biologiques – Presse Univ. France. Paris, 1957 (also in Japanese).

101   REINBERG, A., J. GHATA and E. SIDI – Les variations circadiennes de lactivité cortico-surrénaliènne et le paroxysme nocturne de l'asthme – Ann. d'Endocrinol. 24/3–1963–452.

1   REISINGER, R. C. – Epizootiology of spontaneous cancer in cattle – Ann. N.Y. Acad. Sci. 108/3–1963–855.

1   REISSIG, G. – Der Jahresrhythmus der Geburtenzahlen in Berlin, Zürich und Prag – Z. Ärztl. Fortbild. 33–1959–15.

1 REITER, R. – Wetter und Zahl der Geburten – *D. Med. Wschr.* 77/51–1952–1605.

2 REITER, R. – Beziehungen zwischen Sonneneruptionen, Wetterablauf und Reaktionen des Menschen – *Angew. Meteorol.* 1/10–1953.

3 REITER, R. – Verkehrsunfallziffern aus dem Raum Mitteleuropa und ihre Beziehungen zu biometeorologischen Indikatoren – *Münch. Med. Wschr.* 95/2–1953–98.

4 REITER, R. – Neuere Untersuchungen zum Problem der Wetterabhängigkeit des Menschen – *Arch. Meteorol. Geophys. Bioklimatol.* 4B/3–1953–327.

5 REITER, R. – Umwelteinflüsse auf die Reaktionszeit des gesunden Menschen – *Münch. Med. Wschr.* 96–1954–479, 526.

1 REMANE, A. – *Biologische und ökologische Rhythmen im Tierreich* – Ref. 1953a, p. 63.

1 REMLER, O. – Untersuchungen an Blinden über die 24- Stunden-Rhythmik – *Klin. Mon.bl. Augenhlk.* 113–1948–116.

1 REMMERT, H. – Untersuchungen über das tageszeitlich gebundene Schlüpfen von *Pseudosmittia arenaria* – *Z. Vergl. Physiol.* 37–1955–338.

1 RENBOURN, E. T. – *Variation over a Period of a Year in Resting Pulse Rate and Oral Temperature in Young Men* – Ref. 1960d, p. 366.

1 RENNER, M. – Die Haltung von Bienen in geschlossenen, künstlich beleuchteten Räumen – *Naturwiss.* 42–1955–539.

2 RENNER, M. – Ein Transozeanversuch zum Zeitsinn der Honigbiene – *Naturwiss.* 42–1955–540.

3 RENNER, M. – Der Zeitsinn der Bienen – *Natur u. Volk* 86–1956–185.

4 RENNER, M. – Neue Versuche über den Zeitsinn der Honigbiene – *Z. Vergl. Physiol.* 40–1957–85.

5 RENNER, M. – Der Zeitsinn der Arthropoden – *Erg. Biol.* 20–1958–127.

6 RENNER, M. – Über ein weiteres Versetzungsexperiment zur Analyse des Zeitsinnes und der Sonnenorientierung der Honigbiene – *Z. Vergl. Physiol.* 42–1959–449.

7 RENNER, M. – *The Contribution of the Honey Bee to the Study of Time-Sense and Astronomical Orientation* – Ref. 1960c, p. 361.

8 RENNER, M. – Zeitsinn und astronomische Orientierung der Honigbiene – *Naturwiss. Rundschau* 14/8–1961–296.

1 RENSING, L. – Daily rhythmicity of corpus allatum and neurosecretary cells in *Drosophila* – *Science* 144/3626–1964–1586.

100 RENSING, L., H. OBERDORFER and G. BIRUKOW – Orientierungsrhythmik und tagesperiodische Aktivität beim Wasserläufer *Velia currens* F. – *Naturwiss.* 46/2–1959–91.

1 RHODIN, J. – *Correlation of ultrastructural organization and function in normal and experimentally changed proximal convoluted tubule cells of the mouse kidney* – A.B. Godvil. Stockholm, 1954.

100 RICH, S. and P. E. WAGGONER – Atmospheric concentration of *Cladosporium* spores – *Science* 137/3534–1962–962.

100 RICHARDS, G.A. and F. HALBERG – Variance spectra of oxygen consumption in the American cockroach – *Experientia* 20–1864–40.

1 RICHDALE, L. E. – Seasonal fluctuations in weights of penguins and petrels – *Wilson Bull.* 59–1947–160.

1 RICHTER, C. P. – Behaviouristic study of the activity of the rat – *Comp. Psych. Monogr.* 1–1922.

2 RICHTER, C. P. – Animal behaviour and internal drives – *Quart. Rev. Biol.* 2–1927–307.

3 RICHTER, C. P. – *Experimental Production of Cycles in Behaviour and Physiology in Animals* – Ref. 1953a, p. 36.

4 RICHTER, C. P. – Hormones and rhythms in man and animals – *Rec. Progr. Horm. Res.* 13–1957–105.

5 RICHTER, C. P. – Biological clocks in medicine and psychiatry; shock-phase hypothesis – *Proc. Nat. Acad. Sci.* 46/11–1960–1506.

6 RICHTER, C. P. – The role played by the thyroid gland in the production of gross bodily activity – *Endocrinology* 17–1933–73.

300 RICHTER, G. and A. PIRSON – Enzyme von Hydrodictyon und ihre

Beeinflussung durch Beleuchtungs-
periodik – *Flora* 144–1957–562.

400 RICHTER, H. R. – *Zur elektrischen
Aktivität des Gehirns bei Tag und
Nacht* – Ref. 1953a, p. 199.

1 RIEBOLD, G. – *Einblicke in den periodischen Ablauf des Lebens* – Stuttgart, 1942.

1 RIETSCHEL, H. – Die Sommersterb-
lichkeit der Säuglinge – *Erg. Inn.
Med. Kinderhlk.* 6–1910–369.

1 RILEY, G. M. – Light regulation of
sexual activity in the male sparrow
– *Proc. Soc. Exp. Biol.* 34–1936–331.

100 RILEY, G. M. and E. WITSCHI – Comparative effects of light stimulation
and administration of gonadotropic
hormones on female sparrows –
Endocrinol. 23–1938–618.

1 RINGOEN, A. R. – Effects of continuous green and red light illumination on gonadal response in the
English sparrow – *Physiol. Zool.* 71–
1942–99.

1 RIVERA, J. A. – *Cilia, Ciliated Epithelium and Ciliary Activity* – Pergamon. New York, 1962.

100 RIVERS, T. M. and L. A. ELDRIDGE –
Relation of varicellae to herpes
zoster – *J. Exp. Med.* 49–1929–899.

100 ROBBINS, E. and P. J. MARCUS –
Mitotically synchronized mammalian
cells – *Science* 144/3622–1964–1153.

1 ROBERT, P. – *Les migrations orien-
teés du Hanneton commun* – Ref.
1962d, p. 135.

1 ROBERTS, S. K. DE F. – "Clock"
controlled activity rhythms in the
fruit fly – *Science* 124/3213–1956–
172.

2 ROBERTS, S. K. de F. – *Circadian
Activity Rhythms in Cockroaches* –
Univ. Princeton. Thesis, 1959.

3 ROBERTS, S. K. DE F. – Circadian
activity rhythms in cockroaches I –
J. Cell. Comp. Physiol. 55/1–1960–
99.

1 ROBERTSON, A. G. – The nocturnal
activity of crane-flies – *J. Anim.
Ecol.* 8–1939–300.

1 ROCARD, Y. – *Dynamics of Vibrations* – Lockwood Sons. London,
1960.

2 ROCARD, Y. – *Le signal du Sourcier* –
Dunod, Paris 1964.

1 ROHRACHER, H. – Neuere Untersuchungen über biologische Mikro-

schwingungen – *Anz. Phil. Hist. kl.
Österreich. Akad. Wiss.* 9–1952–153.

2 ROHRACHER, H. – Wärmehaushalt
und Mikrovibration – *Acta Neuroveg.*
11–1955–187.

1 ROMELL, L. G. – Eine neue anschei-
nend tagesautonome Periodizität –
Svensk Bot. Tidskr. 12–1918–446.

2 ROMELL, L. G. – *Nagot om Rytm och
Periodism hos Växter* – Ref. 1941a,
p. 8.

1 ROMEYKE, K. – *Frühjahrseosinophilie beim gesunden Organismus* (Diss.)
– Ernst-Mortiz-Arndt-Univ. Greifswald, 1934.

1 ROSE, M. – Contribution a l'étude
de la biologie du plankton – *Arch.
Zool. Exp. Gen.* 64–1925–387.

100 ROSENBAUM, J. D., B. C. FERGUSON,
R. K. DAVIS and E. C. ROSSMEISL –
The influence of cortisone upon the
diurnal rhythm of renal excretory
function – *J. Clin. Invest.* 31–1952–
507.

1 ROTH, A. – *Rytmiska Företeelser i
Universum* – Ref. 1941a, p. 3.

1 ROWAN, W. – Relation of light to
bird migration and developmental
changes – *Nature* 115–1925–494.

2 ROWAN, W. – On photoperiodism,
reproductive periodicity, and the
annual migration of birds and certain fishes – *Proc. Boston Soc. Nat.
Hist.* 38–1926–147.

3 ROWAN, W. – Experiments in bird
migration I – *Proc. Boston Soc.
Nat. Hist.* 39–1929–151.

4 ROWAN, W. – Experiments in bird
navigation II–III – *Proc. Nat. Acad.
Sci. Wash.* 16–1930–520; 18–1932–
639.

5 ROWAN, W. – Light and seasonal
reproduction in animals – *Biol. Rev.*
13–1938–374.

6 ROWAN, W. – Experiments in bird
migration – *Trans. Roy. Soc. Canada*
40–1946–123.

7 ROWAN, W. – *Reflections on the Biology of Animal Cycles* – Ref. 1954b,
p. 52.

100 ROWLEY, P. T. and B. KLIMAN –
The effect of sodium loading and
depletion on muscular strength and
aldosterone excretion in familial
periodic paralysis – *Am. J. Med.*
28–1960–376.

1 ROYER, C. – Essai sur le sommeil des

plantes – *Ann. Sci. Natur. Bot.* 9V–
1868–345.

100 RUCH, T. C. and J. F. FULTON –
Medical Physiology and Biophysics
– 18th Ed., Saunders. Philadelphia,
1960.

1 RUD, F. – *The Eosinophil Count in
Health and Mental Disease; a Bio-
metrical Study* – Tanum Forl. Oslo,
1947.

1 RUDDER, B. DE – Luftkörperwech-
sel und atmosphärische Unstetig-
keitsschichten als Krankheitsfaktoren – *Erg. Inn. Med. Kinderhlk.*
36–1929–273.

2 RUDDER, B. DE – *Wetter und Jahreszeit als Krankheitsfaktoren* – Berlin,
1931.

3 RUDDER, B. DE – Das Problem der
Saisonkrankheiten – *Strahlenther.* 39
–1931–223.

4 RUDDER, B. DE – Der Wintergipfel
von Krankheiten – *D. Med. Wschr.*
49/–1932–1909.

5 RUDDER, B. De–Atmosphärische und
klimatische Einflüsse auf den kindlichen Organismus für die Auslösung von Krankheiten – *Mschr.
Kinderhlk.* 56–1933–102.

7 RUDDER, B. DE – Die Frühjahreosi-
nophilie – *Klin. Wschr.* 13/5–1934–
167.

6 RUDDER, B. DE – Meteorotrope
Krankheiten – *Der Balneologe* 1–
1934–265.

8 RUDDER, B. DE – Steuerung des Organismus hinsichtlich seiner atmosphärischen Umwelt – *"Normale und
krankhafte Steuerung im menschlichen Organismus".* Fisher. Jena,
1937.

9 RUDDER, B. DE – Der Tuberkulose-
Frühjahrsgipfel – *Beitr. Klin. Tuberk.* 89/3–1937–286.

10 RUDDER, B. DE – *Meteorobiologie des
Menschen* – Berlin, 1938.

11 RUDDER, B. DE – Jahreszeit und
Wetter in der Biologie des Menschen
– *Naturwiss.* 26/41–1938–672.

12 RUDDER, B. DE – Über ein allgemei-
neis Reiz-Reizantwort-Gesetz in der
Biologie – *Naturwiss.* (49–50)–1943–
577.

13 RUDDER, B. DE – *Über sogenannte
"kosmische" Rhythmen beim Menschen* – Thieme. Stuttgart, 1948.

14 RUDDER, B. DE – *Grundriss einer*

Meteorobiologie des Menschen –Berlin, 1952.

15 RUDDER, B. DE – *Epidemiologie und
Klinik der Poliomyelitis* – Verh. 40.
Kongr. Orthop. Ges. Enke. Stutt-
gart, 1953.

16 RUDDER, B. DE – Some aspects on
poliomyelitis waves (Über Polio-
myelitiswellen, Erkenntnisse und
Rätsel)) – *Triangle* 2/1–1955–15.

17 RUDDER, B. DE – Der Mensch im
Jahreszeitenrhythmus – *Stud. Gen.*
8/12–1955–776.

100 RUDDER, B. DE and F. GALLENKAMP
– Die dispositionelle Bedingtheit des
Wintergipfels der Diphterie – *Der
Balneologe* 3/10–1936–464.

101 RUDDER, B. DE and G. A. PETERSEN
– Zur Tagesperiodik der Körper-
temperatur beim Menschen – *Klin.
Wschr.* 14/51–1935–1814.

1 RÜPPELL, W. – Heimfindeversuche
mit Staren – *J. Ornithol.* 83–1935–
462.

2 RÜPPELL, W. – Versuche über Heim-
finden ziehender Nebelkrähen nach
Verfrachtung – *J. Ornithol.* 92–1944
106.

100 RUOSTEENOJA, R., E. LINKO, J.
LIND and A. SOLLBERGER – Heart
volume changes at rest and during
exercise – *Acta Med. Scand.* 162–
1958–263.

1 RUSSEL, B. – *The ABC of Relativity* –
– George, Allen & Unwin. London,
1958.

200 RUSSELL, F. S. – The vertical distribution of plankton in the sea – *Biol.
Rev.* – 2–1927–213.

1 RUSZNYAK, S. – Krankheiten und
Jahreszeiten – *Wien. Arch. Klin.
Med.* 3–1922–379.

1 RUTENFRANZ, J. – Zur Frage einer
Tagesrhythmik des elektrischen
Hautwiderstandes beim Menschen –
Internat. Z. Angew. Physiol. 16–
1955–152.

2 RUTENFRANZ, J. – *The Development
of Circadian System Functions during Infancy and Childhood* – Ref.
1961a, p. 38.

100 RUTENFRANZ, J., T. HELLBRÜGGE
and W. NIGGESCHMIDT – Über die
Tagesrhythmik des elektrischen
Hautwiderstandes bei 11-jährigen
Kindern – *Z. Kinderhlk.* 78–1956–
144.

101 RUTENFRANZ, J. and T. HELLBRÜG-
GE – Über Tagesschwankungen der
Rechengeschwindigkeit bei 11-jähri-
gen Kindern – *Z. Kinderhlk.* 80–
1957–65.

102 RUTENFRANZ, J. and T. HETTINGER
– Die physiologischen Folgen einer
raschen Änderung der Ortszeit
durch Übersee–Luftreisen für die
Leistungsfähigkeit von Sportlern –
Sportmed. 8–1957–195.

1 RYBAK, B. – Les caractères fonda-
mentaux de l'èlectrocardiogramme
déduits de l'analyse expérimentale –
Pathol.-Biol. 11/(9-10)–1963–639.

2 RYBAK, B. – Enregistrement simul-
tané du debit coronaire et des contraction mitrales et ventriculaires du
coeur de lapin extirpé de l'organisme
– *J. Physiol.* 55/2–1963–333.

100 SABIN, F. R., R. S. CUNNINGHAM,
C. J. DOAN and J. A. KINDWALL –
The normal rhythm of the white
blood cells – *Bull. Hopk. Hosp.*
37–1925–14.

1 SACHS, J. – Über das Bewegungs-
organ und die periodischen Bewegungen der Blätter von *Phaseolus*
und *Oxalis* – *Bot. Z.* 15/47–1857–
814.

2 SACHS, J. – Die vorübergehenden
Starre-Zustände periodisch beweg-
licher und reizbarer Pflanzenorgane
II – *Flora* 30–1863–469.

200 SACHS, R. M. – Floral initiation in
Cestrum nocturnum I – *Plant Physiol.* 31–1956–185.

201 SACHS, R. M. – *Dual Day Length
Requirements for Floral Initiation*
– Ref. 1957f, p. 315.

1 SACHSE, P. – *Gleichzeitige Untersuchungen der 24-Stunden-Schwankun-
gen der Blutzuckers und Blutdrucks
beim Menschen* – Diss. Düsseldorf,
1937.

1 SAETREN, H. – Organismens dögns-
rytmer – *Nord. Med.* 67/10–1962–
318.

100 SAGE, A. P., K. E. JUSTICE and J. L.
MELSA – Study and research on
electronic simulation of the biologic
clock I–II – Wright-Patterson Air
Force Base, Ohio, Repts. ASD–
TDR–62–191; ASD–TDR–63–136.

1 SAGROMSKY, H. – Der Einfluss des
Lichtes auf die rhythmische Koni-
dienbildung von *Penicillium* – *Flora*
139–1952–30.

2 SAGROMSKY, H. – Lichtinduzierte
Ringbildung bei Pilzen II – *Flora*
139–1952–560.

3 SAGROMSKY, H. – Wodurch entstehen "Hexenringe" bei Pilzen? –
Umschau 13–1956–396.

4 SAGROMSKY, H. – Zur Lichtinduzier-
ten Ringbildung bei Pilzen III, V –
Biol. Zentr. Blatt 75/(7–8)–1956–
385; 78/4–1959–589.

5 SAGROMSKY, H. – Lichtinduzierte
Ringbildung IV – *Ber.D.Bot.Ges.*
72/4–1959–169.

6 SAGROMSKY, H. – Durch Licht–Dun-
kel-Wechsel induzierter Rhythmus
in der Entleerung der Tetrasporan-
gien von *Nitophyllum punctatum* –
Publ. Staz. Zool. Napoli 32–1960–
29.

7 SAGROMSKY, H. – Tagesperiodische
Ausschüttung der Tetrasporen bei
Rotalgen – *Naturwiss.* 47/6–1960–
141.

1 SAHLENAU, V. – *Metode Matematice
in Cercetarea Medico–Biologica* –
Ed. Medicala. Bucarest, 1957.

1 SAINT GIRONS, H. – Données histo-
physiologiques sur le cycle annuel
des glands endocrines et de leurs
effecteurs chez l'orvet – *Arch.
d'Anat. Micr. Morph. Exper.*
52/1–1963–1.

1 SALANKI, J. – Die Rolle der Afferen-
tation in der Regulation des lang-
samen Rhythmus der periodischen
Aktivität der Muskeln – *Acta Physiol. Hung.* 16/suppl. 10–1959–113.

2 SALANKI, J. – *On the Regulation of the
Slow Rhythm of the Periodic Activity
in Fresh-Water Mussel* – Ref. 1960a,
p. 129.

3 SALANKI, J. – On the dependence of
the slow rhythm of periodic activity
of *Anodonta cygnea* on the condition of sulfhydryl groups in protein
bodies – *J. Gen. Biol. Acad. USSR*
21/3–1960–229.

4 SALANKI, J. – The effect of serotonin
and catecholamines on the nervous
control of periodic activity in
fresh-water mussel – *Comp. Biochem. Physiol.* 8–1963–163.

1 SALISBURY, F. B. – *Influence of Certain Growth Regulators on Flowering
of the Cocklebur* – Ref. 1957f, p. 381.

2 SALISBURY, F.B. – *The flowering pro-*

cess – Perganon, London 1963.

1 SAND, A. – The function of the ampullae of Lorenzini, with some observations on the effect of temperature on sensory rhythms – *Proc. Roy. Soc.* 125–1938–524.

100 SANDEEN, M. J., G. C. STEPHENS and F. A. BROWN JR – Persistent daily and tidal rhythms of oxygen consumption in two species of marine snails – *Physiol. Zool.* 27–1954–350.

1 SANDOZ, A. G. – *Probleme der Photosynthese* – Ausgewählte Kapitel aus der allgemeinen Biochemie –3/4– 277.

1 SANTSCHI, F. – Comment s'orientent les formis? – *Rev. Suisse Zool.* 19– 1911–303.

1 SARGENT, F. D. – Biometeorology – *AIBS Bull.* 13/3–1963–20.

1 SAUER, F. – Zugorientierung einer Mönchsgrasmücke unter künstlichem Sternehimmel – *Naturwiss.* 43 –1956–231.

2 SAUER, F. – Die Sternenorientierung nächtlich ziehender Grasmücken – *Z. Tierpsychol.* 14–1957–29.

3 SAUER, F. – Astronavigatorische Orientierung einer unter künstlichen Sternenhimmel verfrachteten Klappergrasmücke – *Naturwiss.* 44– 1957–71.

4 SAUER, F. – Celestial navigation by birds – *Scient. Am.* 199–1958–42.

100 SAUER, F. and E. – Zur Frage der nächtlichen Zugorientierung von Grasmücken – *Rev. Suisse Zool.* 62– 1955–250.

101 SAUER, F. and E. – Nächtliche Zugorientierung europäischer Vögel in Südwestafrika – *Vogelwarte* 20–1959 –4.

102 SAUER, F. and E. – *Star Navigation of Nocturnal Migrating Birds* –Ref. 1960c, p. 463.

200 SAUER, K. – *Untersuchungen über den 24-Stunden-Rhythmus der Menschen unter besonderer Berücksichtigung des Kreislaufs* – Diss. Tübingen, 1941.

400 SAUER, E. G. F. – *Geographische Prägung, Tag- und Nachtorientierung trans-ozeanisch wandernder pazifischer Goldregenpfeiffer* – Ref. 1962d, p. 280.

100 SAVAGE, I. R., M. M. RAO and F. HALBERG – Test of peak values in

physiopathologic time series – *Univ. Minn. Dept. Stat. Rep.* 3–1962.

101 SAVAGE, I. R., M. M. RAO and F. HALBERG – Test of peak values in physiopathologic time series – *Exp. Med. and Surg.* 20–1962–309.

1 SAVVATEEV, V.B. – On diurnal rhythmicity of conditioned reflex activity in hens [in Russian]–*Biul. Eksp. Biol. Med.* 44–1957–18.

1 SCHADE – Untersuchungen in der Erkältungsfrage–*Münch. Med. Wschr.* 1919–1021.

100 SCHAEFER, H. F. and G. HILDEBRANDT – Praktisch-balneologische Erfahrungen mit dem Puls-Atem-Quotienten – *Arch. Physical. Ther.* 6/5–1954–375.

200 SCHAEFER, K. E. – *Rhythm of Respiration and Respiratory Response to CO_2* – Ref. 1955a, p. 142.

201 SCHAEFER, K. E. – *Man's Dependence on the Earthly Atmosphere* – McMillan. New York, 1962.

500 SCHÄFER, K. H. and R. NETH – *Tagesrhythmus im Serumeisenspiegel* – Ref. 1963a.

1 SCHARRER, E. – *General Concepts and Historical Background* – Ref. 1963b.

1 SCHALTENBRAND, G. (Ed.) – Zeit in nervenärztlicher Sicht – Enke, Stuttgart 1963.

100 SCHECHTER, M. S., S. R. DUTKY and W. N. SULLIVAN – Recording circadian rhythms of the cockroach with a capacity-sensing devise – *J. Econ. Entomol.* 56/1–1963.

1 SCHEIDT, W. – *Die menschlichen Inbilder* (Naturgeschichte des Lebenslaufs) Urban & Schwarzenberg 1954 and 1965.

1 SCHENK, P. – Der Einfluss der Tageszeit auf den Menschen –*Grenzgeb. Med.* 2–1949–138.

100 SCHERBAUM, O. and E. ZEUTHEN – Induction of synchronous cell division in mass culture of *Tetrahymena* – *Exp. Cell. Res.* 6–1954–221.

1 SCHIESSL, G. – *Über tagesperiodische Veränderungen des Blutzuckers bei Schulkindern* – Diss. Ludwig-Maximilian–Univ. München, 1959.

1 SCHILDMACHER, H. – Zur Physiologie des Zugtriebes I–IV – *Vogelzug* 4–1933–21; 5–1934–1; 8–1937–107; 9–1938–146.

2 SCHILDMACHER, H. – Über die künst-

liche Aktivierung der Hoden einiger Vogelarten im Herbst durch Belichtung und Vorderlappenhormone – *Biol. Zbl.* 59–1939–653.

3 SCHILDMACHER, H. – Photoperiodizität des Stoffwechsels beim Vogel – *Acta* 11*th Internat. Ornithol. Congr.* Basel 1954, p. 655.

4 SCHILDMACHER, H. – Physiologische Untersuchungen am Grünfinken im künstlichen Kurztag und nach "hormonaler" Sterilisierung – *Biol. Zbl.* 75–1956–327.

100 SCHILDMACHER, H. and W. RAUTENBERG – Legetätigkeit und Fettansatz der Hausgans unter dem Einfluss künstlich veränderter Photoperiode – *Arch. Geflügelzucht und Kleintierkde* 6/(1–2)–1957–1.

1 SCHLIEPER, H. – *Der Rhythmus des Lebendigen* – Diederichs. Jena, 1909.

1 SCHMID, A. – *Biologische Wirkungen der Luft-Elektrizität* – Haupt. Bern, 1936.

2 SCHMID, A. – Über direkte Einwirkungen kurzdauernder solarer Vorgänge auf das menschliche Leben – *Schweiz. Arch. Angev. Wiss. Techn.* 4–1937–1.

200 SCHMID JR., A – *Die Bedeutung der Periodik des diastolischen Blutdruckes* – Ref. 1955a, p. 143.

300 SCHMID JR., A. and P. COTTIER – Besonderheiten in der Korrelation zwischen Blutdruckperiodik und Nierendurchblutung – *Cardiologia* 27/(4–5)–1955–230.

301 SCHMID JR., A. and F. REUBI – Der Zusammenhang zwischen Blutdrucksperiodik und Nierendurchblutung – *Schweiz. Med. Wschr.* 84/28–1954–760.

302 SCHMID JR., A. and R. SAUTER – Pathogenetischer Deutungsversuch gewisser Hypertonieformen auf Grund einer "Anpassungsstörung" der Arteriolen – *Helv. Med. Acta* 21/3–1954–223.

1 SCHMIDLE, A. – Die Tagesperiodizität der asexuellen Reproduktion von *Pilobolus sphaerosporus* – *Arch. Mikrobiol.* 16–1951–80.

1 SCHMID-MONNRAD E. – Einfluss der Jahreszeit und der Schule auf das Wachstum – *Jb. Kinderhlk.* 40–1895–84.

100 SCHMIDT, R.A. and T.J. COHEN –

Particle accretion rates, variation with latitude – *Science* 145/3635–1964–924.

1 SCHMIDT-KOENIG, K. – *Neuere Aspekte über die Orientierungsleistungen von Brieftauben* – Ref. 1962d, p. 286.

2 SCHMIDT-KOENIG, K. – Sun compass orientation of pigeons upon equatorial and transequatorial displacement – *Biol. Bull.* 124/3–1963–311.

3 SCHMIDT-KOENIG, K. – On the role of the loft, the distance and site of release in pigeon homing – *Biol. Bull.* 125/1–1963–154.

4 SCHMIDT-KOENIG, K. – Der Einfluss experimentell veränderter Zeitschätzung auf das Heimfindevermögen bei Brieftauben – *Naturwiss.* 45–1958–47.

5 SCHMIDT-KOENIG, K. – Experimentelle Einflussnahme auf die 24-Stunden-Periodik bei Brieftauben und deren Auswirkungen unter besonderer Berücksichtigung des Heimfindevermögens – *Z. Tierpsychol.* 15–1958–301.

6 SCHMIDT-KOENIG, K. – *Internal Clocks and Homing* – Ref. 1960c, p. 389.

7 SCHMIDT-KOENIG, K. – The sun–azimut compass; one factor in the orientation of homing pigeons – *Science* 131/3403–1960–826.

8 SCHMIDT-KOENIG, K. – Sun navigation in birds? – *Nature* 190–1961–1025.

1 SCHMITT, O. H. – *Biophysical and Mathematical Models of Circadian Rhythms* – Ref. 1960c p. 207.

2 SCHMITT, O. H. – *Adaptive Analog Models for Biological Rhythms* – Ref. 1961c, p. 846.

3 SCHMITT, O. H. – *Oscillatory Systems as Models of Periodicity* – Ref. 1961a p. 27.

4 SCHMITT, O.H. – Averaging techniques employing several simultaneous physiological variaties – *Ann. N.Y. Acad. Sci.* 115/2–1964–952.

1 SCHMITZ, H. – Die periodischen Bewegungen der Blätter von *Coleus penzigii* – *Z. Bot.* 27–1934–353.

200 SCHMITZ, J. – Über Beziehungen zwischen Blütenbildung in verschiedene Licht-Dunkelkombinationen und Atmungsrhythmik bei wechseln-

den photoperiodischen Bedingungen – *Planta* 39–1951–271.

1   SCHNEIDER, C. F. – Ein Beitrag zur Ermittelung der Sterblichkeitsverhältnisse in Berlin nach den Tageszeiten – *Arch. Path. Anat. Physiol. Klin. Med.* 16–1895–95.

200   SCHNEIDER, G. H. – Die Orientierung der Brieftauben – *Z. Psych. Phys. Sinnesorgane* 40–1906–252.

2   SCHNEIDER, C. – *Periodizität des Lebens und der Kultur* – Akad. Verlagsgesell. Leipzig, 1926.

400   SCHNEIDER, F. – *Ultraoptische Orientierung des Maikäfers in künstlichen elektrischen und magnetischen Feldern* –Ref. 1962d, p. 147.

1   SCHÖN, W. J. – Periodische Schwankungen der Photosynthese und Atmung bei *Hydrodictyon* – *Flora* 142–1955–347.

1   SCHOSTAKOWITSCH, W. B. – Periodische Schwankungen in den vitalen Prozessen und kosmische Einflüsse auf die Lebewesen – *Bioklim. Beiblätter* 3–1936–137.

100   SCHOUR, I and S.R. STEADMAN – The growth pattern and daily rhythm of the incisor of the rat – *Anat. Rev.* 63–1935–325.

1   SCHOVE, D.J. – *Solar cycle and the spectrum of time since 200 B.C.* – Ref. 1961e, p. 107.

1   SCHÜBLER, G. – *Einfluss des Mondes auf die Veränderungen unserer Atmosphäre* – Baumgärtner. Leipzig, 1830.

100   SCHULMAN, J. L. and E. D. KILBOURNE – *Seasonal Variations in the Transmission of Influenza Virus Infection in Mice* – Ref. 1963c.

1   SCHULTE, W. – *Schlafrhythmusstörungen* – Ref. 1955a, p. 148.

1   SCHULTZ, N. A. – I globuli bianchi e le macchie solari – *Geofisica Meteorologica* 7/(5–6)–1960–2.

2   SCHULTZ, N. A. – Lymphocytose relative et activité solaire – *Rev. Méd. (Nancy)* 1961–541.

3   SCHULTZ, N. A. – L'activité solaire et les maladies cardio–vasculaires – *Ann. Méd. (Nancy)* 1962–177.

4   SCHULTZ, N. A. – Leukozytenteste der Sonnenaktivität – *Fol. Haematol.* 79/4–1962–401.

500   SCHULTZ, N. A.–Variabilité de la formule du sang normal au cours des années dernières – *Ann. Méd. (Nancy)* 1963–822.

200   SCHULTZ, J. H. – Lebensrhythmus und Psychotherapie – *D. Med. Wschr.* 64–1938–996.

100   SCHULZ, K. H. – *Untersuchungen über die biologische Wirkung der Elektro-Aerosole und der direkten Aufladungstherapie auf das vegetative Nervensystem* – Ref. 1963c.

100   SCHUNK, J. and G. SCHMITT – Tagesschwankungen der Magenazidität – *D. Med. Wschr.* 80–1955–347.

1   SCHUSTER, A. – On the investigation of hidden periodicities with application to a supposed 26 day period of meteorological phenomena – *Terr. Magn.* 3–1898–13.

2   SCHUSTER, A. – The periodogram of the magnetic declination as obtained from the records of the Greenwich Observatory during the years 1871–1895 – *Trans. Cambr. Philos. Soc.* 18–1900–107.

3   SCHUSTER, A. – On the periodicities of sun-spots – *Philos. Trans. Roy. Soc.* 206A–1906–69.

4   SCHUSTER, A. – The periodogram and its optical analogy – *Proc. Roy. Soc.* 77A–1906–136.

5   SCHUSTER, A. – On sun-spot periodicities – *Proc. Roy. Soc.* 77A–1906–141.

1   SCHWABE, W. W. – Photoperiodic cycles of lengths differing from 24-hours in relation to the endogenous rhythms – *Physiol. Plant.* 8–1955–263.

1   SCHWARTZE, A. – *Vegetative Tagesrhythmik bei erholungsbedürftigen Kindern während einer Klimakur an der Nordsee* – Diss. Hamburg, 1960.

1   SCHWASSMANN, H. O. – *Environmental Cues in the Orientation Rhythm of Fish* – Ref. 1960c, p. 443.

1   SCHWEMMLE, B. – Über die tagesperiodischen Änderungen des Reaktionsvermögens von Keimpflanzen auf niedrige Temperatur – *Planta* 43–1953–98.

2   SCHWEMMLE, B. – Zur Temperaturabhängigkeit der Blütenbildung und der endogenen Tagesrhythmik bei *Kalanchoë blossfeldiana* – *Naturwiss.* 44–1957–356.

3   SCHWEMMLE, B. – *Thermoperiodic*

Effects and Circadian Rhythms in Flowering of Plants – Ref. 1960c, p. 239.

4 SCHWEMMLE, B. – Unterschiedliche Schwankungen der Temperaturempfindlichkeit bei Lang- und Kurztagspflanzen – *Naturwiss.* 47–1960–68.

100 SCHWEMMLE, B. and O. L. LANGE – Neue Beobachtungen über die endogene Tagesrhythmik – *Nachr. Ges. Wiss. Göttingen, Math.-Phys. Kl.* 1959–29.

101 SCHWEMMLE, B. and O. L. LANGE – Endogen-tagesperiodische Schwankungen der Hitzeresistenz bei *Kalanchoë blossfeldiana* – *Planta* 53–1959–134.

102 SCHWEMMLE, B. and K. MEYER – Tagesperiodische Änderungen des Temperatur-Reaktions-vermögens bei Keimpflanzen – *Naturwiss.* 47–1960–69.

1 SCHWING, H. – *Über Biorhythmen und deren technische Anwendung* – Leeman. Zürich, 1939.

1 SCOTT, B. I. H. – Electric oscillations by plant roots and a possible feedback mechanism for them – *Austr. J. Biol. Sci.* 10/12–1957–164.

2 SCOTT, B. I. H. – *Feedback-Induced Oscillations of Five-Minute Period in the Electric Field of the Bean Root* – Ref. 1961c, p. 890.

3 SCOTT, B. I. H. – Electricity in plants – *Sci. Am.* 207/4–1962–107.

100 SCOTT, B. I. H., A. L. McAULEY and P. JEYES – Correlation between the electric current generated by a bean root growing in water and the rate of elongation of the root – *Austr. J. Biol. Sci.* 8/1–1955–36.

101 SCOTT, B. I. H. and D. W. MARTIN – Bioelectric fields of bean roots and their relation to salt accumulation – *Austr. J. Biol. Sci.* 15/1–1962–83.

300 SCOTT, H. M. and L. F. PAYNE – Light in relation to the experimental modification of the breeding season of turkeys – *Poultry Sci.* 16–1937–90.

400 SCOTT, W. N. – An experimental analysis of the factors governing the hour of emergence of adult insects from their pupae – *Trans. Roy(London) Entomol. Soc.* 85–1936–303.

1 SCRUGGS, W. M. – The epithelial

components and their seasonal changes in the pituitary gland of the carp and goldfish – *J. Morph.* 88–1951–441.

1 SCURFIELD, G. – The effects of temperature and daylength on species of *Eucalyptus* – *Austr. J. Bot.* 9–1961–37.

100 SEARS, F. W. and M. W. ZEMANSKY – *University Physics* – Addison–Wesley. Reading, Mass., 1957.

100 SEASHORE, C. E. and C. H. KENT – Periodicity and progressive change in continuous mental work – *Psychol. Rev.* 6/5 suppl.–1905–47.

100 SECKEL, H. P. G. and K. KATO – Development of the diurnal cycle of liver function in nursing rats – – *Arch. Pathol.* 25–1938–347.

1 SEIBERT, H. C. – Differences between migrant and non-migrant birds in food and water intake at various photoperiods and temperatures – *Auk* 66–1949–128.

1 SEIDL, E. C. – *Über tagesrhythmische Veränderungen der Körpertemperatur im Kindesalter* – München, 1958.

1 SEIFRITZ, W. – A theory of protoplasmic streaming – *Science* 86–1937 –397.

2 SEIFRITZ, W. – Protoplasmic streaming – *Bot. Review* 9–1943–49.

3 SEIFRITZ, W. – in Frey-Wyssling, *"Deformation and Flow in Biological Systems* – North-Holland Publ. Amsterdam, 1952 (pp 3-156).

4 SEIFRITZ, W. – The physical chemistry of cytoplasm – *Handb. Pflanzenphysiol.* 1–1955–340.

1 SELBACH, H. – *Endogene Rhythmik in der Neuropsychiatrie* – Ref. 1955a. p. 18.

2 SELBACH, H. – *The Principle of Relaxation Oscillation as a Special Instance of the Law of Initial Value in Cybernetic Functions* – Ref. 1961c, p. 1221.

100 SELBACH, H. and C. – Das Regelkreis-Prinzip in der Neuropsychiatrie – *Wien. Klin. Wschr.* 69/(38–39)–1957–727.

100 SELHIME, A. G., M. H. MUMA, and D. W. CLANCY – Biological, chemical and ecological studies on the predatory thrips in Florida citrus groves – *Ann. Entomol. Soc. Am.* 56/5–1963–709.

1 SELYE, H. – *The Physiology and Pathology of Exposure to Stress* – Med. Publ. Inc. Montreal, 1950.

1 SEMON, R. – Über die Erblichkeit der Tagesperiode – *Biol. Zbl.* 25–1905–241.

2 SEMON, R. – Hat der Rhythmus der Tageszeiten bei Pflanzen erbliche Eindrücke hinterlassen? – *Biol. Zbl.* 28–1908–225.

100 SEYDERHOLM, R. and C. OESTRICH – Das Tagesprofil des Blutzuckers beim Gesunden und beim Diabetiker – *Z. Klin. Med.* 109–1929–35.

1 SHAKHBAZOV, V.G. – The reaction to the length of daylight and the light receptor of the pupa of the Chinese oak silkworm [in Russian]–*Dokl. Akad. Nauk.SSSR* 140/1–1961–249.

1 SHAKHNOWITSCH – Ein seltner Fall von intermetthierender Paraplegie – *Russ. Vratsh.* 32–1882–537.

100 SHANNON, C. E. and W. WEAVER – *The Mathematical Theory of Communication* – Univ. Illinois Press. Urbana, 1959.

1 SHAPIRO, A. – *Observations on some Periodic and Non-Periodic Phenomena in Human Sleep* – Ref. 1961c, p. 1139.

1 SHARP, G. W. G. – *Simultaneous Reversal of Diurnal Rhythms of Urine and Electrolyte Excretion, Leucocytes and Sleep/Wakefulness* – Ref. 1960a, p. 133.

2 SHARP, G. W. G. – Reversal of diurnal rhythms of water and electrolyte excretion in man – *J. Endocrinol.* 31–1960–97.

3 SHARP, G. W. G. – Reversal of diurnal leucocyte variations in man – *J. Endocrinol.* 21–1960–107.

4 SHARP, G. W. G. – The effect of light on diurnal leucocyte variations – *J. Endocrinol.* 21–1960–213.

5 SHARP, G. W. G. – The effect of light on the morning increase in urine flow – *J. Endocrinol.* 21–1960–219.

6 SHARP, G. W. G. – Persistence of the diurnal rhythms of flow of urine – *Nature* 193–1962–37.

700 SHARP, G. W. G. – Reversal of diurnal temperature rhythms in man – *Nature* 190/4771–1961–146.

100 SHARP, G. W. G., S. A. SLORACH and H. J. VIPOND – Diurnal rhythms of keto- and ketogenic steroid excretion and the adaptation to changes of the activity–sleep routine – *J. Endocrinol.* 22–1961–377.

1 SHAW, A. F. B. – The diurnal tides of the leucocytes of man – *J. Path.* 30–1927–1.

100 SHIPTON, H. W., J. W. EMDE and G. E. FOLK JR. – A multiple point recorder of small animal locomotor activity – *Proc. Iowa Acad. Sci.* 66–1959–407.

1 SHIRLEY, M. – Studies in activity II – *J. Comp. Psychol.* 8–1928–159.

1 SHÖN, W. J. – Periodische Schwankungen der Photosynthese und Atmung bei *Hydrodicton* – *Flora* 142–1955–347.

100 SHOLITON, L. J., E. E. WERK JR. and R. T. MARNELL – Diurnal variation of adrenocortical function in non-endocrine disease states – *Metabolism* 10/8–1961–632.

100 SHORR, E., A. R. BERNHEIM and H. TAUSSKY – The relation of urinary citric acid excretion to the menstrual cycle and the steroidal reproductive hormones – *Science* 95/2476–1942–606.

1 SHULL, F. – The effect of intensity and duration of light and of duration of darkness, partly modified by temperature, upon wing-production in aphids – *Roux' Arch. Entw.–Mech.* 115–1929–825.

100 SHWAYRI, E. and N. TUTUNJI – Periodic disease – *Arch. Int. Med.* 95–1955–337.

100 SHY, G. M., T. WANKO, P. T. ROWLEY and A. G. ENGEL – Studies in familial periodic analysis – *Exp. Neurol.* 3–1961–53.

100 SIDERIS, C. P., H. J. YOUNG and H. H. Q. CHUN – Diurnal changes and growth rates associated with ascorbic acid, titrable acidity, carbohydrate and nitrogenous fractions in the leaves of *Ananas comosus* – *Plant. Physiol.* 23–1948–38.

1 SIEBER H. – Über den normalen Rest-N-Gehalt des Blutes und seine Tagesschwankungen bei Hühnern – Diss. Wien, 1938. (*Wien. Tierärztl. Mschr.* 26–1939–636).

1 SIEGAL, S. – Periodic disease–*JAMA* 141–1949–738.

100 SIEGEL, R. B. and A. M. GUHL –
The measurement of some diurnal
rhythms in the activity of white
leghorn cockerels – *Poultry Sci.* 35–
1956–1340.

200 SIEGEL, S. – *Non-Parametric Statistics for the Behavioral Sciences* –
McGraw Hill. New York, 1956.

400 SIEGEL, P.S. – Food intake in the
rat in relation to the dark-light
cycle – *J. Comp. Physiol. Psychol.*
54–1961–294.

500 SIEGEL, P.S. and H.L. STUCKEY –
The diurnal course of water and food
intake in the normal mature rat –
J. Comp. Physiol. Psychol. 40–1947–
365.

1 SIEMS, O. H. – *Der 24-Stunden-Rhyth-
mus der Todesstunde* – Diss. Hamburg, 1949.

100 SIIVONEN, L. and J. KOSKIMIES –
*Population Fluctuations and the
Lunar Cycle* – Pap. Game-Res. Hels-
ingfors, 1955, no. 14.

100 SIMON, C. W. and W. H. EMMONS, –
EEG, consciousness, and sleep –
Science 124–1956–1066.

200 SIMON, S. V. – Studien über die Periodizität der Lebensprozesse der in
dauernd feuchten Tropengebieten
heimischen Bäume – *Jb. Wiss. Bot.*
54–1914–71.

1 SIMPSON, G. E. – Diurnal variations
in the rate of urine excretion for
two hour intervals – *J. Biol. Chem.*
59–1924–107.

2 SIMPSON, G. E. – The effect of sleep
on urinary chlorides and pH–*J.
Biol. Chem.* 67/2–1926–505.

300 SIMPSON, S. and J. J. GALBRAITH –
An investigation in the diurnal
variation of the body temperature
of nocturnal and other birds, and a
few mammals – *J. Physiol.* 33–
1905–25.

100 SINNOTT, E. W. and K. S. WILSON –
Botany, Principles and Problems –
McGraw-Hill. New York, 1955.

1 SIRÉN, G. – Tree rings and climate
forecasts – *New. Sci.* 19/346–1963–
18.

100 SIROHI, G. S. and K. C. HAMNER –
Inhibitory effects of long days on
the flowering of soybean – *Proc.
9th Internat. Bot. Congr. 2, Univ.
Toronto Press.* Toronto, 1959.

101 SIROHI, G. S. and K. C. HAMNER –

Automatic device for controlling
lengths of light and dark periods in
cycles of any desired duration –
Plant Phys. 35–1960–276.

100 SIROTA, J. H., D. S. BALDWIN and
H. VILLARREAL – Diurnal varia-
tions of renal function in man – *J.
Clin. Invest.* 29–1950–187.

100 SJÖGREN, B., T. NORDENSKJÖLD, H.
HOLMGREN and J. MÖLLERSTRÖM –
Beitrag zur Kenntnis der Leber-
rhythmik – *Pflüger's Arch.* 240–
1938–427.

100 SKOOG, F., T. C. BROYER and K. A.
GROSSENBACHER – Effects of auxin
on rates, periodicity and osmotic
relations in exudation – *Am. J. Bot.*
25–1938–749.

1 SKRABAL, A. – *Homogenkinetik* –
Steinkopff. Leipzig, 1941.

1 SKRAMLIK, E. VON – Über die Stren-
ge des Rhythmus bei biologischen
Vorgängen – *Naturwiss.* 28–1940–
759.

1 SLAVINA, E. E. – On diurnal variations in the excitability of the cerebral hemispheres and the effect of
lack of sleep – *Arkh. Biol. Nauk*
41–1936–9.

1 SLATER, L. – *Biotelemetry* – Pergamon Press. New York, 1962.

1 SLATYER, R.O. – The significance
of the permanent wilting percentage
in studies of plant and soil water relations – *Bot. Rev.* 23/10–1957–586.

1 SLOBODKIN, L. B. – Population dynamics in *Daphnia Obtusa* Kurz –
Biol. Monogr. 24/1–1954–69.

2 SLOBODKIN, L. B. – Conditions for
population equilibrium – *Ecology*
36/3–1955–530.

3 SLOBODKIN, L. B. – Ecological energy
relationships at the population
level – *Am. Naturalist* 94/876–1960
–213.

100 SLOBODKIN, L. B. and S. RICHMAN –
The effect of removal of fixed percentages of the newborn on size and
variability in populations of *Daphnia pulicaria* (Forbes) – *Limnol.
Oceanogr.* 1/3–1956–209.

100 SLONIM, A. D., R. P. OLNJANSKAJA
and S. O. RUTTENBURG – *Versuche
zur Erforschung der Dynamik der
physiologischen Funktionen des Menschen unter den Bedingungen des
Transpolargebietes* – Bykow, Ref. 1,

p. 206.

101 SLONIM, A. D. and O. P. STSCHERBA-
KOWA – *Beobachtungen über den
Nachtschlaf bei Affen* – Bykow, Ref.
1, p. 155.

102 SLONIM, A. D. and O. P. STSCHER-
BAKOWA – *Stoffwechsel und physiologische Besonderheiten des Winter-
schlafs beim Dachs* – Bykow, Ref. 1,
p. 166.

1 SLUTZKY E. – The summation of
random causes as the source of
cycle processes – *Econometria* 5–
1937–105.

100 SMITH, C. and McDOWELL – Normal
rhythm of white blood cells in
women – *Arch. Int. Med.* 43–1929–
68.

101 SMITH, C. and PRIEST – Further
observation on the normal variations in erythrocyte values in
women – *Am. J. Physiol.* 99–(1931–
1932)–562.

200 SMITH, C. A. B. – *Biomathematics* –
Griffin. London, 1954.

400 SMITH, O. J. M. – *Feedback Control
Systems* – Mc Graw-Hill. New York,
1958.

700 SMITH, J. T., D. T. MAYER and C. P.
MERILAN – Seasonal variation in
the succinic dehydrogenase activity
of bovine spermatozoa – *J. Dairy.
Sci.* 40–1957–516.

1 SNEDECOR, G. W. – *Statistical Methods* – 4th Ed. Iowa State College
Press. Iowa, 1948.

1 SNYDER, W. E. – Effect of light and
temperature on floral initiation in
Biloxi soy bean – *Bot. Gaz.* 102–
1940–302.

2 SNYDER, W. E. – Mechanism of the
photoperiodic response of *Plantago
lunceolata* L.; a long-day plant –
Am. J. Bot. 35–1948–520.

1 SOLLBERGER, A. – *Tagesschwankungen in der Streuung biologischer
Werte* – Ref. 1953a, p. 69.

2 SOLLBERGER, A. – A study of biological variation – *Acta Anat.* 22–
1954–127.

3 SOLLBERGER, A. – *Studies of Temporal Variations in Biological Variates*
– Suppl. Ref. 1955a.

4 SOLLBERGER, A. – *24-Hour Rhythm
of Citric Acid in Diabetes* – Ref.
1955a, p. 149.

5 SOLLBERGER, A. – Statistical aspects

of diurnal biorhythm – *Acta Anat.*
23–1955–97.

6 SOLLBERGER, A. – Diurnal changes
in biological variability – *Acta Anat.*
23–1955–259.

7 SOLLBERGER, A. – *Outlines of a Statistical Method of Separating Exogenous
and Endogenous Components in Biological Cycles* – Ref. 1960a, p. 138.

8 SOLLBERGER, A. – Frequency distributions arising from biological
movement – *Acta Morph. Neerl.-
Scand.* 3/2–1960–179.

9 SOLLBERGER, A. – *General Properties
of Biological Rhythms* – Ref. 1961c,
p. 757.

10 SOLLBERGER, A. – Symposium du
"Cold Spring Harbor" sur le temps
biologique – *Concours Méd.* 83/16–
1961–2320.

11 SOLLBERGER, A. – VIIe Conférence
internationale de la société des
rythmes biologiques – *Concours
Méd.* 83/17–1961–2457.

12 SOLLBERGER, A. – *Biological Rhythms
in Medicine* – Ref. 1962a.

13 SOLLBERGER, A. – Conférence sur les
fonctions rythmiques du système
biologique – *Concours Méd.* 84/46–
1962–6223.

14 SOLLBERGER, A. – Los ritmos biologicos en medicina – *Fol. Clin.
Internac.* 13/1–1963–18.

15 SOLLBERGER, A. – *The Control of
Circadian Glycogen Rhythms* – Ref.
1963b, p. 519.

16 SOLLBERGER, A. – Biologische Rhythmen in der Medizin – *Hippokrates*
34/16–1963–629.

17 SOLLBERGER, A. – Ritmos biologicos
en medicina – *Prensa Med. Mex.*
28/(3–4)–1963–140.

18 SOLLBERGER, A. – *Statistical Peculiarities of Time Series and the Problem
of identifying External Influences
in Biological Rhythm Data* – Ref.
1963a.

19 SOLLBERGER, A. – *Significance of Biological Rhythm Study for Human
Biometeorology* – Ref. 1963c.

100 SOLLBERGER, A. and U. STRÖMBERG
– The biological moving variate –
Acta Anat. 29–1957–20.

100 SONDEN, K. and R. TIGERSTEDT –
Die Respiration und der Gesamt-
stoffwechsel des Menschen III, –
Skand. Arch. Physiol. 6–1895–1.

1   SONESSON, B. – Förlossningsfrekven-
    sen under olika årstider – *Svenska
    Läkartidning* 55/31–1956–1966.

1   SOTAVALTA, O. – Recordings of high
    wing-stroke and thoracic vibration
    frequency in some midges – *Biol.
    Bull.* 104–1953–439.

100 SOTGIU, G. and A. LODI – *Le Bio-
    rythme Saisonnier du Cortico–Sur-
    rénal* – Ref. 1960a, p. 145.

1   SOUTHERN, H. N. – Periodicity of
    refection in the wild rabbit – *Natu-
    re* 149–1942–553.

1   SPEAR, J. – *Metabolic Aspects of
    Photoperiodism in Plants* – Ref.
    1957f, p. 289.

100 SPEAR, J. and K. V. THIMANN – The
    interrelation between CO_2 meta-
    bolism and photoperiodism in *Ka-
    lanchoë* – *Plant Physiol.* 29–1954–
    414.

1   SPEIRS, J. M. – Fluctuations in
    numbers of birds in the Toronto
    region – *Auk* 56–1939–411.

1   SPENCER, W. P. – Day and night
    periodicity in four species of fresh-
    water fish–*Anat. Rec.* 44–1929–197.

2   SPENCER, W. P. – Diurnal activity
    in fresh-water fishes – *Ohio J. Sci.*
    39–1939–119.

100 SPRENGER, F. and W. GOCKELL –
    Welchen Vorteil bietet die abend-
    liche Injection von Penicillin – *Die
    Medizinische* 1954–126.

1   STACEY, C. M. – Cyclical measures:
    some tidal aspects concerning equi-
    noctial years – *Ann. N.Y. Acad.
    Sci.* 105/7–1963–421.

1   STADDON, J.E.R. – Reinforcement as
    input: Cyclic variable-interval sche-
    dule – *Science* 145/3630–1964–410.

1   STADLER, D. R. – Genetic control of
    a cyclic growth pattern in *Neuros-
    pora* – *Nature* 184–1959–170.

1   STAEHELIN, J. E. – *Über die Beein-
    flussung der Periodizität bei psy-
    chischen Störungen* – Ref. 1953a, p.
    119.

1   STALFELDT, M. G. – Ein neuer Fall
    von tagesperiodischem Rhythmus –
    Svensk Bot. Tidskr. 14–1920–186.

2   STALFELT, M. G. – Studien über die
    Periodizität der Zellteilung – *Kungl.
    Svenska Vetenskapsakad. Handl.* 62/
    1–1921–1.

3   STALFELDT, M. G. – Pulsierende
    Blattgewebe – *Planta* 7–1929–720.

4   STALFELT, M. G. – The influence of
    light upon the viscosity of proto-
    plasm – *Ark. Bot. (Swed.)* 33A/4–
    1946–1.

5   STALFELT, M. G. – The effect of
    light on the protoplasmic viscosity
    – *Physiol. Plant.* 4–1951–255.

6   STALFELT, M. G. – The protoplasmic
    viscosity of terrestrial plants and
    its sensitivity to light – *Protoplasma*
    45/3–1955–285.

1   STAFFE, A. – Belichtung und Lege-
    leistung beim Huhn – *Experientia
    (Basel)* 7–1951–399.

1   STAHLE, J. – Variation in the 24-
    hour rhythm of hepatic glycogen in
    the rabbit following hypophysecto-
    my – *Acta Endocrinol.* 2–1949–128.

1   STALLING, W. – Veränderungen der
    Pulsfrequenzregulation im Zusam-
    menhang mit vegetativen Umstel-
    lungen während der CO_2-Bäderkur
    in Bad Orb – *Arch. Physikal. Ther.*
    12/2–1960–127.

100 STANBURY, S. W. and A. E. THOMP-
    SON – Diurnal variations in electro-
    lyte excretion – *Clin. Sci.* 10–1951–
    267.

1   STARK, L. – *The Effects of Visual
    Blocking of Theta Rhythm* – Ref.
    1955a, p. 150.

2   STARK, L. – *Oscillations of a Neuro-
    logical Servomechanism Predicted by
    the Nyquist Stability Criterion* –
    Yale Univ. Press, 1959.

3   STARK, L. – Stability, oscillations
    and noise in the human pupil servo-
    mechanism – *Proc. IRE* 47/11–1959
    –1925.

4   STARK, L. – *Biological Rhythms, Noi-
    se, and Asymmetry in the Pupil–
    Retinal Control System* – Ref. 1961c,
    p. 1096.

5   STARK, L. – Environmental clamping
    of biological systems; pupil servo-
    mechanism – *J. Opt. Soc. Am.* 52/8–
    1962–925.

100 STARK, L. and F. BAKER – Stability
    and oscillations in a neurological
    servomechanism – *J. Neurophysiol.*
    22–1959–156.

101 STARK, L., F. W. CAMPBELL and J.
    ATWOOD – Pupil unrest; an exam-
    ple of noise in a biological servo-
    mechanism – *Nature* 182–1958–857.

102 STARK, L. and T. N. CORNSWEET
    Testing a servoanalytic hypothesis

for pupil oscillations – *Science* 127–1958–588.

103 STARK, L. and H. T. HERMAN – The transfer function of a photoreceptor organ – *Kybernetik* 1/3–1961–124.

104 STARK, L. and P. M. SHERMAN – A servoanalytic study of the consensual pupil reflex to light – *J. Neurophysiol.* 20–1957–17.

105 STARK, L., G. VOSSIUS and L. R. YOUNG – Predictive control of eye tracking movements – *I.R.E. Trans. Human Factors in Electronics* HFE 3 /2–1962–52.

106 STARK, L. and L. R. YOUNG – *Defining Human Feedback Control* – Ref. 1963b.

107 STARK, L., A.A. SANDBERG, S. STANTEN, P.A. WILLIS and J.F. DICKSON – On-line digital computer used in biological experiments and modeling – *Ann. N.Y. Acad. Sci.* 115/2–1964–338.

1 STAUBER, L.A. – Factors influencing the asexual periodicity of avian malarias – *J. Parasitol.* 25–1939–95.

1 STAUDER, K. H. – Anfall, Schlaf, Periodizität – *Nervenarzt* 19–1948–107.

1 STEGEMAN, J. – Über den Einfluss sinusförmiger Leuchtdichteänderungen auf die Pupillweite – *Pflüger's Arch. Ges. Physiol.* 264–1957–113.

100 STEPHEN, W. and N. E. GRAY – Evidence for a 400 year cycle in human ability – *J. Cycle Res.* (Ref. J.d.) 7/2–1958–49.

1 STEPHENS, G. C. – *Activity Rhythms in the Mud Snail Nassa obsoleta* – Ref. 1955a, p. 151.

2 STEPHENS, G. C. – *Twenty-four Hour Cycles in Marine Organisms* – Ref. 1956b, p. 135.

3 STEPHENS, G. C. – Influences of temperature fluctuations on the diurnal melanophore rhythm of the fiddler crab – *Physiol. Zool.* 30–1957–55.

4 STEPHENS, G. C. – *Populations as Circadian Systems* – Ref. 1961a, p. 83.

5 STEPHENS, G. C. – *Circadian melanophore rhythms of fiddler crab; interaction between animals* – Ref. 1961c, p. 926.

6 STEPHENS, G. C. – Induction of moulting in the crayfish, *Cambarus,*

by modification of daily photoperiod – *Biol. Bull. Woods Hole* 108–1955–235.

100 STEPHENS, G. C., M. I. SANDEEN and H. M. WEBB – A persistant tidal rhythm of activity in the mud snail – *Anat. Rec.* 117–1953–635.

100 STERN, K. and E. BÜNNING – Über die tagesperiodischen Bewegungen der Primärblätter von *Phaseolus multiflorus* I – *Ber. D. Bot. Ges.* 47–1929–565.

1 STERZINGER, O. – Das menschliche Zeitbewusstsein – *Umschau* 1936–43.

1 STEWART, C. C. – Variations in daily activity with description of recording methods – *Amer. J. Physiol.* 1–1898–40.

200 STEWART, J. L. – *Circuit Theory and Design* – Wiley Sons. New York, 1956.

1 STIER, T. J. B. – Diurnal changes in activities and geotropism in *Thyone briareus* – *Biol. Bull.* 64–1933–326.

1 STINSON, R. H. – The timing of the activity pattern of peromyscus in constant darkness – *Can. J. Zool.* 38–1960–51.

100 STOLPE, M. and K. ZIMMER – Das Geheimnis des Kolibrifluges – *Umschau* 42/20–1939–462.

1 STOPPEL, R. – Über den Einfluss des Lichtes auf das Öffnen und Schliessen einiger Blüten – *Z. Bot.* 2–1910–369.

2 STOPPEL, R. – Über die Bewegungen der Blätter von *Phaseolus* bei Konstanz der Aussenbedingungen – *Ber. D. Bot. Ges.* 30–1912–29.

3 STOPPEL, R. – Die Abhängigkeit der Schlafbewegungen von *Phaseolus multiflorus* von verschiedenen Aussenfaktoren – *Z. Bot.* 8–1916–609.

4 STOPPEL, R. – Leitfähigkeit und Jonengehalt der Atmosphäre im geschlossenen Raum bei konstanten Licht- und Temperaturverhältnissen – *Nachr. Kgl. Ges. Wiss. Göttingen, Math. phys. Kl.* 1919.

5 STOPPEL, R. – Die Schlafbewegungen der Blätter von *Phaseolus multiflorus* in Island zur Zeit der Mitternachtssonne – *Planta* 2/(2–3)–1926–343.

6 STOPPEL, R. – Die Beziehung tagesperiodischer Erscheinungen beim

Tier und bei der Pflanze zu den tagesperiodischen Intensitätsschwankungen der elektrischen Leitfähigkeit der Atmosphäre – *Planta* 2/(2–3)–1926–357.

7 STOPPEL, R. – Beitrag zum Problem der Leitfähigkeit der Atmosphäre – – *Physik. Z.* 27–1926–755.

8 STOPPEL, R. – Untersuchungen über die Schwankungen der lokalen elektrischen Ladung der Erde – *Gerlands Beitr. Geophys.* 21/1–1929–116.

9 STOPPEL, R. – Tagesperiodische Erscheinungen bei Pflanzen – *Hb. Norm. Pathol. Physiol.* 18–1932–448.

10 STOPPEL, R. – Die Raumladung in ihrer Beziehung zu den chemischen Komponenten der Atmosphäre – *Z. Physik* 78/(11–12)–1932–849.

11 STOPPEL, R. – Die Schlafbewegungen etiolierter Blätter von *Phaseolus multiflorus* sind tageszeitlich von der Wirkung eines unbekannten Faktors abhängig – *Ber. D. Bot. Ges.* 66–1938–177.

12 STOPPEL, R. – *Analyse der tagesrhythmischen Blattbewegung von Phaseolus multiflorus* – Ref. 1939a, p. 45.

13 STOPPEL, R. – Einfluss des Chlorophylls auf die Schlafbewegungen der Bohnenblätter und eine Analyse der Bewegungen – *Planta* 30–1940–695.

100 STOPPEL, R. and H. KNIEP – Weitere Untersuchungen über das Öffnen und Schliessen der Blüten – *Z. Bot.* 3–1911–369.

101 STOPPEL, R. and H. G. MÖLLER – Das Zustandekommen der Schlafbewegungen der Pflanzen – *Phyton* 8/(1–2)–1959–62.

1 STRANDGAARD, N. J. – Seasonal variation of the weight of tuberculous patients – *Acta Med. Scand.* 57–1923–275.

1 STRATMAN, F. W. – *Die Bedeutung der Tageszeit für die Insulinapplication bei der Diabetesbehandlung* – Ref. 1955a, p. 156.

1 STRAUB, H. – Über Schwankungen in der Tätigkeit des Atemzentrums speziell im Schlaf – *D. Arch. Klin. Med.* 117–1915–397.

100 STRAUB, H., K. GOLLWITZER-MEYER and SCHLAGINTWEIT – Die Kohlen-säurebindungskurve des Blutes und ihre Jahresschwankungen – *Z. Exp. Med.* 32–1923–229.

100 STROUN, M., C. C. MATHON, M. SANDMEIER, F. CHODAT and A. GIROUD – *Long-day effect as a function of interrelation between light quality, duration of photoperiod, and developmental phases in* Perilla nankinensis *Voss* – Ref. 1960b, p. 384.

1 STRUGHOLD, H. – Physiological day–night cycle in global flights – *J. Aviat. Med.* 23–1952–464.

2 STRUGHOLD, H. – *Day–Night Cycling in Atmospheric Flight, Space Flight, and other Celestial Bodies* – Ref. 1961c, p. 1109.

100 STRUVE, O., B. LYNDS and H. PILLANS – *Elementary Astronomy* – Oxford Univ. Press. New York, 1959.

1 STSCHERBAKOWA, O. P. – *24-Stunden Periodik physiologischer Funktionen bei einigen Säugetierordnungen* – Bykow, Ref. 1, p. 13.

2 STSCHERBAKOWA, O. P. – *Experimentelle Untersuchungen über den 24-Stunden-Rhythmus physiologischer Funktionen bei Affen* – Bykow, Ref. 1, p. 40.

3 STSCHERBAKOWA, O. P. – *Jahreszeitliche und 24-Stündige Schwankungen der Bewegungsaktivität bei Affen* – Bykow, Ref. 1, p. 143.

1 STUBBS, P. – Why should the moon affect the weather – *New Sci.* 17/329–1963–507.

1 STUMPFF, K. – *Grundlagen und Methoden der Periodenforschung* – Springer. Berlin, 1937.

2 STUMPFF, K. – *Tafeln und Aufgaben zur harmonischen Analyse und Periodogrammrechung* – Springer. Berlin, 1939.

100 STUSSI, T. and A. HEUSNER – Variation nycthémérale de la consommation d'oxygène chez quelques espèces d'Insectes, – *C.R. Séances Soc. Biol.* 157/7–1963–1509.

1 SUCKLING, E. E. – *Bioelectricity* – McGraw-Hill. New York, 1961.

1 SUGANO, H. – Studies on the microvibration – *Kurume Med. J.* 4–1957–97.

100 SUGANO, H. and K. INANAGA – Studies on minor tremor – *Jap. J. Physiol.* 10/3–1960–246.

100 SULLIVAN, W. N., M. S. SCHECHTER, S. R. DUTKY and J. C. KELLER – Monitoring electrophysiological responses of cockroaches for space research – *J. Econ. Entomol.* 55/6–1962–985.

1 SUOMALAINEN, P. – Sur le sommeil hibernal du hérisson II – *Biochem.* 295–1938–145.

2 SUOMALAINEN, P. – Production of artificial hibernation – *Nature* 142–1938–1157.

3 SUOMALAINEN, P. – The alarm reaction and the hibernating gland – *Science* 114–1951–300.

4 SUOMALAINEN, P. – Hibernation, the natural hypothermia of mammals – *Triangle* 2–1956–227.

100 SUOMALAINEN, P. and L. SAURE – *Hibernation and the Islets of Langerhans* – Ref. 1955a, p. 157.

1 SUTERMEISTER, H. – Über Rhythmusforschung in der Medizin – *Praxis* 35–1949–1.

1 SUTTON, J – Long-term cycles in the evolution of the continents – *Nature* 198 – 1963–731.

200 SUTTON, G. – Micrometeorology – *Sci. Am.* 211/4–1964–62.

1 SWEENEY, B. M. – *The Photosynthetic Rhythm in Single Cells of Gonyaulax polyedra* – Ref. 1960c, p. 145.

100 SWEENY, B. M., F. T. HAXO and J. W. HASTINGS – Action spectra for two effects of light on the luminescence of *Gonyaulax polyedra* – *J. Gen. Physiol.* 43–1959–285.

101 SWEENEY, B. M. and J. W. HASTINGS – Characteristics of the diurnal rhythm of luminescence in *Gonyaulax polyedra* – *J. Cell. Comp. Physiol.* 49–1957–115.

102 SWEENEY, B. M. and J. W. HASTINGS – Rhythmic cell division in populations of *Gonyaulaux polyedra* – *J. Protozool.* 5–1958–217.

103 SWEENEY, B. M. and J. W. HASTINGS – Effects of Temperature upon Diurnal Rhythms – Ref. 1960c, p. 87.

200 SWEENEY, J. S. – Twenty-four hour blood-sugar variations in fasting and in non-fasting subjects – *Arch. Intern. Med.* 45–1930–257.

1 SWENSSON, Å. – Contributions to the knowledge of the effect of exogenous insulin on the glycogen storage of normal animals – *Acta Physiol. Scand.* 11/suppl. 33–1945.

1 SWIFT, D. R. – Seasonal variations in the growth rate, thyroid gland activity and food reserves of brown trout – *J. Exp. Biol.* 32–1955–751.

100 SZWARC, H. and B. KIELSZEWSKI – *Investigations on Daily Rhythms in Man, The Effect of Physical Exertion on the Functioning of the Pituitary – Adrenal System* – Ref. 1963c.

1 SZÉNT-GYÖRGYI, A. – *Introduction to Submolecular Biology* – Academic Press. New York, 1960.

1 SZYMANSKY, J. – Eine Methode zur Untersuchung der Ruhe- und Aktivitätsperiode bei Tieren – *Pflüger's Arch.* 152–1914–343.

2 SZYMANSKY, J. – Die Haupttiertypen in Bezug auf die Verteilung der Ruhe- und Aktivitätsperioden im 24-stündigen Zyklus – *Biol. Zbl.* 36–1916–537.

3 SZYMANSKY, J. – Die Verteilung der Ruhe- und Aktivitätsperioden bei weissen Ratten und Tänzmäusen – *Pflüger's Arch.* 171–1918–324.

1 TABOR, T. – The 24-hour rhythm of activity in the common buzzard and in the rough-legged buzzard in different conditions at lighting – *Acta Biol. Exp. (Wars.)* 17–1956–5.

100 TAGEEVA, S. V. and A. B. BRANDT – *Study of Optical Properties of Leaves Depending on the Angle of Light Incidence* – Ref. 1960b, p. 163.

1 TAKAGI, K. – Rhythmical changes in the cutaneous blood vessels of man studied by means of the photoelectric plethysmograph – *Int. J. Biometeorol.* 7/1–1963–78.

100 TAKATA, M. and T. MURASUGI – Flockungszahlstöhrung im gesunden menschlichen Blutserum – *Bioklimat. Beibl.* 1941–17.

100 TAKEBE, K., K. NAKAGAWA and S. MATSUKI – *Diurnal Variations of Adrenocortical Hormone in Hyperthyroid Patients* – Ref. 1962c.

1 TAKIMOTO, A. – Flowering response to various combinations of light and dark periods in *Silene armeria* – *Bot. Mag. (Tokyo)* 68–1955–308.

2 TAKIMOTO, A. – Photoperiodic induction in *Silene armeria* as influenced by various light sources – *Bot. Mag. (Tokyo)* 70–1957–312.

3 TAKIMOTO, A. – Two processes in-

volved in the light period of inductive photoperiodic cycles in *Silene armeria* – *Bot. Mag. (Tokyo)* 70–1957–321.

1 TALBOTT, J. H. – Periodic paralysis, a clinical syndrome – *Medicine* 20–1941–85.

100 TALSO, P. J., M. F. GLYNN, Y. T. OESTER and J. FUDEMA – Body composition in hypokalemic familial periodic paralysis – *Ann. N.Y. Acad. Sci.* 110/II–1963–993.

100 TAMIYA, H., K. SHIBATA, T. SASA, T. IWAMURA and Y. MORIMURA – Effect of diurnally intermittent illumination on the growth and some cellular characteristics of *Chlorella*. – J. S. Burlew, "*Algal Culture*", 1953, p. 76.

1 TANAKA, Y. – Studies of hibernation with special reference to photoperiodicity and breeding of the Chinese Tussar-silkworm – *J. Ser. Sci. Jap.* 19–1950–580.

100 TARANTA, A., M. SPAGNUOLO, R. SNIJDER, D.S. GERBARG and J.J. HOFLER – Automatic analysis of phonocardiograms–*Ann. N.Y. Aced. Sci.* 115/2–1964–1062.

1 TASHIMA, Y. – Effect of daylength on the seedlings of pines and other conifers – *Kagoshima Univ. Facul. Agr. Bull.* 4–1955–127.

1 TATAI, K. – Diurnal fluctuation in sleeping – *Publ. Health (Jap.)* 18/4–1954–21 [in Japanese].

2 TATAI, K. – Bioclimatology and stress theory – *Weather (Jap.)* 1/7–1954–225 (in Japanese).

3 TATAI, K. – *Rhythmical Changes in the Calibre of Peripheral Blood Vessels* – Ref. 1962c.

4 TATAI, K. – *Photoelectric Recording and a Simulating System for the Microcirculatory Rhythm* – Ref. 1963a.

100 TATAI, K., M. ASANO, K. YOHIDA, Y. OSADA and K. TATAI – *Rhythmic Circulatory Changes in the Peripheral Vasculature* – Ref. 1961c, p. 1069.

101 TATAI, K. and S. OGAWA – A study of diurnal variations in circulating eosinophils especially with reference to sleep in healthy individuals – *Jap. J. Physiol.* 1/4–1951–328.

102 TATAI, K. and K. – Pain threshold measurement with thermal radia-

tion, particularly in reference to the menstrual period in young women – *Bull. Inst. Publ. Health Jap.* 1953–5.

103 TATAI, K. and K. and M. ASANO – *Studies on the Rhythmic Change of Circulation in the Peripheral Vascular System* – Ref. 1960a, p. 149.

1 TAUSSKY, H. H. – *Rhythm of Endogenous Urinary Citric Acid Excretion* – Ref. 1960a, p. 150.

1 TAYLOR, J. L. – *Rhythmic Behaviour of Lizards in Controlled Regular or Random Cyclic and Constant Temperature Environments* – Ref. 1960a, p. 153.

300 TAYLOR, L. R. and H. KALMUS – Dawn and dusk flight of *Drosophila* – *Nature* 174–1954–221.

1 TCHIJEWSKY, A. L. – *Sur la Périodicité de la Mortalité* – Med. Prophylactique. Charkov, 1930.

2 TCHIJEWSKY, A. L. – *Influence des Perturbations dans l'Activité du Soleil sur la Mortalité* – Moscow, 1930.

3 TCHIJEWSKY, A. L. – *Influence des Variations de l'Electricité atmosphérique sur la Natalité et la Mortalité* – Côte d'Azur Méd. Toulon, 1930.

4 TCHIJEWSKY, A. L. – Action de l'activité périodique solaire sur la mortalité générale – *Trait. Climatol. Biol. Méd.* 2–Paris, 1934.

5 TCHIJEWSKY, A. L. – Die Wege des Eindringens von Luftionen in den Organismus und die physiologische Wirkung von Luftionen – *Acta Med. Scand.* 83–1934–219.

6 TCHIJEWSKY, A. L. – L'activité corpusculaire électro-mágnetique et périodique du soleil et l'électricité atmosphérique comme régulateur de la distribution, dans la suite de temps, des maladies épidémiques et de la mortalité générale – *Acta Med. Scand.* 91–1937–491.

7 TCHIJEWSKY, A. L. – *Cosmobiologie et Rhythme du Milieu Extérieur* – Ref. 1939a, p. 211.

100 TEIXEIRA-PINTO, A.A., L.L. NEJELSKI, J.L. CUTLER and J.H. HELLER – The behaviour of unicellular organisms in an electromagnetic field– *Exp. Cell. Res.* 20–1960–548.

1 TEMBROCK, G. – Zur Aktiviätsperiodik bei *Vulpes* und *Alopex* – *Zool.*

Jb. Phys. 68–1958–297.

1 TENCKHOFF-EIKMANNS, I. – Licht-und Erdschwereorientierung beim Mehlkäfer *Tenebrio molitor* L. und bei einigen anderen Insekten – *Zool. Beitr.* 4 NF/3–1959–307.

100 THARP, G.D. and G.E. FOLK, JR. – Analysis of daily rhythms in isolated hearts – *Am. Zool.* 3/4–1963.

1 THEDERING, F. – Zur vegetativen Steuerung des Serumeisens – *Klin. Wschr.* 27–1949–496.

100 THIERFELDER, A. and G. WANNINGER – Wochenrhythmus – *Zbl. Arbeitsmed.* 4–1954–7.

1 THIES, K. – *Zur Tagesrhythmik der Magensaftsekretion bei Magengesunden und Magenkranken* – Diss. Hamburg, 1947.

1 THIIS-EVENSEN, E. – Skiftarbeid og helse – Eidanger Salpeterfabriker, Oslo, 1958.

1 THOMAS, D.G. – Periodic phenomena observed with spherical particles in horizontal pipes – *Science* 144/3618–1964–534.

1 THOMPSON, A. P. – Relation of retinal stimulation to oestrus in the ferret – *J. Physiol.* 113–1951–425.

100 THOMPSON, A. P. and S. ZUCKERMAN – The effect of pituitary-stalk section on light-induced oestrus in ferrets – *Proc. Roy. Soc. (London)* 142B–1954–437.

300 THOMPSON, E. M. and M. A. KIGHT – Effect of high environmental temperature on basal metabolism and concentrations of serum protein-bound iodine and total cholesterol – *Am. J. Clin. Nutr.* 13/4–1963–219.

1 THORSON, J. – Dynamics of motion perception in the desert locust – *Science* 145/3627–1964–69.

1 THREADGOLD, L. T. – The annual gonad cycle of the male jackdaw – *Cellule* 58/1–1956.

2 THREADGOLD, L. T. – Photoperiodic response of the house sparrow – *Nature* 182–1958–407.

3 THREADGOLD, L. T. – A study of the annual cycle of the house sparrow at various latitudes – *Condor* 62/3–1960–190.

1 TIETZE, K. – *Zur formalen Genese des 28-tägigen weiblichen generativen Rhythmus* – Ref. 1949a, p. 147.

100 TIMMERMAN, J. C., G. E. FOLK JR.

and S. M. HORVATH – Day–night differences of body temperature and heart rate after exercise – *Quart. J. Exp. Physiol.* 44/3–1959–258.

100 TINBERGEN L. and H. KLOMP – Conditions for damping of Nicholson oscillations in parasite-host systems – *Arch. Neerl. Zool.* 13/3–1960–344.

1 TINTNER, G. – *The Variate difference Method* – Principia Press. Bloomington, 1940.

100 TISDALL, F. and A. BROWN – Seasonal variation of the antirachitic effect of sunshine – *Am J. Dis. Child.* 34–1927–721.

101 TISDALL, F., A. BROWN and A. KELLY – The age, sex and seasonal incidence of certain diseases of children – *Am. J. Dis. Child.* 39–1930–163.

1 TOCANTINS, L. M. – Seasonal variations in the number of platelets in arterial, venous and cutaneous blood of man – *Am. J. Pysiol.* 119–1937–439.

1 TOCQUET, R. – *Cycles et Rhythmes* – Dunond. Paris, 1951.

100 TOLLIN, G., P. B. SOGO and M. CALVIN – *Energy Transfer in Ordered and Unordered Photochemical Systems* – Ref. 1957f, p. 47.

1 TOMPKINS, P. – Use of basal temperature graphs in determining date of ovulation – *JAMA* 124–1944–698.

1 TONACK, W. – *Frühjahrseosinophilie und Ultraviolettstrahlung* – Diss. Ernst-Mortiz-Arndt-Univ. Greifswald, 1934.

1 TONGIORGI, P. – Effects of reversal of the rhythm of nychthemeral illumination on astronomical orientation and diurnal activity in *Arctosa variana* – *Arch. Ital. Biol.* 97–1959–251.

1 TOOLE, E. H. – *Effect of Light on the Germination of Seeds* – Ref. 1957f, p. 89.

1 TOPITZ, A. – *Neue Gedanken über Beziehungen biologischer Rhythmen zu Klima und Wetter* – Ref. 1955a, p. 161.

1 TRÄNKLE, W. – *Rhythmologische Abläufe als psychophysischer Ausdruck* – Ref. 1955a, p. 167.

1 TRELOAR, A. E. – *Basic Statistical*

Aspects of Circadian Systems – Ref. 1961a, p. 21.

1 TRIBUKAIT, B. – Aktivitätsperiodik der Maus im künstlich verkürtzten Tag – *Naturwiss.* 41–1954–92.

2 TRIBUKAIT, B. – *Die Aktivitätsperiodik von Nagern im Kunsttag von 16-29 Stunden Länge* – Ref. 1955a, p. 163.

3 TRIBUKAIT, B. – Die Aktivitätsperiodik der weissen Maus im Kunsttag von 16-29 Stunden Länge – *Z. Verg. Physiol.* 38–1956–479.

100 TRIMBLE, H. C. and S. J. MADDOCK – The fluctuations of the capillary bloodsugar in normal young men during a 24-hour period – *J. Biol. Chem.* 81–1929–595.

1 TROJAN, W. – *Vergleichende Messungen der täglichen Schwankungen der Körpertemperatur bei Aufenthalt an der Erdoberfläche und in einem Bergwerk* – Diss. Hamburg, 1937.

1 TROMP, S. W. – *Medical Biometeorology* – Elsevier. Amsterdam, 1963.

1 TRONCHET, A. – *Présentation d'un Film sur les Mouvements Périodiques des Feuilles et sur la Nutation Révolutive de Tiges Volubiles et de Vrilles* – Ref. 1958b, p. 41.

2 TRONCHET, A. – *Périodicité et Nutation Révolutive des Vrilles* – Ref. 1958b, p. 71.

100 TRONCHET, A. and J. – Description schématique de la nutation révolutive des vrilles – *C. R. Acad. Sci.* 233–1950–817.

101 TRONCHET, A. and J. and E. CRINQUAND – Nouvelles observations sur le mouvement revolutif des vrilles – *Ann. Sci. Univ. Besançon, Bot.* 1–1951–1.

200 TRONCHET, J. – *Variations Périodiques de Masse Fraiche des Plantules de Cuscuta gronovii Cultivées en Conditions Constantes* – Ref. 1958b, p. 43.

1 TSCHERKOWITSCH, G. M. – *Einfluss des Phenamins auf den 24-Stunden-Rhythmus physiologischer Prozesse bei Affen* – Bykow, Ref. 1, p. 77.

2 TSCHERKOVITSCH, G.M. – Studies of neurosis produced by changes of diurnal rhythm in monkeys [in Russian] – *Biul. Eksp. Biol. Med.* 48–1959–21.

1 TUKEY, J. W. – The sampling theory of power spectrum estimates – Symp. on appl. of autocorrelation. Woods Hole, Mass, June 1949. – *J. Cycle Res.* (Ref. J. d.) reprint 6/2–1957–31.

1 TUQAN, N. A. – Periodic disease; a clinicopathologic study – *Ann. Int. Med.* 49/4–1958–885.

1 TURNER, C. L. – The seasonal cycle in the spermary of the perch – *J. Morph.* 32–1919–681.

300 TURNER, H. J. and D. L. BELDING – The tidal migration of *Donax variabilis* – *Limnol. and Oceanogr.* 2–1957–120.

1 UEBELMESSER, E. R. – Über den endonomen Rhythmus der Sporangienträger-Bildung von *Pilobolus* – *Arch. Mirobiol.* 20–1954–1.

1 UMBARGER, H. E. – Evidence for a negative-feedback mechanism in the biosynthesis of Isoleucine – *Science* 123/3202–1956–848.

2 UMBARGER, H.E. – Intracellular regulatory mechanisms – *Science* 145/3633–1964–674.

100 UMBARGER, H. E. and B. BROWN – Isoleucine and valine metabolism in *Escherichia coli VII* – *J. Biol. Chem.* 233–1958–415.

2 UNDT, W. – Der Tagesgang markanter Kaltfrontdurchgänge in Wien – *Wetter und Leben* 8/3–4).

1 UNGAR, F. – In vitro Studies of *Adrenal–Pituitary Circadian Rhythms in the Mouse* – Ref. 1963b.

100 UNGAR, F. and F. HALBERG – Circadian rhythm in the *in vitro* response of mouse adrenal to adrenocorticotropic hormone – *Science* 137/3535–1962–1058.

101 UNGAR, F. and F. HALBERG – *In vitro* demonstration of circadian rhythm in adrenocorticotropic activity of C mouse hypophysis – *Experientia (Basel)* 19–1963–158.

1 UNGER, H. – Tag- und Nachtbelastungen des Blutzuckers und Blutbildes mit Traubenzucker, Insulin und Adrenalin – *Z. Ges. Inn. Med. Grenzgeb.* 9/6–1954–272.

100 URSPRUNG, A. and G. BLUM – Über die periodische Schwankungen des osmotischen Wertes – *Ber. D. Bot. Ges.* 34–1916.

1 UTIDA, S. – *Population Fluctuation, an Experimental and Theoretical*

Approach – Ref. 1957d, p. 139.

1 UVAROV, B. P. – Revision of the genus *Locusta* L. with a new theory of the periodicity and migration of locusts – *Bull. Entomol. Res.* 12–1921–135.

1 VAARTAJA, O. – Evidence of photoperiodic ecotypes in trees – *Ecol. Monogr.* 29–1959–91.

2 VAARTAJA, O. – Photoperiodic ecotypes in trees – *Rec. Adv. Bot.* 1961–1331.

3 VAARTAJA, O. – Ecotypic variation in photoperiodism of trees – *Can. J. Bot.* 40–1962–849.

4 VAARTAJA, O. – Photoperiodic response in trees from warm climates – *Int. J. Biomet.* 6/2–1963–91.

1 VARA, P. – *Fötales EKG in situ beim Menschen* – Ref. 1953a, p. 153.

1 VASAMA, R. – The diurnal rhythm of mitotic activity in the corneal epithelium of mice – *Ann. Univ. Turkuensis (Finland)* 2/29–1961–1.

100 VASAMA R. and R. – On the diurnal cycle of mitotic activity in the corneal epithelium of mice – *Acta Anat.* 33–1958–230.

100 VASTOLA, E. F. and C. A. BERTRAND – Intracellular water and potassium in periodic paralysis – *Neurology* 6–1956–523.

100 VAUGIEN, L. and M. VAUGIEN – Sur le comportement alimentaire du Moineau domestique séjourment à la lumière naturelle ou à l'obscurité complete–*C. R. Acad. Sci.* 254/25–1962–4357.

101 VAUGIEN, L. and M. VAUGIEN – Le Moineau domestique synchronise le milieu de sa période alimentaire avec le milieu de la période journalière de lumière artificielle–*C.R. Acad. Sci.* 257/14–1964–2040.

100 VEEDER, B. S. and E. H. ROHLFING – Studies in pubescent growth with special reference to periodic gain – *Am. J. Dis. Child.* 34–1927–211.

100 VEEN, R. V. D. and G. MEIJER – *Critical Daylength of the Short-Day Plant Salvia occidentalis in Red and Far-Red Radiation* – Ref. 1960b, p. 389.

1 VENTER, J. – Untersuchungen über tagesperiodische Amylaseaktivitätsschwankungen – *Z. Bot.* 44–1956–59.

1 VERHEIJEN, F. J. – The mechanisms of the trapping effect of artificial light sources upon animals – *Arch. Neerl. Zool.* 13/1–1958–1.

100 VERHOEVEN, B. and G. J. v. OORDT – The influence of light and temperature on the sexual cycle of the Bitterling – *Proc. Kon. Ned. Akad. Wet.* 58–1955–628.

1 VERING, F. – *Zur Hygiene der Arbeit* – Wien, 1948.

2 VERING, F. – Die Rhythmusforschung in der experimentellen Hygiene – *Mitteil. Österreich. Sanitätsvervaltung* 51/(6–7)–1950–1.

3 VERING, F. – Einfluss der Tag- und Nachtschicht auf den Arbeiter – *Wien. Med. Wschr.* 100/(37–38)–1950–652.

4 VERING, F. – Bioklimatologie und Rhythmusforschung im Dienste der Arbeitshygiene–*Wiener Med. Wschr.* 101/17–1951–310.

5 VERING, F. – *Arbeitsklima* – 2. Österr. Tag. Arbeitsmed., Wien, 1952, p. 300.

6 VERING, F. – *Nachweiss extraterrestrischer Einflüsse auf mikrobiologische Systeme* – Ref. 1958c, p. 177.

100 VERMUND, H., F. HALBERG, C. P. BARNUM, C. W. NASH and J. J. BITTNER – Physiologic 24–hour periodicity and hepatic phospholipid metabolism in relation to the mouse adrenal cortex – *Am. J. Physiol.* 186–1956–414.

1 VESTINE, E.H. – *Solar influences on geomagnetic and related phenomena* – Ref. 1961e, p. 3.

100 VILLEE, C. A., W. F. WALKER and F. E. SMITH – *General Zoology* – Saunders. Philadelphia, 1958.

1 VINOGRADOVA, G. A. – The influence of the reparative regeneration of the liver on the mitotic activity in the epithelium of cornea and the epidermis in rats – *Bull. Exp. Biol. Med. USSR.* 11–1960–105.

1 VIRGIN, H. I. – The relation between the viscosity of the cytoplasm, the plasma flow and the motive force – *Physiol. Plant.* 2–1949–157.

2 VIRGIN, H. I. – The effect of light on the protoplasmic viscosity – *Physiol. Plant.* 4–1951–255.

3 VIRGIN, H. I. – An action spectrum for the light-indiced changes in the

viscocity of plant protoplasm – *Physiol. Plant.* 5–1952–575.

4   VIRGIN, H. I. – Physical properties of protoplasm – *Ann. Rev. Plant Physiol.* 4–1953–363.

5   VIRGIN, H. I. – Further studies of the action spectrum for light–induced changes in the protoplasmic viscosity of *Helodea densa* – *Physiol. Plant.* 7–1954–343.

6   VIRGIN, H. I. – The distortion of fluorescent spectra in leaves by light scattering and its reduction by infiltration – *Physiol. Plant* 7–1954–560.

7   VIRGIN, H. I. – The conversion of protochlorophyll to chlorophyll *a* in continuous and intermittent light – *Physiol. Plant.* 8–1955–389.

8   VIRGIN, H. I. – Protochlorophyll formation and greening in etiolated barley leaves – *Physiol. Plant.* 8–1955–630.

9   VIRGIN, H. I. – Light-induced stomatal movements in wheat leaves recorded as transpiration – *Physiol. Plant.* 9–1956–280.

10 VIRGIN, H. I. – Light-induced stomatal transpiration of etiolated wheat leaves as related to chlorophyll *a* content – *Physiol. Plant.* 9–1956–482.

100 VIRGIN, H. I. and L. EHRENBERG – Effects of β- and γ-rays on the protoplasmic viscosity of *Helodea* cells – *Physiol. Plant.* 6–1953–159.

1   VIRZI, T. – Etude sur les mouvements périodiques de feuilles des *Oxalis* – *Bull. Soc. Bot. (Genéve)* 22 II–1930–1.

100 VISSCHER, M. B. and F. HALBERG – Daily rhythms in numbers of circulating eosinophils and some related phenomena – *Ann. N.Y. Acad. Sci.* 59–1955–834.

1   VÖLKER, H. – Über die tagesperiodischen Schwankungen einiger Lebensvorgänge des Menschen – *Pflüger's Arch.* 215–1927–43.

200 VÖLKER, R. – *Das Verhalten der Spontanrhythmik der Kreislaufperipherie* – Ref. 1955a, p. 181.

1   VOGEL, G. – Über tageszeitliche Blutzuckerschwankungen – *Z. Ges. Inn. Med.* 3–1948–606.

100 VOGEL, G. and W. WESTPHAL – *Die lokomotorische Aktivität und ihr endogener Rhythmus von Albinomäusen unter dem Einfluss verschiedener Wirkstoffe der Nebennierenrinde* – Ref. 1955a, p. 180.

1   VOLLMAN, R. F. – Über Fertilität und Sterilität der Frau innerhalb des Menstruationszyklus – *Arch. Gyn.* 182–(1952–53)–602.

1   VOLPE, P. – *Sulla Possibilità di Controllare il Ritmo Biologico* – Ref. 1960a, p. 153.

1   VOLTERRA, V. – Variations and fluctuations of the number of individuals in animal species, living together – p. 409, R. N. Chapman, *Animal Ecology".* Mc Graw–Hill. New York, 1931.

1   VOLZ, W. – *Der Begriff des "Rhythmus" in der Geographie* – Mitteil. Ges. Erdkde. Hirt u Sohn, Leipzig, 1926, p. 8.

2   VOLZ, W. – Geographische Ganzheitlichkeit – *Ber. Math.-Phys. Kl. Sächs. Akad. Wiss.(Leipzig)* 84–1931–91.

3   VOLZ, W. – Ganzheit, Rhythmus und Harmonie in der Geographie – *Die Erde* 1951–97.

1   VOROBJEVA, I. A. – *About Certain Peculiarities of Biological Action of U.V.-rays with Different Wave Length* – Ref. 1960b, p. 173.

1   VOSKRESENSKAYA, N. P. – *Effect of Various Rays of the Visual Region of the Spectrum on the Absorption of Oxygen by Green and Non-Green Plant Leaves* – Ref. 1960b, p. 149.

1   VOSS, G. V. – Über die Schwankungen der geistigen Arbeitsleistung – *Psychol. Arb.* 2–1899–399.

1   VOSSIUS, G. – *Die Parameter der Augenbewegung und ihre physiologische Bedeutung* – Ref. 1960a, p. 159.

2   VOSSIUS, G. – Das System der Augenbewegungen – *Z. Biol.* 112–1960–27.

1   VOWLES, D. M. – Sensitivity of ants to polarized light – *Nature* 165–1950–282.

1   WACHHOLDER, K. – *Die allgemeinen physiologischen Grundlagen der Entstehung von Lebensrhythmen* – Ref. 1953a, p. 21.

100 WACHHOLDER, K. and A. BECKMANN – *Rhythmische, reziprok alternierende Schwankungen des weissen*

Blutbildes und ihre Bedeutung für die Erkenntnis der Funktionsweise des vegetativen Zentralnervensystem – Ref. 1949a, p. 79.

1 WACHSMUTH, G. – *Tagesperiodik in den Organismen von Erde und Mensch* – Ref. 1953a, p. 104.

1 W.A.D.D. (WRIGHT AIR DEVELOP-MENT DIVISION) – Bionics symposium, Dec. 1960, W.A.D.D. TR 60–600, Wright-Patterson Air Force Base, Ohio, U.S.A.

100 WADSWORTH, G. L., F. HALBERG, P. ALBRECHT and G. SKAFF – Peak urinary excretion of 5-hydroxyindoleacetic acid following arousal in human beings – *The Physiologist* 1–1957–86.

1 WAGNER, H. – Schwingungen im Verlauf der Körpertemperatur und ihre Kopplung mit föhnartigen Verhältnissen – *Angew. Meteorol.* 1/7–1952–193.

2 WAGNER, H. – Sonnenschein und Körpertemperatur; Änderungen in der jahreszeitlichen Reaktionsweise bei Kurpatienten – *Naturwiss.* 45/6–1958–143.

3 WAGNER, H. – Der zyklische Wandel der vegetativen Tonuslage durch die Ovarialhormone – *Med. Welt* 1–1960–50.

4 WAGNER, H. – Zur Frage der Blutdruckveränderungen nach bestimmten Ausgangswerten – *Biometr. Z.* 2/2–1960–117.

100 WAGNER, H. and H. JORDAN – Frühniveau und Tagesperiodik als Kennzeichen der Körpertemperaturrhythmik – *Naturwiss.* 41/23–1954–557.

200 WAGNER, H. O. – Über Jahres- und Tagesrhythmus bei Zugvögeln – *Z. Tierpsychol.* 13–1956–82.

201 WAGNER, H. O. – Die Bedeutung von Umweltfaktoren und Geschlechtshormonen für den Jahresrhythmus von Zugvögeln – *Z. Vergl. Physiol.* 38–1956–355.

400 WAGNER, K. W. – *Einführung in die Lehre von den Schwingungen und Wellen* – Wiesbaden, 1947.

600 WAGNER, R. – *Probleme und Beispiele biologischer Regelung* – Thieme. Stuttgart, 1954.

601 WAGNER, R. – *Die Beziehungen zwischen biologischer Regelung und*

biologischen Rhythmen – Ref. 1955a, p. 24.

602 WAGNER, R. – Wesen und Bedeutung biologischer Regelung für die Medizin – *Fortschr. Med.* 75–1957–658.

1 WAHL, O. – Neue Untersuchungen über das Zeitgedächtnis der Bienen – *Z. Vergl. Physiol.* 16–1932–529.

2 WAHL, O. – Beitrag zur Frage von der biologischen Bedeutung des Zeitgedächtnisses der Bienen – *Z. Vergl. Physiol.* 18–1933–709.

1 WAHLSTRÖM, G. – *Influence of Psychopharmacological Agents on Circadian Rhythm in the Canary studied by Self-Selection of Light and Darkness* – Ref. 1963b, p. 320.

1 WALD, A. – Long cycles as a result of repeated integration – *Ann. Math. Mthly* 46–1939–136.

1 WALDOW, F. – *Die Bedeutung des biologischen Lebensrhythmus für die Nacht- und Schichtarbeit* – Diss. Bonn, 1957.

1 WALDRON, J. – Courtship sound production in two sympatric sibling *Drosophila* species – *Science* 144/3615–1964–191.

1 WALKER, T. J. – The taxonomy and calline songs of United States tree crickets II – *Ann. Entomol. Soc. Am.* 56/6–1963–772.

1 WALLGREN, A. – Meteorologiska faktorer som sjukdomsorsak – *Nord. Med. Tidskr.* 11–1936–625.

100 WALLIS, W. A. and H. V. ROBERTS – *Statistics; A New Approach* – Methuen Co. London, 1957.

200 WALLIS, R. L. – Spring migration of the six-spotted leafhopper in the Western great plains – *J. Econ. Entomol.* 55/6–1962–871.

1 WALLRAFF, H. G. – Über den Einfluss der Erfahrung auf das Heimfindevermögen von Brieftauben – *Z. Tierpsychol.* 16–1959–424.

2 WALLRAFF, H. G. – Örtlich und zeitlich bedingte Variabilität des Heimkehrverhaltens von Brieftauben – *Z. Tierpsychol.* 16/5–1959–513.

3 WALLRAFF, H. G. – *Does Celestial Navigation Exist in Animals* – Ref. 1960c, p. 451.

4 WALLRAFF, H. G. – Über Zusammenhänge des Heimkehrverhaltens von Brieftauben mit meteorologischen

und geophysikalischen Faktoren – *Z. Tierpsychol.* 17/1–1960–82.

5 WALLRAFF, H. G. – Können Grasmücken mit Hilfe des Sternenhimmels navigieren – *Z. Tierpsychol.* 17/2–1960–165.

1 WALOFF, Z. – Seasonal breeding and migrations of the desert locust in eastern Africa – *Antilocust Mem.* 1–1946–1.

100 WANGERSKY, P. J. and W. J. CUNNINGHAM – On time lags in equations of growth – *Proc. Nat. Acad. Sci.* 42–1956–676.

101 WANGERSKY, P. J. and W. J. CUNNINGHAM – *Time Lag in Population Models* – Ref. 1957d, p. 329.

100 WARBURG O., W. SCHRÖDER and H. W. GATTUNG – Züchtung der Chlorella mit fluktuierender Lichtintensität – *Z. Naturforsch.* 11–1956–654.

1 WARD, H. C. – The hourly variations in the quantity of hemoglobin and in the number of the corpuscles in human blood – *Am. J. Physiol.* 11–1904–394.

300 WARD, F. and R. SHAPIRO – *Solar, geomagnetic and meteorological periodicities* – Ref. 1961e, p. 200.

1 WAREING, P. F. – Growth studies in woody species V. – *Physiol. Plant.* 6–1953–692.

2 WAREING, P. F. – Experiments on the "light-break" effect in short-day plants – *Physiol. Plant.* 7–1954–157.

3 WAREING, P. F. – *Photoperiodism in Seeds and Birds* – Ref. 1957f, p. 73.

100 WARREN, D. M. and M. B. WILKINS – An endogenous rhythm in the rate of dark-fixation of carbon dioxide in leaves of *Bryophyllum fedtschenkoi* – *Nature* 191/4789–1961–686.

1 WASSERMAN, L. – Die Auslösung endogen-tagesperiodischer Vorgänge bei Pflanzen durch einmalige Reize – *Planta* 53–1959–647.

100 WASSINK, E. L., P. J. A. L. de LINT and J. BENSINK – *Some Effects of High-Intensity Irradiation of Narrow Spectral Regions* – Ref. 1957f, p. 111.

1 WATANABE, G. – *Bio-Rhythms represented by the Uropepsin Output* – Ref. 1962e.

300 WATANABE, T., F. INOUE and A.

NAKAGAWA – Studies on a sense of rhythm – *Nat. Sci. Rep. Ochanomzu Univ. (Japan)* 8/2–1957–105.

1 WATERMAN, T. H. – *Polarized Light Orientation by Aquatic Arthropods* – Ref. 1960b, p. 214.

2 WATERMAN, T. H. – *The Analysis of Spatial Orientation* – Ref. 1962d, p. 98.

1 WATSON, G. S. – Goodness-of-fit tests on a circle (I–II) – *Biometrica* 48–1961–109; 49–1962–57.

100 WAY, M. J. and B. A. HOPKINS – The influence of photoperiod and temperature on the induction of diapause in *Diataraxia oleracea* L. – *J. Exp. Biol.* 27–1950–365.

1 WEBB, H. M. – Diurnal variations in response to light in the fiddler crab – *Physiol. Zool.* 23–1950–316.

100 WEBB, H. M. and F. A. BROWN JR. – The repetition of pattern in the respiration of *Uca pugnax* – *Biol. Bull.* 115–1958–303.

101 WEBB, H. M. and F. A. BROWN JR. – Timing long-cycle physiological rhythms – *Physiol. Rev.* 3–1959–127.

102 WEBB, H. M., F. A. BROWN JR. and W. J. BRETT – Effects of imposed electrostatic fields on rate of locomotion in *Ilyanassa* – *Biol. Bull.* 117–1959–430.

103 WEBB, H. M., F. A. BROWN JR. and T. E. SCHROEDER – Organismic responses to differences in weak horizontal electrostatic fields – *Biol. Bull.* 121–1961–413.

1 WEBER, A. – Über Koronarsklerose, vorwiegend bei Ärzten – *Z. Kreislaufforsch.* 48–1959–717.

1 WEBSTER, J. H. D. – *The Periodicity and Cause of Cancer, Leucemia and Allied Tumours* – Baillière, Tindall and Cox. London, 1940.

2 WEBSTER, J. H. D. – Periodic inspiration in poetry and music – *Poetry Review* 34/4–1943–137.

3 WEBSTER, J. H. D. – The periodicity of the "sevens" in mind, man and nature, a neohippocratic study – *Brit. J. Med. Psychol.* 24/4–1951–277.

4 WEBSTER, J. H. D. – *The Endogenous 7.6 Month Period* – Ref. 1960a, p. 1962.

100 WEHMEYER, H. and H. CASPERS –

Bioelektrische Registrierung der Schlaf–Wach Periodik beim Tier – *Pflüger Arch.Ges.Physiol.* 267–1958–298.

1   WEHNER, A.P. – Growth of microorganisms in electrostatic fields – *Int. J. Biometeorol.* 7/3–1964–277.

1   WEICKER, B. – Über rhythmische Kontraktionen der Tunica dartos und ihre Beeinflussung durch mechanische, physikalische, psychische und pharmakologische Mittel, durch Schlaf und infektiöse Erkrankung – *Z. Ges. Exp. Med.* 54–1927–169.

1   WEIL, P. – Über Leukocyten und Lungentuberculose III – *Z. Tuberk.* 30–1919–76.

1   WEINBERG, A. M. – A case of biological periodicity – *Growth* 2–1933–81.

100 WEINER, A. D. and R. K. GHORMLEY – Periodic benign synovitis – *J. Bone Joint Surg.* 38A–1956– 1039.

100 WEITZ, W. and W. VOLLERS – Studien über Magenbewegungen – *Z. Ges. Exp. Med.* 47–1925–42.

101 WEITZ, W. and W. VOLLERS – Über rhythmische Kontraktionen der glatten Muskulatur an verschiedenen Organen – *Z. Ges. Exp. Med.* 52–1926–721.

1   WELLENSIEK, S. J. – Photoperiodism and temperature in *Perilla* – *Proc. Kon. Ned. Akad. Wetensch.* 55C–1952–701.

1   WELLINGTON, W. G. – Motor responses evoked by the dorsal ocelli of *Sarcophga aldrichi* Parker and the orientation of the fly to plane polarized light – *Nature* 172–1953–1177.

1   WELLS, G. P. – Studies on the physiology of *Arenicola marina.* L. – (I), *J. Exp. Biol.* 14–1937–117.

2   WELLS, G. P. – The behaviour of *Arenicola marina.* L. in sand, and the role of spontaneous activity cycles – *J. Mar. Biol. Ass. U.K.* 28–1949–465.

3   WELLS, G. P. – Spontaneous activity cycles in polychaete worms – J. F. Danielli and R. Brown, *Physiological Mechanisms in Animal Behaiour''.* Cambridge, 1950.

4   WELLS, G. P. – *Spontaneous Activity Cycles in the Behaviour of Worms –* Ref. 1953a, p. 57.

5   WELLS, G. P. – Defaecation in relation to the spontaneous activity cycles of *Arenicola marina* L. – *J. Mar. Biol. Ass. U.K.* 32–1953–51.

100 WELLS, G. P. and E. B. ALBRECHT – The integration of activity cycles in the behaviour of *Arenicola marina,* L – *J. Exp. Biol,* 28–1951–41.

101 WELLS, G. P. and E. B. ALBRECHT – The role of oesophageal rhythms in the behaviour of *Arenicola ecaudata* Johnston – *J. Exp. Biol.* 28–1951–51.

102 WELLS, G. P. and R. P. DALES – Spontaneous activity patterns in animal behaviour – *J. Mar. Biol. Ass. U.K.* 29–1951–661.

200 WELLS, L. J. – *Experiments on Light and Temperature in a Wild Mammal with an Annual Breeding Season –* Ref. 1957f, p. 801.

1   WELSH, J. H. – Diurnal rhythm of the distal pigment cells in the eyes of certain crustaceans – *Proc. Nat. Acad. Sci.* 16–1930–386.

2   WELSH, J. H. – The mechanics of migration of the distant pigment cells in the eyes of *Palaemonetes* – *J. Exp. Zool.* 56–1930–459.

3   WELSH, J. H. – Further evidence of a diurnal rhythm in the movement of pigment cells in eyes of crustaceans – *Biol. Bull.* 68/2–1935–247.

4   WELSH, J. H. – Diurnal movements of the eye pigments of anchistioides – *Biol. Bull.* 70/2–1936–217.

5   WELSH, J. H. – Diurnal rhythms – *Quart. Rev. Biol.* 13/2–1938–123.

6   WELSH, J. H. – The sinus gland and twenty-four hour cycles of retinal pigment migration in crayfish – *J. Exp. Zool.* 86–1941–35.

100 WELSH, J. H., F. A. CHASE and R. F. NUNEMACHER – The diurnal migration of deep-water animals – *Biol. Bull.* 73/2–1937–185.

101 WELSH, J. H. and C. M. OSBORN – Diurnal changes in the retina of the catfish *Ameiurus nebulosus* – *J. Comp. Neurol.* 66–1937–349.

1   WENT, F. W. – Plant growth under controlled conditions II – *Am. J. Bot.* 31–1944–135.

2   WENT, F. W. – The effect of temperature on plant growth – *Ann. Rev. Plant. Physiol.* 4–1953–347.

3   WENT, F. W. – The roleen of vironment in plant growth – *Am. Sci.* 44/4–1956–378.

4   WENT, F. W. – *The Periodic Aspect of Photoperiodism and Thermoperiodicity* – Ref. 1957f, p. 551.

5   WENT, F. W. – *The Experimental Control of Plant Growth* – Walthman, Mass. 1957.

6   WENT, F. W. – *Photo- and Thermoperiodic Effects in Plant Growth* – Ref. 1960c, p. 221.

7   WENT, F. W. – *Ecological Implications of the Autonomous 24-Hour Rhythm in Plants* – Ref. 1961c, p. 886.

1   WERNER, G. – Tänze und Zeitempfinden der Honigbiene in Abhängigkeit von Stoffwechsel – *Z. Vergl. Physiol.* 36–1954–464.

1   WERNLI, H. J. – *Biorhythm* – Crown Publ. Inc. New York, 1961.

1   WETZEL, U. – *Biologischer Rhythmus des Serumeisens beim Menschen* – Ref. 1949a, p. 135.

1   WEVER, R. – *Possibilities of Phase-Control demonstrated by an Electronic Model* – Ref. 1960c, p. 197.

2   WEVER, R. – Zum Mechanismus der biologischen 24–Stunden-Periodik – *Kybernetik* 1/4–1962–139.

3   WEVER, R. – *Mathematische Analyse der 24-Stunden-Periodik*–Ref. 1963a.

4   WEVER, R. – Zum Mechanismus der biologischen 24-Stunden-Periodik II – *Kybernetik* 6–1963–213.

100   WEYSSEE, A. and B. R. LUTZ – Diurnal variations in arterial blood pressure – *Am. J. Physiol.* 37–1915–330.

100   WHEELER, J. F. G. and F. A. BROWN – The periodic swarming of *Anchistioides antiguensis* (Schmitt) *(Crustacea, Decapoda)* at Bermuda – *J. Linn. Soc. Lond. (Zool.)* 39–1936–413.

1   WHITAKER, W. L. – Some effects of artificial illumination on reproduction in the white-footed mouse – *J. Exp. Zool.* 83–1940–33.

1   WHITE, P. D. – *Heart Disease* – 3rd Ed. Mac Millan. New York, 1949.

300   WHITE, G. H. JR., K. O. LANGE and R. R. COERMANN – The effects of simulated buffeting on the internal pressure of man – *Human factors* Oct. 1962–275.

100   WHITEHOUSE, H. L. K. and E. A. ARMSTRONG – Rhythms in the breeding behaviour of the European wren – *Behaviour* 5–1953–261.

1   WHITMEE, S. J. – On the habits of *Palola viridis* – *Proc. Zool. Soc. (London)* 1875–496.

1   WHITROW, G. S. – The natural philosophy of time – Harper 1961.

1   WHYTE, L. L. – Note on the structural philosophy of organism – *Brit. J. Philos. Sci.* 5/20–1955–332.

1   WIENER, N. – Generalized harmonic analysis – *Acta Math.* 55–1930–117.

2   WIENER, N. – *Cybernetics* – Wiley. New York, 1948 and 1961.

3   WIENER, N. – *The Human Use of Human Beings; Cybernetics and Society* – H. Mifflin Co. Boston, 1950.

1   WIESINGER, K. – *Über den Einfluss des Höhenklimas auf einige Rhythmen* – Ref. 1953a, p. 194.

1   WIGAND, R. – Der Tod des Menschen an inneren Krankheiten in seinen Beziehungen zu den Tages- und Jahreszeiten–*D.Med.Wschr.*60–1934 II–1709.

100   WIJK, B. and S. ÅHLUND – *Some Investigations Concerning the Glycogen Fraction Problem* – Ref. 1955a p. 176.

200   WIJK, W. R. VAN – *Physics of Plant Environment* – North-Holland Publ. Amsterdam, 1963.

1   WILDE, J. DE – Extrinsic control of endocrine functions in insects – *Bull. Res. Counc. Israel* 10B/(1–2)–1961–36.

100   WILDE, J. de, C.S. DUINTJER and L. MOOK – Physiology of diapause in the adult Colorado beetle. I – *J. Insect. Physiol.* 3–1959–75.

1   WILDER, J. – Das "Ausgangswert-Gesetz", ein unbeachtetes biologisches Gesetz und seine Bedeutung für Forschung und Praxis – *Z. Neur. Psychiatr.* 137–1931–317.

2   WILDER, J. – Das "Ausgangswert-Gesetz", – ein unbeachtetes biologisches Gesetz; seine Bedeutung für Forschung und Praxis – *Klin. Wschr.* 10/41–1931–1889.

3   WILDER, J. – Das Ausgangswertgesetz – *Ars Med.* 43/11–1953–752.

4   WILDER, J. – Adrenalin and the law of initial value – *Exp. Med. Surg.* 15/1–1957–47.

5 WILDER, J. – The law of initial value in neurology and psychiatry – *J. Nerv. Ment. Dis.* 125/1–1957–73.

6 WILDER, J. – Paradoxic reactions to treatment – *N.Y. State J. Med.* 57/20–1957–3348.

7 WILDER, J. – The law of initial value in medicine – *World Sci. Rev.* 1958.

8 WILDER, J. – Zur Kritik des Aus-gangswert-Gesetzes – *Klin. Wschr.* 36/4–1958–148.

9 WILDER, J. – Modern psychophysiology and the law of initial value – *Am. J. Psychother.* 12/2–1958–199.

10 WILDER, J. – *Principles of Basimetry, with Special Reference to Biological Rhythms* – Ref. 1960a, p. 169.

11 WILDER, J. – Basimetric Approach to Biologic Rhythms – Ref. 1961c, p. 1211.

12 WILDER, J. – Recent development in the law of initial value – *Exp. Med. Surg.* 20/(1–2)–1962–126.

200 WILDER, C. S. – Acute respiratory illnesses reported to the U.S. National Health Survey during 1957–1962 – *Am. Rev. Resp. Dis.* 88/3 (part 2)–1963–14.

1 WILHELMI, H. – Zur Frage der endogenen Rhythmus beim kindlichen Diabetes mellitus – *D. Med. Wschr.* 74–1949–1466.

1 WILKINS, M. B. – *Rhythmic Phenomena in Plants* – Thesis Univ. London, 1958.

2 WILKINS, M. B. – An endogenous rhythm in the rate of carbon dioxide output of *Bryophyllum* I–III – *J. Exp. Bot.* 10/30-1959-377; 11/32–1960–269; *Proc. Roy. Soc. (London)* 156B–1962–220.

3 WILKINS, M. B. – *Studies of the Endogenous Rhythm in the Rate of Carbon Dioxide Output of Excised Leaves of Bryophyllum* – Ref. 1960a, p. 164.

4 WILKINS, M. B. – *The Effect of Light upon Plant Rhythms* – Ref. 1960c, p. 115.

5 WILKINS, M. B. – A temperature-dependent endogenous rhythm in the rate of carbon dioxide output of *periplaneta americana* – *Nature* 185/4711–1960–481.

1 WILLIAMS, C. B. – The times of activity of certain nocturnal insects, chiefly *Lepidoptera,* as indicated by a light trap – *Trans. Roy. Entomol, Soc.* 85–1935–523.

2 WILLIAMS, C. B. – The influence of moonlight on the activity of certain nocturnal insects, particularly of the family *Noctuidae,* as indicated by a light trap – *Phil. Trans.* 1936–357.

100 WILLIAMS C. B. and B. P. SINGH – Effects of moon-light on insect activity – *Nature* 167–1951–853.

101 WILLIAMS C. B., B. P. SINGH and S. EL ZIADY – An investigation into the possible effects of moon-light on the activity of insects in the field – *Proc. Roy. Entomol. Soc. (London)* 31A–1957–135.

200 WILLIAMS, G. – Seasonal and diurnal activity of *Carabidae* – *J. Anim. Ecol.* 28–1959–309.

400 WILLIAMS, E. S. – Sleep and wakefulness at high altitudes – *Brit. Med. J.* 1959 I–197.

700 WILLIAMS, C.M. and P.L. ADKISSON –Photoperiodic control of pupal diapause in the silkworm–*Science* 144/3618–1964–569.

800 WILLIAMS, D. – *Sunspot cycle correlations* – Ref. 1961e, p. 78.

1 WILLIER, B. H. – *Development of Rhythmic Structure and Design* – Ref. 1957c.

1 WILSON, C. – On diurnal and nocturnal excretion of urine – *Lancet* 1889–1299.

300 WILSON, H. L., E. J. and H. W. NEWMAN – Diurnal variation in rate of alcohol metabolism – *J. Appl. Physiol.* 8–1956–556.

400 WILSON, W. O. – *Photocontrol of Oviposition in Gallinaceous Birds* – Ref. 1963b.

500 WILSON, W. O. and H. ABPLANALP – Intermittent light stimuli in egg production of chickens – *Poultry Sci.* 35/3–1956–533.

501 WILSON, W. O., E. H. MCNALLY and H. OTA – Temperature and calorimeter study on hens in individual cages – *Poultry Sci.* 36/6–1957–1254.

502 WILSON, W. O. and A. E. WOODARD – *Egg Production of Chickens in Darkness* – Ref. 1957f, p. 787.

503 WILSON, W. O., A. E. WOODARD and H. ABPLANALP – The effect and after–effect of varied exposure to light on chicken development – *Biol.* 111/3–1956–415.

600 WILSON, D.M. – Relative refractoriness and patterned discharge of locust flight motor neurons,–*J. Exp. Biol.* 41/1–1964–191.

1 WING, L. W. – Time chart measurements of Norwegian lemming and rodent cycles – *J. Cycles Res.* (Ref. J. d.) 6/1–1957–3.

2 WING, L. W. – Latitudinal passage behavior – *J. Cycle Res.* (Ref. J. d.) 7/3–1958–67.

3 WING, L. W. – A possible 3.6-quarter year cycle in a variable star, the earth and the sun – *Cycles* (Ref. J. c.) 11/10–1960–233.

4 WING, L. W. – *The Effect of Latitude on Cycles* – Ref. 1961c, p. 1202.

5 WING, L. W. – The 3.9-year lemming cycle and latitudinal passage in temperature – *J. Cycle Res.* (Ref. J. d.) 10/2–1961–59.

6 WING, L. W. – Lemmings – *Cycles* (Ref. J. c.) 14/5–1963–121.

7 WING, L.W. – *Latitudinal passage: a principle of solar–terrestrial cycle behaviour* – Ref. 1961e, p. 381.

100 WINGET, C.M., C.A. MEPHAM, D.R. PATTIE and A.M. WALKER – Scleral contact filters for domestic birds – *Proc. Soc. Exp. Biol. Med.* 112–1963–412.

101 WINGET, C.M., A.H. SMITH and C.F. KELLY–Effects of chronic accelleration on induced nystagmus in the fowl –*J. Appl. Physiol.* 17/4–1962–709.

1 WINZENRIED, F. J. M. – Über langfristige Rhythmen in der Psychiatrie – Ref. 1963a.

1 WITHROW, R. B. – *A Kinetic Analysis of Photoperiodism* – Ref. 1957f, p. 439.

1 WITTEKINDT, W. – Experimentelle Auslösung von Tänzen der Honigbiene – *Naturwiss.* 42–1955–567.

1 WITTEN, L. – *Gravitation, an Introduction to Current Research* – Wiley, 1963.

100 WITTWER, S. H. and M. J. BUKOVAC – *Effects of Gibberellin on the Photoperiodic Responses of some Higher Plants* – Ref. 1957f, p. 373.

1 WOLD, H. O. A. – A short-cut method for distinguishing between rigid and disturbed periodicity – *Proc. Int. Stat. Conf.* 3–1947–302.

2 WOLD, H. O. A. – *Series Cronologicas Estacionarias* – Monografias de Ciencia Moderna no. 28. Madrid, 1951.

3 WOLD, H. O. A. – *A Study in the Analysis of Stationary Time Series* – Almqvist and Wiksell. Uppsala, 1954.

4 WOLD, H. O. A. – *Forecasting by the Chain Principle* – Ref. 1962b, p. 471.

1 WOLF, E. – Über das Heimkehrvermögen der Bienen – *Z. Vergl. Physiol.* 6–1927–221.

2 WOLF, E. – Die Aktivität der japanischen Tanzmaus und ihre rhythmische Verteilung – *Z. Vergl. Physiol.* 11–1930–321.

200 WOLF, F. T. – *Chemical Nature of the Photoreceptor Pigment inducing Fruiting of Plasmodia of Physarum Polycephalum* – Ref. 1957f, p. 321.

400 WOLF, R. – *Mitteilungen über die Sonnenflecken* – 10, 13–1839.

1 WOLFE, H. H. – Periodicity in the sequence of irregular time intervals between successive appearances of the moon in perigee – *J. Cycle Res.* (Ref. J. d.) 8/4–1959–99.

1 WOLFSON, A. – Regulation of spring migration in *Juncos* – *Condor* 44–1942–237.

2 WOLFSON, A. – The role of the pituitary, fat disposition and body weight in bird migration – *Condor* 47–1945–95.

3 WOLFSON, A. – Fat deposition as a response to photoperiodism in migratory birds – *Anat. Rec.* 99–1947–44.

4 WOLFSON, A. – Day length, migration and breeding cycles in birds – *Science Mthly* 74–1952–191.

5 WOLFSON, A. – Body weight and fat deposition in captive white-throated sparrows in relation to mechanics of migration – *Wilson Bull.* 66–1954–112.

6 WOLFSON, A. – Production of repeated gonadal, fat and molt cycles whithin one year in the *Junco* and white-crowned sparrow by manipulation of day length – *J. Exp. Zool.* 125–1954–353.

7 WOLFSON, A. – Weight and fat disposition in relation to spring migration in transient white-throated sparrows – *Auk* 71–1954–413.

8 WOLFSON, A. – *The Role of Light and*

Darkness in the Regulation of Spring Migration and Reproductive Cycles in Birds – Ref. 1957f, p. 679.

9 WOLFSON, A. – Role of light in the progressive phase of the photoperiodic responses of migratory birds – *Biol. Bull.* 117–1959–601.

10 WOLFSON, A. – *Regulation of Annual Periodicity in the Migration and Reproduction of Birds* – Ref. 1960c, p. 507.

100 WOLFSON, A. and D. P. WINCHESTER – Effect of photoperiod on the gonadal cycle in an equatorial bird – *Nature* 184–1959–1658.

1 WOLLENSCHLÄGER, I. – Alternans- und Periodenbildung bei künstlicher Reizung des Rückenmarksfrosches und andere Reflexphänomene – *Pflüger's Arch.* 239–1937–246.

1 WURSTER, K. – Untersuchungen zur Frage tagesperiodischer, lunarer und meteorologischer Einflüsse auf den Wehenbeginn – *Zbl. Gyn.* 2–1949–159.

100 WURTMAN, R.J., J. AXELROD and J.E. FISCHER, – Melatonin synthesis in the anneal gland: Effect of light mediated by the sympathetic nervous system–*Science* 143/3612–1964–1328.

100 YAMAMOTO, S. and K. TAKAGI – *Rhythms in the Electromyogram during Shivering* – Ref. 1962c.

1 YEATES, N. T. M. – Influence of variation in length of day upon the breeding season in sheep – *Nature* 160–1947–429.

2 YEATES, N. T. M. – The breeding season of the sheep with particular reference to its modification by artificial means using light – *J. Agricult. Sci.* 39–1949–1.

1 YOUNG, L. R. – *A Sampled Data Model for Eye Tracking Movements* – Diss. M.I.T. Cambridge. Mass., 1962.

100 YOUNG L. R. and L. STARK – Discontinuous biological control of the eye movement system – 15. *Ann Conf. Engin. in Med. and Biol., Chicago, Nov.* 5-7, 1962.

1 YULE, G. U. – On the time correlation problem, with special reference to the variate-difference correlation method – *J. Roy. Stat. Soc.* 84–1921–497.

2 YULE, G. U. – Why do we sometimes get nonsense-correlations between time series? – *J. Roy. Stat. Soc.* 89–1926–1.

3 YULE, G. U. – On a method of investigating periodicities in disturbed series – *Proc. Roy. Soc.* 226A–1927–267.

100 YULE, G. U. and M. G. KENDALL – *An Introduction to the Theory of Statistics* – 14th Ed., Griffin. London, 1950.

100 ZANDER, H. A., J. WAERHAUG and F. HALBERG – Effect of hypophysectomy upon cyclic mitotic activity in the retromolar mucosa of rats – *J. Clin. Endocrinol. Metab.* 14–1954–829.

1 ZEEUW, D. DE – Flowering of *Xanthium* under long-day conditions – *Nature* 180–1957–588.

1 ZEILON, N. – On dominant frequencies in the praxis of curve analysis – *Göteborgs Kgl. Vetensk.-Vitterhetssamh. Handl. (Swed.)* 1B/9 (6th series)–1941–1.

100 ZEITLIN, R.A., L.D. CADY, L.J. TICK, and M.A. WOODBURY – Combined analog digital processing of cardiograms – *Ann. N.Y. Acad. Sci.* 115/2–1964–1106.

1 ZEUTHEN, E. – Biochemistry and metabolism of cleavage in the sea urchin egg, as resolved into its mitotic steps – *Arch. Neerl. Zool.* 10/suppl. 1–1953–31.

1 ZIMMERMANN, H. – Untersuchungen zur Tagesperiodizität der Meiosis – *Z. Bot.* 42–1954–283.

100 ZINK, O. and W. KUHNKE – Die biologische Bedeutung der langwelligen Hochfrequenzstrahlung der Atmosphäre – *Schweiz. Med. Wschr.* 82/45–1952–1168.

1 ZINN, J. G. – Von dem Schlafe der Pflanzen – *Hamb. Mag.* 22–1759–40.

1 ZINNER, E. – *Alte Sonnenuhren an europäischen Gebäuden* – Steiner, 1963.

1 ZIPF, H. F. – Zum "Ausgangswertgesetz" von Wilder – *Klin. Wschr.* 24–25/(35–36)–1947–545.

100 ZIRM and BAUERMEISTER – Über physiologische Tagesschwankungen der Leukocyten – *Z. Klin. Med.* 125–1933–282.

SUBJECT-INDEX

Unfortunately, biological rhythms cover almost the whole biological spectrum, and is also overflowing with synonyms. The index has, therefore, been severely compressed, though retaining numerous cross references. The subjects tend to be grouped under rather broad headings, but are often enumerated under these, in parentheses. If you do not find a particular item, look up the wider class in which it belongs. The code is:

subject (related concepts), cross references, paragraph numbers.

These *numbers* do not only indicate where the definition is to be found, but also all places at which the subject is mentioned. You can thus follow the development and all connections of a concept.

The *cross references* are given in alphabetical order, separated by commas. Reference words in square brackets, like e.g.: [angular] velocity, or [harmonic] motion, do not constitute entries, but have to be looked up under – velocity, angular –, and – motion, harmonic –, respectively.

The *related concepts* include:
(1) synonyms under which the subject may be referred to in the text;
(2) subheadings belonging to the subject and grouped here;
(3) closely related subjects, included here for simplicity;
(4) sometimes even antitheses of the subject in question.

A

acceleration, 8.19; 4.5,8,10; 18.7,17; 19. 6,8-9; 22.2; 23.3,23.

accidents, 25.42; 26.16; 27.17,19.

acidity (acidosis, blood bicarbonate, pH, ß-hydroxybutyric acid), 2.2,11; 6.5, 18; 7.4.23; 8.5,10: 25.12,28,33-34,44; 27.15,21.

acoustics, 19.22-23.

action spectrum, 13.5-6; 20.8; 24.30; 27.3.

activity, 6.17,33,35; 7.5,10; 8.8,11; 9.6,8; 12.4; 13.16; 14.2; 16.9; 20.7-8; 24.26-27,30,40; 25.6; 27.4,8,15.

activity, day and night (day and night peaks), 5.16; 13,18; 18.19; 24.27-28; 25.13,26; 26.8;.

activity, mental, 1.15; 6.2,25-27; 25.42; 26.16.

activity rhythm (twenty four-hour), 1.3; 6.5,10-11; 13.22; 18.18; 25.2,5-6,12-20; 27.7.

activity rhythms (tidal, 7-day, seasonal), 26.2,5-6,11.

activity statistics, 1.34; 7.16; 20.6.

actogram (actograph), 6.17; 7.5,10; 9.6; 20.8; 27.8.

adaptation. 1.4; 2.1-2; 3.17,27; 4.20; 19. 19; 25.9.

additivity, 19.13,21-23; 21.9; 22.4-5,13,17

adrenal gland, 25.4,29,32,34-36,47

adrenalectomy (or insufficiency), 25.4,32, 35-36

adsorption spectrum, 13.5

autonomous nervous system (neurovegetative system), 2.2; 4.20; 6.2, 5,16,
31; 7.25; 8.3,8,16; 11.3; 13.16; 15.4;
19.33; 24.38, 40; 25.9,34,42
— rhythm, 4.26
autophasing (frequency transformation),
1.22-23; 7.6; 12.17; 13.21; 16.13;
19.24; 23.28,35; 24.4-5, 11,32-26
average (arithmetic and geometric mean,
median, middle value, mid-time,
mode), 1.37; 10.4; 20.14-16,31,33;
21.2-3,6,8,16
— curve (cycle, path), 1.39; 16.9; 20.6,29,
33
— frequency (period), 1.23; 13.21; 19.22;
24.5,11
—,horizontal and vertical, 1.37; 20.33
—,moving, 1.39; 20.15,33; 21.6,13
awakening, 5.24-25
azimuth, 18.6,10-13,16,18

B

backlash, 3.21,28; 19.16
'backward' rhythm, 19.35
bacteria, 15.6; 25.44
balneotherapy, 8.2; 15.1; 25.12,37; 27.19
basal state, 27.14-15
base-line(resting level, trend), 19.8,23;
20.14-17,22; 21.23,28; 24.21
— — characteristics (slope,linearity,loga-
rithmic, sine-shape), 20.15-17,22
— — crossing, 20.24
basimetry (L.I.V.), 8.16; 11.1-12; 20.2
bats, 1.15; 6.22; 7.11; 19.31; 25.15,25
beach fleas, 1.18; 18.12-13; 25.19; 27.5
bean plants (*Phaseolus,* peas), 6.3; 13.25
beats, 6.8,13,29; 12.16; 17.3,5; 19.22-23,
31; 23.26-28,30; 24.29,36; 25.11,40;
27.11,24
—,extra, intercalated, missed 1.26;
19.27,34; 23.31
bee dances, 7.18; 18.8,13
bees, 1.18; 5.23; 7.11,18; 13.26; 18.8, 12-
13; 25.19
beetles, 6.21; 25.19; 26.11
beta-diagram, 23.42
bias, 24.10
bile (bile pigments, bilirubin, coproporphyrin, urobilin), 7.23; 14.7; 25.6,26,31
bimodal curve, 20.25; 24.27-28,40; 25.5,26
bio- (bioamplitude, bioduration, biofrequency, biolevel, biooscillation, bioperiod, biophase); see corresponding
parameter without prefix; 20.10
biological meaning (significance), 1.35;
6.17; 20.11,34; 21.18,25

bioluminescence, 7.4,7,11, 16,18; 25.23
biometeorology (bioclimatology); see meteorotropism; 15.1-6
biorhythm, 20.10
bird-banding, 18.9
— song, 6.22
birds (blackcaps, crows, finches, garden
warblers, grouse, hawks, humming
birds, owls, penguins, sooty tern,
sparrows); see poultry
—,chickens, pigeons, starlings, 1.18; 5.18,
23; 6.20-21,33; 7.22; 9.1,8-9; 10.2;
13.17,27; 18.2,8-9,15-19; 20.8; 24.10,
41-42; 25.6,16,24-25,34; 26.6,8,14;
27.4-7
birth;hatching; 9.2-3,7-8; 25.6,12,45;26.16
— control, 7.24; 20.10
— rate, 24.42,46; 25.45; 26.5,16; 27.11,21
— trauma, 9.7; 11.11
bit, 19.13,36
biting (stinging); see mosquitos; 25.14,
19; 26.11
black box, 2.3-4,22; 3.17; 23.37; 24.1-2
blinding (blindness), 13.17,20; 24.39; 25.4,
34; 26.17; 27.11
blood; see various blood cells, serum,
vascular; 2.14; 6.16-18, 37; 7.23; 8.4,
6,8,10,13,18; 13.17; 20.21
— disorders (anemia, leucemia), 8.4,10,13
— physiology (circulation, coagulation,
flow, volume), 4.4,6; 6.16-17,31; 25.
36,38,41
— pressure, 1.7,15; 2.11,14; 6.17,31; 8.6-7,
10; 9.7; 11.3; 20.14; 24.29; 25.12,37-38
— sugar (glucose, hypo- and hyperglycemia), 1.7,13; 2.11; 7.23; 8.10; 9.5;
11.9; 13.17; 20.19; 24.18; 25.5,24,27;
26.13; 27.11,15
body characteristics (shape, size, surface),
6.20; 9.11; 10.6; 14.2; 27.14,16
— weight (birth weight), 7.23; 8.10;
25.46; 26.14,16
bone diseases, 8.13
— marrow (blood formation), 8.6,8,13;
13.17
brain; see electroencephalogram, epilepsy, hypophysis, hypothalamus, nervous, neuro-, psycho-; 3.16; 6.10-15,
19; 8.7-16; 13.14-17; 24.16; 25.4,7,
31; 27.17
— lesions (surgery), 8.7-8, 14-15; 24.16;
25.4,35
— waves, 6.10-11,13,15
branching (ramification), 19.4; 27.3
business (economy), 1.13,36; 3.24; 6.42;
10.5; 17.10,12; 21.1; 26.22
buzzer, 4.2,15

C

calculation, mental, 6.26

cancer (tumour), 8.4,6,8,13; 16.4; 24.16,
39,46; 25.12,32,47; 26.17

—,gastric, 24.38; 25.12; 27.19

capacitance (capacitor, condenser), 3.15;
4.2,9,13,25,30; 23.24,31; 24.31

— forcing, 23.24; 24.31

capacity, 4.6,27; 9.2; 24.37

—,organ (diffusion), 7.15; 24.11

carbohydrate metabolism (KREBS cycle,
citric acid, pentoses, pyruvic acid);
see blood sugar, gluco-, glyco-; 1.13;
2.11,15; 3.11; 6.3; 7.23; 8.10; 13.7;
20.19; 23.3; 25.26-28; 26.10

carbon dioxide; see acidity; 2.11,17; 3.11,
15; 6.5,8,34; 7.4,23; 13.7,20; 15.3;
24.20; 25.30; 26.13

cardiac, see heart

carrier, 1.20; 12.11; 15.5; 16.5,9; 19.14-15
17,31

cell characteristics (mitochondria, morphology, populations, pulsations);
see mitosis, protoplasm; 6.29-30; 7.
15; 19.5; 20.34; 24.2,7,40; 25.46

— membrane (equilibrium, potential),
1.20; 4.20; 6.21;30; 7.13; 15.5; 16.10;
24.9

centre of cycle, 20.15

—,rhythm, see [master] clock

cerebrospinal fluid, 8.6; 25.42

change, poststimulus (step), 11.1-4; 23.11;
24.25

charge (electric, grid), 4.9-10,12; 15.5;
16.4; 24.31

chemical independence, 7.18-19; 14.9; 24.
34

chemistry; see [chemical] equilibrum,
metabolism, [physical] oscillator;
4.16-19,28; 7.18-19; 19.13

chemoreception, 12.4

chewing, 1.15; 6.2,13

chicken (hens); see egg-laying; 5.18; 6.33;
9.8-9; 13.27; 14.10; 20.3; 24.23,27,
42; 25.13,24-27, 30-31; 26.14

children (infants, newborn), 3.17; 5.25;
6.10, 13,16,18,35; 8.16; 9.5-7; 11.11;
14.7; 25.6-7,14,25,27,31-33,37,40; 26.
6

chlorophyll, 13.2,5-8,10-11; 27.2

chronobiological variation (active, passive, regular, irregular), 1.2,8-9;2.2;
20.9

chronopathology, 8.1-19

cilia, 1.15; 6.2,23; 19.9

cinematography, 6.12

circadian (endodiurnal); see freerunning,
twentyfour-hour rhythm; 1.16-18;
5.16-25; 7.1-19,27; 8.17; 9.1,3; 13.7,
11-12, 17-23; 14.3-4; 16.12-13; 18.8,
18,20; 19.34-36; 20.10; 24.3-5,9,13-
16,26-31,33-34,43,45; 25.8,11; 26.8-
10; 27.2,4,11,13

— chart (map), 24.18, 22; 25.5; 27.16

— frequency (period), 1.16-17,23; 4.26;
5.13; 6.1,37,39; 7.3,10-12; 9.1,8;
12.11, 17; 13.18,20-22; 14.3,9; 19.35;
23.21; 24.11, 26,33-34; 25.11

— graph, 7.10

— quotient; see amplitude quotient; 21.
31; 24.38; 25.6,11

— theory, 1.16-17,23; 4.26; 5.3,16-20;
6.37,39; 7.3,6-19; 9.8; 12.9,17; 13.18-
22; 14.9; 16.13; 18.8; 23.21,32; 24.5,
11,13-16,19-20,26-31,33-34,38-39;
25.4-5

circle, curve generator, 19.7,9

circuit, electronic, 4.9-10,30; 5.8; 19.30;
24.31

circular distribution (circular table, direction chart); see polar coordinates;
18.11; 20.12

— motion (cyclic motion, circus contraction), 2.23; 4.4-6; 6.28-29; 19.35

circulation; see blood, heart, pulse wave,
vascular; 2.11; 4.6; 8.6; 16.3; 18.17;
25.5,37-38; 26.16-17; 27.19

circum-lunar (circum-monthly), 7.20,27;
24.40

— -nutation, see nutation

— seasonal (circannular, endogenous seasonal), 7.2,20,22,27; 24.40; 26.9

clams (mussels, oysters), 1.15; 6.33; 16.9;
25.20; 26.2

clinical trial, 27.20

clock, biological, 1.18; 5.10-25; 7.11; 18.1,
8,11-13,16-20; 24.35,37; 25.4; 27.2,5

—,endogenous and exogenous, 5.10-13;
7.13,19

— graph, see circular distribution

— levels (homeostatic, tissue), 8.12

—,living (bird, flower), 1.18; 5.22-23

—,lunar, 5.21; 18.19; 26.1

—,master, 5.13,25; 8.12; 24.12; 27.11

—,physical (alarm clock, chronometer);
see [interval] timer, 1.22; 4.3,25; 5.7-
11,19; 16.11; 18.1,6-7; 23.3

—,seasonal (annual), 5.21; 26.1

closed systems; see feedback; 2.18,20,26;
4.4; 6.3; 23.2

clue (cue), see synchronization

cockroaches, 6.34; 9.13; 13.12,26; 24.16,
38; 25.14,19

dark-shock, 13.19; 14.4

Dauerdunkel (Dauerlicht), 13.22

dawn and dusk (light-on and -off), 1.24, 30; 5.14,17; 12.13-14; 19.15,32; 23. 12,16; 24.5,8,14,16,27,30,36

day, see circadian, [day] activity, twenty-four-hour

— -length (light duration), 5.18; 13.1,4; 14.5; 18.16; 24.33,41; 26.8

—,lunar, 1.21; 16.9; 17.3; 21.24; 25.5; 26.1-3

—,sidereal, 1.21; 17.2

—,solar, 1.21; 16.9; 17.1-3; 19.20; 21.24

—,time of (fixed, 04 and 16 o'clock); see dawn and dusk, evening, morning, noon; 5.10,19; 13.4; 19.35; 24.18; 25.31,44; 27.13

—,travelling, 18.8

DD, 13.22

dead point, 27.19

— space (time, zone), 3.21,26,28; 8.16; 11.6; 19.16

death (death rate, mortality, suicide), 1.2; 2.23; 4.33; 8.17; 16.6; 20.6,34; 24.46; 25.12,44; 26.5,16-18

decay, exponential, 4.10-11; 23.2

decrement, logarithmic, 3.20

delay, synaptic; see phase lag; 6.19

demultiplication, see frequency

density effect (direct, indirect), 10.6-7

—,spectral, 21.30

dental tissues, 19.4; 25.46

derivatives (differentiation); see differential; 1.31; 19.6,9,12; 21.6,9; 22.2-6; 23.6,40

desert (dessiciation, dryness), 9.13; 14.2; 26.4; 27.7

desynchronization, 7.7

detoxification, 25.31

development of rhythm (formation, phylogeny); see embryonic; 6.36; 8.16; 9.1-9; 24.11; 25.6

diabetes; see insulin; 1.6,13; 2.11,15; 8.5; 9.11; 14.8; 20.15,19; 25.4,12,27-28, 31-33,44; 27.10-11,15,19,21-22

diagnosis (differential, early); medicine; 2.21; 8.2; 24.38; 25.32; 27.13-16,19

dial (diel = daily), 20.10

difference tone, 19.22-23, 32

differences between cycles (horizontal, vertical), 19.9; 20.30,35

differential curves, 7.8; 24.18; 25.5, 27

— equations (coefficients, degree, homogeneity, nonlinearity, order, system); see derivatives; 1.10; 4.7,10,13,16, 21,23; 11.5; 22.2-7,9-10,17-18; 23.6-7,14-27,30,36-38

diffusion, 1.17; 4.17; 6.29; 7.13,15,19; 14.2,5; 24.7; 27.3

direction, 1.7,24; 3.5-8,25; 4.20; 5.6; 12.15; 19.26; 21.4

— reversal, 6.29

— sense; see animal migration; 1.18

discharge level; see oscillation, relaxation; 24.21

disease, see pathology

—,cyclic (periodic), 1.13; 3.26; 8.8-16,17; 24.17

dispersion (scatter, variability, variance, variation); see distribution, random, [analysis of] variance; 1.35-39; 20.3, 23,27-31; 21.20,28,30; 27.14

dispersion, horizontal, 1.38; 20.30

—, interindividual, 6.13; 20.3; 27.14,16

dissimilation, see utilization

distribution characteristics (cumulative, rectangular, skewness), 20.27, 28,30, 31,34

—,frequency (normal, Gaussian); see dispersion, random; 1.36-37; 20.6, 11-12,27,30; 21.1-2,23

—,non-normal; see time series; 20.6,14, 27-28,30

—,time, 20.30

disturbance (displacement, deviation); see shock, signal; 1.12; 2.4-10,22, 24,26; 3.4,7,15-16,18-19,21; 4.8,30; 6.18; 8.6; 11.1,7; 13.19; 19.16; 23.2, 4,6,33-34; 24.5,35; 27.11,21-22,24

—,random (see noise), 1.8; 4.31; 11.1; 12.2; 19.16; 24.3,37

disturbances, repeated (rhythmic), 24.2,6

disturbed periodicity, 21.21,23,25; 23.11, 30-31; 24.5

dither (jitter); see noise; 3.22; 4.33; 19.32

diuresis, see renal excretion

diurnal (diurnalism); see circadian, twentyfour-hour; 1.3,16; 9.13; 20.10; 25. 1,8

divergence phenomenon, 20.29-30

dogs, 6.32; 13.16; 25.15,35

dreaming, 1.15; 5.4; 6.10,35; 8.17; 25.7

drift, 25.20

drops, 4.14; 19.3

Drosophila (fruit fly), 7.7,18; 13.26; 14.6; 24.13-14; 25.19; 27.4

drug dosage, 11.4; 25.44; 27.21-23

— sensitivity, 5.20; 8.2; 11.11; 24.20; 25.12,44; 27.20-21,23

drugs (atropine, carcinogens, colchicine, digitalis, librium, LSD, papaverine, phenamin, quinine, surface active drugs); see alcohol, hormones, insulin, narcosis, poisons, vitamins;

flight personnel, 25.9
— rhythms, 24.40
flood level, 17.12
flow, see blood physiology, movement, protoplasm
flowers, 5.10,14,17; 7.4; 13.5,9; 25.22; 26.10; 27.2
fluid matrix, see milieu interne
flyback, 24.24
flywheel, 3.5; 4.14
focus, in phase plane, 22.6,10
Föhn, 12.6
foraging, 18.2
force, constant, 23.14-16, 19-20
—,periodic, 3.31; 23.12-13,17-23
—,physical (centripetal, restoring); see electromagnetic and -static fields, energy, power; 4.5,8; 19.6,8,21; 22.2; 23.2-3, 5-7,9,13,26
forcing; see also oscillation, resonance, synchronization; 1.3,14,22; 3.28; 4.8; 5.13; 22.5; 23.10-28; 24.22, 26,29
— function, 22.5; 23.10-14, 17-18, 21-24, 29
— types (capacitive, inductive, resistance), 23.24; 24.31
forestry, 6.42; 27.2
forward rhythm, 19.35
FOURIER functions (point, series, transform); see harmonic analysis; 21.9; 22.1,11,16-17; 23.25
free function, 23.19
— play, 3.21
— radicals, 1.20; 13.2; 15.5; 16.10
freerunning; see circadian; 1.15,19; 4.26; 6.39; 7.1-2,27; 8.5; 9.8; 12.17; 13.18, 21; 18.18; 19.31,36; 24.5,10,39; 25.4,8,11; 26.9; 27.11,13,24
frequency (rate); see synchronization; 1.34,40; 3.19,30; 4.6; 6.2-44; 7.15; 12.2,7-8; 13.2; 14.11; 20.6,10,12, 18,23,34; 21.20; 23.7-8,10,16-17, 19-22,26,28,35,42; 24.2,6,25,28,31, 35; 27.18
— analysis (periodicity analysis); see harmonic analysis; 6.26; 10.4; 12.7; 19.29; 20.12,25; 21.1,10,13,16,20-30; 24.2,29;26.3
—,characteristic (free intrinsic, natural or spontaneous oscillation or rhythm) 1.3,14,22; 4.14,25-27,29-30,35; 6.2-44; 7.6; 13.18; 19.8,26,34-35; 20.23; 22.2,5; 23.10,12-14,16-17,21,27,33,35; 24.10,37; 27.24
—,combined, 6.9
— comparison, 24.32

— coupling (relation), see [relative] coordination
— demultiplication (subharmonics, submultiplication), 1.3,17,22; 4.28-29; 5.9; 6.37; 7.6,21; 19.26,30,34; 23.27; 24.11,37
—,dominant, 21.3,5,8,21; 23.41
—,driving (forcing rhythm), 1.22,40; 4.29; 23.17,19,23,25-27,35; 24.26,35
—,intermediate, 1.26; 23.31; 24.36
— jumps, 19.25
— modulation, 4.20; 6.9,11,22; 19.14; 21.21
—,scanning (recording), 19.35
— spectrum (wave spectrum); see amplitude graphs, periodogram, power spectrum; 6.22; 20.12; 21.3,16,20-21,24,28-30; 23.21
— stability (constancy), 6.1; 7.16; 14.37
— transformation, see autophasing
— variability, 4.27; 6.8; 7.7; 21.21; 23.27,30
friction (coloumb, hydraulic, viscous), 3.14,21,28; 4.2,25; 19.8; 23.5-6,21
frogs, 19.34; 25.47; 26.13
Fühler, 3.2

G

gain, 3.14,29-30; 4.2; 23.35,39-40
—,high and low, 2.25; 3.14,21,24-25; 4.2,30-31; 8.16; 10.6
— –phase–frequency diagrams (BODE and NYQUIST plots), 3.30; 20.12; 23.41-42
ganglion, pulsating, 6.32
gastrointestinal canal, 4.14; 6.32,37; 20.19; 25.2,34,42,47
— disorders, 8.4,10; 24.18; 25.10,12,34; 26.17; 27.19
gating, 6.11
genetics (inheritance); see evolutionary selection; 7.9; 9.1; 18.13; 25.19
geographic location, 10.2; 12.14; 17.13
geotaxis, 16.7; 18.4,19
glandular functions; see gonadal, hypophysis, secretion, thymus, thyroid; 1.15; 3.5; 10.10; 24.40; 25.42,47
glucose (glucosuria, tolerance test); see blood sugar; 20.15,19; 25.27-28
glycogen, liver, 9.8; 14.7,10; 20.7,14-16, 19,22,26-27,31; 23.15; 24.23,27; 25.2,5-6,13,24,26-27,31; 27.12,19
— metabolism; see carbohydrate metabolism; 1.4-6; 2.11,15; 6.3,29; 7.23; 24.18; 25.27-28,34
goal-seeking, 2.24; 3.3,5,7; 18.2

gonadal functions (involution, ovulation, castration), 5.18; 7.24; 13.17; 24.41; 25.34; 26.8,12,14; 27.6

graph; see [graphical] solutions; 1.29; 5.8; 7.10; 19.3,6,29; 20.12; 21.24

—,clock, see circular distribution

grasshoppers (locusts), 6.21; 18.12; 24.16; 25.19; 26.11

gravitation; see geotaxis; 1.18-20; 4.2,7; 5.11; 12.6; 16.2-3,6-7; 17.3,5,7; 18. 17; 26.1-2; 27.11

growth equations (models), 4.21-23; 22.9

—,hair, 25.46

—,individual, 5.6; 6.20; 8.6; 13.17; 14.2; 16.4,7; 19.6; 24.42; 26.1,14,16

— pattern, 1.29; 19.4-5

—,plant (vegetative), 5.10; 6.2; 7.4; 13.1,9-11; 14.4-5; 24.16,43; 25.23; 26.10; 27.3

—,population, 1.13; 4.21-23; 10.3,7; 24.40

guinea-pigs, 6.32; 25.15,26

gynaecology (climacterium), 8.17; 25.45

H

half-day, tidal, 17.3

— -month period, 17.5

hamsters, 13.28; 24.14; 25.15,25,35,47; 26.15

harmonic analysis (FOURIER analysis); see frequency analysis; 1.33,35,39-40; 3.29; 6.17; 20.11, 21.1,7-23,27,29-30, 32; 23.14,24-25; 24.2,37

— analyzers, 21.13

—, fundamental (main frequency or period), 1.35; 21.12,14-15,17,24; 22.16

— overtones (harmonics); see harmonic synchronization, hour-rhythms; 3.21, 29; 6.11,29,37; 19.16,32; 22.15; 23. 12,26,42; 24.3,5,35,37,46; 25.13; 26,5; 27.24

— pattern (FOURIER, frequency or wave pattern or system); see frequency spectrum; 1.40; 8.2; 19.11,16,21; 21.9,17-19; 22.16-17; 23.14,31; 24.3

— response function, 23.41-42

— synchronization, 1.3,22; 4.29; 23.26, 32,35; 24.3,29; 25.11; 26.15

hatching, 9.8; 25.6

heads and tails, 21.3,7

heart, 1.26; 4.14; 6.3-4,16,28; 19.34; 23.12; 24.2; 25.26,38; 27.16

— disease, 1.26; 2.11; 6.7, 16; 8.4; 14.2; 19.34; 25.12,34,40,44; 27.19,21

— rate; see arhythmia, pulse; 1.15; 2.11; 6.2,4-5,7,16,20,31; 7.23; 8.10,18; 9.4-

5,7; 24.29,38; 25.2,6,37; 26.16; 27.9

heat; see temperature; 1.7; 6.32; 9.13; 13.2; 14.2; 16.2,6

hedgehogs, 14.2; 25.15

height, see altitude, amplitude

heliotropic system, 13.15

hemerography, 25.8

hepatectomy, 15.4,35

herd instinct, 14.10

herrings, 17.6; 24.45; 26.4,12

hibernation (forced, obligatory, voluntary); see aestivation, hypothermia; 1.3-4; 7.11; 9.13; 14.2; 25.7; 26.6-8

hidden periodicity, 21.21-22,27-29

high-frequency components, see harmonic overtones and synchronization, hour-rhythms, [high-frequency] oscillation

hippus, pupillary, 1.13; 3.24-25; 8.7

holidays, 14.10

homeostasis, 1.8; 2.1-2,4; 11.8

homeostat, 3.16-17; 4.27; 8.16; 19.16; 23.4,33; 24.2

homeothermy (homeothermia, homoiothermia, homothermia), 7.11; 14.2; 26.6

homing, 1.18; 18.2,8,15,17

Homo, 2.11; 3.25; 5.24-25; 6.10-14, 16-18, 32,37,41-43; 7.23-26; 8.1-18; 9.6-7; 13.28; 14.11; 16.12; 19.36; 20.17,21; 24.23,29,37-38,42,46; 25.2,5-7,9-15, 24-29,31-47; 26.3,5-6,16-20,22-23; 27. 9-23

homogeneity; see differential equations; 4.32; 20.3; 22.2; 25.5

horae minoris resistentia; 27.21

hormone; see endocrine, insulin, neurosecretion, the various glands; 2.13; 3.26; 8.11,18; 25.34

—,melanophore, 13.16-17; 24.39,41; 25. 34; 27.5,10

hormones, adrenal (catecholamines, cortisons), 6.32; 7.23; 8.6; 9.11; 25.34-35

—,plant (auxines, florigen, gibberellin); 6.30; 7.18; 13.9,11

—,sexual; see gonadal, sexual; 7.23,25; 8.10-11; 13.16; 25.34,44; 26.15

hospital regimen, 14.10; 27.11

hot-house, 15.3

hour, biological, 6.35

— -glass, 5.8

— rhythms (4-8 hours); see [high-frequency] oscillation; 6.37; 8.5; 9.8, 10; 21.31; 24.11,14,26,28-29,37-39; 25.6-7,12-13

humidity, 1.19; 9.13; 13.20; 15.2,5; 27.7

hunting, 13.21; 24.5

maximum (minimum); see peak; 7.10; 20.4,17,24

medicine, general; see drugs, pathology, sensitivity; 8.1-19; 20.20; 24.18; 25.2; 27.9-23

—,industrial; see accidents, night activity, shift work; 25.10,42; 27.19

—,preventive, 27.14

—,space, 16.7,12; 25.11; 27.10

medusae, 6.24; 19.33

memory, 1.29; 2.8; 6.10,25; 19.3; 21.8; 25.42

menstrual cycle; see estrus, sexual cycles; 1.13; 3.26; 7.21,23-25; 8.9,12; 24.46; 25.45; 26.5

Messwerk, 2.4; 3.2

metabolism (biochemistry); see chemistry, carbohydrate, lipid, protein; 2.11; 4.17,19; 5.6,12; 6.21,29; 7.5,16, 18-19,23,25; 8.8,10; 13.7,11,16; 14.2, 7-9; 16.9; 19.37; 24.18; 25.2,21,26-31, 34; 26.6,14; 27.10,19-23

— blocking (antimetabolites), 7.18-19; 8.6

—,plant, 7.18; 13.7; 16.9; 25.23; 26.10

—,rate of (BMR, oxygen consumption); see oxygen; 7.15,23; 8.10,18; 9.8; 20.7; 26.16

—,reverse, 3.11; 24.18

—,turning points, 25.26,31

metamorphosis (diapause, eclosion, emergence); see moulting; 5.10; 9.1-2,12; 14.6; 24.13-14,16,40; 25.19; 26.6,8, 11; 27.4-5,7

meteorotropic disease, 26.6,17-19

— receptor, 15.4-5

meteorotropism, 9.13; 15.1-6; 23.11; 25.9; 26.6,17-19; 27.10

meter, 20.10

metronome, 4.25; 6.14

mice; see rats; 6.11; 7.5; 13.20,28; 19.36; 20.3,8; 24.41; 25.15, 25-26,30,35-36, 44,47; 26.2,15; 27.21

micropopulation, 10.3

microrhythms (rapid rhythms), 6.1,9-36, 43; 24.37

migration, see animal migration

milieu (externe, interne), 1.14; 2.2,6

mitosis, 10.8; 20.34; 24.40; 25.21,23,47; 27.3

models, 1.28,33; 19.1-38; 22.1 to 23.36; 24.1-2,4,9,16,19,24-25,31; 27.11-12

—,mathematical, 10.3; 19.1-38; 20.29; 21.9; 22.1-18; 24.35

—,physical, 4.4-24; 19.1-38; 23.1-36; 24.2,24-25,31

modulation (amplitude, frequency, pulse frequency), 1.32; 4.20; 6.9,11,22; 12.11; 15.5; 19.14-16,22,31; 21.21

molecular rhythms, 1.17

monkeys, 5.25; 25.15,25,27; 26.15

monothermia, 9.5

months (anomalistic, calendar, draconic, lunar, nodal, sidereal, synodic, tropical); see [28-day] periods; 7.2,21; 17.4,8,11; 26.3-4

mood, 6.41; 8.10; 25.13

moon; see lunar, [lunar] day and light, months, tide; 1.18; 5.11,21; 15.3; 16.2; 17.3-6; 18.8,12,19; 26.1-5

— phases (quarters, lunation), 17.4-6; 24.44-46; 26.2,4-5,21

morbidity; see death; 9.5; 15.6; 20.6,34; 25.12,44; 26.16-20

morning (morning people and -sickness); see [time of] day; 24.11,40; 25.13,31; 27.13,21

MORSE system, 19.13

mosquitos, 25.14,19; 26.4; 27.7

moths, 6.21; 18.4

motion (movement); see activity, circular motion, locomotion; 1.2,7; 4.33; 5.2; 6.23; 19.6,9-10,33,35; 22.7; 23.2,5-6

—,harmonic (angular, simple), 4.7-8; 19.7-9; 21.9; 22.4; 23.7

motor rhythms, see chewing, locomotion, neuromuscular system, tapping, walking

moulting, 5.10,14; 14.4; 24.40; 26.14-15; 27.5

movement, ear, 1.15; 6.22

—,fetal, 9.4

—,nonlinear, 3.19; 19.6

—,random (Brownian, random walk); see [stationary] time series; 3.17; 4.31; 21.4,7

—,unidirectional, 1.7

—,vertical, 25.20

—,voluntary, 6.13-15; 19.33

moving average; see average

— variate, 5.1; 20.27-30; 21.23; 24.19

multimodal curve, 20.25

muscle, 1.15; 3.5; 4.20; 6.2-4,16,19; 14.11; 23.31; 25.26

— disorders, 8.10; 25.31

—,fibrillar (flight), 6.2,21

— ring, 4.4; 6.28

—,smooth, 6.2,31-33

mushrooms (fungi, yeast), 6.36,38; 7.4; 13.8,24; 19.4; 24.43; 25.23; 27.3

music (music instruments, drum, piano); see sound; 4.8,14; 7.14; 14.10-11; 19.11; 27.20

host cycle; 1.13; 2.16; 3.24; 4.23; 10.3, 6-7; 14.8; 22.9-10; 25.2,14

prediction (anticipation), 1.9; 2.8; 3.7-8, 19,23; 6.42; 17.12; 18.6; 20.24; 21.1

preformed rhythms; see embryonic; 9.2

pregnancy (gestation, labour); see sexual activity and cycles; 8.11; 25.13,25,3 4,36-37,45; 26.15

pressure (intramuscular, intraocular, population, sensory); see blood and atmospheric pressure; 10.3; 12.4; 19.33; 25.42-43

probability–density function, 21.23

probits, 20.6,34

proof, negative, 25.3

propulsion, undulatory, 6.23; 19.9

protein metabolism (amino acids, ammonia, creatine, creatinine, cystine, pyridine, SH-groups); see serum; 2.11, 15; 8.10; 9.5; 25.28-29,31

protoplasmic flow (motility, streaming, viscosity), 1.15; 4.17; 6.2,29; 13.8; 24.7; 25.23; 27.3

psyche; see [mental] activity; 16.12; 25.13,42

psychology (creativity, illusions, learning, performance, reading, religion, teaching, toys, training); see business, memory, mood, pain, perception, [reaction] time, sleep, war; 1.15; 2.21; 3.17; 6.12-14,25-27,41; 12.13; 15.6; 24.10; 25.10-11,21,42

psychopathology (anorexia, anxiety, catatonia, crime, debility, delirium, depression, hallucination, homosex, hysteria, insomnia, kleptomania, mania, nervosity, nymphomania, paranoia, psychosis, pyromania, retardation, stottering, stupor); see death, mood; 1.13; 2.11; 3.17,27; 5.25; 6.8,10,13,41; 8.3,8-10,14-18; 16.4; 19. 37; 25.10-13,27,36; 26.16

puberty, 8.17; 9.5

pulmonary parameters; see respiration; 2.11; 6.3,8,18; 15.5; 20.19; 25. 39,46

pulsatance, 4.7-8; 22.16; 23.14,16

pulse, physical (longitudinal, torsional, transverse); see vibration; 19.3,10, 37; 23.32

— -respiratory coordination (quotient), 6.7,16,20; 19.33; 23.31; 25.37,39

— wave; see heart rate; 1.15,35; 6.17,31; 19.11-12,31; 21.18; 24.2; 27.19

pupillary regulation (reflex); see eye; 1.13; 2.19; 3.5,9,14,14-25; 4.33; 6.3; 7.23; 8.7; 19.32; 25.43

Q

Q_{10}, 1.17; 7.11-15; 14.5

quotients (indices), 20.6,26

R

rabbits, 6.32; 10.2; 13.16; 24.27; 25.15, 26-27,33-34,47; 26.15

radiation, cosmic, 1.20; 12.6,11; 13.3; 15.3; 16.8-9

—,general (corpuscular, heat, UV); see light; 1.19; 3.11; 6.2; 13.2,7-8; 16.2, 6-9; 17.9; 24.13; 27.17

—,solar, 13.4,7; 17.9; 19.13; 20.6; 24.5; 26.3,18

radio, 2.8; 4.31; 12.6; 15.3; 16.6-8; 19.14

random behaviour (differences, movement, variation); see distribution, error, noise, [stationary] time series; 1.38; 3.21; 18.2-3; 19.13,17; 20.12; 21.3-7; 27.14

— control (entrainment, forcing, stimuli); see disturbance, disturbed periodicity, error-control; 3.16-17; 12.2, 13; 24.16,28

— cycles; see [serial] correlation; 10.3-4

— walk, 21.7

range, see amplitude, dispersion

rate, see frequency, heart, metabolism, velocity

— -sensitivity; see unidirectionality; 12. 15; 19.19,33; 24.8

rats; see mice; 8.11; 13.16,28; 16.9; 20.19; 24.26-27,41; 25.6,15,25-27,30-35,45, 47; 26.2-3

réacteur, 2.4; 3.2

receptor, see sensor

recording conditions (long and short, continuous and discontinuous records); see actogram, aliasing, assay, sampling; 1.29; 19.3; 20.4-8,23; 21. 3,5,15-16, 23-29; 27.3

records, single cycle, 21.14-15,17; 24.5, 19,37

red far-red system; see light

reference point, 1.18,21; 17.2,4; 18.5-6

— value (control input or value, desired value), 1.12; 2.24; 3.1-4,18,21,31; 4.27; 27.23

reflex, closed (pupillary, somatic, visceral), 1.13; 2.18-20; 6.3,10,15,19; 14.11; 27.9

Regel-abweichung (-fläche, -güte, -kreis, -strecke, -werk), 3.2,19

regeneration, 25.47

regimen, see environmental and hospita